JOHNSON O'CONNOR
SCIENCE VOCABULARY
BUILDER

BOOKS BY
JOHNSON O'CONNOR

BORN THAT WAY
PSYCHOMETRICS
UNSOLVED BUSINESS PROBLEMS
STRUCTURAL VISUALIZATION
TOO-MANY-APTITUDE WOMAN
APTITUDES AND THE LANGUAGES
IDEAPHORIA
UNIQUE INDIVIDUAL
ENGLISH VOCABULARY BUILDER

JOHNSON O'CONNOR

SCIENCE VOCABULARY

BUILDER

BOSTON

HUMAN ENGINEERING LABORATORY

1956

JOHNSON O'CONNOR RESEARCH FOUNDATION INCORPORATED
11 East 62nd Street New York 21 New York
formerly at Stevens Institute of Technology
Hoboken New Jersey

HUMAN ENGINEERING LABORATORY INCORPORATED
347 Beacon Street Boston 16 Massachusetts

HUMAN ENGINEERING LABORATORY
161 East Erie Street Chicago 11 Illinois
formerly at Illinois Institute of Technology

HUMAN ENGINEERING LABORATORY
302 South Bunker Hill Avenue Los Angeles 17 California

HUMAN ENGINEERING LABORATORY
2012 Delancey Place Philadelphia 3 Pennsylvania

HUMAN ENGINEERING LABORATORY
657 Fifth Avenue Fort Worth 4 Texas

HUMAN ENGINEERING LABORATORY
721 South Guthrie Avenue Tulsa 3 Oklahoma

JOHNSON O'CONNOR RESEARCH FOUNDATION INCORPORATED
240 West Jefferson Street Detroit 26 Michigan

JOHNSON O'CONNOR RESEARCH FOUNDATION
AN ONTARIO CORPORATION
Toronto Ontario

JOHNSON O'CONNOR DE MÉXICO
Apartado 23726
México 10 DF

INTRODUCTION

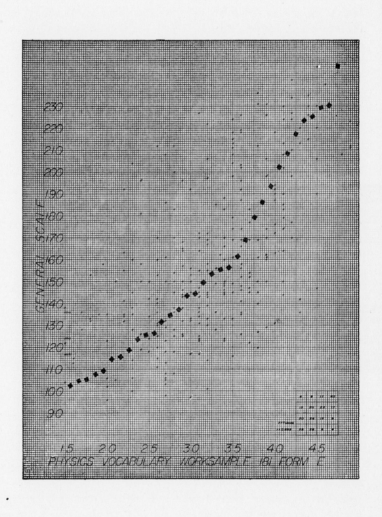

INTRODUCTION

The president of a great engineering school once remarked, in commenting on the English vocabulary scores of his student body: 'We do not teach English; we teach physics'. In the light of recent test results, this statement seems improbable; for a measurable apprehension of physics terms goes too often with an analogous English vocabulary for the two to be unrelated. With engineering institutions engrossed in the sciences, technical terms, it would seem, should be known to graduates, even though wholly wanting in literary words. But this seldom happens.

The interdependence of physics vocabulary and English becomes more definitive as the human sample accumulates. With 277 men in figure 1, where the score in the physics vocabulary test, worksample 181, form E, appears plotted horizontally as abscissa, and the English vocabulary score for the same person vertically as ordinate, the line of relationship is present though ragged; but inspires more confidence in figure 2 based on 476 persons. Finally with a sampling of 909, figure 3, the line smooths sufficiently so that additional cases seem superfluous. With other physics terms, in a second form of the test, the same relationship reappears, figure 8. An exact physics vocabulary goes statistically with a nearly comparable grasp of English words, only seven persons among 909 scoring in the top quarter of the physics test, grade A, to the right on the horizontal scale, and simultaneously in the bottom quarter of English vocabulary, grade D, in the lower right hand almost barren corner of the graph. A physics vocabulary without a somewhat corresponding English vocabulary is an anomaly.

Is a literal translation of divers physics terms, through Greek and Latin, responsible for this correlation; for to the classical scholar, with no deep comprehension of physics, the word PYRHELIOMETER is a combination of the Greek πῦρ (pyr), fire, with the Greek ἕλιο (helio), sun, plus μέτρον (metron), measure, an instrument for measuring the heat of the sun. To answer, each physics item was studied separately. At the top of the list, best known to those high in English vocabulary, is ZEEMAN EFFECT, a proper name where neither Greek nor Latin

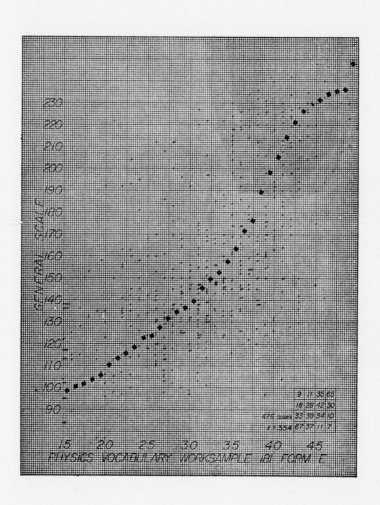

PHYSICS VOCABULARY WORKSAMPLE 181 FORM E

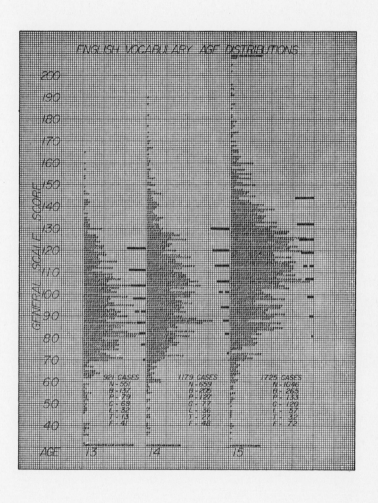

ENGLISH VOCABULARY AGE DISTRIBUTIONS

helps. Second in the list, or near the top, is JOULE-THOMSON EFFECT. The bond between physics and English does not seem to rest exclusively on language knowledge. Though the inference cannot be proved beyond cavil, a large and exact English vocabulary may be a prerequisite not merely to an interpretation of the glossary of physics but to an intellectual mastery of its concepts.

Much as a comprehensive English vocabulary characterizes eminent business executives, so a physics vocabulary, accompanied by a nearly equivalent English vocabulary, characterizes top engineers and scientists. And much as English vocabulary levels go up with executive title, so physics vocabularies rise with engineering position, mechanical engineers in general outranking draftsmen, and these in turn scoring above laboratory technicians. Design engineers average higher than engineers in general, while men who call themselves RESEARCH ENGINEERS, though such job titles are vague, equivocal, and of doubtful interpretation, score one point higher still. Rarely does one who rates low in physics vocabulary establish himself in the technical world; and rarely does one gain a physics vocabulary without an accompanying English vocabulary nearly as high on the general scale.

Both technical and literary vocabularies accrue through life, median or middle scores, obtained independently for each age, soaring rapidly through the early years and then more leisurely, but continuing to mount from 56 at age 10, through 108 at age 15, 133 at age 20, to 159 at age 30, and 171 at age 40, until some 80 per cent, more than three quarters, of the older group tested at age 50 score as high in English vocabulary as the average of the younger generation at 23.

For each separate age the distribution of English vocabulary scores ranges widely, as for age 14, figure 4, where the lowest person scores 18 points on the general scale, through the next highest at 20, both off the bottom of the graph, to 187 and 190 at the top. Counting up from the bottom in this group of 1179 boys and girls tested during the ten-year period 1944 to 1954, the lowest decile or 10th percentile, the top person in the bottom ten per cent, scores 73, shown by the shortest of the horizontal lines. The second decile or 20th percentile, the top

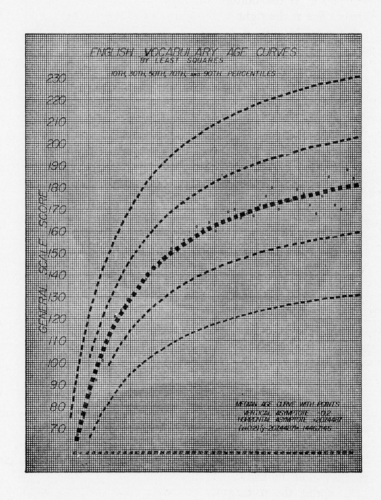

person in the bottom 20 per cent, scores 82, the second horizontal line; while the median or middle score, defined as the top person in the bottom half, shown by the short middle broken line at the right of the distribution, scores 101.

Between the ages of 13 and 25, where the Laboratory does much of its testing and where the cases are many, the medians or mid points form a smooth curve easily traced by eye. But for the younger and older ends, where the persons tested are fewer, the exact position is doubtful. Though a curve can still be sketched approximately, one of the conic sections, a rectangular hyperbola referred to its own asymptotes as axes, fits remarkably well and if correct can be located mathematically. The usual formula:

$$\frac{x^2}{a^2} - \frac{y^2}{b^2} = 1$$

gives a hyperbola with the horizontal or x coordinate as the axis. By rotating this 45 degrees, and assuming it to be rectangular, the expression becomes:

$$xy = 2b^2,$$

or in the more general form:

$$xy - ax - by = c.$$

The ideal type of curve to fit a set of points cannot, I believe, be determined directly. Wholly unsuitable types can be discarded by inspection; but others must be tried. A logarithmic curve for example rises rapidly at first and then more slowly, much as does the vocabulary age curve, and at least two growth curves are thought to be of this type. A colony of bacteria, after an initial lag, grows logarithmically; and tree rings are said to follow the same curve. But when actually tried no sort of logarithmic curve has been found to fit the vocabulary median points within the known standard errors.

Accepting the rectangular hyperbola, and using 43 simultaneous equations, one for each age from 14 to 56, the most probable constants are obtained by least squares. Inserting these, the equation becomes:

$$(y - 207.4)(x + 0.2) = -1446.7$$

This curve, the heaviest line of figure 5, rises steeply from the lower left and swings around to the right, gradually leveling off, approaching but never reaching a horizontal asymptote, located on the general scale by the constant 207.4. Retracing the curve into the younger ages, the lower left arm, pointing downward, approaches but never touches an upright asymptote at zero years of age, actually at +0.30, three tenths of a year after birth. The constant −1446.7 specifies the curvature or the extent to which the hyperbola crowds into the right angle between its asymptotes, one horizontal and the other vertical. Conceding the mathematical extension backward into the early years with no actual points before ages 7 or 8, and no adequate populations before age 9, vocabulary starts almost instantly at birth, certainly within three or four months, and develops more rapidly during the first few years than at any other time in life.

A knowledge of words which goes back to birth is obviously not a reading vocabulary, a fact already surmised from other findings. During the early years, or with reading difficulties, the vocabulary test is read aloud by the administrator. Later, when reading skills have been acquired, the new score, with the test read by the examinee, is about where it should be assuming the original score, when the test was read aloud, to have been correct. The sort of vocabulary measured and studied by the Laboratory seems almost independent of reading skill. Nor is this early vocabulary usable in the sense that it can be spoken. It is thinkable and probably employed even in the very early months as a tool of thought.

The same conic section fitted independently to each decile by least squares, with of course different constants, gives a family of nine hyperbolas, the thinner lines above and below the median, figure 6, apportioning the total population for each age roughly into tenths. The vertical asymptote, the time at which vocabulary starts, seems the same for all, at approximately zero years, +0.30.

The general scale position of the horizontal asymptote differs for each decile, but these parameters trace a surprisingly smooth curve, though each figure was obtained independently by an application of least squares to the actual points. The constant which gives the curvature of the hyperbola is the least accurate and gives the most trouble when the formula is used to compute norms for the younger ages. Only the collection of more cases for ages 6, 7, and 8, and new techniques for measuring a knowledge of words still earlier in life will show whether the hyperbola still fits and reveal more consistent constants.

These hyperbolas express normal, group improvement in vocabulary under the conditions of life and education during the past decade. They are the paths which most persons can expect to pursue who depend on formal education as administered today, even including college, for these age curves contain college students, college graduates, and graduate students. Their remarkable feature is their smoothness, with no recognizable perturbations or distortions, no unmistakable bump at the college period where it was expected at least for the higher scores, and no perceptible leveling off at ages 16, 17, or 18, among the lower scores, when many boys stop formal education, finishing high school without going on to college. Perhaps so large a percentage of one's final vocabulary comes during the first few years of life that variations in the little gained thereafter are not enough to affect the over-all trend.

If the faster climb of the top curves, the 80th and 90th percentiles, is the result of education, as one likes to believe, then it would seem as if the lower ones must be also, for they are drawn with the same mathematical formula and ought to represent the same set of operating causes. Were it impossible to teach low-vocabulary pupils, as many believe, for colleges rarely accept them, the lower curves ought to reach a horizontal plateau with no further improvement. Instead they continue to rise through life, slower but in exactly the same manner as do the top deciles. Whatever education does for the high-vocabulary student it ought also to be able to do for everyone, even for the 10th and 20th percentiles.

These curves are based on data collected during the period 1944 to 1954, and are at some ages as much as 25 percentiles lower than the previous ones for the preceding ten years. Those in turn were lower than still earlier curves. Is the country as a whole dropping in vocabulary, for if so it is serious; or is the Laboratory testing today a more unselected group? Certainly the first group of thirty years ago was highly selected.

Similar curves drawn separately for those tested during the past ten years in each city where a Human Engineering Laboratory is located are all of the same mathematical type, and all spring from the same vertical asymptote, suggesting that vocabulary starts everywhere at the same age. But the horizontal asymptote, the height which each city approaches, differs from place to place. Thus a median age curve based on persons tested exclusively in the New York Laboratory is at every age sensibly above the total population. Just below the New York curve come those for Boston and Philadelphia; and below these Chicago and Los Angeles roughly together; while the vocabulary median for the southwest rises still more slowly. At age 30 the Philadelphia median is 7 points on the general scale below New York; and Chicago 5 points below this; while the southwest median at the same age is 20 points lower still. Expressed differently, the average New York examinee scores as high at the age of 30 as the average Chicago one eight years later; and at 25 the average Chicago examinee scores as high as the average tested in the southwest at 38.

Are these veritable regional dissimilarities? For the Laboratory has measured only a minute portion of the total population in each city, not enough perhaps to be indicative. Furthermore in the southwest it has sampled a larger percentage both of the local community and of the region than in other situations and so may be tapping a more unselected and lower vocabulary stratum. Also in the southwest the percentage of industrial testing is larger. Are these variations between cities a selection of those who have been tested? Perhaps not, for corresponding vocabulary differences in specific occupations and professions excludes industrial testing as an explanation. A current study of college graduates tested in separate Laboratories may throw additional light on selection as a factor.

Does the tense competition of New York City eliminate low vocabularies from the area, leaving a high residue? Or do the city's stimulating opportunities envelop and penetrate? Does its gigantic public library raise the vocabulary of the community, which gains words as an individual absorbs them from his own shelves? Or is the library the product of a high-vocabulary population? There is certainly some relationship, for the vocabulary averages of various cities are roughly proportional to the volumes in their respective libraries. The low-vocabulary individual in any locality should add books to his own library; for there are quiet evenings and rainy weekends when he will reach for a book from his own shelves if just at hand.

The distinction in vocabulary between men as a group and women is slight and not consistent from one city to another. Using New York cases only, the age curves for men and women differ perceptibly, but not a great deal more than the possible errors of the individual points due to inconsistencies in the selection of the two. To age 13 boys and girls improve together. Then boys lag, the median age curve for girls continuing on above. By age 16 the median for girls is twelve or thirteen percentiles above that for boys; or expressed differently girls of 16 score like boys a year and a half older. By age 25 the two curves are parallel once more. Although women still score above men, they improve from this point less rapidly so that by age 30 men overtake them and the age curves cross. Thereafter New York women of each age, those tested in the New York Laboratory, average below men.

Similar curves based on Philadelphia cases repeat this relationship in essence. Those for Chicago rise together to age 13, as do the New York and Philadelphia; then women learn more rapidly, and from this age on remain above men through life, not loitering as in New York and Philadelphia. Are these differences the result of selection? Or is it environment and opportunity? Or is there an aptitude difference?

A recently isolated trait, measured by worksample 376 and given the sobriquet SILOGRAMS, the name of its designer spelt backward, manifests the sort of age curve thought to characterize an aptitude, one which ascends in this case to age 18, and droops later. Yet the trait correlates with English vocabulary and so is thought to be a language-learning aptitude. As three quarters of women score as high as the top half of men, it may help them to acquire more words. As the difference between men and women in the aptitude is 25 percentiles at the men's median and no more than half this in vocabulary, other factors as well as this aptitude must contribute.

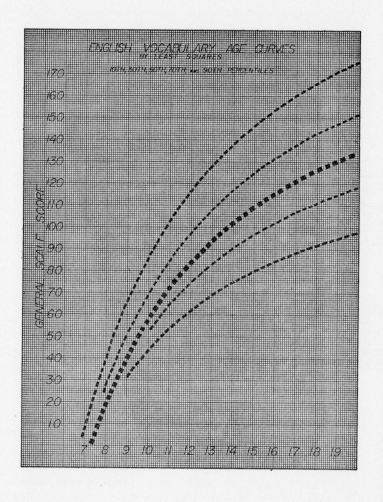

Vocabulary differences start early in life and are hard to overcome. Even at age 10 the spread is forty points from the 10th percentile to the 90th, charted more clearly in figure 6, based on the same data as figure 5, but for the younger ages only, enabling the bottom scale to be extended. Here the 10th-percentile boy, who scores 43, the top boy in the bottom tenth of the distribution, who makes normal improvement in vocabulary from year to year, needs 1.4 years to score as high as the average age-10 boy, at 57 on the general scale, a figure which the 10th-percentile age-10 boy does not attain until between the ages of 11 and 12, more exactly at age 11.4. At age 10 a boy who scores at the 10th percentile may be regarded as a year and a half retarded. If he improves normally a year and a half will pass before he scores as high as he should have scored at age 10. For age 11 the average or median is 72; and the bottom line reaches 72 at age 13.6. Here the bottom tenth is two and a half years retarded, for it will take the 10th-percentile boy two and a half years of normal improvement to score as high as he should have scored at 11. Starting from age 13, the bottom decile line requires five and a half years to reach a score equal to the 13-year average. For the 15-year-old boy, at the bottom decile for his age, who makes normal improvement for a boy in this position, ten years will pass, he will be 25 years of age, before he scores as high as the 15-year-old average. Although with normal effort, a boy at the 10th percentile stays there through life, in terms of years retarded such a boy drops gradually further behind.

Can the individual ever break away from these mathematical lines? Does the failure of each curve to rise above its own horizontal asymptote mean that no one climbs higher than some foreseen and predictable ceiling? Rare persons certainly do. A 17-year-old boy, below the 5th percentile for his age, rose a year later to the 16th for his new age; and by the end of another year attained the 26th. The next year he scored at the 56th percentile and insisted on taking three independent forms to eliminate any possible doubt about this unusual progress. Single measures, one at the beginning of a period and a second at the end, may either be wrong; but a series of four scores showing gradual improvement are convincing. An older man, a salesman, lifted his English vocabulary, with persistent work, from the 5th percentile to the 83d. It took eleven years and he was tested seven times during the period. A nine-year-old raised his English vocabulary from the 11th percentile to the 33d in two years. A youngster tested at age 13, at the 23d percentile, returned twelve years later, a successful development engineer, scoring at the 89th percentile, a vocabulary improvement which he asserted sprang largely from the impression which the Laboratory made on him at the age of 13.

Nor are these sporadic instances. Each year a constantly increasing number of boys and girls who have been tested by the Johnson O'Connor Research Foundation or by the Human Engineering Laboratory return to have their English vocabularies and technical vocabularies remeasured and so confirm their improvement. With those who score low at their first appointment these organizations do everything in their power to urge more words. In a study of 450 persons who returned in this way, 74 per cent of those who originally graded in the bottom quarter show more than normal improvement, go up faster than the lines of figures 5 and 6.

What is it which enables an individual, whether boy or girl, man or woman, to leave these rigidly mathematical curves? Probably many factors, for the vocabulary score distribution fits almost exactly the normal probability curve built originally on the theoretical assumption of an infinite number of contributing variables. But in the hope of enabling each student to gain words with a greater economy of time the Laboratory has formulated three laws of learning. They are:

First Law of Learning: Each English word and scientific term has its own strict order of difficulty with respect to others, indicated statistically by the percentage of persons who recognize the meaning when the word appears in such a test item as:

The power of a lens with a focal length of one meter.
    anastigmat   sagitta   umbra   diopter   hefner

where one of the five choices, and only one, is correct. This order of difficulty is remarkably reproducible, though the numerical percentages differ unexpectedly from one sampling of persons to another, due apparently to fortuitous selection.

Three hundred and seventy-one technical terms appear in this book in their order of familiarity, starting with FUSELAGE, marked correctly by 513 persons out of 515 whose test scores have been tabulated, advancing through RADIAL ENGINE, answered correctly by only 440 of the same 515 persons, and culminating in LAMBERT and CORIOLIS, unknown except to the rare physicist. These words come from eight separate technical vocabulary tests, each of fifty items. Three contain physics terms; three others, mathematical; one, radio; and one, aviation.

The percentage of examinees who know each word, as that appears at the top of each page, is adjusted for lucky guessing, on the assumption that the number who mark an item correctly in a vocabulary test exceeds the number who confidently know its meaning. Examinees wholly ignorant of a word should select each of the five choices about equally often. As the choices consist of four misleads and the correct answer, they should mark the latter by chance as often as the average mislead. Dividing by four, the number of persons who fail on a particular item, gives the average number of persons who mark each of the misleads in that item. A similar number probably mark the correct answer by good fortune. Subtracting this number from the total who actually mark the correct answer gives the number who probably know the meaning.

When the four misleads are equally attractive, marked by approximately equal numbers of persons, this method is sound. But where a substantial number hesitate only between the correct choice and its opposite, as between CATHODE and ANODE, or between the correct choice and a near-synonym, as between CONVECTION and CONDUCTION, rejecting other choices, only those who have no idea at all of the correct answer mark the least frequently marked mislead, the least probable answer. This number can be subtracted from each of the other four choices on the assumption that those who have no idea of the answer mark each of the five choices equally often.

The number of persons who mark the second least frequently marked mislead, minus those who mark the least frequently marked, gives the number who know just enough not to mark the least attractive and so have one chance in four of the correct answer. This number is subtracted from what remains of those who mark the other three choices. And so on. Mathematically this is equivalent to subtracting those who mark the most frequently marked mislead from those who mark the correct answer to obtain the number who know the correct answer, and is probably more accurate than subtracting the average of the four misleads. The words of this book are arranged in the order of the number of persons believed to know the correct answer as computed by this last method.

Discounting erratic variations, the present word sequence is the same in Fort Worth (FW), Texas; in Tulsa (TU), Oklahoma; in Los Angeles (LA); Philadelphia (PH); Chicago (CH); Boston (BO); and New York (NY); and is not therefore due to some school, or teacher, or textbook, but seems inherent in words themselves. The most difficult tenth average less than two letters longer than the easiest tenth. Length is a factor, but almost negligible in determining difficulty. Words from Anglo-Saxon are easier than those from Latin; and those in turn easier than words from Greek. But again this is no more than a partial explanation of the empirical findings. Ancient words, dating back in the language, are more widely known than recently coined ones; the easiest ideas for the human mind to grasp were probably the first to be named historically. Granting exceptions, word age influences current difficulty. But it is still necessary to include each word in a vocabulary test and, after administering it, determine the number of persons who mark each word correctly before its difficulty in relation to other words is assured.

Second Law of Learning: Leaving the statistical group for the individual, each distinct person knows practically every word in this sequence of familiarity up to an inchoate section where his or her vocabulary becomes doubtful. He then knows fewer and fewer words in a short learning range, and literally none beyond. This second law is the remarkable finding that all Americans acquire words in the same order. Were it natural, or even possible, to learn beyond one's immediate level, then a vocabulary test, with the words in order of statistical familiarity, ought to disclose persons who know difficult words, toward the end of the test, and fail to know easier ones, or persons who know some of the easy ones and some of the hard. This all but never happens, except with the foreign-born student. Nearly every native American who takes the test knows virtually every word within the confines of his present knowledge, and none beyond.

This word sequence has its consequences in human relations. A New England organization experienced constant trouble with a factory which it tried to operate in the South. When tested, the disconcerting group scored at a lower vocabulary level. The foremen were lower than the home foremen, the manager lower, the workers lower. High-vocabulary men transferred to the southern factory never survived. The two groups thought differently; for words are used not only in communication but apparently in rigorous thinking. The same happened in reverse with a national organization which developed a very high-vocabulary branch in the Middle West. There was constant wrangling. Finally the high-vocabulary man at the head of the western group was discharged.

In general, executive success goes with a large and exact English vocabulary, technical success with a physics vocabulary; but it is not quite so simple as this sounds. A major executive, who scores superior in English vocabulary, failed recently. Secure in his own preeminence, he had not lifted his subordinates, but left a hiatus between his vocabulary and theirs.

Wishing to raise the level of an organization which sold largely to a professional clientele, the district manager added knowingly a high-vocabulary man, whom he liked. After struggling for two years to amalgamate him with the group, he let him go as a failure. There was too great a gap between the vocabulary of the new employee and the group. If words are used in thinking as well as in communication, then the very high- and the very low-vocabulary man do not think alike.

As individuals differ widely, so do communities and cities, and so must whole countries. And much as the low-vocabulary boy in a high-vocabulary school, frustrated by the words about him, covertly rebels, closing his mind, hearing nothing, or turns openly truculent, so must entire nations. Is America, which probably furnishes the most education to the largest percentage of its citizenry, elevating its own vocabulary too far beyond the world as a whole, leaving a widening and dangerous chasm between itself and others? Is it doing enough to raise the vocabularies of the rest of the world? For the survival of the very high-vocabulary man does not necessitate holding himself back, restraining his own growth, but raising the vocabularies of others.

Third Law of Learning: In the sequence of words arranged in order of difficulty, rate of learning is greatest just at the beginning of the nebulous stretch between the known and the unknown. For easy words, already familiar, rate of learning is zero. While difficult words, even if laboriously committed to memory, do not become working parts of one's vocabulary. They are too obvious when used and are soon forgotten.

To assemble a vocabulary, either English or physics, with economy of time and effort, each student should locate his own vocabulary border and, starting at that point, add new words in the exact order of their determined familiarity. The average student, or one a bit above, can do just this naturally. But in almost every college class, some freshman scores as low in English vocabulary as the average 7th grade pupil, five or six years retarded. This third law of learning states that these low-vocabulary students cannot learn college-freshman words until they know those of seventh and eighth grade difficulty. Could they start at their own vocabulary level they would learn rapidly. Instead they now sit daily listening to rarefied words beyond their immediate learning range.

With some 2000 colleges and universities in the United States a selected few should devote themselves exclusively to this low-vocabulary group, for there is every reason to believe that it can be raised significantly more rapidly than at present. As a step in this direction the Human Engineering Laboratory and the Johnson O'Connor Research Foundation recommend recently founded colleges to those who score low in vocabulary, for as a man goes up in vocabulary with age so probably does an educational institution. Also the younger organizations are apt to have younger faculties whose own vocabularies are not yet quite so high as they will be later. And finally there is the feeling that a young group ought to undertake one of the problems of education and not merely follow in the footsteps of the established institutions.

At the top of the scale, in the same freshman class, are high-vocabulary students, six or seven years in advance of the average, scoring like third and fourth year graduate students. They also gain little or nothing from teaching aimed at the average, only occasionally hearing a new word which interests them, wasting most of their days in the region they know well, learning to be bored, indifferent, supercilious, with the result that in one carefully followed group every man who scored in the top five per cent in vocabulary left college without finishing, not because of failure but for personal reasons. The old colleges should devote themselves to this high-vocabulary group.

A study of the misleads chosen in various sections of the vocabulary tests reveals steps in the acquisition of a new word, in the narrow region between the known and the unknown. With test items presented in order of difficulty, the first are familiar to everyone and universally marked correctly. The first word mismarked, in the midst of the easy ones, should be almost known, but not quite. It should be just at the brink of the examinee's knowledge. A study of these nearly known words reveals the exact opposite of the accepted meaning as the popular misconception. One who falters between CENTRIFUGAL and CENTRIPETAL recognizes the sound of both, knows the situation to which both apply, everything except which is which. Distinguishing a word from its opposite with confidence concludes the learning process.

As an examinee progresses with a vocabulary test toward the less familiar, he errs more often, the words growing gradually more remote; and he begins to confuse those occurring in the same situation. Knowing that MANTISSA relates to logarithms, he marks ANTILOG or even LOG. Advancing further, he knows only an occasional item. Here he marks a word which sounds like the test word, PARAMETER for PERIMETER, or the synonym of a word which sounds like the test word, confusing sounds.

Interpreting backward in the test, from the unknown end toward the known at the beginning, one who hears a completely unfamiliar word such as CORIOLIS should be content to get its sound, to hear it clearly, to pronounce it easily. Next, begin to use it in the right situation, without worrying too much about its more precise meaning. Learn that the

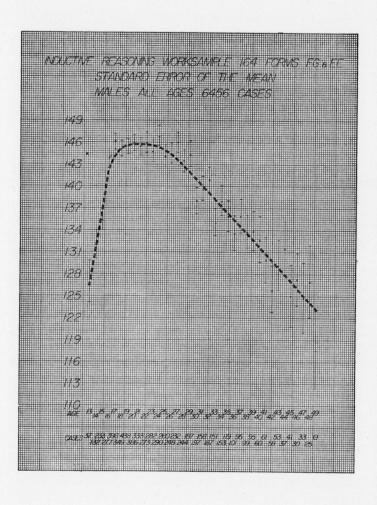

TYMPANUM is a part of the ear, and that ACCOMMODATION may apply to the eye, without being more specific. Then cease to be content with this inclusive sense and restrict it. Learn to distinguish explicitly between CONVECTION and CONDUCTION and, in airplane construction, between STACK and MANIFOLD. Finally connect the word with its exact opposite and so ultimately learn which is which, differentiating OBTUSE from ACUTE; SUBTRAHEND from MINUEND; WAVE LENGTH from FREQUENCY; MANTISSA from CHARACTERISTIC; and ABSCISSA from ORDINATE.

While a sure knowledge of these technical terms mounts through life, the boy who would distinguish himself in science cannot wait for time to give him words. For brilliant achievement is the product not solely of knowledge but of a synthesis with aptitudes; and at least one of these, inductive reasoning, significant to the pure scientist, deteriorates by age 24. In the inductive reasoning test, worksample 164, scores go up through the early years, to ages 18 or 19, not unlike vocabulary, reach a peak at 21, and turn down immediately.

Inverting the picture, the corporate enterprise or the government, the employer whoever he may be, who retires the older man loses with him an accumulation of knowledge which it will take years to replace; for only five per cent of the younger men aged 22 have the English vocabulary and technical vocabularies of the average man at 55. But the employer who needs aptitudes should seek the younger man.

Of INDUCTION the Oxford New English Dictionary says: 'The process of inferring a general law or principle from the observation of particular instances'. From Inductive Logic by Fowler, 1876, comes: 'Induction is the inference from the particular to the general'; and from Natural Philosophy, 1812, by John Playfair, the Scottish mathematician and physicist: 'It is from INDUCTION that all certain and accurate knowledge of the laws of nature is derived'. At a still earlier date, 1656, Thomas Stanley says in his History of Philosophy: 'INDUCTION is every method of reason which proceedeth from singulars to generals'. If induction or inductive reasoning as defined in these quotations is the trait which the Human Engineering Laboratory measures by means of worksample 164 and which is plotted in figure 7, then eminent scientists of the past should have pro-

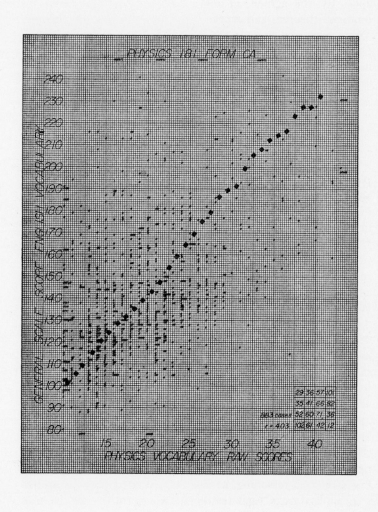

PHYSICS 181 FORM CA

pounded their laws of nature and general principles between the opportune ages of 18 and 24, with the trait at its precocious apex. By the age of 23 Isaac Newton had discovered the binomial theorem and worked on infinite series and fluxions. Writing later he says: 'In the same year (1666 at the age of 24) I began to think of gravity extending to the orb of the Moon, having thereby compared the force requisite to keep the Moon in her orb with the force of gravity at the surface of the Earth and found them to answer pretty nearly. All this was in the two years 1665 and 1666 for in those years I was in the prime of my age.' During the years to which Newton refers he was 23 and 24, for he was born in 1642. Albert Einstein announced relativity at the age of 26. Linnaeus published his classification of plants at 28. Carnot published his steam cycle at the same age; and Bohr announced his structure of the atom. Campbell and Garnett tell how the young Clerk Maxwell, Junior, at age 15, communicated a paper to the Edinburgh Royal Society on Oval Curves with a Plurality of Foci. Under present conditions in the United States boys at the summit of their inductive aptitude have neither opportunity for basic research, nor encouragement; and, though this country is justly noted for its applied engineering, its pure science must be suffering.

Compare the age curves for inductive reasoning and English vocabulary. Between 20 and 22 the inductive aptitude attains its height, with knowledge, as symbolized by vocabulary, significantly lower than it will be subsequently. The older man, with whom knowledge predominates, leans on the past and its accumulated findings. The younger generation, with more aptitudes than knowledge, seeks new laws, penetrates the unknown in both science and human affairs; for much as induction leads the technically minded boy to the perception of natural laws, so it draws the non-technical toward human laws. For inductive reasoning, at least as measured by worksample 164, approximates legal reasoning, and seems to be the trait which stimulates youth movements, without always sufficient knowledge to recognize historical prototypes. For this reason the older man should not be judged by what he was earlier, for at 40 he is a different person, higher in vocabulary and materially lower in the aptitude, or in its effective use.

To capitalize on inductive reasoning at its zenith, formal education, the colleges, science societies, and even the United States government, should give opportunity to apply this important aptitude at its height, in government if the technical trait, structural visualization, is low, or in pure science when this is high. More important still, education should proffer knowledge of these fields, science and government, well before ages 17 or 18, in time for it to be available during the years of maximum aptitude.

For inductive reasoning demands knowledge. Other aptitudes can be exercised at low-vocabulary levels. The mechanic uses structural visualization and yet may score below average in vocabulary. The clerk uses accounting aptitude; the factory assembler, finger dexterity. But no known work demands inductive reasoning without a comparably large and exact English vocabulary. Magazine editors rank high in inductive reasoning, but high also in English vocabulary. Lawyers average high inductive reasoning and high vocabulary. College professors score high in both.

To put into vigorous action the inductive-reasoning aptitude in a lasting contribution to pure science a boy must not count on present-day schools and colleges to furnish the needed technical knowledge, for laboratory physics rarely begins before junior or senior year of high school. Instead he must assemble his own equipment at home, lenses, mirrors, balances, magnets, coils, and gain a science vocabulary from books on his own shelves, in his own room, always available, and in great enough variety to answer any technical question; for authors differ widely in aptitudes and in the manner of expressing and explaining the same subject. Furthermore a boy should start even before he comprehends the printed text; for he will soon know the pictures, even the diagrams, and surprisingly quickly will fetch the right book from his own collection to have the answers to his incessant queries read aloud.

Far too often the child and even the adult is held or holds himself to reading one book through to the end before he feels he can buy another. Instead he should absorb a little from each, perhaps no more than a new word for which he is ready. The aviation term FUSELAGE, number one in the following pages, belongs among the first which the scientifically minded youngster should acquire. Of like difficulty are the technical terms GENERATOR, from electrical engineering, and PRODUCT, from mathematics. Though in three different books, these three words should all be learned before the remote ASPECT RATIO, DIHEDRAL, and GEODETIC, from the same book as FUSELAGE. To work in this way a boy should refer to numerous textbooks, and not re-read endlessly some abstruse page in one.

At age 24 as the effective use of inductive reasoning, and of other aptitudes, begins to wain, at first imperceptibly but nevertheless measurably, another problem confronts the aging individual. Knowledge, as indicated by vocabularies of various sorts, must replace the fall of inherent power, and to a degree dependent almost directly on how high one aspires; for in the population as a whole, vocabulary appears to be a continuous variable, distributed gradually from low to high. By contrast, each aptitude seems all or none, present in full or absent, and not in proportion to the test score. It is possessed more certainly by those who score high than by those nearer the median, but to no greater extent, scores varying because of extraneous factors, not because of a variation in the amount of the aptitude. Many persons tested show an aptitude pattern for eminence; but few have the requisite knowledge, few score as high as the top person in four thousand, the ratio, according to Francis Galton, in his Hereditary Genius, of the eminent.

Nearly every outstanding man and woman who has been tested scores high in the specialized terminology of his or her occupation or profession, and equally high in English vocabulary; and a surprisingly large percentage of those who score high reach the top. A boy or girl who remains low lacks this measurable trait of the successful person. Gaining a vocabulary may not infallibly lead to world renown; but its absence holds one back. In the theory of functions, in studying conditions for the convergence of series, there is an expression familiar to mathematicians: NECESSARY but not SUFFICIENT. A large and exact vocabulary acquired through diligence may not by itself be SUFFICIENT, but at this stage of research seems one of the NECESSARY conditions to eminence.

PRONUNCIATION

In this book no attempt has been made to give exact vowel sounds. In addition to the accent only two phonetic marks have been used, the long and the short. This book does not replace a dictionary; it is not primarily a reference book, but is an attempt to answer a few specific questions with which the general reader is frequently faced.

ă	CAP (*kăp*), FAT (*făt*), BLACK (*blăk*)
ā	MAKE (*māk*), CAGE (*kāj*), DAY (*dā*)
ĕ	MET (*mĕt*), TEN (*tĕn*), BELL (*bĕl*)
ē	DEEP (*dēp*), NEAT (*nēt*), SEEM (*sēm*)
ĭ	DIP (*dĭp*), IT (*ĭt*), THIS (*thĭs*)
ī	FIVE (*fīv*), LIKE (*līk*), FLY (*flī*)
ŏ	LOG (*lŏg*), ON (*ŏn*), TOP (*tŏp*)
ō	BONE (*bōn*), ROLL (*rōl*), NO (*nō*)
ŭ	UP (*ŭp*), SUN (*sŭn*), TUB (*tŭb*)
ū	TUNE (*tūn*), DUKE (*dūk*), USE (*ūz*)
ah	FAR (*fahr*), STAR (*stahr*), FATHER (*fah'-ther*)
aw	LAW (*law*), SAW (*saw*), CAUGHT (*kawt*)
er	HER (*her*), TURN (*tern*), DIRT (*dert*)
or	FOR (*for*), ORDER (*or'-der*), HORSE (*hors*)
oo	SCHOOL (*skool*), FOOD (*food*), BOOT (*boot*)
ŏŏ	BOOK (*bŏŏk*), LOOK (*lŏŏk*), FOOT (*fŏŏt*)

Only one accent mark (') has been used; the secondary accent, when it occurs, having been omitted. LESSON (*lĕs'-sŏn*); RAILROAD (*rāl'-rōd*); ELEPHANT (*ĕl'-ĕ-fănt*); EVERLASTING (*ĕv-er-lăs'-tĭng*).

1. *FUSELAGE* (*fū'-sē-lahj*) *n*. The framework of the body
   of an airplane to which the wings and tail assembly are
attached.

To the question: 'The body of an airplane', 18 persons out of
18 tested in Fort Worth, Texas, whose scores have been tabulated for the aviation vocabulary test, form A, answer correctly
FUSELAGE; and in Los Angeles, 54 out of 54. In New York 36
out of 37 answered correctly in one study; and 66 out of 66
in another. Adding the third New York group and the Philadelphia figures, 513 out of 515 answer FUSELAGE. The entire
population has learned this new term remarkably rapidly; for
FUSELAGE does not appear in the great ten-volumed Oxford
New English Dictionary built on historical principles, which
contains some 300,000 words, compiled in England and edited
by James A. H. Murray, the first volume dated 1888. Nor does
FUSELAGE appear in the six-volume Century Dictionary done in
America at about the same time.

According to the supplement to the Oxford New English
Dictionary, which appeared in 1933, FUSELAGE derives from the
French *fuseler*, to shape like a spindle, from *fuseau*, a spindle.
From the same language come other terms in modern aviation,
such as EMPENNAGE, LONGERON, and NACELLE, surviving perhaps from early ballooning days where the French led the
world. The word FUSELAGE itself may have been suggested by
the shape of the dirigible, which preceded the airplane, for
the lighter-than-air balloon designed by Tissanier and his
brother, and flown in 1883 and 1884, was called: 'Spindle
shaped'; and the balloon La France, of a year later, was called
FUSIFORM, spindle shaped, or in modern times STREAMLINED.

In the revised form AA, the mislead PROPELLER, which attracted no one and which seems remote, was changed to CHAS-
SIS. The word CHASSIS (*shǎs'-sē*) was used as early as 1870 for
the lower part of a gun carriage, which enables the gun to move
back and forth. Then CHASSIS became the frame of an automobile; and then the base frame of an airplane. Though the word
CHASSIS is associated with the wheels and with the structure
which holds them, it has attracted 3 out of 63 persons whose
scores have been tabulated for form AA, and is undoubtedly too
near a right answer to use as a mislead.

Writing in 1913, A. E. Berriman says: 'Another French word at present in common use is FUSELAGE, meaning the girder-like backbone employed in modern aeroplane design. This member also forms the body of the machine.' The French dictionary Larousse, in the 1935 edition, says: 'FUSELAGE, Ensemble des longerons, entrecises, tubes, etc., qui constituent la charpente d'un aëroplane'; assembly of longerons, braces, tubes, etc., which constitute the frame of an airplane. Assen Jordanoff, in his Illustrated Aviation Dictionary, defines the FUSELAGE as the

Form A. The body of an airplane.
Form AA. The frame of the body of an airplane.

FORM A. I.	FW	LA	NY	NY	NY	PH	SUM	FORM AA. I.	NY
FUSELAGE	18	54	36	66	139	200	513	FUSELAGE	60
tail	0	0	0	0	1	0	1	cabane	0
propeller	0	0	0	0	0	0	0	chassis	3
wing	0	0	0	0	0	0	0	wing	0
engine	0	0	0	0	0	0	0	engine	0
unmarked	0	0	1	0	0	0	1	unmarked	0
total	18	54	37	66	140	200	515	total	63

body to which the wings and tail unit are attached. In his illustration he shows clearly the framework, without its covering, with no seats for passengers or crew and no form of protection. Despite another dictionary of aviation defining the FUSELAGE as the body of an airplane which houses the crew, passengers, cargo, etc., the word FUSELAGE should be used for the framework, comparable to the structural steel of a building, and, though a part of the body in the complete plane as seen by the layman, means body only when this is an integral part of the structure.

2. *GENERATOR* (jĕn'-ĕ-rā-tor) *n.* A machine which uses mechanical energy to produce an electric current.

A GENERATOR is the opposite of a MOTOR. A MOTOR changes electricity into motion; a GENERATOR changes motion into electricity. A GENERATOR is fundamentally a coil of wire revolving between the poles of a magnet. The coil may be turned by hand in a very small generator; by a MOTOR in a MOTOR-GEN-

ERATOR set; by a turbine; or by any sort of independent engine. The motion of the coil of the GENERATOR, through the magnetic field, produces electricity in the wires of the coil.

GENERATOR, DYNAMO, and MAGNETO, are nearly synonymous. A MAGNETO (măg-nē'-tō) is a small generator, usually with permanent magnets, frequently today one which furnishes electricity to a spark coil which ignites gasoline or petrol vapor in an internal combustion engine.

The word DYNAMO antedates GENERATOR, and itself replaced a still earlier DYNAMO-ELECTRIC MACHINE. According to Silvanus P. Thompson, later principal of and professor of physics in the City and Guilds of London Technical College, Finsbury, writing in 1882, the name DYNAMO-ELECTRIC MACHINE was first applied by Dr. Werner Siemens (zē'-měnz), of Siemens Halske, in a communication made to the Berlin Academy in January, 1867. He there described a machine for generating electric

A machine for creating electric current.

FORM E. 3.	BO	FW	LA	NY	NY	NY	NY	PH	TU	SUM
eliminator	0	0	0	0	0	0	0	1	0	1
antenna	0	0	0	0	0	0	0	0	0	0
GENERATOR	27	48	32	20	20	40	210	99	28	524
turbine	1	1	1	0	0	0	6	0	0	9
spark coil	0	0	0	0	0	0	1	0	0	1
unmarked	0	1	0	0	0	0	1	0	0	2
total	28	50	33	20	20	40	218	100	28	537

power by the application of mechanical power, the currents being induced in the coils of a rotating armature by the action of electromagnets which were themselves excited by the currents so generated. The machine was, in fact, a self-exciting dynamo. In the same year Professor Thompson wrote that: 'The word DYNAMO is now being used as a noun in the place of DYNAMO-ELECTRIC MACHINE, and from its convenience it will probably soon become the generic term'.

Two years later, 1884, in Dynamo-electric Machinery, Professor Thompson continued: 'A DYNAMO is a DYNAMO, in fact, whether its magnets are excited by the whole of its own current, or by a current from an independent source'. 'The arbitrary distinction between so-called MAGNETO-ELECTRIC MA-CHINES fails when examined carefully. In all of these machines a magnet, whether permanently excited, independently excited, or self-excited, is employed to provide a field of magnetic force'. Today all such machines especially if large are called GENERATORS.

The word GENERATOR comes through the French *générateur* (*jā-nā-ră-ter'*) from the Latin *generator*. This noun comes in turn from the Latin verb *generare*, to generate, produce, beget, procreate, from *genus, generis,* kind, race, family. Directly from the Latin *genus* comes the botanical and zoological term

A machine for creating electric current.

FORM E. 3.   ENGLISH VOCABULARY

	HIGH	LOW
eliminator	0	0
antenna	0	0
GENERATOR	40	35
turbine	0	5
spark coil	0	0
unmarked	0	0
total	40	40

GENUS, a group of species, a classification more general and in-clusive than a SPECIES, and smaller than a FAMILY. From the same Latin source come the English verb to GENERATE, to pro-duce, create, the noun a GENERATION, a group produced, created, and the chemical terms HYDROGEN, water producing, and OXY-GEN, literally, by derivation, acid producing.

With the definition: 'A machine for creating electric cur-rent', nearly everyone answers GENERATOR, 524 persons out of 537, but 9 answer TURBINE. A TURBINE converts moving water, or steam under pressure, into mechanical power. A TURBINE may turn the coil in a GENERATOR. The GENERATOR then converts this mechanical motion into electricity.

In a small separate study of the relation of physics vocabu-lary to English vocabulary, TURBINE is the mislead marked by the low-English-vocabulary group, by 5 persons out of 40 who score between 76 and 114 on the English vocabulary general scale; while the mislead TURBINE is not marked by those who score high in English vocabulary.

Of 28 persons tested in Boston on the physics vocabulary test called worksample 181, 27 mark GENERATOR, and 1 TURBINE; in Fort Worth, of 50 persons, 48 mark GENERATOR, 1 TURBINE, while 1 person for some reason skipped the item and marked nothing. In each city, and even with samplings as small as twenty persons, the figures show the word GENERATOR to be widely understood and so a simple item when used in a vocabulary test. This implies some feature in the word GENERATOR or in the concept GENERATOR which makes the word easy to learn and remember.

In constructing a vocabulary test, the initial item should be easy to give the examinee confidence both in his own knowledge and in having understood the directions. A difficult first item discourages a low-vocabulary person enough sometimes to arouse rebellion to the rest of the test; but after marking one item correctly there seems a tendency to try a bit harder to find the right answer to the next. As 524 persons out of 537 mark the present item correctly, perhaps no change should be made in the revised form. But of the four misleads neither ANTENNA nor SPARK COIL has been marked by anyone, and there seems little reason for either in the test. Both have been changed in the new form, one to MOTOR, the motive part of a MOTOR-GENERATOR SET, and the other to CONDENSER.

3. *PRODUCT* (*prŏd'-ŭkt*) *n.* In mathematics, the result of multiplying one quantity by another.

The noun PRODUCT comes from Latin, as do many mathematical terms, from *productum*, the neuter of *productus*, the past participle of *producere*, to lead forth, produce, bring forward. This Latin verb is in turn a combination of *pro*, forward, and *ducere*, to lead, to bring. From the verb *ducere*, to lead, come a host of English words, many of them starting with such common Latin prefixes as: *re-*, back; *de-*, from; *in-*, in, on; and *con-*, with. From the past participle *ductus* come the verb to DEDUCT, to take away, subtract; the nouns AQUEDUCT for leading water, and VIADUCT, a structure for leading or bringing a road across a valley; as well as the adjective DUCTILE, easily led, and so bendable, malleable. From the same past participle and starting with *con-* comes the verb to CONDUCT, to lead, guide. From the verb *ducere*, to lead, and the prefix *re-*, back, comes the English verb to REDUCE, by derivation to lead back, as: 'To REDUCE a statement to simple terms', to lead it back to simplicity. To DEDUCE is to lead from, to draw a conclusion from facts. To INDUCE is to lead someone into some-

The result of multiplying two values.

FORM A. 17.	BO	NY	SUM	FORM AA. I.	NY
moment	o	o	o	aggregate	I
multiplier	o	o	o	multiplier	o
multiplicand	I	o	I	multiplicand	7
PRODUCT	19	41	60	PRODUCT	124
sigma	o	o	o	commutant	o
unmarked	o	o	o	unmarked	o
total	20	41	61	total	132

thing, or in science to lead on from observations and laboratory experiments to a general law. Even the verb to EDUCATE comes from *ducere*, to lead, to bring, for to EDUCATE is by derivation to bring up. The fact that many mathematical terms come from the same Latin sources as literary words may be one of the reasons for the unexpectedly high correlation between a knowledge of technical terms and a large and exact English literary vocabulary.

To the question: 'The result of multiplying two values', nearly everyone who has taken the vocabulary of mathematics and whose scores have been tabulated answers correctly PRODUCT. Only three quarters of those tested know the mathematical term EXPONENT which appears farther on in this book. Near the middle of the book half of those tested know the trigonometrical term SINE; while only a quarter know CONVERSE, as applied to a proposition, and COMMENSURABLE, measurable in the same units. At the end of this book no more than the one person in five who, by the laws of chance, should guess the answer from among five choices, marks correctly POSTULATE, HYPOCYCLOID, and PERMUTATION.

To return to PRODUCT, in the simple equation: $10 \times 3 = 30$, the PRODUCT of multiplying 10 by 3 is 30. The MULTIPLICAND, a mislead in the test marked by 7 persons out of 132, is 10, the larger of two numbers to be multiplied. The MULTIPLIER, by which the MULTIPLICAND is to be multiplied, is 3; and the PRODUCT is 30.

The outcome of an addition is the SUM; the outcome of a subtraction is the DIFFERENCE; the outcome of a division is the QUOTIENT; the outcome of a multiplication, the PRODUCT.

4. *OBTUSE* (*ŏb-tūs'*) *adj.* In mathematics, blunt, dull, applied to an angle greater than a right angle; or as E. Coles, Schoolmaſter, and Teacher of the Tongue to Foreigners, says in his English Dictionary of 1724 explaining the Difficult Terms that are uſed in Divinity, Huſbandry, Phyſick, Philoſophy, Law, Navigation, Mathematicks, and other Arts and Sciences: 'OBTUSE Angle, when two lines include more than a Right'.

OBTUSE is used in literature to mean dull-witted, heavy, impervious to reason: 'An OBTUSE mind', 'An OBTUSE person'.

The adjective OBTUSE comes from the Latin *obtusus*, blunt, dull, blunted, the past participle of *obtundere*, to OBTUND, to dull, blunt, originally to strike upon, beat; for *obtundere* is a combination of *ob*, upon, and *tundere*, to strike. The familiar CONTUSION comes from the Latin *con-*, together, and the same verb *tundere*, to strike. A CONTUSION (*kŏn-tū'-zhŏn*, not *kŏntŭsh'-ŏn*) is a bruise from a blunt instrument. The unusual adjective PERTUSE, from *per*, through, and the same past participle, *tusus*, of the verb *tundere*, means struck through, with holes, and so punched, perforated.

OBTUSE is one of the easiest of the mathematical terms which have been studied, judged by the fact that: 'Angle greater than 90 degrees', is answered correctly by 349 persons out of 357, only 4 answering the opposite ACUTE, the most frequently marked mislead.

From the first English translation of Euclid's Elements, published in London in 1570 with the title: The Elements of Geometrie of the most auncient Philosopher Euclide of Megara. Faithfully (now first) translated into the Englishe toung by H. Billingsley, Citizen of London, comes: 'An OBTUSE angle is that which is greater than a right angle'. Despite H. Billingsley there seem to have been two Euclids. Euclid of Megara was a Greek philosopher a hundred years or more before Euclid of Alexandria, the author of The Elements of Geometrie.

A term such as OBTUSE may be really easy, generally known, or may occasionally be marked correctly because of poor misleads. Were OBTUSE difficult, it would no doubt be confused more often with ACUTE, for such an exact opposite of the cor-

Angle greater than 90 degrees.

B. 3.	NY	MISC.	SUM
acute	1	3	4
OBTUSE	47	302	349
exterior	0	3	3
inferior	0	0	0
vertical	0	0	0
unmarked	0	1	1
total	48	309	357

rect answer is often the most frequently marked mislead which can be found. With so easy a word, no mislead is apt to be marked; and though a mislead chosen by no one is ordinarily regarded as a failure, in this instance no changes have been made.

Each revision of a test must for a time be scored on the norms computed for the previous version, at least until cases collect and new norms can be computed. To avoid serious inaccuracies in this interim relatively few changes should be made at each step.

5. *BISECT* (*bī-sĕkt'*) *v.* To cut in half, partition once, divide into two equal parts.

BISECT is a combination of the Latin *bi-*, two, and *sectus*. The Latin *bi-* is the combining form of the Latin *bis*, two, and appears in BICYCLE, a two-cycled vehicle, two-wheeled velocipede; in the statistical term BIMODAL, with two MODES, two peaks in a curve; in BINOMIAL (*bī-nō'-mĭ-ăl*), two-termed; and in BIFOCAL, having two foci. From the same Latin *bis*, two, comes the adjective *binus*, which in the plural becomes *bini*, as in BINOCULAR, two-eyed, designed for two eyes.

The Latin *sectus*, the second part of BISECT, is the past participle of the verb *secare*, to cut. From *sectus* come the verb to INTERSECT, literally to cut between, to cut across, pass over, and INTERSECTION, the corresponding noun; and from *secare*, to cut, comes SECANT, a line cutting a circle.

To the question: 'To divide in two', 122 persons out of 132 answer BISECT; while 6 answer FACTOR. The verb to FACTOR is to divide a number into other smaller numbers which when multiplied together give the original number. Thus 2 and 3 are

To divide in two.

FORM A. 44.	BO	NY	SUM	FORM AA. 2.	NY
differentiate	0	0	0	intersect	1
BISECT	19	39	58	BISECT	122
trisect	0	0	0	trisect	3
subtract	0	1	1	subtract	0
factor	0	1	1	factor	6
unmarked	1	0	1	unmarked	0
total	20	41	61	total	132

FACTORS of 6. The noun FACTOR is also used more generally for one of the elements which enters a problem. To FACTOR is to divide into smaller parts and so is conceivably a correct answer of: 'Divide in two'.

The verb BISECT applies ordinarily to a line or geometric figure. Although occasionally to BISECT is to cut merely in two parts, in geometry the word has its original meaning of cut in two equal parts, divide in half. There is also a noun, BISECTION, the act of cutting in half; and BISECTOR, the line or plane which does the cutting.

6. *EQUILIBRIUM* (*ē-kwĭ-lĭb'-rē-ŭm*) *n.* A state in which the forces on a body balance one another, the situation when the sum of the forces pulling in any direction equals the sum of the forces pulling in the opposite direction, and the sum of the moments tending to rotate clockwise around any line or axis equals the sum of the moments tending to rotate counterclockwise around the same line or axis.

In the Dictionary of Joseph E. Worcester, published in Boston in 1865, based on his own earlier Universal and Critical Dictionary of 1846, which in turn was based on Todd's edition of Samuel Johnson's Dictionary of 1755, appears: 'EQUILIBRIUM: The state of rest produced by the mutual counter action of two or more forces; equipoise'.

Ephraim Chambers, in his five-volumed folio-sized Cyclopaedia first published in 1728, writes: 'A balance is in *equilibrio* when the two ends are so exactly poised that neither of them ascends or descends, but both retain their parallel position to the horizon. From this circumstance the word is originally taken, as being a compound of *aequus*, equal, and *libra*, balance; whence we frequently use the word BALANCE in lieu thereof.'

Existing conditions are balanced and balance maintained.

FORM E. 4.	BO	FW	LA	NY	NY	NY	NY	PH	TU	SUM
nul vector	1	0	0	0	0	1	1	1	0	4
congruence	0	0	0	0	0	0	5	0	0	5
EQUILIBRIUM	27	46	32	19	20	39	209	98	26	516
parallelism	0	4	1	1	0	0	1	1	2	10
alternation	0	0	0	0	0	0	2	0	0	2
unmarked	0	0	0	0	0	0	0	0	0	0
total	28	50	33	20	20	40	218	100	28	537

The Latin phrase: *in equilibrio* rarely appears in English dictionaries but is used occasionally by English authors. From the same Latin *aequus*, equal, come the adjective EQUINOCTIAL and the corresponding noun EQUINOX, the time at which the sun crosses the equator so that everywhere on earth day and night are of equal length. From the Latin *libra*, a balance, comes the French *livre*, a pound, with the letter v in the French word in place of the Latin B. Also from the Latin *libra*, balance, come the unusual verb to LIBRATE, to oscillate like the beam of a balance, and the corresponding noun LIBRATION.

If FUSELAGE (1) and GENERATOR (2) are marked correctly by nearly everyone because they are tangible machines which can be seen, the same is not true of EQUILIBRIUM, an abstract concept. With the exception of FUSELAGE, the first word in this book, easy words as a whole, those marked correctly by a large percentage of examinees, date further back in the language than lesser known ones. This may mean that the ideas named by these early words are easier to grasp. EQUILIBRIUM, marked correctly by 516 out of 537 persons, was used by Robert Boyle in the first of his published studies, printed at Oxford in 1660: New Experiments, phyſico-mechanical, touching the ſpring of the air and its effects, where it was spelt AEQUILIBRIUM.

PARALLELISM, marked by 10 persons out of 537, the most frequently marked mislead, is the state of being parallel. Two forces may be parallel but pull in the same direction and so not be in EQUILIBRIUM. Or parallel forces may pull in opposite di-

Existing conditions are balanced and balance maintained.

FORM E. 4.   ENGLISH VOCABULARY

	HIGH	LOW
nul vector	0	0
congruence	0	0
EQUILIBRIUM	40	39
parallelism	0	0
alternation	0	0
unmarked	0	1
total	40	40

rections but not at the same point and so again not be in EQUILIBRIUM. Sir Robert Stawell Ball, astronomer royal of Ireland, in his Experimental Mechanics, says: 'When at rest under the action of two equal and opposite forces, a point is said to be in EQUILIBRIUM'.

7. *FOCAL LENGTH* (fō'-kăl lĕngth). Distance from the optical center of a lens to the point at which parallel rays of light converge and cross after meeting the lens.

The adjective FOCAL comes from the noun FOCUS. This word FOCUS as applied to a lens was introduced into physics by Johann Kepler in 1604. It comes from the Latin *focus*, fireplace, hearth, the center of the household. The Oxford New English Dictionary conjectures that Kepler chose the word to signify the burning point of the lens; for strong rays, as from the sun, burn paper held at the FOCUS. A FOCUS is any point at which rays come to a point. Light from a source so distant that the rays are practically parallel, after passing through a converging lens, meet at a point called the PRINCIPAL FOCUS, the FOCUS of rays which were parallel to one another and to the principal axis of the lens before striking the lens.

The FOCAL LENGTH is the distance from the optical center of the lens to this particular focus, the PRINCIPAL FOCUS. For a given kind of glass or transparent material, the thicker the lens

Distance from a lens to the image of a distant object.

FORM E. 18.	BO	FW	LA	NY	NY	NY	NY	PH	TU	SUM
axis	0	0	0	0	0	1	4	2	0	7
foot-candle	0	0	0	1	0	0	3	0	0	4
penumbra	0	1	2	1	0	0	1	0	0	5
incidence	1	1	0	1	2	0	7	2	0	14
FOCAL LENGTH	25	48	30	17	18	37	203	96	28	502
unmarked	2	0	1	0	0	2	0	0	0	5
total	28	50	33	20	20	40	218	100	28	537

the more sharply the rays bend, the more quickly they converge, and the shorter the FOCAL LENGTH. With a thin double-convex lens, with the same radius of curvature on the two sides, the OPTICAL CENTER, from which the FOCAL LENGTH is measured,

Distance from a lens to the image of a distant object.

FORM E. 18.   ENGLISH VOCABULARY

	HIGH	LOW
axis	0	2
foot-candle	0	2
penumbra	1	0
incidence	1	1
FOCAL LENGTH	38	34
unmarked	0	1
total	40	40

is the geometric center of the lens. With a plano-convex lens the OPTICAL CENTER is where the principal axis meets the curved face. With other types, the OPTICAL CENTER is outside the lens on the concave side.

With a concave reflecting mirror the FOCAL LENGTH is the distance from the mirror to the point at which parallel rays reflected back from the mirror converge and cross.

With a diverging lens the FOCAL LENGTH is the distance from the lens to the point where the diverging rays from a distant object would meet if extended backwards.

To the question: 'Distance from the lens to the image of a distant object', 502 persons out of 537 answer correctly FOCAL LENGTH; and no significant number concentrate on any other particular answer. FOCAL LENGTH seems to be one of the easier concepts in physics.

8. *ANTENNA* (ăn-tĕn'-nah) *n.* A wire, or combination of wires, supported in the air for sending electric waves into space, or for receiving them, a long wire mounted preferably in an exposed position.

As early as 1898 Marconi discovered the importance of grounding the receiving ANTENNA, the earth and the ANTENNA acting like the two plates of a huge condenser.

To the question: 'Wire suspended so as to receive short wave radiations', 218 persons out of 224 answer correctly ANTENNA. This easiest word of the radio-and-physics test dates far back in the language, though certainly not with its modern meaning.

Wire suspended so as to receive short wave radiations.

FORM A. 2.	NY	NY	NY	SUM
line	1	1	0	2
ANTENNA	35	38	145	218
ground	0	0	1	1
contact	1	0	1	2
bridge	0	1	0	1
unmarked	0	0	0	0
total	37	40	147	224

The Latin *antenna* originally meant a sail-yard. The first application of the word to mean the feelers of an insect seems to have occurred in a Latin translation of Aristotle. In 1813 John Mason Good wrote: 'ANTENNAE, ANTENNAS, the horn-like processes projecting from the head of insects'. And from Huxley in the Crayfish, 1880, comes: 'The ANTENNAE are organs of touch'. But in the first edition of the Oxford New English Dictionary the initial volume of which appeared in 1888 the word ANTENNA is designated as not naturalized, meaning they regarded it even then as still a Latin word.

In 1899 Marconi used the word AERIAL: 'A vertical conductor which I will call the AERIAL conductor'. By 1906 AERIAL conductor and AERIAL wire, where AERIAL is an adjective, had been shortened to AERIAL the noun. Writing for the Encyclopaedia Britannica in 1902 J. A. Fleming, the devisor of Fleming's right-hand and left-hand rules for the direction of motion in generators and motors, said: 'The great improvement introduced by Marconi was the employment of this vertical air-wire, AERIAL, ANTENNA, or elevated conductor'. This was one of the earliest uses of the word ANTENNA in this sense, for Fleming was interested in words and felt the need here of giving several synonyms. When the two words are differentiated that part of the ANTENNA which is suspended in the air is called the AERIAL.

The ANTENNA is connected with the ground through a coil, one of the coils of a transformer. Radio waves induce small alternating electromotive forces in the ANTENNA and cause electrons to surge through the coil to the earth and back repeatedly.

9. *CIRCUIT* (*ser′-kĭt*) *n.* A closed course traversed by an electric current, closed path of a current.

CIRCUIT goes back through Middle English to the Latin *circuitus*, a going around, from *circuire*, a contraction of *circum-ire*, to go around, a combination of *circum*, around, and *ire*, to go. Not until 1800 was the word CIRCUIT used in the Medical Journal for the path of an electric current. Three hundred years earlier, in 1494, a CIRCUIT was the journey of a judge through his appointed area. More than a hundred years before that a CIRCUIT, as used by John Wyclif (*wĭk′-lĭf*) in 1382 and by Chaucer in 1386, was an imaginary line drawn around an area, or the course followed in going around. The idea of an imaginary line and of going around an area both survive in today's technical term CIRCUIT.

Many substances through which electricity may flow, as for example a CONDUCTOR or an ELECTROLYTE, are not CIRCUITS. A

CIRCUIT must be closed. The phrase: OPEN CIRCUIT suggests a break in what would otherwise be a CIRCUIT. The phrase: CLOSED CIRCUIT is justified only to call attention to a previous break which has been closed.

To the question: 'Path through which a current flows', 497 persons out of 537 answer CIRCUIT; but 19 answer CYCLE. A

Path through which a current flows.

FORM E. 12.	BO	FW	LA	NY	NY	NY	NY	PH	TU	SUM
cycle	3	3	0	2	0	3	7	0	1	19
CIRCUIT	21	46	32	18	20	37	197	100	26	497
battery	0	0	0	0	0	0	0	0	0	0
oscillator	0	0	0	0	0	0	1	0	0	1
coil	2	0	1	0	0	0	13	0	1	17
unmarked	2	1	0	0	0	0	0	0	0	3
total	28	50	33	20	20	40	218	100	28	537

subsequent study of a small selected group shows that of 40 persons high in English literary vocabulary all mark CIRCUIT correctly; while of 40 low in English vocabulary 7 mark CYCLE. The English CYCLE and the corresponding French *cycle* go back to the Greek κύκλος (kyklos), a ring, circle, wheel, disk,

Path through which a current flows.

FORM E. 12. ENGLISH VOCABULARY		
	HIGH	LOW
cycle	0	7
CIRCUIT	40	31
battery	0	0
oscillator	0	0
coil	0	2
unmarked	0	0
total	40	40

orbit, revolution. The original meaning of CYCLE in English was an imaginary circle or orbit in the heavens. Both a CYCLE in this sense and a CIRCUIT are imaginary lines representing closed paths. A CYCLE may be the path of a heavenly body; a CIRCUIT the path of an electric current.

10. *AMPHIBIAN* (*ăm-fĭb'-ĭ-ăn*) *adj.* An airplane designed to rise from and alight on either land or water. With an AMPHIBIAN the wheels are drawn back, retracted, except when alighting on land.

The word AMPHIBIAN comes from the Greek ἀμφίβιος (amphibios), living a double life, a combination of ἀμφί (amphi), on both sides, and βίος (bios), life. In zoology, the AMPHIBIA are animals which can live both on the land and in the water,

A plane equipped for landing on water or land.

FORM A. 2.	FW	LA	NY	NY	NY	PH	SUM	FORM AA. 2.	NY
monoplane	0	0	1	0	1	1	3	monoplane	0
biplane	0	0	0	0	4	1	5	composite	0
AMPHIBIAN	17	54	35	65	123	193	487	AMPHIBIAN	59
seaplane	1	0	1	1	12	5	20	seaplane	4
flying boat	0	0	0	0	0	0	0	tandem	0
unmarked	0	0	0	0	0	0	0	unmarked	0
total	18	54	37	66	140	200	515	total	63

though they are not able to breathe under water. They include the frogs, turtles, crocodiles, seals, walruses, otters, beavers, and hippopotami. From the Greek βίος (bios) come BIOLOGY, the science of life, BIOGRAPHY, the story of a life, and BIOCHEMISTRY, the chemistry of living things.

To the question: 'A plane equipped for landing on water or land', the only popular misconception is SEAPLANE, marked by 1 person out of 18 in Fort Worth, Texas, by 5 out of 200 in Philadelphia, and 4 out of 63 in the newly revised form AA. A SEAPLANE is any airplane designed to rise from and alight on the water. It may have floats or be the boat type, a FLYING BOAT.

Unlike FUSELAGE (1), which is new to the English language, AMPHIBIAN goes back at least to 1609, for Philemon Holland used the word in one of his translations: 'Some live on land and water both, whereupon they are named AMPHIBIA'. Ben Jonson used the word in the same year.

11. *BRACKETS* (*brăk'-kĕts*) *pl. n.* In mathematics, [ ], used in algebra to show that a group of symbols are to be treated together as one; used in literature to enclose a reference, ex-

planation, or note, to separate it from the context. BRACKETS were formerly called CROTCHETS (*krŏt'-chĕts*).

PARENTHESES (*pah-rĕn'-thē-sēz*), the plural, a pair of upright curves, are used more commonly for this purpose than BRACKETS. Thus the expression: (a + b) x means that a and b are added together and their sum then multiplied by x. The expression could be rewritten: ax + bx. The same expression without

[ ].

FORM C. 2.	CH	FORM CA. 2.	CH	LA	NY	NY	PH	SUM
braces	3	braces	0	1	5	12	5	23
BRACKETS	60	BRACKETS	39	35	86	241	68	469
times	3	times	1	1	2	17	0	21
groups	2	groups	0	0	3	1	0	4
coefficients	0	coefficients	0	0	1	3	1	5
unmarked	0	unmarked	0	0	0	3	0	3
total	68	total	40	37	97	277	74	525

FORM CB. 1.	NY
braces	4
BRACKETS	75
times	0
groups	3
vincula	1
unmarked	3
total	86

the PARENTHESES: a + bx means multiply b times x and then add this product to a. In numbers (2 + 3)4 = 5 × 4 = 20; while 2 + 3 × 4 = 2 + 12 = 14.

BRACKETS indicate a large group of symbols including within it a smaller group enclosed in PARENTHESES. For a still larger group BRACES { } are customary. For a still smaller group within the PARENTHESES a straight horizontal line is drawn over the symbols to be grouped. This is called a VINCULUM, from the Latin *vincere*, to bind.

To the question: '[ ]', 469 persons out of 525 answer BRACKETS; and 23 BRACES. The three terms: BRACES, BRACKETS, and PARENTHESES, have not always been differentiated. BRACES are made like this: { }; BRACKETS are square: [ ]; and PARENTHESES rounded: ( ). But the word PARENTHESIS has sometimes in the past included the square form, now called BRACKET.

Little is known with certainty of the derivation of the word with this meaning. It is connected with Spanish and Portuguese words for a projecting molding, and BRACKET is used today in architecture for a supporting piece on a wall.

In algebra, PARENTHESES, BRACKETS, and BRACES, are often essential parts of the mathematical manipulation, and frequently real aids in thinking. In literature they often take the place of a writer's ability to construct an English sentence. Those unacquainted with A Dictionary of Modern English Usage by H. W. Fowler should read his article on the PARENTHESIS; and, under the heading STOPS, his comments on BRACKETS and double dashes.

Writing on Poetry, A Rhapsody, in 1733, Dean Swift says:

> The Muse invoked, sit down to write;
> Blot out, correct, insert, refine,
> Enlarge, diminish, interline;
> Be mindful, when invention fails,
> To scratch your head, and bite your nails.
>   Your poem finish'd, next your care
> Is needful to transcribe it fair.
> In modern wit all printed trash is
> Set off with numerous breaks and dashes.

12. *SQUARE* (*skwār*) *adj.* A quantity multiplied by itself, with 2 as an exponent, a quantity raised to the second power, of the second degree.

The s at the beginning of this word goes back through Old French, and appears in the Spanish, Portuguese, and Italian words for SQUARE, but was not in the original Latin *quadra*, a square. This was the feminine of the adjective *quadrus*, four-cornered, from *quatuor*, four. From *quadra* come QUADRATIC, involving the square and no higher power of the unknown, and QUADRILATERAL, four-sided.

Given the expression: 'x^2', 120 persons out of 132 answer correctly x-SQUARE. This means x times x, x multiplied by itself.

The expression 3^2 equals 9; 4^2 equals 16. The expression x^3 is read x cube or x third; and x^4 is read x to the fourth power or x

$$x^2.$$

FORM A. 9.	BO	NY	SUM	FORM AA. 6.	NY
two x	1	1	2	two x	4
x sub 2	0	0	0	half x	1
X-SQUARE	19	38	57	X-SQUARE	120
square root of x	0	1	1	square root of x	4
x second	0	1	1	x second	3
unmarked	0	0	0	unmarked	0
total	20	41	61	total	132

fourth; and x^2 is correctly read x second and should not be a mislead in the test.

13. *CELL* (sĕl) *n.* Two metals immersed in a dilute acid for the purpose of generating electricity by chemical action, a receptacle containing electrodes in an electrolyte.

The English word CELL comes from the Latin *cella*, a small room, an apartment, sometimes a store closet, a prison cell, or a

An electrical system involving two metals immersed in a dilute acid.

FORM F. 2.	BO
CELL	9
condenser	2
transmitter	0
Tesla-transformer	0
stator	0
unmarked	0
total	11

slave's room. The Latin *cella* always suggested one of several rooms in a building. The same word designated one of the compartments or cells of a honeycomb; some say the original application. The English CELL was first applied technically in electricity to one of the compartments of the wooden trough of Cruikshank's voltaic battery; and later to one of the divisions or CELLS of Children's battery, designed by John George Children, an English physicist who lived from 1777 to 1852. Henry Watts in the first volume of his Dictionary of Chemistry, which appeared in 1863, says: 'In Daniell's battery, each CELL consists of a copper cylinder, within which is placed a CELL of porous earthenware'. Here CELL means the containing vessel and not one compartment in a group of several. More recently Cassell's Encyclopaedic Dictionary defines a CELL as: 'A single jar, bath, or division of a compound vessel containing a couple of plates, say copper and zinc, united to their opposites or to each other usually by a wire'.

To the question: 'An electrical system involving two metals immersed in a dilute acid', the popular wrong answer is CONDENSER. A CONDENSER is fundamentally two metal plates, as called for in the definition; but they are not immersed in a dilute acid. Instead they are separated by some sort of dielectric or nonconducting substance. The charge on a CONDENSER depends upon the space between the plates not becoming ionized and upon a spark not jumping across. A CELL depends upon ions moving constantly from one metal plate to the other.

14. *VOLUME* (*vŏl'-ūm*) *n*. Determinate bulk, solid contents, size, amount, measure of tridimensional space.

The word VOLUME comes from the Latin *volumen*, a roll, coil, as a roll of manuscript, a written document rolled up, a scroll, from *volvere*, to roll round. This Latin *volvere*, and its past participle *vulsus*, are the source of enough English words so that it should be learned and remembered. From the verb *volvere* come the English verb to REVOLVE, to turn about an axis, and the noun REVOLVER; also INVOLVED, turned back into itself and so complicated; EVOLUTION, a gradual unrolling of the future; CONVOLUTIONS, a word used of the turns of a sea shell; and finally from the past participle *vulsus* the literary word REVULSION, a turning away.

The original meaning of VOLUME in English was a roll of parchment for writing. The word was used in this way by Wyclif (*wĭk'-lĭf*) in 1382. From this, VOLUME came to mean any sort of written material, and so a book. By 1530 VOLUME was used for something the size and bulk of a book; and finally from this, a hundred years later, VOLUME came to be used for the abstract quality bulk, contents, amount, solid mass.

To the question: 'Quantitative content of a solid body', 120 persons out of 132 answer VOLUME; while 10 answer AREA. AREA refers to the surface, often to a plane. The AREA of a circle

Quantitative content of a solid body.

FORM A. 35.	BO	NY	SUM	FORM AA. 3.	NY
area	1	2	3	area	10
sigma	0	0	0	section	1
integral	0	0	0	surface	0
moment	0	0	0	moment	1
VOLUME	18	39	57	VOLUME	120
unmarked	1	0	1	unmarked	0
total	20	41	61	total	132

is πr^2; the VOLUME of a sphere is $4/3 \pi r^3$. AREA is two dimensional; VOLUME, three dimensional. Even the surface AREA of a sphere, $4 \pi r^2$, is expressed as a square, VOLUME as a cube.

15. *DIAGONAL* (dī-ăg'-ō-năl) *n*. A straight line from one corner of a figure to the opposite corner.

George Crabb, an English lawyer, author of Dictionary of English Synonyms, says in his little known Technological Dictionary of 1833: 'A straight line drawn across a figure from one angle to another, which by some is called a DIAMETER'. Crabb continues: 'DIAGONALS principally belong to quadrilateral figures, and divide them into two equal parts'.

To the question: 'A line passing through non-adjacent corners of a four-sided figure', 325 persons out of 357 answer DIAGONAL; while the others divide almost evenly among the four misleads.

The word DIAGONAL comes from the Greek διαγών (diagon), διαγώνιος (diagonios), literally from angle to angle, a combination of διά (dia), across, and γωνία (gonia), angle. The Greek διά (dia), across, through, appears also in DIAMETER, the measure across or through a circle. The Greek γωνία (gonia), angle, occurs in numerous geometrical terms. PENTAGONAL (pĕn-tăg'-ō-năl) means five-cornered, five-angled; HEXAGONAL, six-cornered; OCTAGONAL, eight-cornered; and POLYGONAL (pō-lĭg'-ō-

năl), many-cornered. From Billingsley's English translation of Euclid, 1570, comes: 'DIAGONAL lines drawn from the opposite angles'.

Despite some 300,000 English words in the Oxford New English Dictionary, three fifty-word forms of the mathematics vocabulary test, with a total of 150 test words and 600 misleads, nearly exhaust the vocabulary of mathematics. Though SECANT

A line passing through non-adjacent corners of a four-sided figure.

FORM B. 7.	NY	MISC.	SUM
perpendicular	0	5	5
vector	1	9	10
DIAGONAL	43	282	325
normal	4	3	7
secant	0	8	8
unmarked	0	2	2
total	48	309	357

appears elsewhere in form BB, the mislead has been retained here, partly because it is marked by 8 persons, the second most frequently marked mislead, and partly for want of an apparently better choice.

16. *PERPENDICULAR* (*per-pĕn-dĭk′-ū-lahr*) *adj.* Meeting another line so as to form equal angles on the two sides, making a right angle with another straight line.

The word PERPENDICULAR comes from the Latin *perpendiculum*, a plumb line, plummet, from *perpendere*, to hang downward, a combination of *per-*, through, and *pendere*, to weigh, to hang. Like the Latin *ducere*, to lead, and *volvere*, to roll, the Latin verb *pendere*, to hang, is the source of numerous English literary words. From *pendere*, to hang, come the English adjective PENDENT, hanging, and the noun PENDANT, a hanging ornament. From the same *pendere*, to hang, come DEPENDENT, hanging down from something and so needing something for support; and the opposite, INDEPENDENT, self-reliant; also IMPENDING, hanging over one's head and so threatening; as well as PENTHOUSE, originally a roof attached to a wall.

Although dictionaries define PERPENDICULAR as VERTICAL, at right angles to the horizon, up and down, the word is used in geometry to mean at right angles to any line or to any surface, with equal angles on every side; and a large majority of those who have been tested distinguish PERPENDICULAR from VERTICAL, for to the question: 'A line at right angles to another line', 124 out of 132 persons answer PERPENDICULAR, and only 3 VERTICAL. VERTICAL means at right angles to the horizon. PERPENDICULAR means at right angles to any reference line.

The new mislead OBLIQUE ($\breve{o}b$-$l\bar{e}k'$) means deviating from the perpendicular, not at right angles. An OBLIQUE angle may be

A line at right angles to another line.

FORM A. 41.	BO	NY	SUM	FORM AA. 5.	NY
coordinate	0	0	0	straight	1
vertical	0	3	3	vertical	3
vector	0	0	0	oblique	4
PERPENDICULAR	18	38	56	PERPENDICULAR	124
bisector	1	0	1	bisector	0
unmarked	1	0	1	unmarked	0
total	20	41	61	total	132

ACUTE, less than 90 degrees, or OBTUSE, greater than 90 degrees, but is not a right angle, not 90 degrees. An OBLIQUE line is not PERPENDICULAR, not at right angles.

17. *RADIUS* ($r\bar{a}'$-$d\breve{i}$-$\breve{u}s$) *n.* In mathematics, any straight line from the center of a circle to the circumference, to the edge of the circle; also the length of such a line all such lines being equal; also a line from the center of a sphere to its surface, half the diameter.

According to Noah Webster who, in the first edition of his Dictionary in 1828 often expressed simple concepts in elegant language: 'In geometry, a right line drawn or extending from the center of a circle to the periphery, and hence the semi-diameter of the circle'.

The plural of RADIUS follows the Latin, RADII ($r\bar{a}'$-$d\breve{i}$-$\bar{i}$), as the plural of FOCUS ($f\bar{o}'$-$k\breve{u}s$) is FOCI ($f\bar{o}'$-$s\bar{i}$); the plural of BACILLUS, BACILLI ($b\breve{a}$-$s\breve{i}l'$-$l\bar{i}$); and FUNGUS, FUNGI ($f\breve{u}n'$-$j\bar{i}$).

The word RADIUS comes from the Latin *radius*, rod, staff, also spoke of a wheel, and from this half the diameter of a circle, like the spoke of a wheel. The Latin *radiare* is to furnish with spokes. From this comes the past participle *radiatus*, which in turn leads to the English verb to RADIATE, originally to give out rays, and so finally to shine. From RADIATE, meaning to issue

Distance from the center to the circumference of a circle.

FORM C. I.	CH	FORM CA. I.	CH	LA	NY	NY	PH	SUM
pi	2	pi	0	0	2	9	1	12
chord	0	chord	0	0	1	6	0	7
diameter	0	diameter	4	2	2	6	2	16
secant	0	secant	0	0	0	1	1	2
RADIUS	66	RADIUS	36	34	92	255	70	487
unmarked	0	unmarked	0	1	0	0	0	1
total	68	total	40	37	97	277	74	525

in RAYS or straight lines from a center, to emit rays, comes RADIUS, any one of a number of lines drawn from a center. From the same source comes the adjective RADIANT, sparkling, shining. An old word from this same source is RAY, the noun, going back to 1300 or 1400; whereas the English RADIUS goes back no further than 1600.

The strange volume II of Nathan Bailey's Dictionary dated 1737 includes: 'RADIUS (in mechan.), a spoke, or fellow of a

Distance from the center to the edge of a circle.

FORM CB. 2.	NY
pi	0
circumference	0
diameter	1
axis	0
RADIUS	85
unmarked	0
total	86

wheel, because they issue like rays from the center of it'. Bailey himself, in his own dictionary of 1721, a hundred years before Webster and thirty-five years before Dr. Johnson, seldom if ever makes an error; but volume II, though called Bailey's Dictionary, never seems quite like his work. Its use of FELLOW as apparently synonymous with spoke is wrong, for FELLOW, also written FELLOE, is the rim of a wheel into which the spokes fit.

To the question: 'Distance from the center to the circumference of a circle', 487 out of 525 mark RADIUS correctly; while 16 mark DIAMETER. The word DIAMETER is a combination of the Greek διά (dia), through, a prefix which appears so often in technical terms that it should be learned in connection with this simple word, and μέτρον (metron), a measure. The DIAMETER is the measure through the circle, from one side to the other through the center. The RADIUS is half the DIAMETER. The difficulty may be the term CIRCUMFERENCE in the definition, probably about as difficult a word as RADIUS. In the revised form CB, CIRCUMFERENCE has been replaced by the simpler EDGE; and in this form 85 persons out of 86 mark RADIUS correctly, while only 1 marks DIAMETER.

18. *RADIAL ENGINE* (rā'-dǐ-ăl ĕn'-jǐn). An engine having stationary cylinders arranged like the spokes of a wheel around a point on a common crankshaft. Reread RADIUS (17). The adjective RADIAL comes through the French *radial*, from the Latin *radius*, ray, radius, spoke of a wheel, staff, rod, the source of the English mathematical noun RADIUS, the distance from the center of a circle to its edge. The adjective ending -AL comes from the Latin adjective ending *-alis*, with the accusative *-alem*. In Latin this meant pertaining to, of the nature of, of the kind of. Thus MANUAL, from the Latin *manus*, hand, and the ending -AL, means of the nature of the hand, in this case done by hand. ORAL, ending in the same -AL, comes from the Latin *os*, *oris*, mouth, and means of the nature of the mouth, pertaining to the mouth. RADIAL means like the radius of a circle, like the spokes of a wheel.

To the question: 'Engine having cylinders evenly arranged around the crankshaft in the same circular plane', 440 persons out of 515 answer correctly RADIAL-TYPE ENGINE; but 17 answer FOUR-CYCLE ENGINE, the popular misconception also in the newly revised form AA. The term FOUR-CYCLE applies to the operation within each cylinder. The four strokes of a four-cycle engine, perhaps more correctly called FOUR-STROKE engine, or sometimes FOUR-STROKE-CYCLE engine, are: the intake or induction stroke down; the compression stroke up; the power or firing stroke down; and the exhaust stroke up, the crankshaft turning twice for one power stroke. This FOUR-STROKE engine is used in practically all aircraft with internal combustion engines, including the RADIAL type.

A SINGLE-ROW RADIAL engine has an odd number of cylinders, often three to nine, arranged in a circle. Every other one fires in turn, the first, third, and fifth, in a five-cylinder engine, and then, the crankshaft having made one turn, the second fires and the fourth, when, the crankshaft having made two turns, the first fires again. In a DOUBLE-ROW RADIAL engine the cylinders

Form A. Engine having cylinders evenly arranged around the crankshaft in the same circular plane.

Form AA. Type of engine with cylinders in circular plane around the crankshaft.

FORM A. 35.	FW	LA	NY	NY	NY	PH	SUM	FORM AA. 3.	NY
in-line type engine	0	0	2	1	7	4	14	in-line	0
V-type engine	0	0	1	0	11	3	15	V	3
four-cycle engine	0	0	3	1	8	5	17	four-cycle	6
RADIAL-TYPE ENGINE	18	52	28	54	109	179	440	RADIAL	53
opposed-type engine	0	1	1	1	3	0	6	opposed	0
unmarked	0	1	2	9	2	9	23	unmarked	1
total	18	54	37	66	140	200	515	total	63

are in two planes, one behind the other, each still with an odd number, each cylinder of the rear circle located directly behind the space between two cylinders in the front circle, cylinders in both circles being cooled by air in the slipstream. The RADIAL ENGINE has the lowest weight per horsepower of all types of internal-combustion engines; but for an airplane it has a large frontal area difficult to streamline.

19. *SPEED OF LIGHT* (*spēd ŏv līt*). 186,285 miles per second in vacuum, 299,712 kilometers per second in air, 299,796 plus or minus 4 kilometers per second in vacuum, another more recent measurement gives 299,774 kilometers per second in vacuum.

To the question: 'Speed of light', nearly every high-school student answers correctly 186,000 miles per second, 485 persons out of 537.

The speed of light was first successfully measured in 1675 by Olaf Römer (Roemer), a Danish astronomer working in Paris at the invitation of Colbert, director-general for Louis XIV. One of the planet Jupiter's four largest satellites is eclipsed by the planet's shadow at intervals of approximately 42½ hours. When Jupiter and the earth are on the same side of the sun, relatively near to one another, these eclipses occur regu-

Speed of light.

FORM E. 17.	BO	FW	LA	NY	NY	NY	NY	PH	TU	SUM
25,478 miles per second	0	3	0	0	0	0	9	0	1	13
7,214 miles per second	2	2	0	0	0	1	9	0	0	14
200,578 miles per minute	0	1	0	0	0	0	2	2	1	6
186,285 miles per second	23	42	32	18	20	39	189	97	25	485
5,017,599 miles per second	1	2	1	2	0	0	9	1	1	17
unmarked	2	0	0	0	0	0	0	0	0	2
total	28	50	33	20	20	40	218	100	28	537

larly. But as the earth moves around the sun, away from Jupiter, the eclipses seem to be delayed. When the earth is on the opposite side of the sun from Jupiter the eclipses again occur at intervals of 42½ hours but are all delayed nearly 17 minutes, or about 1000 seconds behind schedule. Römer surmised that the apparent delay was the time required for light to cross the earth's orbit, 186,000,000 miles. Dividing this distance by the delay of a thousand seconds gives the speed of light as 186,000 miles per second, the correct value. Römer would have obtained this answer except that in his day the radius of the earth's orbit was thought to be 96,000,000 miles.

Fifty years later, in 1727, James Bradley, astronomer royal of England from 1742, obtained the speed of light from a study of aberration.

In the period 1880 to 1882 A. A. Michelson, working at the Case School of Applied Science at Cleveland, Ohio, determined the speed of light by flashes from a revolving mirror which were reflected back and caught by the next face of the revolving mirror if it turned fast enough. From the speed of the mirror and the distance the light traveled, it was possible to compute its velocity. In the first experiment this proved to be 299,853 kilometers per second.

In the period 1926 to 1929 Michelson repeated the study in California flashing light from an eight-sided mirror on Mount Wilson 22½ miles to a stationary mirror on Mount San Antonio and back. This gave a value of 299,712 kilometers per second in air or 299,796 kilometers per second in vacuum, equivalent to 186,285 miles per second, a speed which according to the theory of relativity can never be exceeded by anything.

20. *EVAPORATION* (ē-văp-ō-rā'-shŏn) n. The escape of rapidly moving molecules from the exposed surface of a liquid so that the liquid gradually lessens in amount.

EVAPORATION and the corresponding verb to EVAPORATE come from the Latin *evaporare*, to disperse in vapor, a combination of *e*, out, and *vapor*. From this Latin *vapor*, steam, exhalation, particularly a warm exhalation, comes the English noun VAPOR. From the same source come the Latin *vapidus*, and the English VAPID. Of this word VAPID the Rev. James Stormonth says in his dictionary of 1885: 'Originally something which has exhaled its flavor, particularly wine which has been opened to the air, that has lost its life and spirit, as by EVAPORATION; and so spiritless; flat; dull; mawkish'.

To the question: 'The escape of rapidly moving particles from the free surface of a liquid', 490 persons out of 537 mark EVAPORATION; but 20 mark DISCHARGE, and 14 OSMOSIS. The word OSMOSIS comes from the Greek ὠσμός (osmos), impulsion, pushing, thrust. Both OSMOSIS (*ŏs-mō'-sĭs*) and EVAPORATION are due to the escape of rapidly moving molecules or atoms. The term OSMOSIS can apply to either a liquid or a gas; while EVAPORATION applies to a liquid only. But the important difference is that OSMOSIS is the escape of particles through a membrane which stops large or different ones; while EVAPORATION is the escape of particles from an uncovered surface.

The warmer and drier the surrounding air the more rapid the EVAPORATION, but EVAPORATION takes place to some extent at any temperature. In contrast to EVAPORATION, BOILING goes on inside a liquid and occurs at a definite temperature. The word BOILING designates rapid conversion accompanied by bubbling. Some authors limit the term EVAPORATION to the slow

The escape of rapidly moving molecules from the free surface of a liquid.

FORM E. 7.	BO	FW	LA	NY	NY	NY	NY	PH	TU	SUM
attraction	0	2	0	0	0	0	0	0	0	2
discharge	1	1	0	4	0	1	9	2	2	20
EVAPORATION	26	43	33	16	19	37	192	98	26	490
decomposition	0	1	0	0	0	0	10	0	0	11
osmosis	1	3	0	0	1	2	7	0	0	14
unmarked	0	0	0	0	0	0	0	0	0	0
total	28	50	33	20	20	40	218	100	28	537

process which takes place only at the surface of a liquid. Thus Balfour Stewart, the Scottish physicist, in his Elementary Treatise on Heat, 1871, wrote: 'EVAPORATION, where the liquid is converted into a gas quietly, and without the formation of bubbles'. But EVAPORATION should be the general term for any transformation from a liquid to a gas. BOILING then becomes rapid EVAPORATION.

21. *AMPLIFIER* (*ăm'-plĭ-fī-er*) *n.* A device to magnify electric impulses.
The verb to AMPLIFY, to enlarge, increase, augment, goes back in English nearly to 1400. It comes through Middle English and Old French from the Latin *amplificare*, to enlarge. This comes in turn from the Latin *amplus*, large, and *facere*, to

make, represented only by the last two letters of the verb, -FY. From *amplus* comes the English adjective AMPLE, spacious, roomy, large in size, abundant, plentiful; while from *facere* come a host of English words of which FACTORY is one of the most common. To AMPLIFY is to make large, to increase the size of an object by the aid of a microscope, or to increase sound by reflection from a concave mirror, or to increase an electric impulse by aid of a vacuum tube.

To the question: 'Unit which increases gain', 206 persons out of 224 mark AMPLIFIER, while the few others scatter. Incoming signals, picked up by the ANTENNA (8) from passing electromagnetic waves sent out originally from the transmitter, con-

Unit which increases gain.

FORM A. 7.	NY	NY	NY	SUM
echo	0	0	3	3
Clark cell	3	1	1	5
ferromagnet	1	0	6	7
AMPLIFIER	33	38	135	206
hysteresis	0	1	2	3
unmarked	0	0	0	0
total	37	40	147	224

trol the voltage of the grid. Small changes in grid voltage cause large changes in plate current. Extremely weak signal currents cause grid voltage changes large enough to control comparatively large filament-plate currents. A weak signal is AMPLIFIED, strengthened, enlarged, magnified.

22. *ACUTE* (ă-kūt') *adj*. Sharp at the end, pointed, coming to a sharp point, less than a right angle. Reread OBTUSE (4). The word ACUTE occurs in literature in numerous ways, as: 'ACUTE hearing', sharp, keen; 'An ACUTE mind', again sharp, keen. The word comes from the Latin *acutus*, the past participle of *acuere*, to sharpen. From this comes the literary word ACUMEN, sharpness of mind, keenness of wit, mental penetration, quickness of perception; and the unusual ACUMINATE, pointed, or, as a verb, to sharpen, bring to a point.

Billingsley, in his translation of Euclid of 1570, says: 'An ACUTE angle is that which is less than a right angle'. This great textbook of geometry was written in Greek about 300 B.C., translated into Arabic a thousand years later, about 800 A.D.; from Arabic into Latin; and finally in 1570 into English by H. Billingsley, the first man to use in English many of the mathematical terms of Latin origin which we now take for granted.

To the question in the mathematics vocabulary test: 'An angle less than 90 degrees', 121 persons out of 132 mark ACUTE; while 7 mark OBTUSE, the most frequently marked mislead. The

An angle less than 90 degrees.

FORM A. 4.	BO	NY	SUM	FORM AA. 4.	NY
obtuse	2	2	4	obtuse	7
right	0	0	0	explemental	3
ACUTE	18	38	56	ACUTE	121
vertical	0	1	1	vertical	1
interior	0	0	0	interior	0
unmarked	0	0	0	unmarked	0
total	20	41	61	total	132

confusion of a word with its opposite is a natural step in the learning process, the last before a final grasp of the correct meaning. OBTUSE (4) is dull, blunt, greater than 90 degrees. ACUTE is sharp, pointed, less than 90 degrees.

23. *PERIMETER* (pĕ-rĭm'-ē-ter) *n.* Border, outer boundary, periphery.

The word PERIMETER comes through the Latin *perimetros*, from the Greek περίμετρος (perimetros), a combination of περί (peri), around, about, also near, and μέτρον (metron), measure, the same μέτρον (metron) which has already appeared in DIAMETER, discussed under RADIUS (17). The prefix περί (peri) appears in the noun PERICARDIUM, a sac around the heart, the adjective PERIPATETIC, walking around, and the verb to PERIPHRASE, to talk in a roundabout way. This prefix περί (peri) is usually attached to a word of Greek origin, and so differs from its Latin equivalent *circum-*, prefixed to almost any word.

To the question: 'Sum of the lengths of the sides of a plane enclosed figure', 450 persons out of 525 answer PERIMETER; while 28 answer VECTOR SUM, misled by the word SUM, and 24 PARAMETER. This is no doubt a confusion of sound rather than meaning. The word PARAMETER has several uses in mathematics. The meaning selected for item 44 of form BB is a constant in

Sum of the lengths of the sides of a plane enclosed figure.

FORM C. 40.	CH	FORM CA. 5.	CH	LA	NY	NY	PH	SUM
parameter	4	parameter	1	2	3	12	6	24
PERIMETER	50	PERIMETER	36	33	86	228	67	450
conjugate	1	area	2	1	7	4	0	14
perigon	3	perigon	0	0	0	8	0	8
vector sum	10	vector sum	1	1	1	24	1	28
unmarked	0	unmarked	0	0	0	1	0	1
total	68	total	40	37	97	277	74	525

the equation of a curve such that if the constant be changed the same type of curve is obtained but of different proportions or in a different position. This meaning of PARAMETER is far more difficult than the present word PERIMETER.

PERIPHERY ($p\breve{e}$-$r\breve{i}f'$-$\breve{e}$-$r\bar{e}$), by derivation carried about, moving around, from the same Greek περί (peri), around, and the

Sum of the lengths of the sides of a plane enclosed figure.

FORM CB. 4.	NY
parameter	4
PERIMETER	78
area	3
apothem	0
vector sum	1
unmarked	0
total	86

verb φέρειν (pherein), to bear, carry, similar in derivation to the Latin CIRCUMFERENCE, and PERIMETER, by derivation the measure around, are in actual usage practically synonymous. The meaning of PERIMETER is an exact translation of the Greek from which it comes, the measure around a geometric figure.

24. *SPEAKER* (*spē'-ker*) *n.* A device like a telephone receiver which produces sounds loud enough to be heard without holding it close to the ear, final link in a radio system, usually called LOUD-SPEAKER.

The verb to SPEAK, with the past tense SPOKE, goes directly back to Anglo-Saxon, appearing as early as the year 800, one of the old words of the language. To SPEAK is to utter sounds, articulate words, express opinions, talk. The ending -ER is also of Anglo-Saxon origin, and is added to verbs to make the noun, the agent, as: BAKER, one who BAKES; DRIVER, one who DRIVES; READER; and WRITER.

To the question as it appeared in form A: 'A unit which produces audible vibrations', 204 persons out of 224 answer SPEAKER; while 9 answer COIL. The so-called MOVING-COIL SPEAKER consists of a small movable coil, attached to the diaphragm and moved at right angles to the lines of force by an

Unit which produces audible vibrations.

FORM A. 4.	NY	NY	NY	SUM
Crookes tube	1	1	2	4
photon	0	0	3	3
SPEAKER	35	33	136	204
kilocycle	1	2	1	4
coil	0	4	5	9
unmarked	0	0	0	0
total	37	40	147	224

alternating current flowing through the coil. The words AUDIBLE, capable of being heard, and VIBRATION are too difficult for the definition of so easy a word as SPEAKER. Both have been removed in the revised form AA, which reads: 'A unit which produces sounds which can be heard'.

The SPEAKER translates electrical energy into sound. The equivalent of a tiny motor converts electrical energy into mechanical, which is imparted to the diaphragm. The diaphragm vibrates and sets air in motion to form sound impulses. There are HORN SPEAKERS and DIAPHRAGM SPEAKERS. In these last a small cone transmits high frequencies, a large cone low frequencies, so that radio receivers sometimes have both.

25. *SLIPSTREAM* (*slĭp'-strēm*) *n.* Current of air forced to the
   rear by the propeller, stream of air urged astern.

The velocity of the SLIPSTREAM depends upon the throttle
setting and on the angle of attack. For normal flight the velocity of the SLIPSTREAM is a little greater than the air speed;
for steep climb, much greater.

The verb to SLIP, which goes back in English to the year
1300, is related to Dutch and Scandinavian words, but comes
perhaps more directly from German. It appears in numerous
compounds, as: SLIPKNOT, a knot which slips along a cord; and
SLIP-NOOSE; as well as in the word SLIPPER. The noun STREAM,
the second part of SLIPSTREAM, goes directly back to Anglo-
Saxon, to the year 875.

To the question: 'Current of air driven astern by a propeller',
419 persons out of 515 answer correctly SLIPSTREAM; but 40
answer DOWNWASH, also the popular mislead in the revised form
AA. Both the DOWNWASH and the SLIPSTREAM are currents of

Current of air driven astern by a propeller.

FORM A. 20.	FW	LA	NY	NY	NY	PH	SUM	FORM AA. 4.	NY
blade element	0	1	4	0	2	4	11	blade element	1
downwash	1	4	4	3	15	13	40	downwash	8
sweepback	0	1	4	5	19	9	38	sweepback	7
SLIPSTREAM	17	48	24	56	104	170	419	SLIPSTREAM	46
tail plane	0	0	0	0	0	0	0	gust	1
unmarked	0	0	1	2	0	4	7	unmarked	0
total	18	54	37	66	140	200	515	total	63

air. The DOWNWASH is the air turned downward by the forward
motion of the wing or other lifting surface which, in lifting
the plane, turns the air downward. The SLIPSTREAM is the air
driven straight astern by the propeller.

26. *CALORIMETRY* (*kăl-ō-rĭm'-ē-trē*) *n.* The quantitative
   measurement of heat, including specific heats.

The word CALORIMETRY, like many technical terms, is a combination of Latin and Greek; for there are few pure Greek
scientific words ending in -METRY like GEOMETRY, the art of
measuring the earth, and the erudite STICHOMETRY, the art of

measuring a manuscript in terms of the number of lines. CAL-ORIMETRY comes from the Latin *calor*, heat, the source of CALORIE, a unit of heat, from the verb *calere*, to be hot. One small CALORIE of heat, measured with a CALORIMETER, raises one gram of water from 14.5 to 15.5 degrees centigrade. The same amount of heat raises other substances to different tem-peratures. As the amount of heat needed to produce a result differs from the temperature of a body at any moment, so CALORIMETRY differs from THERMOMETRY (*ther-mŏm'-e-trē*) or

Heat measurements.

FORM E. 39.	BO	FW	LA	NY	NY	NY	NY	PH	TU	SUM
seismology	0	1	1	0	0	0	6	0	0	8
electrology	0	2	0	1	1	0	1	2	0	7
CALORIMETRY	24	43	31	16	19	36	199	97	26	491
electrostriction	1	0	0	2	0	0	5	0	0	8
humidity	0	4	1	1	0	2	4	0	2	14
unmarked	3	0	0	0	0	2	3	1	0	9
total	28	50	33	20	20	40	218	100	28	537

PYROMETRY (*pī-rŏm'-e-trē*). The second part of the word CALORIMETRY comes from the Greek -μετρία (-metria), the ac-tion of measuring, from the word μέτρον (metron). The Greek μέτρον (metron) means measure, as in: DIAMETER, the measure across, and PERIMETER (23), the measure around. The Greek -μετρία (-metria) suggests the process of measuring, the art of measuring. Thus CALORIMETRY is the art of measuring heat.

To the definition: 'Heat measurement', 40 persons high in English vocabulary all answer CALORIMETRY; but among 40 persons low in English vocabulary 2 answer HUMIDITY. In the total sampling of 537 persons, 491 answer CALORIMETRY; but 14 answer HUMIDITY. HUMIDITY is the relative amount of water vapor in the air, the ratio of the water vapor actually in the air at the moment to the amount which would saturate it. This last varies with the temperature; the higher the temperature the more water vapor the air can hold. In summer heat, HUMID air is a perpetual source of complaint; and it may be this con-nection of HEAT and HUMIDITY which leads 3 per cent to mark HUMIDITY as heat measurement.

In 1871 Clerk Maxwell defined CALORIMETRY, in his Theory of Heat, as the method of measuring heat. Still earlier, 1858, Dionysius Lardner used the word as a chapter title in his Natural Philosophy. In his Dictionary of Chemistry, 1863, planned as a new edition of Andrew Ure's Dictionary of Chemistry and

Heat measurements.

FORM E. 39.   ENGLISH VOCABULARY

	HIGH	LOW
seismology	0	0
electrology	0	0
CALORIMETRY	40	38
electrostriction	0	0
humidity	0	2
unmarked	0	0
total	40	40

Mineralogy, 1821, but actually a new work, Henry Watts says: 'The measurement of temperature, or THERMOMETRY, is a preliminary to the measurement of heat, or CALORIMETRY'.

27. *THERMODYNAMICS* (*ther-mō-dī-năm'-ĭks*) *n.* That department of physics which treats of heat and mechanical energy and of the conversion of either into the other; branch of science dealing with the relations between heat and work.

An enthusiastic authority defines THERMODYNAMICS as the branch of science which deals with the transformations of energy, and continues to say that all natural phenomena and physical processes involve changes of energy, so that THERMODYNAMICS is one of the most comprehensive of the physical sciences. This makes the principles of THERMODYNAMICS the foundations for a large part of physics and chemistry.

But the term comes from the Greek θέρμη (therme), heat, with the plural θέρμαι (thermai) which meant hot baths. These come from the adjective θερμός (thermos), warm, from the verb θέρειν (therein), to make hot, burn. From the same source come the English word THERMOMETER, by derivation a measure of heat, more exactly of temperature, and THERMOSTAT, an instrument for holding the temperature static.

DYNAMICS, the second part of THERMODYNAMICS, is the mathematical theory of force; W. K. Clifford says: 'The investigation of the circumstances under which particular motions take place'. DYNAMICS comes from the Greek δυναμικός (dynamikos), powerful, efficacious, from δύναμις (dynamis), power, might, strength, vigor, faculty, capacity, force, from

The science which deals with the relationship of heat energy to mechanical energy.

FORM E. 8.	BO	FW	LA	NY	NY	NY	NY	PH	TU	SUM
calorescence	3	1	0	1	1	3	17	0	0	26
electrodynamics	1	3	0	1	0	4	7	1	0	17
flux	0	1	0	0	0	0	3	0	0	4
thermostatics	0	3	0	1	2	4	16	2	2	30
THERMODYNAMICS	24	42	33	17	17	28	174	97	26	458
unmarked	0	0	0	0	0	1	1	0	0	2
total	28	50	33	20	20	40	218	100	28	537

δύνασθαι (dynasthai), to be able, capable, strong enough. From the same source comes the noun DYNAMO, a shortened form of the earlier DYNAMO-ELECTRIC MACHINE. The term THERMO-DYNAMICS should be reserved for the relation of heat and mechanical energy, for the transformation of heat into motive power or the reverse.

To the question: 'The science which deals with the relationship of heat energy to mechanical energy', 458 persons in 537 answer correctly THERMODYNAMICS; but 30 answer THERMO-STATICS; 26, CALORESCENCE; and 17 ELECTRODYNAMICS. In Electricity, 1870, Robert M. Ferguson says: 'ELECTRODYNAMICS treats of the mutual attractions and repulsions of currents on currents, and currents on magnets'. Since electricity in motion, the subject of ELECTRODYNAMICS, always creates a magnetic field, ELECTRODYNAMICS is also called ELECTROMAGNETICS. In his Theory of Heat, 1871, Clerk Maxwell says: 'The theory of the equilibrium of heat might be called THERMOSTATICS, and that of the motion of heat THERMOKINEMATICS'; but the term THERMO-STATICS is rarely seen today.

This is one of the early physics terms which the small group who score low in English vocabulary mark differently from those high, for many of the comparatively easy items up to this point are answered correctly by nearly the whole of both groups. As these physics items become more difficult the relation between physics vocabulary and English vocabulary becomes closer and more apparent. Of students who score low in English vocabulary, 76 to 114 on the general scale, only 23 out

FORM E. 8.   ENGLISH VOCABULARY

	HIGH	LOW
calorescence	1	5
electrodynamics	0	6
flux	0	1
thermostatics	0	5
THERMODYNAMICS	39	23
unmarked	0	0
total	40	40

of 40 answer THERMODYNAMICS compared with 39 out of 40 who score high in English vocabulary. Possibly in this instance a knowledge of Greek aids both in scoring high in the English vocabulary test and in the correct interpretation of this word; possibly a broad and exact knowledge of English words aids in breaking THERMODYNAMICS into its two obvious parts.

ENGINEERING THERMODYNAMICS includes the generation of power by fuel-burning power plants and the removal of heat and subsequent reduction of temperature for refrigeration and air conditioning.

28. *ALTITUDE* (*ăl'-tĭ-tūd*) *n.* The height of a triangle measured by a perpendicular dropped from the top point to the base, the height of any figure measured at right angles to the base. Read also HYPOTENUSE (29).

The end of this word, the suffix -TUDE, comes from the Latin *-tudo, -tudinem*, through the French *-tude*. This Latin ending is added to adjectives to form the corresponding abstract noun. Thus: FORTITUDE, bravery, strength, comes from the Latin adjective *fortis*, brave, strong; the English AMPLITUDE and the corresponding Latin *amplitudo*, largeness, come from *amplus*, large; while the more unusual HEBETUDE, dullness, obtuseness, comes from *hebes*, dull, blunt, obtuse. TURPITUDE, and the Latin *turpitudo*, baseness, vileness, wickedness, depravity, come from the adjective *turpis*, base. APTITUDE and LATITUDE come in the same way from the corresponding adjectives. The English abstract noun ALTITUDE comes from the Latin *altitudo*, height, tallness, and this from the adjective *altus*, high, tall.

To the question: 'Distance measured at right angles to the base of a triangle in plane geometry', 318 persons out of 357 answer ALTITUDE, while 26 answer HYPOTENUSE, the only frequently marked mislead. The HYPOTENUSE, a word used ex-

Distance measured at right angles to the base of a triangle in plane geometry.

FORM B. I.	NY	MISC.	SUM
secant	1	2	3
ALTITUDE	41	277	318
hypotenuse	6	20	26
base	0	3	3
versine	0	4	4
unmarked	0	3	3
total	48	309	357

clusively of a right-angled triangle, is the long side opposite the right angle. The BASE is the side on which the triangle rests, the horizontal bottom of the triangle; while in a right-angled triangle the ALTITUDE is the upright or vertical side.

29. *HYPOTENUSE* (*hĭ-pŏt′-ē-nūs*) *n*. The side of a right triangle opposite the right angle, the side which subtends the right angle. Reread ALTITUDE (28).

The usual spelling and pronunciation of this term with TH, *hypothenuse*, is an error, first made apparently in the 16th century. Edward Phillips in his New World of Words, 1658, gives only the adjective: 'HYPOTHENUSAL line', spelling it with the TH. John Harris, in his Lexicon Technicum of 1704, says: 'HYPOTHENUSE, in a Right-angled Triangle, is that side which subtends the Right-angle, and consequently is the longest'. John Kersey, who wrote Elements of Algebra in 1673, edited a new edition of Edward Phillips in 1706, and published Anglo-

Britannicum or a general English Dictionary in 1708, gives only HYPOTHENUSE in his 1715 edition. Nathan Bailey, a few years later, 1721, uses the same spelling; while Ephraim Chambers, 1728, who rarely errs, lists the word under HYPOTHENUSE but says: 'HYPOTHENUSE, or rather HYPOTENUSE'. A quarter of a century later, 1755, Dr. Johnson gives only the correct spelling, HYPOTENUSE. Errors which enrich the language, as they often

The side of a right triangle opposite the right angle.

FORM B. 27.	NY	MISC.	SUM
leg	1	4	5
base	0	7	7
altitude	1	4	5
HYPOTENUSE	45	270	315
perpendicular	1	2	3
unmarked	0	22	22
total	48	309	357

do, with new words and new meanings ought to be kept, but this TH adds nothing. Where did this strange mistake originate, for it appears in no other language, and why should it survive in English?

The word HYPOTENUSE comes from the Greek ὑποτείνουσα (hypoteinousa), the feminine form of the present participle, spelt with τ(t) and not θ(th). The full expression in Greek meant the line or side subtending the right angle: ἡ τὴν ὀρθὴν γωνίαν ὑποτείνουσα. In this expression ὀρθὴν (orthen), with TH, means right, and appears in the English word ORTHODOX, of the right opinion, and in ORTHOGONAL, at right angles. The Greek γωνίαν (gonian) means angle, as in HEXAGON, a figure of six angles; OCTAGON, eight angles; and POLYGON, many angles; as well as in the Greek word for TRIANGLE, τρίγωνον (trigonon). The final word in this phrase ὑποτείνουσα (hypoteinousa) is the source of the English HYPOTENUSE and means to subtend. The beginning of this word is the same HYPO-, under, which appears in HYPOCYCLOID, the curve traced by a point on a small circle which rolls under, inside, a larger one. From the second part of the word comes TENSION, stretch; so that the Latin SUBTEND is an exact translation of the Greek HYPOTENUSE. An arc or a chord which subtends an angle stretches across it exactly as the HYPOTENUSE stretches across a triangle subtending the right angle.

To the question: 'The side of a right triangle opposite the right angle', 315 persons out of 357 answer correctly HYPOTENUSE.

From a Geometrical Practice named Pantometria, written by Leonard Digges and published by his son Thomas Digges in 1571, a year after his father's death, comes: 'Ye squares of the two contayning sides ioyned to gither, are equall to the square of ye HYPOTHENUSA'. From M. Blundeville his Exercises, six treatises on cosmography, astronomy, geography, and the art of navigation, London, 1594, in which Thomas Blundeville describes Mercator's charts and globes, comes: 'They cal the line SECANT the HIPOTHENUSE, because it subtendeth the right angle'. This quotation gives an easy way of remembering the SECANT, for originally the trigonometric functions were lengths of lines and the SECANT was the length of the HYPOTENUSE when the base of the triangle was unity. From Logisticelogia, or Arithmetic surveighed and reviewed, 1674, by Samuel Jeake: 'The PERPENDICULAR, the BASE, and the HYPOTENUSA'.

30. *OHM'S LAW* (ōmz). A law which connects the electromotive force, the resistance, and the current; the current in a circuit equals the electromotive force divided by the resistance, the current flowing through any resistance equals the voltage across that resistance divided by the OHMS of that resistance.

Georg Simon Ohm (ōm) was professor of mathematics in the Jesuits' college at Cologne in Germany from 1817 and it is said that his enunciation of this law in 1827 aroused such bitter antagonism that he lost his position. In 1833 he began teaching in the polytechnicum in Nürnberg (Nuremberg).

In mathematical symbols, and to avoid the fractional form, this is usually written:

$$E = IR$$

where E stands for electromotive force measured in volts, the difference in potential between the terminals; I, for current intensity measured in amperes; and R for resistance in OHMS. Several physics textbooks as late as 1900 wrote this formula as:

$$c = \frac{V}{R}$$

where c is current; v is voltage; and R is resistance. Silvanus Thompson in 1894 uses:

$$c = \frac{E}{R}$$

and in a footnote says intensity of current is old-fashioned and misleading; but the symbol I has nevertheless survived.

To the question: 'Law stating that voltage equals resistance times current', 201 persons out of 224 answer OHM's, and 11 WATT's. The technical term WATT, named for James Watt, is more difficult for it is unknown to 55 per cent. A WATT is a unit of electrical power. It is volts times amperes, electromotive

Law stating that voltage equals resistance times current.

FORM A. 10.	NY	NY	NY	SUM
Peltier's	1	0	5	6
Ohm's	33	34	134	201
Seebeck's	0	1	1	2
Watt's	3	2	6	11
Thomson's	0	3	1	4
unmarked	0	0	0	0
total	37	40	147	224

force multiplied by intensity of current. OHM's LAW also involves volts and amperes, for it says volts divided by amperes gives RESISTANCE, electromotive force divided by intensity of current equals RESISTANCE.

OHM's LAW is identical with FOURIER's LAW for the propagation of heat, using potential in place of temperature, and electric current in place of flux of heat. For a direct-current circuit OHM's LAW says: The strength of an electric current, or the quantity of electricity passing a section of the conductor in unit time, is directly proportional to the whole electromotive force in operation, and inversely proportional to the sum of all the resistances in the circuit; for an alternating-current circuit: The current flowing through any impedance equals the voltage across that impedance divided by the OHMS of that impedance:

$$I = \frac{E}{Z}.$$

31. *CONCENTRIC* (*kŏn-sĕn'-trĭk*) *adj.* Having the same center, with a common center.

Both the English CON- and the Latin *con-* come from the Latin prefix *com-*, with, together, which becomes *con-*, spelt with an N, before a word beginning with C, as in CONCAVE, hollow, CONCLAVE, a group locked together with a key, and CONCENTRIC, a combination of *con-*, together, and *centrum*, center. The English word CENTER, usually spelt CENTRE in England but

Figures whose centers are identical.

FORM A. 39.	BO	NY	SUM	FORM AA. 10.	NY
eccentric	0	2	2	eccentric	2
acentric	1	1	2	acentric	7
inscribed	1	2	3	inscribed	14
CONCENTRIC	17	33	50	CONCENTRIC	93
circumscribed	0	3	3	circumscribed	13
unmarked	1	0	1	unmarked	3
total	20	41	61	total	132

CENTER in America, goes back through the French *centre*, and the Latin *centrum*, to the Greek κέντρον (centron), any sharp point, goad, spur, pin, also the stationary point of a pair of compasses, and so from this the center of a circle. The Greek noun comes from the verb κεντεῖν (centein), to prick, goad. The CENTER is a point. CENTRIC, the second part of the word CONCENTRIC, goes back to the Greek κεντρικός (centricos), pertaining to the center. ECCENTRIC, from the Latin *ex-*, from, is the opposite of CONCENTRIC and means not having the same center.

To the question: 'Figures whose centers are identical', 93 persons out of 132 answer CONCENTRIC; while 14 answer INSCRIBED, and 13 CIRCUMSCRIBED, both of the latter ending with the Latin *scribere*, to write. In literature, to INSCRIBE is by derivation to cut into; for *scribere* meant not only to write, but originally to scratch. In geometry, INSCRIBED means drawn inside. A many-sided figure is INSCRIBED in a circle or curve when every point or vertex of the figure touches the curve. In this instance the circle or curve is CIRCUMSCRIBED about the many-sided figure; for CIRCUMSCRIBED starts with the Latin *circum*, around, about, and ends with the same Latin *scribere*, to write. A many-sided figure is CIRCUMSCRIBED about a curve when every side of the figure is tangent to the curve. A regular five-sided figure, six-sided figure, or eight-sided figure, any regular polygon, has exactly the same center as a CIRCUMSCRIBED or INSCRIBED circle; the two are CONCENTRIC. But the center of a circle and the center of an irregular, scalene triangle about which it is CIR-CUMSCRIBED may differ radically. CIRCUMSCRIBED means drawn about, around; INSCRIBED means drawn within; CONCENTRIC means having the same center.

32. *INTERSECTION* (*in-ter-sĕk'-shŏn*) *n.* A cutting, place of crossing, point common to two lines, or a point common to a line and a surface, or a line common to two planes.
The noun INTERSECTION comes from the past participle *sectus* of the Latin verb *secare*, to cut, already discussed under BISECT (5), a verb which plays a part in a number of English words. The past participle is the source of the words SECTION, a slice; DISSECTION, a cutting apart; and of the mathematical terms to BISECT (5), to cut in two; BISECTION, a cutting in two; and SECANT, by derivation a line which cuts another. A little-known meaning of the word SECANT is a line drawn across a circle so that it cuts the circle in two places. The line between the two INTERSECTIONS of the SECANT and the circle is a CHORD; the whole straight line including the CHORD and extending beyond the circle is the SECANT.

To the question: 'Point at which lines or planes meet', 300 persons out of 357 answer INTERSECTION; and 33 INTERCEPT; two words which are almost inseparable. The INTERCEPT is the part of a line between INTERSECTIONS. Both INTERCEPT and INTER-SECTION start with the Latin *inter*, between. INTERCEPT comes from the Latin *interceptus*, to take between, from *capere*, to take. Nathan Bailey, with his own school at Stepney near Lon-don, in the third edition of his Dictionary dated 1726, a quarter

of a century before Dr. Johnson and one of the first to attempt
a complete representation of words, uses the verb INTERCEPT:
'Right ascension is an arc of the equator, reckoned toward the
east, INTERCEPTED between the beginning of Aries and the point

FORM B. 2.	NY	MISC.	SUM
origin	3	16	19
root	0	1	1
center	1	3	4
intercept	5	28	33
INTERSECTION	39	261	300
unmarked	0	0	0
total	48	309	357

of the equator which rises at the same time with the sun or star
in a right sphere'. INTERSECTION is the point of crossing. An
INTERCEPT is a distance; an INTERSECTION is a point.

33. *ARITHMETIC PROGRESSION* (ă-rĭth-mĕt'-ĭk prō-
grĕsh'-shŏn). A succession of numbers where each differs
from the one before by a constant amount, where each figure
can be obtained from the preceding by adding to it always the
same number.

The first term of an ARITHMETIC PROGRESSION can be any
quantity or number. The second term is then related to the first
by a constant difference; and every other term differs from the
one before by the same difference. The general form of an
ARITHMETIC PROGRESSION is:

$$a, a + d, a + 2d, a + 3d;$$

and the formula for any term is:

$$N = a + (n - 1) d$$

where N is any term,
      a, the first term,
      n, the number of the term in the sequence, and
      d, the constant difference.

The word ARITHMETIC comes through the Latin *arithmetica*,
from the Greek ἀριθμητική (arithmetica), the science of reckoning, from ἀριθμεῖν (arithmein), to reckon, count, number, which
in turn comes from ἀριθμός (arithmos), number. The spelling

ARITHMETIC in English goes back only to the 16th century. Before that, the word was commonly spelt *arsmetrike*.

To the question: 'A series of values constructed by adding a constant to the first to obtain the second, the same constant to the second term to obtain the third, et cetera', 88 persons out of 132 answer ARITHMETIC PROGRESSION; while 17 answer GEOMETRIC PROGRESSION; and 17 others EXPONENTIAL SERIES. A GEOMETRIC PROGRESSION is a succession of numbers where each is obtained by multiplying the one before by a constant, as:

A series of values constructed by adding a constant to the first to obtain the second, the same constant to the second term to obtain the third, et cetera.

FORM A. 16.	BO	NY	SUM	FORM AA. 9.	NY
ARITHMETIC PROGRESSION	16	34	50	ARITHMETIC	88
geometric progression	1	4	5	geometric	17
Fourier's series	0	0	0	converging	7
Taylor's series	0	0	0	diverging	3
exponential series	2	2	4	exponential	17
unmarked	1	1	2	unmarked	0
total	20	41	61	total	132

3, 9, 27, 81, 243, where each number is the one before multiplied by 3. The adjective GEOMETRIC is used because problems involving multiplication were at one time solved by geometry and not by arithmetic. An ARITHMETIC PROGRESSION is obtained by adding. A falling body, starting from rest, drops approximately 16 feet in the first second, 48 feet in the next second, 80 feet in the third second, where each number is 32 added to the one before: 16, 48, 80, 112, 144, is an ARITHMETIC PROGRESSION.

34. *ISOSCELES* (*ī-sŏs'-sĕ-lēz*) *adj*. Having two legs which are equal, with two and only two equal sides.

ISOSCELES is directly from the Latin *isosceles,* and this in turn from the Greek ἰσοσκελής (isosceles), with equal legs, a combination of ἴσος (isos), equal, and σκέλος (skelos), leg. This same Greek ἰσο (iso-) appears in ISOBAR, a term in meteorology for a line drawn on a weather map through places with the same barometric pressure; also in the recent ISOTOPES, chemical elements in the same place in the periodic table; and in ISOGONIC, literally with the same angle. The Greek ἴσος (isos) applied to things alike in number, appearance, or size.

To the question: 'Any triangle with two equal sides', 424 persons out of 525 answer ISOSCELES; and 71 EQUILATERAL. This may be the wording of the question. EQUILATERAL comes from the Latin *aequus*, equal, the source of the first part of the word EQUILIBRIUM; and *latus, lateris*, side, the source of LATERAL, sidewise. In geometry, EQUILATERAL may be an adjective and mean all sides equal, or it may be a noun, a figure all of whose

Any triangle with two equal sides.

FORM C. 15.	CH	FORM CA. 4.	CH	LA	NY	NY	PH	SUM
scalene	2	scalene	0	0	0	4	1	5
ISOSCELES	55	ISOSCELES	32	29	75	222	66	424
equilateral	9	equilateral	6	4	16	40	5	71
asymmetric	1	isogonal	0	1	0	2	0	3
equiangular	1	equiangular	2	3	6	9	2	22
unmarked	0	unmarked	0	0	0	0	0	0
total	68	total	40	37	97	277	74	525

sides are equal. In the revised form the definition has been made more exact: 'Any triangle with only two sides equal'; and 8 persons out of 86, practically the same percentage, still mark EQUILATERAL. ISOGONAL, marked by only 3 persons in the previous form CA, has also been changed in form CB to AMBLYGONAL, having an obtuse angle, a choice which in actual practice proves no more attractive.

From the translation of Euclid by Sir Henry Billingsley, done in 1570: 'ISOSCELES, is a triangle, which hath onely two sides equall'. From the next year, 1571, A Geometrical Practice named Pantometria, by Leonard and Thomas Digges: 'ISOSCHELES is such a triangle as hath onely two sides like, the thirde being unequall, and that is the Base'. A still earlier quotation, 1551, comes from the Pathway to Knowledge by Robert Recorde: 'There is also an other distinction of the names of triangles, according to their sides, two sydes bee equall and the thyrd unequall, which the Greekes call ISOSCELES, the Latine men *aequicurio*, and in English *tweyleke* may they be called'.

35. *MULTIPLICAND* (*mŭl'-tĭ-plĭ-kănd*) *n.* A number which is to be multiplied by another. William Henry P. Phyfe in his Ten Thousand Words often Mispronounced accents this word on the first syllable but adds that Worcester, Stormonth, and Haldeman accent the last syllable. Reread PRODUCT (3).

The word MULTIPLICAND was used in the year 1600, in Arithmetick by Thomas Hill, an English astrologer about whom little is known: 'The two numbers given or assigned in every multiplication have each of them a peculiar name, for the greater is called the MULTIPLICAND, and the lesser is named the MULTIPLIER'.

The term MULTIPLICAND comes from the Latin *multiplicandus*, the gerundive or verbal adjective of *multiplicare*, to multiply, increase, make manifold, from *multiplex*, manifold.

A quantity which is to be multiplied by another quantity.

FORM B. 47.	NY	MISC.	SUM
MULTIPLICAND	38	258	296
multiplier	5	20	25
product	1	0	1
power	0	0	0
radical	0	1	1
unmarked	4	30	34
total	48	309	357

This in turn is a combination of *multus*, many, the source of the English MULTITUDE, many, and *plicare*, to fold. From *plicare*, to fold, come DUPLICATE, by derivation twice folded, COMPLICATED, with many folds, IMPLICATED, folded into a situation, involved, infolded, the verb to IMPLY, as well as the simple word REPLY, originally to fold back, now to answer, respond.

To the question: 'A quantity which is to be multiplied by another quantity', 296 persons out of 357 answer MULTIPLICAND; while 25 answer MULTIPLIER. Though the PRODUCT (3), the answer, is the same when two numbers are multiplied together no matter which is taken as the MULTIPLICAND and which the MULTIPLIER, it is customary, for ease of operation, to write the longer number first, the MULTIPLICAND, and the shorter number below as the MULTIPLIER.

36. *AIRFOIL* (*ăr'-foil*) *n.* Any surface designed to obtain a
reaction from the air through which it moves.

The noun FOIL goes back through Middle English and Old
French words meaning sheet of paper and sheet of metal to the
Latin *folium*, a leaf, and the Greek φύλλον (phullon), also a leaf.
From the same source come FOLIAGE, growing leaves in general,
and FOLIO, a large book in which two facing pages when open

Any surface designed to obtain reaction from the air through
which it moves.

FORM A. 13.	FW	LA	NY	NY	NY	PH	SUM	FORM AA. 6.	NY
flap	1	5	6	8	29	24	73	flap	15
rib	0	1	0	0	0	0	1	leading edge	5
aileron	0	5	6	11	18	18	58	aileron	7
AIRFOIL	17	43	22	46	88	153	369	AIRFOIL	36
strut	0	0	2	0	5	4	11	strut	0
unmarked	0	0	1	1	0	1	3	unmarked	0
total	18	54	37	66	140	200	515	total	63

are the size of a printer's sheet, originally used only in the
phrase: 'In FOLIO', where it meant in a single sheet. TIN FOIL is
a thin sheet of tin. There is also GOLD FOIL, called GOLD-LEAF
when it is very thin. An AIRFOIL is a sheet of metal designed to
produce a reaction with the air stream through which it moves.
The verb to FOIL, with its modern meaning of baffle, frustrate,
balk, comes from another source and, though spelt the same
today, is a different word.

To the question: 'Any surface designed to obtain reaction
from the air through which it moves', 369 persons out of 515
mark AIRFOIL, while 73 mark FLAP and 58 AILERON; the popular
misleads also in the revised form AA. A FLAP is an AIRFOIL, the
rear part of a larger AIRFOIL, hinged so that it can be moved to
vary the effective camber. It is a part of the trailing edge of a
larger AIRFOIL. A WING FLAP, a hinged section, the trailing
edge of a wing, extends from the fuselage to the inboard end
of the AILERON. The AILERON, the second most frequently
marked mislead, is the rear part of a wing, hinged like a FLAP,
and like a FLAP it is a part of the trailing edge of a wing. The

WING FLAPS, on opposite sides of the fuselage, lift and lower together. The AILERONS are connected in such a way as simultaneously to lift one wing and depress the other. Other important AIRFOILS are the wings, rudder, and elevators; but AIRFOIL is the general term for any such surface.

37. *BAND* (*bănd*) *n.* Any range of frequencies, sequence of wave lengths.

There are at least two nouns, both spelt BAND, probably from the same ultimate source, but more or less distinct even in Anglo-Saxon, and yet constantly confused. One is a shackle, bond, used for binding; the other a flat strip. This last is used figuratively in radio to mean a range of frequencies.

To the question: 'A range of broadcast frequencies', 183 persons out of 224 answer BAND; while 28 answer MODULATION. It is MODULATION which adds the signal to the carrier wave. To

A range of broadcast frequencies.

FORM A.	NY	NY	NY	SUM
modulation	2	7	19	28
BAND	31	30	122	183
ratio	2	0	3	5
gap	1	0	0	1
intermediate	1	3	3	7
unmarked	0	0	0	0
total	37	40	147	224

MODULATE is to vary the height, amplitude, of a wave train in some characteristic way; or to vary the frequency. This last may lead to the popularity of MODULATION.

Each transmitting station requires a BAND of frequencies about 10 kilocycles wide for ordinary broadcasting, and twice as wide for high-fidelity. This BAND of frequencies assigned to a station is called a radio CHANNEL. To prevent interference between two stations their carrier frequencies should differ perhaps by as much as 10 kilocycles. In the broadcasting range or broadcast BAND from 500 to 1600 kilocycles there are 1100 kilocycles or, with stations 10 kilocycles apart, 110 CHANNELS. BAND is the general term for any range of frequencies.

38. *ELASTIC LIMIT* (ē-lăs′-tĭk lĭm′-ĭt). That point or pressure or stress beyond which further stress would cause a
permanent set, the limit within which a given stress produces
no permanent deformation.

The Reverend Walter W. Skeat, professor of Anglo-Saxon
at Cambridge, England, in his Etymological Dictionary of the

In a stressed body, that point beyond which the smallest stress
of any kind will cause a permanent set.

FORM E. 34.	BO	FW	LA	NY	NY	NY	NY	PH	TU	SUM
elastic range	0	4	2	0	1	2	10	1	0	20
latitude	0	0	0	0	0	0	2	2	1	5
ELASTIC LIMIT	20	39	29	15	19	32	175	96	26	451
range of force	3	2	2	1	0	2	11	1	0	22
stretch coefficient	2	5	0	4	0	3	17	0	1	32
unmarked	3	0	0	0	0	1	3	0	0	7
total	28	50	33	20	20	40	218	100	28	537

English Language, calls ELASTIC a scientific term coined from
the Greek ἐλατήρ (elater), a driver to hurl missiles by the force
of a spring, hurler, catapult.

From the Minor Encyclopedia by the Reverend Thaddeus
M. Harris, published in Boston in 1803, comes: 'ELASTICITY,
that property of bodies, whereby they reſtore themſelves to

FORM E. 34.	ENGLISH VOCABULARY	
	HIGH	LOW
elastic range	0	4
latitude	2	0
ELASTIC LIMIT	38	23
range of force	0	6
stretch coefficient	0	7
unmarked	0	0
total	40	40

their former figure, after any external preſſure; being the ſame
with what is otherwiſe called ſpringineſs, very obſervable in a
bent bow, ſteel ſprings, and the like. A perfectly elaſtic body,
is that which reſtores itſelf with the ſame force wherewith it

was bent, or depreſſed; thoſe which do not ſo reſtore themſelves with exactly the ſame force, being called imperfectly
elaſtic bodies.' Since 'All known bodies are in ſome degree or
other elaſtic', the ELASTIC LIMIT is the stress, deformation,
within which the body is perfectly elastic and beyond which it
becomes imperfectly elastic.

To the question: 'In a stressed body, that point beyond which
the smallest stress of any kind will cause a permanent set', 451
persons out of 537 answer ELASTIC LIMIT; but 32 answer
STRETCH COEFFICIENT. This last group seem to come largely
from those who score low in the English literary vocabulary,
for in the special study no one high in English vocabulary
marked this mislead, 38 out of 40 marking the correct answer;
while in the group low in English vocabulary only 23 mark
ELASTIC LIMIT and 7 STRETCH COEFFICIENT. STRETCH COEFFICIENT
is another term for MODULUS OF ELASTICITY or YOUNG'S MODU-
LUS. It is a ratio: stretching force divided by stretch produced.
The ELASTIC LIMIT is the point beyond which a body when
thus stretched fails to return to its original length.

39. *ABSOLUTE ZERO* (ăb'-sō-lūt zē'-rō). The temperature
at which molecular kinetic energy is zero, the temperature
at which the particles whose motion constitutes heat would be
at rest, approximately −273 degrees centigrade.

To the question: 'Absolute zero', 448 persons out of 537, or
83 per cent, answer correctly −273 degrees centigrade; while
49 answer zero degrees centigrade. The CENTIGRADE ZERO is the
melting point of ice, chosen by Celsius as the zero for his thermometer scale, 100 on his scale being the boiling point of water.
ABSOLUTE ZERO is far below the freezing point of water. It is the
point at which molecular motion ceases.

To the same sort of question differently worded in another
form of the physics vocabulary test, studied in 1936, 82 per cent
answer ABSOLUTE, and 10 per cent RÉAUMUR. The thermometric
scale of René Réaumur started with zero at the freezing point
of water. The tube was then graduated so that each degree
represented an expansion of one thousandth of the amount of
alcohol in the bulb when at zero degrees. This chanced to bring
the boiling point of water at 80 degrees.

Words such as ABSOLUTE and ZERO are so familiar that one forgets their histories. ABSOLUTE comes from the Latin *absolutus*, complete, unrestricted, the past participle of *absolvere*, to loosen from, the source also of the verb to ABSOLVE, to set free from some obligation, release from consequences. This is

Absolute zero.

FORM E. 33.	BO	FW	LA	NY	NY	NY	NY	PH	TU	SUM
0° F.	0	3	2	2	0	0	9	0	1	17
—273° C.	23	40	30	13	19	34	170	95	24	448
0° C.	2	6	0	4	1	3	29	3	1	49
—22° K.	0	0	1	0	0	0	2	0	1	4
—127° C.	0	1	0	1	0	2	5	2	1	12
unmarked	3	0	0	0	0	1	3	0	0	7
total	28	50	33	20	20	40	218	100	28	537

a combination of the Latin *ab*, from, and *solvere*, to loosen. The adjective ABSOLUTE, in such a phrase as: 'ABSOLUTE authority', means unrestricted. As used scientifically ABSOLUTE means independent of other things, not merely relative, in

Thermometric scale with boiling point of water at 373.

FORM AB. 11.	NY
Celsius	2
fahrenheit	0
ABSOLUTE	82
Réaumur	10
centigrade	6
unmarked	0
total	100

terms of phenomena of universal occurrence. The phrase ABSOLUTE SYSTEM OF UNITS is said to have been introduced by Gauss in 1832 in expressing the earth's magnetic field in units of length, mass, and time. The zero of the RÉAUMUR SCALE is the temperature of melting ice; the zero of the fahrenheit scale, the lowest temperature observed in the winter of 1709. ABSOLUTE ZERO is free of these personal choices. It is the lowest possible temperature which the nature of heat admits.

40. *RESONANCE* (rĕz'-ō-năns) *n*. In general, the abnormally
large response of a system having a natural vibration period
to a stimulus of the same, or nearly the same, frequency. In
radio, the phenomenon when inductive and capacitive reactances are equal.

Although 169 persons out of 224 answer correctly the question: 'The phenomenon when inductive and capacitive reactances are equal', the idea underlying RESONANCE seems much
harder than the statistics indicate; and any discussion of this
meaning of RESONANCE involves difficult terms. INTERFERENCE,
the most frequently marked mislead chosen by 21 out of 224

The phenomenon when inductive and capacitive reactances
are equal.

FORM A. 15.	NY	NY	NY	SUM
interference	4	6	11	21
beats	1	1	8	10
tone	0	1	8	9
load	1	1	12	14
RESONANCE	30	31	108	169
unmarked	1	0	0	1
total	37	40	147	224

persons, is nearly a correct statement of what actually happens;
but the word is not used in this situation. REACTANCES may be
positive or negative. When the CAPACITIVE REACTANCE equals
the INDUCTIVE REACTANCE, the effects cancel, and the IMPEDANCE
is equal to the resistance in ohms alone. This occurs at a single
frequency only.

Another way of describing the same phenomenon is to say
that current due to INDUCTIVE REACTANCE lags behind its voltage
by 90 degrees. Current due to CAPACITIVE REACTANCE leads
its voltage by 90 degrees. The effects of the two are therefore
180 degrees out of phase. When the two are adjusted so that
they are equal at some frequency the circuit is in RESONANCE.

The word RESONANCE comes from the Latin *resonans, re-
sonantis*, the present participle of *resonare*, to echo, to sound
back, resound, a combination of *re*, again, and *sonare*, to sound.
From *sonare* come DISSONANCE, PERSON, and SOUND itself.

One who tunes a radio receiver to a particular station adjusts the alternating current circuits, Professor Richard F. Deimel says: 'Really the capacitances which correspond to spring in a vibrating elastic system', so that a condition of RESONANCE exists, one of the most interesting phenomena in alternating current theory. A RESONANT circuit must contain both INDUCTANCE and CAPACITANCE, both a coil and a condenser. At low frequencies, the REACTANCE of the condenser is high, so that little current flows. At zero frequency, that is direct current, none passes the condenser. At high frequencies the REACTANCE of the coil is high, so that little current flows. At intermediate frequencies, more current flows. When the voltage across the condenser and the INDUCTANCE are equal and opposite in sign, the impedance or total resistance is a minimum and the current a maximum.

41. *DEW POINT* (*dū point*). The temperature at which water vapor condenses out of the air.

In his book Physiography, first published in 1877 and reprinted twenty times in the next twenty-five years, T. H. Huxley says, in the chapter on Rain and Dew: 'Moisture deposited upon any cold surface, without production of mist, is

Temperature at which air when cooled becomes saturated.

FORM E. 11.	BO	FW	LA	NY	NY	NY	NY	PH	TU	SUM
latent heat	1	2	0	0	0	1	8	1	0	13
DEW POINT	23	41	31	16	19	32	182	93	24	461
absorption coefficient	2	3	2	3	1	4	10	5	3	33
boiling point	1	1	0	1	0	0	9	1	0	13
100° F.	0	3	0	0	0	2	9	0	0	14
unmarked	1	0	0	0	0	1	0	0	1	3
total	28	50	33	20	20	40	218	100	28	537

termed DEW. The proportion of watery vapour that can be held in the atmosphere depends principally on the temperature of the air; the lower the temperature the less it retains. If charged so highly with moisture that it can take up no more, the air is then said to be SATURATED. When a body of moist air is cooled, the point of saturation is gradually reached; and, when saturated, any further cooling causes a deposition of DEW; hence the temperature at which this occurs is called the DEW-POINT.'

To the question: 'Temperature at which air when cooled becomes saturated', 461 out of 537 answer DEW POINT; but 33 answer ABSORPTION COEFFICIENT. All 40 high in the English literary vocabulary answer DEW POINT; but only 32 of the 40 who score low, 4 answering ABSORPTION COEFFICIENT. Henry Watts says: 'The volume of a gas which, under certain fixed conditions of temperature and pressure, is absorbed by the unit volume of any solid or liquid, is a fixed and definite

FORM E. 11.	ENGLISH VOCABULARY	
	HIGH	LOW
latent heat	0	1
DEW POINT	40	32
absorption coefficient	0	4
boiling point	0	2
100° F.	0	1
unmarked	0	0
total	40	40

quantity, and is called the COEFFICIENT OF ABSORPTION of the body for that particular gas. These COEFFICIENTS OF ABSORPTION have been determined with accuracy for various liquid and gaseous bodies and certain relations existing between the volume of gas and the temperature and pressure under which it is absorbed have been satisfactorily established.' Earlier in the same paragraph Watts says: 'We are as yet altogether unacquainted with the law which regulates the amount of gas absorbed by any solid or liquid substance under any condition whatever; any knowledge which we possess concerning the absorptive powers of bodies for gases must therefore be entirely empirical'.

The DEW POINT is a temperature; and the term is used only of the air. The DEW POINT, which varies with the amount of moisture in the air, is low with dry air and higher with air which contains much water vapor. At zero degrees centigrade,

32 degrees fahrenheit, the air can hold 4.84 grams of water and no more. At 40 degrees centigrade it can hold 50.70 grams of water or less but again no more. Air which contains 30.04 grams of water can cool to 30 degrees centigrade before water condenses out.

The moisture on cold spectacles in a warm room and the drops of water on the outside of a cold pitcher are both DEW.

42. *EXPONENT* (*ĕks'-pō-nĕnt*) *n.* A figure indicating how many times a quantity is to be multiplied by itself, a symbol written above and at the right of another to show the power to which it is to be raised, the number of times it is to be multiplied by itself. Reread SQUARE (12).

René Descartes introduced the modern system of EXPONENTS in La Geometrie in 1637. Hume had written the EXPONENT up and to the right, in the same position as today, but had used

Symbol indicating how many times a variable is to be employed as a factor, or to what power it is to be raised.

FORM A. 5.	BO	NY	SUM	FORM AA. 13.	NY
index	2	3	5	index	8
EXPONENT	17	32	49	EXPONENT	103
coefficient	0	3	3	coefficient	18
root	0	1	1	modulus	0
constant	0	2	2	constant	3
unmarked	1	0	1	unmarked	0
total	20	41	61	total	132

Roman numerals, as: 5a^{IV}. Hérigone used Arabic numbers written to the right, but of the same size as the coefficient and on the same line, not lifted, as: 5a4. Descartes was the first to write as mathematicians do today: 5a^4.

In the expression a^4, the EXPONENT is 4 and signifies that a is to be multiplied by itself four times: $a \times a \times a \times a$, or as Harriot preferred: aaaa. From Ephraim Chambers comes: 'The multiplication of letters, and as the number of thofe may be fo great as to become incommodious; the method is only to write down the root, and on the right hand to write the index of the power, that is, the number of letters whereof the power to be expreſſed does conſiſt; as a^2, a^3, a^4, a^5; the laſt of which ſignifies as much as a multiplied five times into itſelf; and ſo of the reſt'.

The word EXPONENT comes from the Latin *exponens, exponentis*, the present participle of *exponere*, to set forth, indicate, expound, a combination of *ex*, out, forth, and *ponere*, to set, put, place. Though the derivation of EXPONENT helps little in remembering the meaning of the term, for it is by derivation no more than an indicator, the Latin verb *ponere* from which it comes enters so many English words that it should be learned and remembered. Through the past participle *positus* come EXPOSE, to put forth, set out; COMPOSE, to put to-

The ½ in $x^{½}$.

FORM B. 13.	NY	MISC.	SUM
EXPONENT	43	238	281
delta	0	5	5
radical	0	10	10
log	2	4	6
coefficient	3	44	47
unmarked	0	8	8
total	48	309	357

gether; PROPOSE, to put forward; and IMPOSE, to put upon. COMPONENTS, a combination of *com-*, together, and *ponere*, to put, are things put together, ingredients which go together to make a whole. To PROPOUND, from *pro*, forward, and the same *ponere*, to put, is to put forward, offer for consideration; while PROPONENT is one who makes a proposal, offers a proposition. From the same source come the noun PROPOSITION and the unusual PROPONE, to put forward. To EXPOUND is to enlarge upon, explain; while in literature an EXPONENT is one who expounds, explains, or one who stands for a cause, represents it.

To the question: 'The ½ in $x^{½}$' 281 persons out of 357 answer correctly EXPONENT; while 47 answer COEFFICIENT. To a differently worded question in another form of the mathematics vocabulary tests: 'Symbol indicating how many times a variable is to be employed as a factor, or to what power it is to be raised', 103 persons out of 132 answer EXPONENT; while

18 answer COEFFICIENT, and 8 INDEX. COEFFICIENT and EXPO-
NENT are confused in other items of these mathematical tests.
A COEFFICIENT indicates how many times a number is to be
added to itself; an EXPONENT how many times it is to be multiplied by itself. By tradition the COEFFICIENT is written first
and in the same type as what follows, as 3a, which means
a + a + a. The EXPONENT is written above and to the right
and in smaller type, as a^3, which means a × a × a.

43. > An algebraic sign indicating GREATER THAN, as: a > b,
      a is greater than b, occasionally read: a contains b. The
same symbol is used in music for diminishing.
Writing in 1728, Ephraim Chambers says: ' 7 Is the sign of
MAJORITY, or of the excess of one quantity beyond another:
some use this ⌐, or this ⌐'. Chambers continues: ' ∠ Is the
sign of MINORITY. These two characters were first introduced
by Harriot, and have been since used by Wallis and Lamy.
Other authors use others: some this ⌐'. Thomas Harriot,

>.

FORM B. 37.	NY	MISC.	SUM
unequal to	2	3	5
GREATER THAN	39	244	283
less than	4	24	28
similar to	1	7	8
opposite	0	3	3
unmarked	2	28	30
total	48	309	357

born at Oxford, England, in 1560, mathematician and astronomer, tutor to Sir Walter Raleigh, was the author of Artis
Analyticae Praxis ad Aequationes Algebraicas Resolvendas,
published in London in 1631, after Harriot's death in 1621.
Harriot was responsible for some of the great strides made
in the 17th century in algebraic notations and the more or less
general acceptance of such signs of operation as: +, −, ×; and
such signs of relation as: =, >, and <, though he wrote the
last three much longer than is customary today:

'Comparationis signa in sequentibus vsurpanda. Aequalitatis === ut a === b, significet a aequalem ipi b. Maioritatis > ut a > b, significet a maiorem quam b. Minoritatis < ut a < b, significet a minorem quam b.'

To the question: '>', 283 persons out of 357 answer GREATER THAN; but 28 answer LESS THAN. The expression a > b is read: a is greater than b. The larger value is written on the open side of the symbol; the smaller at the pointed end.

44. < This symbol is read LESS THAN. It is due to the same Thomas Harriot who devised the previous symbol GREATER THAN (43) and was published in his algebra in 1631, after his own death. Reread GREATER THAN (43).

Given the symbol: < 48 persons out of 61 interpret it correctly as LESS THAN; while 9 call it GREATER THAN. When placed between two numbers or letters or expressions, the small end

<.

FORM A. 8.	BO	NY	SUM
LESS THAN	14	34	48
equal to	1	0	1
unequal to	0	0	0
greater than	4	5	9
similar to	0	2	2
unmarked	1	0	1
total	20	41	61

of the symbol points to the smaller of the two, while the large wide end opens toward the greater or larger of the two.

The signs > and < are included in different forms of the mathematics vocabulary test, rarely taken by the same person, and yet these two symbols have come out unknown to practically the same percentage of persons, as one might expect, except that in dealing with human beings it is always a surprise when actual results agree with anticipations.

In commenting on these symbols in his History of Mathematical Notations, published in two volumes in 1928, Florian Cajori remarks that both are symmetrical about the horizontal axis and so easier to remember than the earlier symbols for greater and less which were asymmetrical both horizontally and vertically, and which were confused even by their own devisers. Despite their simplicity and seeming obviousness, these notations are still confused, and have been even by mathematicians themselves. In his Principles of Algebra published in London in 1796, John Frend defined: < as GREATER THAN, and > as LESS THAN, the exact opposite of the more generally accepted interpretation.

That William Oughtred (ŏt'-rĕd), who published his Clavis Mathematicae in 1631, and to whom with Harriot is due much of today's standardization of mathematical notation, recognized the importance is shown by his statement: 'This specious and symbolicall manner, neither racketh the memory with multiplicity of words nor chargeth the phantasie with comparing and laying things together; but plainly presenteth to the eye the whole course and processe of every operation and augmentation'.

As learning a symbol may differ in some way from learning a word, it has been decided to separate the two in different tests so that they can be studied independently more easily than if they are combined as at present.

45. *QUOTIENT* (kwō'-shĕnt) *n.* The result of dividing, the number of times one number is contained in another.

The word QUOTIENT comes from the Latin *quoties, quotiens,*

Result of dividing one number by another.

FORM A. 36.	BO	NY	SUM	FORM AA. 12.	NY
dividend	1	5	6	dividend	27
remainder	1	3	4	remainder	10
index	0	0	0	residual	0
QUOTIENT	17	32	49	QUOTIENT	94
divisor	0	1	1	divisor	1
unmarked	1	0	1	unmarked	0
total	20	41	61	total	132

how often, how many times, from *quot,* how many. To QUOTE on the stock market is to give a price, how many. A QUOTATION in commerce is a statement of how much, how many.

To the question: 'Result of dividing one number by another', 94 persons out of 132 answer QUOTIENT; but 27 answer DIVIDEND. The DIVIDEND is the quantity to be broken into parts, to be divided by another. The DIVIDEND of a stock company is really the amount to be divided among the stockholders, not the amount each receives, for mathematically this is the QUOTIENT. The result of multiplication is the PRODUCT (3); the result of division is the QUOTIENT.

46. *INVERSE PROPORTION* (*in-vers′ prō-pōr′-shŏn*). One quantity growing larger as another grows smaller, one quantity varying as the reciprocal of the other, two quantities related in such a way that their product is constant.

The word INVERSE and the French *inverse*, spelt in the same way, come from the Latin *inversus*, the past participle of *invertere*, to turn about, invert. This is a combination of *in*, in, toward, and *vertere*, to turn, a Latin verb which plays a part in so many English words that it ought to be remembered. From it come OBVERSE, the side turned toward one, in a coin the important side, usually the one with the head; and REVERSE,

Describing a variable which decreases as another variable increases, in constant ratio.

FORM A. 45.	BO	NY	SUM	FORM AA. 14.	NY
direct proportion	0	5	5	direct	7
positive correlation	0	1	1	positive correlation	21
operational function	0	2	2	operational	2
INVERSE PROPORTION	17	31	48	INVERSE	89
geometric progression	1	2	3	geometric	10
unmarked	2	0	2	unmarked	3
total	20	41	61	total	132

the other side, turned away from one; also AVERSE, as: 'AVERSE to going', turned against it; the more difficult noun CONVERSE, the same statement but with the subject and object interchanged, unknown to 77 per cent of those whose scores in the mathematics test have been tabulated, a word discussed later in this volume; and VERSATILE, turning easily to a new subject. INVERSE means turned upside down, inverted.

To the question: 'Describing a variable which decreases as another variable increases, in constant ratio', 48 persons out of 61 answer correctly INVERSE PROPORTION; while 5 answer DIRECT PROPORTION. A PROPORTION is an equality between two ratios, a statement that two ratios are equal. A DIRECT PROPORTION may be written:

$$2 : 4 = 3 : 6 \text{ or } 2 / 4 = 3 / 6$$

or in symbols:

$$a : b = c : d \text{ or } a / b = c / d$$

which is read: the ratio of b to a equals the ratio of d to c, or a over b equals c over d; or in still a third way:

$$2 : 4 :: 3 : 6$$
$$a : b :: c : d$$

which is read: a is to b as c is to d. All of these mean the same:

$$2 / 4 \text{ is constant, or}$$
$$a / b \text{ is constant, } a = kb.$$

The statement: 'b is proportional to a' means: $b = ka$. The statement: 'b varies inversely as a' means:

$$b = \frac{k}{a}; \text{ or } b = k\frac{1}{a}.$$

One quantity is INVERSELY PROPORTIONAL to another if the product of the two is a constant.

In the more recent study 89 persons out of 132 answer correctly INVERSE PROPORTION; while 21 answer POSITIVE CORRELATION. A CORRELATION is any sort of relation between two variables. In a POSITIVE CORRELATION both variables increase together. In a NEGATIVE CORRELATION one decreases while the other increases. But the word CORRELATION does not imply a constant ratio as does the word PROPORTION.

47. *FACTOR* (făk'-tŏr) *n.* One of two or more numbers which, multiplied together, produce a product. Reread PRODUCT (3).

John Kersey who, in addition to editing an English Dictionary, 1708, wrote Elements of Algebra, 1673, says: 'The quantities given to be multiplied one by the other are called FACTORS'. A hundred years later, 1780, Charles Hutton, who lived from 1737 to 1823, wrote: 'For that xy may be positive, the signs of the two FACTORS x and y must be alike'. And from Herbert Spencer, 1855: 'Error in either FACTOR must involve error in the product'.

The noun FACTOR comes from the Latin *factor*, an agent, from the verb *facere*, to do, to make. From this come the English FACTORY and MANUFACTURE, to make by hand, *manus*. The English word FACTOR still appears occasionally in literature with its Latin meaning, an agent, one who acts for another.

To the question: 'Any quantities whose product makes up a given number', 275 persons out of 357 answer correctly FACTORS; while 29 answer DERIVATIVES, and 17 EXPONENTS. An

Any quantities whose product makes up a given number.

FORM B. 11.	NY	MISC.	SUM
extractives	2	8	10
powers	0	16	16
FACTORS	39	236	275
exponents	3	14	17
derivatives	3	26	29
unmarked	1	9	10
total	48	309	357

EXPONENT (42) is the small number written above and to the right of another which indicates how many times the lower number is to be multiplied by itself to produce another. Thus in the expression x^2, the figure 2 is the EXPONENT. A DERIVATIVE, the most frequently marked mislead, is a limit. It is the limit of a ratio, the ratio of two increments, two small additions, an increment to a function divided by an increment to the independent variable as the latter approaches zero. It is the fundamental concept of calculus.

In mathematics, FACTORS are parts of a whole which when multiplied together produce the whole. In literature and often in the sciences the FACTORS involved are the contributing elements, the causes which combine to produce a result.

The word FACTOR has proved so familiar that the term PRODUCT in the definition may be too hard, though it is marked correctly by everyone in another form of the mathematics test and so is known to a larger percentage of persons than FACTOR.

48. *EMPENNAGE* (ŏm-pĕn-nahj́) *n.* The tail unit of an airplane, the horizontal and vertical stabilizers and their attached controlling surfaces which are the rudder and the
elevator, the tail assembly.

EMPENNAGE comes from the French verb *empenner,* to
feather an arrow so that it will fly straight. This comes in turn
from the French noun *penne,* a feather, quill, pen, from the
Latin *penna,* which even in Latin was used for the feather of

Form A. The group of parts composing the tail.
Form AA. The tail assembly or tail unit.

FORM A. 5.	FW	LA	NY	NY	NY	PH	SUM	FORM AA. 10. NY	
rudder	0	3	7	7	24	20	61	rudder	12
EMPENNAGE	16	42	17	54	83	141	353	EMPENNAGE	25
stabilizer	2	3	6	5	19	24	59	stabilizer	21
fin	0	2	2	0	6	7	17	fin	3
elevator	0	2	2	0	8	6	18	terminal fittings	2
unmarked	0	2	3	0	0	2	7	unmarked	0
total	18	54	37	66	140	200	515	total	63

an arrow. The EMPENNAGE is an arrangement of stabilizing
planes at the stern of an aircraft, the tail-surfaces or tail-plane.
A. Berget, in 1909 in Conquest of Air, wrote: 'The EMPENNAGE
will comprise a surface placed well to the rear of the sustaining
surface'.

To the question: 'The group of parts composing the tail',
353 persons out of 515 answer correctly EMPENNAGE. Others
divide almost evenly between STABILIZER and RUDDER, both
parts of the EMPENNAGE or tail assembly.

49. *WORK* (*work*) *n.* Force multiplied by the distance
through which the force acts.
The Oxford New English Dictionary devotes more than nine
full pages to the single word WORK, tracing its history back
to before 1000. The modern word goes back through many
spellings to an Old English *weorc.* The original meaning was
something done, an act or deed done by a person, with no
sense of the time taken, but only of the deed done.

In physics WORK is measured or expressed in terms of the earth's pull. WORK is done when a weight is lifted directly up against gravity. Doubling the weight doubles the WORK. Doubling the distance through which the weight is lifted doubles the WORK. Thomson and Tait in their Natural Philosophy of 1879 say: 'In lifting coals from a pit, the amount of work done is proportional to the weight of the coals lifted; that is, to the force overcome in raising them; and also to the height through which they are raised'.

The units in which WORK is measured are a combination of weight and distance. British engineers use the FOOT-POUND, the work spent in raising one pound one foot against the pull of

Product of force and distance.

FORM E. 2.	BO	FW	LA	NY	NY	NY	NY	PH	TU	SUM
length	2	2	1	0	0	1	5	2	0	13
WORK	22	38	28	16	20	32	182	93	25	456
loudness	0	1	1	0	0	0	2	1	0	5
intensity	1	4	0	4	0	3	17	2	0	31
expansion	3	4	3	0	0	4	11	2	3	30
unmarked	0	1	0	0	0	0	1	0	0	2
total	28	50	33	20	20	40	218	100	28	537

gravity. Continental and electrical engineers and all physicists use the KILOGRAM-METER, or the work done in lifting one kilogram one meter against the pull of gravity.

But WORK is also done in pushing a weight over a level surface against friction even though it is not lifted up against gravity; so that WORK is ordinarily defined not merely as weight times distance but as force times distance. The Scotch physicist James Clerk Maxwell, in his Electricity and Magnetism of 1873, says: 'The unit of WORK is the WORK done by the unit of force acting through the unit of length measured in its own direction'.

To the question: 'Product of force and distance', 456 persons out of 537 answer WORK; but 31 answer INTENSITY; and 30 EXPANSION. In the parallel study concerning the relation of English literary vocabulary to physics vocabulary, all 40 high in English vocabulary mark WORK correctly, compared with only

30 out of 40 who score low in English vocabulary, 4 marking INTENSITY and 3 EXPANSION. The term EXPANSION may be used in a literary sense as synonymous with DISTANCE, but in physics EXPANSION more often means increase in DISTANCE, increase in length, in area, in volume. The term EXPANSION does not include or imply the FORCE which brings about the EXPANSION or the WORK done. EXPANSION is pure distance. INTENSITY is almost synonymous with FORCE. The INTENSITY of an electric or magnetic field is the FORCE on a unit charge or pole at that point. WORK is FORCE times DISTANCE.

Another Scottish physicist William John Macquorn Rankine wrote in 1855, the year in which he became professor of civil engineering in the University of Glasgow: 'WORK is the variation of an accident by an effort, and is a term comprehending all phenomena in which physical change takes place. Quantity

FORM E. 2.	ENGLISH	VOCABULARY
	HIGH	LOW
length	0	2
WORK	40	30
loudness	0	1
intensity	0	4
expansion	0	3
unmarked	0	0
total	40	40

of WORK is measured by the product of the variation of the passive accident by the magnitude of the effort when this is constant; or by the integral of the effort with respect to the passive accident when the effort is variable.' In this definition Rankine uses the word ACCIDENT in its original sense of anything that happens.

In reading the galley proof of this book Professor Deimel notes in the margin: 'Mention this as an example of incomprehensible jargon; Rankine was my textbook as a student'. And he quotes Professor Ennis: 'Rankine rose to the height of obscurity'. Every student should use many books; for what is incomprehensible to one may seem clear to another, as this must have to Rankine when he wrote it.

50. *ELECTROLYSIS* (*ē-lĕk-trŏl'-ĭ-sĭs*) *n*. The decomposition
of a solution by a current of electricity.

Michael Faraday, a journeyman bookbinder, became laboratory assistant to Sir Humphrey Davy in 1813, after hearing him
lecture, and then in 1825 director of the Royal Institution. In
paragraph 662 in one of his papers dated 1834 he says: 'To
avoid, therefore, confusion and circumlocution, and for the
sake of greater precision of expression than I can otherwise
obtain I have deliberately considered the subject with two
friends, and with their assistance and concurrence in framing

The decomposition of a solution by a current of electricity.

FORM C. I.	NY	FORM CA.	BO	NY HIGH	NY NEXT	NY REST	NY MISC.	SUM
osmosis	1	electro-statics	0	2	2	98	4	106
polarization	15	polarization	2	4	7	107	4	124
ELECTROLYSIS	366	ELECTROL-YSIS	94	394	386	697	216	1787
hysteresis	6	hysteresis	1	0	1	88	1	91
electrophoresis	12	electropho-resis	3	0	4	110	8	125
unmarked	0	unmarked	0	0	0	0	1	1
total	400	total	100	400	400	1100	234	2234

them, I propose henceforward using certain terms, which I will
now define'; and then on little more than a single page he coins
the words ANODE, CATHODE, ION, ANION, CATION, ELECTRODE,
ELECTROLYTE, and ELECTRO-CHEMICAL EQUIVALENT, as well as
ELECTROLYSIS, all so familiar today that they are accepted with
little realization that they were invented by one man as recently
as 1834.

The combining form ELECTRO appears in ELECTRO-CHEMISTRY,
the study of chemical changes produced by electricity; also in
ELECTROPLATING and ELECTROTYPING. It comes from the Greek
ἤλεκτρον (electron), a word which originally meant amber, a
hard brittle substance, pale yellow, brown, or red in color, the
mineralized resin of extinct pine trees. The Greek ἤλεκτρον
(electron) then came to mean the negative charge which
amber acquires when rubbed, and so ELECTRICITY.

The ending -LYSIS from the Greek λύειν (lyein), to loosen, resolve, appears in the English word ANALYSIS ($ă$-$năl'$-$ĭ$-$sĭs$), the separation of a compound into its elements, the resolution of an idea into its parts, a loosening, taking apart. CATALYSIS ($kă$-$tăl'$-$ĭ$-$sĭs$), from the Greek κατά (cata-), down, and -LYSIS, originally meant a shaking apart which resulted in destruction. CATALYSIS is now a chemical reaction which takes place only in the presence of a third substance which breaks down the previous stability. ELECTROLYSIS is a taking apart by electricity.

Passage of an electric current decomposes a copper-sulphate ($CuSO_4$) solution into copper (Cu) particles and sulphate (SO_4) particles. The formula is:

$$CuSO_4 = Cu^{++} + SO_4^{--}$$

The positively charged copper $(Cu)^{++}$ particles, called IONS, move to the negative pole, the cathode, and are deposited there. The sulphate $(SO_4)^{--}$ negatively charged particles move to the positive pole, the anode.

To the question: 'The decomposition of a solution by a current of electricity', 80 per cent of 2234 persons answer ELECTROLYSIS, 6 per cent POLARIZATION, and practically the same number ELECTROPHORESIS. In the previous study based on 400 persons POLARIZATION, there the most frequently marked mislead, attracted 4 per cent, and ELECTROPHORESIS, the second, 3 per cent. ELECTROPHORESIS ($ē$-$lĕk$-$trō$-$fō$-$rē'$-$sĭs$), a combination of the same ELECTRO- and the Greek φέριεν (pherien), to carry, bear, is the motion or migration of particles or ions in a fluid under the influence of an electric field. ELECTROLYSIS is the breaking down of a fluid into ions which then migrate.

POLARIZATION is the gathering of hydrogen at the cathode. When electricity decomposes a dilute solution of sulphuric acid into hydrogen (H) and sulphate (SO_4) particles or IONS:

$$H_2SO_4 \text{ into } 2H^+ + SO_4^{--}$$

the positively charged hydrogen collects on the cathode. Unless removed, it introduces resistance in the circuit and ultimately sets up a counter-electromotive force. As thus used the word POLARIZATION, which designates the accumulation of a film of gas on the negative electrode, is almost an opposite of ELECTROLYSIS, for the phenomenon stops the flow of current and so puts an end to the breaking up of the solution.

51. *FREQUENCY* (frĕ'-kwĕn-sē) *n.* The number of times a
given thing happens in some unit period, the number of occurrences in a second of a regularly repeated event.
It is hard a realize the recency of the present meaning of
FREQUENCY as used in physics. The word originally meant a
crowd, throng, from *frequentia*, a crowd, throng, from *fre-
quens, frequentis*, crowded, crammed, repeated, frequent. As a
third meaning of FREQUENCY the Century Dictionary says:
'The ratio of the number of times that an event occurs to the
number of occasions on which it might occur; with a few
recent writers on physics, the number of regularly recurring

Number of oscillations per second.

FORM A. I.	NY	NY	NY	SUM
cycle	7	6	17	30
FREQUENCY	28	29	122	179
amplitude	1	1	4	6
wave number	0	4	3	7
speed	1	0	1	2
unmarked	0	0	0	0
total	37	40	147	224

events of any given kind in a given time'. This last is the usual
meaning of FREQUENCY in physics today. As early as 1831 David
Brewster wrote of sound: 'The pitch or FREQUENCY of vibration'; but Ellis the philologist in his translation of Helmholtz of
1875 speaks of VIBRATIONAL NUMBER, and rarely if ever of
FREQUENCY.

To the question: 'Number of oscillations per second', 179
persons out of 224 answer FREQUENCY; while 30 answer CYCLE.
CYCLE comes through the French *cycle*, from the Greek
κύκλος (cyclos), a ring, wheel, disk, circle, orb, revolution,
orbit, a round of operations. A CYCLE is one complete revolution; but the term is used constantly in stating the FREQUENCY,
as: 'Alternating current used for house lighting is 60 CYCLES',
meaning a FREQUENCY of 60 CYCLES per second. On ships and
airplanes, generators often produce 500-CYCLE currents. But
the CYCLE is still one turn of a wheel, one unit in a periodic
series. FREQUENCY is the number of such units per second.

52. *EFFICIENCY* (*ĕf-fĭsh'-ĕn-sē*) *n*. The ratio of the useful work performed by a prime mover to the energy expended, ratio of the useful energy derived from a system to the energy communicated to it over a protracted period of operation.

The word EFFICIENCY comes from the Latin *efficientia*, efficiency, from *efficiens, efficientis*, efficient, the source of the English adjective EFFICIENT. This in turn is the present participle of *efficere*, to effect, accomplish, bring to pass, do, complete, a combination of *ex*, out, and *facere*, to do.

EFFICIENCY is a relative term. It is a ratio showing how much useful work is got out of a total amount of work supplied.

$$\text{EFFICIENCY} = \frac{\text{USEFUL OUTPUT}}{\text{INPUT}} = \frac{\text{USEFUL OUTPUT}}{\text{OUTPUT} + \text{LOSSES}}$$

or

$$\text{EFFICIENCY} = \frac{\text{ENERGY USED OR CONVERTED}}{\text{ENERGY SUPPLIED}}$$

To the question: 'The power out / power in', 159 persons out of 224 answer EFFICIENCY, and 46 GAIN. The word GAIN is used ordinarily for an amount, increment, access, not for a ratio. In mechanics, work done in overcoming friction is wasted as heat,

The power out divided by the power in.

FORM A. 14.	NY	NY	NY	SUM
EFFICIENCY	27	28	104	159
gain	6	6	34	46
baffle	0	3	3	6
lead	2	0	2	4
fundamental	1	3	2	6
unmarked	1	0	2	3
total	37	40	147	224

so that the useful work out of a system is always less than the work which goes in. The power out, or useful power, divided by the power in is always less than one. There is always a loss.

The EFFICIENCY of a machine is the work accomplished divided by the work put into the machine. The EFFICIENCY of an engine is the ratio of the heat actually turned into mechanical work to the amount of heat given by the fuel consumed.

In an automobile engine the useful work done may be as low as 20 per cent. The losses out of the exhaust may be as high as 35 per cent, in cooling water another 35 per cent, and in friction 10 per cent. The EFFICIENCY in this instance is 20 per cent.

53. *SOLENOID* (*sō'-lē-noid*) *n.* A cylindrical coil of wire, the length of which is greater than the diameter, wound as cotton on a reel, a helix of wire used to produce a magnetic field or to excite an electromagnet.

The Century Dictionary gives only one pronunciation (*sō-lē'-noid*). The Oxford New English Dictionary offers two: (*sō-lē'-noid*) first, followed by (*sō'-lē-noid*). Cassell's Encyclopaedic Dictionary of 1887, clearer and more accurate in scientific terms than most such reference books, gives (*sō'-lĕn-oid*).

SOLENOID comes from the Greek σωλήν (solen), channel, pipe, plus εἶδος (eidos), form, resemblance, likeness. The termination -OID is really an adjective ending which means having the form of, resembling, as: ANTHROPOID, like man, resembling man, HYDROID, like water, and CRYSTALLOID, like crystal. There is no

An electrically energized coil of many turns.

FORM EA. 15.	BO
SOLENOID	19
permanent magnet	9
Bronson resistance	1
diode	1
kenotron	1
total	31

other common English word from σωλήν (solen), pipe, though there are a number of technical terms in various sciences. Thus the SOLENIDAE (*sō-lĕn'-ĭ-dē*) are a family of bivalve mollusks, the razor shells, the SOLENOSTOMIDAE (*sō-lē-nō-stŏm'-ĭ-dē*) are a family of fishes, and the SOLENODONTIDAE (*sō-lē-nō-dŏn'-tĭ-dē*) are a family of mammals.

To the question: 'An electrically energized coil of many turns', the popular mislead is PERMANENT MAGNET. An electrically energized SOLENOID acts in every way like a bar magnet; but the word SOLENOID designates the coil of wire, not its mag-

netic properties when energized; though the combination COIL
AND PLUNGER is sometimes called a SOLENOID. But an electrically
energized SOLENOID is not a permanent magnet, for this term
refers to a magnet of hard, cobalt, or tungsten steel as opposed
to a temporary magnet of soft iron.

54. *COEFFICIENT OF FRICTION* (kō-ĕf-fĭsh'-ĕnt ŏv frĭk'-
shŏn). A ratio, the force dragging an object parallel to a
surface divided by the force pressing it against the surface.
The word COEFFICIENT is a combination of the Latin prefix
CO-, together, and EFFICIENT. In algebra, a COEFFICIENT is a
number or a quantity usually placed before and multiplying
another quantity which may be known or unknown. In the
expression 2x, the COEFFICIENT is the figure 2. In physics, a
COEFFICIENT is also a multiplier which expresses usually some
property of a particular substance. This latter type of CO-

Ratio of the force dragging an object over a surface to the
force pressing the object to the surface.

FORM E. 27.	BO	FW	LA	NY	NY	NY	NY	PH	TU	SUM
critical pressure	0	0	0	0	0	0	6	2	0	8
slope	1	3	0	2	0	1	5	1	0	13
resolution of forces	2	2	1	1	2	3	24	11	1	47
COEFFICIENT										
OF FRICTION	22	44	32	16	18	34	179	85	26	456
attrition	0	0	0	1	0	1	1	1	1	5
unmarked	3	1	0	0	0	1	3	0	0	8
total	28	50	33	20	20	40	218	100	28	537

EFFICIENT is almost always of necessity a ratio. Thus the
COEFFICIENT OF EXPANSION is the actual expansion of a given
substance divided by the initial length, and then divided by the
change in temperature; expansion per unit length, per degree
change in temperature. There is a COEFFICIENT OF RIGIDITY and
several COEFFICIENTS OF ELASTICITY, all ratios, primarily the
effect produced divided by the force producing it. The CO-
EFFICIENT OF FRICTION is the ratio between two forces, the
force needed to push an object over a surface divided by the
force pressing it down.

With the definition: 'Ratio of the force dragging an object over a surface to the force pressing the object to the surface', 456 persons out of 537 mark the correct answer COEFFICIENT OF FRICTION; but 47 mark RESOLUTION OF FORCES. From Charles Hutton, A Course of Mathematics, 1798, comes: 'The RESOLUTION OF FORCES is the finding of two or more forces which acting in any different directions shall have the same effect as any given single force'. From Kater and Lardner, Mechanics, 1830, comes: 'It is frequently expedient to substitute for a single force two or more forces to which it is mechanically equivalent or of which it is the resultant. This process is called the RESOLUTION OF FORCE'.

This is another item which those low in the English literary vocabulary do poorly, only 26 out of 40 persons answering

Ratio of the force dragging an object over a surface to the force pressing the object to the surface.

FORM E. 27.	ENGLISH VOCABULARY	
	HIGH	LOW
critical pressure	1	0
slope	2	3
resolution of forces	0	8
COEFFICIENT OF FRICTION	36	26
attrition	1	3
unmarked	0	0
total	40	40

correctly, 8 marking RESOLUTION OF FORCES, compared with the small group high in English vocabulary where not one marked this mislead.

Without lubrication the COEFFICIENT OF FRICTION ranges from about 0.1 to 0.4; that is the force required to push an object horizontally is one tenth to four tenths the weight of the object. A hundred pound weight needs a force of ten to forty pounds to move it horizontally. If the bearing surface is lubricated the force needed to move the weight is enormously reduced. The force may be reduced to 0.01; or with good lubrication even to 0.002, to one tenth or even one hundredth of the force needed without lubrication.

The COEFFICIENT OF FRICTION for a solid body is directly proportional to the force pressing the body down, but is independent of the area of the surface in contact, and with solids nearly independent of the speed of motion. This is not true of friction in liquids. STATIC FRICTION is the friction which must be overcome in order to start a body moving, and may be expressed by the COEFFICIENT OF STARTING FRICTION. KINETIC FRICTION, which is less, is the friction which must be overcome in order to keep a body moving after it has started, expressed by the COEFFICIENT OF SLIDING FRICTION.

55. *EQUATION* (*ē-kwā'-shŏn*) *n.* A formula stating the sameness of two quantitative expressions.
Noah Webster in the first edition of his American Dictionary of the English Language, published in America in 1828 and in

An algebraic statement of equality.

FORM B. 6.	NY	MISC.	SUM
identity	4	41	45
derivation	0	2	2
congruity	2	18	20
homogeneity	0	3	3
EQUATION	42	244	286
unmarked	0	1	1
total	48	309	357

England in 1832, says: 'In algebra, a proposition asserting the equality of two quantities, and expressed by the sign = between them'. The Imperial Dictionary, based on Webster, and published in Edinburgh in 1850, quotes this exactly.

The word EQUATION comes from the Latin *aequation, aequationen,* from the verb *aequare,* to make equal. This comes in turn from the adjective *aequus,* equal. Of AE, written Æ, Noah Webster says: 'A diphthong in the Latin language; used also by the Saxon writers. It answers to the Greek αι (ai). In derivatives from the learned languages, it is most superseded by E, and convenience seems to require it to be wholly rejected in anglicized words'. The original *ae* of the Latin *aequus* is now always written E in English, probably because of the age of the English word EQUAL. The same sort of *ae* is today usually retained in AESTHETIC, coined more recently from the Greek, though even this word is sometimes changed to ESTHETIC. Webster does not include it at all in his first edition; and the Imperial, 1850, says: 'ESTHETICS or AESTHETICS'. The AE is usually kept in the word ENCYCLOPAEDIA; though Webster, 1828, following his own advice, spells it ENCYCLOPEDIA.

To the question: 'An algebraic statement of equality', 286 persons out of 357 answer EQUATION; but 45 answer IDENTITY, the most frequently marked mislead. From New School Algebra by G. A. Wentworth, published by Ginn and Company in 1898, comes: 'An equation containing letters, if true for all values of the letters involved, is called an IDENTICAL EQUATION; but if it is true only for certain particular values of the letters involved, it is called an EQUATION OF CONDITION. For brevity, an IDENTICAL EQUATION is called an IDENTITY, and an EQUATION OF CONDITION is called simply an EQUATION.'

56. *LOCUS* (*lō'-kŭs*) *n.* A figure generated by a point, a line, or a plane, moving in accordance with defined conditions, a line or surface which embodies all of the points satisfying a particular equation. The plural follows the Latin LOCI (*lō'sī*), as the plural of FOCUS is FOCI (*fō'-sī*).

Ephraim Chambers was born in Westmorland, in the northwest of England. As a youth he was apprenticed to a globemaker in London; but how he shifted from this to compiling one of the first and still one of the greatest of all encyclopaedias is unknown. Fifty years later a French translation of Chambers led to the French Encyclopédie of Denis Diderot (*dē-drō'*) and d'Alembert, the mathematician. From the Cyclopaedia or Universal Dictionary of Arts and Sciences by Ephraim Chambers which came out through subscription in two folio volumes in 1728 comes: 'A LOCUS is a line, any point of which may equally solve an indeterminate problem'; and still from Ephraim Chambers: 'All LOCI of the second degree are conic sections'.

The word LOCUS comes directly from the Latin *locus*, a place, the source of the adjective LOCAL, belonging to the place, and LOCALITY, the place, as well as the verbs to LOCATE, to place, and DISLOCATE, to get out of place. From the same source comes the French *lieu*, pronounced almost (*lē-er'*), place; and from this comes LIEUTENANT, one who acts in the place of another.

To the question: 'All positions of a moving point', 260 persons out of 357 answer LOCUS; and 22, SUMMATION, the most frequently marked mislead. The word SUMMATION is used technically for the sum of a series and the sign of SUMMATION is the Greek capital sigma: Σ(S).

William Kingdon Clifford, an English mathematician and philosopher, 1845 to 1879, one more of the great theoretical scientists who must have done much of his thinking early in life, perhaps even between the years twenty one and twenty three or twenty four when the Laboratory finds the trait in-

All positions of a moving point.

FORM B. 36.	NY	MISC.	SUM
summation	2	20	22
differential	0	15	15
asymptote	1	10	11
area	3	12	15
LOCUS	39	221	260
unmarked	3	31	34
total	48	309	357

ductive reasoning at its height, for Clifford died at the age of thirty four, wrote a Classification of Loci in 1878. From his Seeing and Thinking, 1879, a series of popular science lectures, comes: 'When a point moves along a line, that line is the LOCUS of the successive positions of the moving point'.

57. *CARRIER* (*kăr'-rĭ-er*) *n.* A continuous electromagnetic wave motion, of constant height and frequency, sent out by a radio transmitter; a steady high-frequency current, which contains no signal, which is unmodulated. Called also a CARRIER WAVE. Reread BAND (37).

When energy is fed into the antenna circuit, the high-frequency current sets up magnetic and electric fields. As the current alternates these two fields are constantly pushed away from the antenna (8). For this phenomenon to occur the frequency of vibration must be 15,000 cycles per second or more.

To the question: 'A steady unmodulated radio-frequency output', 172 persons out of 224 answer CARRIER, and 24 answer MODULATOR. A MODULATED WAVE is one in which either the amplitude, the frequency, or the phase, is varied. The voice wave of a person speaking has a much lower frequency (51) than the CARRIER WAVE, and varies in both frequency and amplitude. Audible frequencies, those which affect the ear, range from 20 cycles per second to 10,000 or more but not high enough to radiate out through space. Audible frequencies will

A steady unmodulated radio frequency output.

FORM A. 13.	NY	NY	NY	SUM
modulator	6	7	11	24
speech	0	3	3	6
CARRIER	30	26	116	172
receiver	1	1	4	6
shunt	0	3	12	15
unmarked	0	0	1	1
total	37	40	147	224

not radiate. High frequencies, often called RADIO FREQUENCIES, cannot be heard. Therefore the high constant frequency and constant amplitude of the CARRIER WAVE are altered, often by keeping the frequency the same but altering the height of the vibration. By modulation of the CARRIER WAVE, impulses caused by sounds at the transmitting end are conveyed by it to the receiver. While the long audible wave is at its maximum, its own strength is added to the peak of each CARRIER WAVE, so that the peaks of hundreds of CARRIER WAVES all connected by a line make the audible wave.

58. *CAM* (kăm) *n.* A projection on the edge of a wheel designed to impart an alternating motion to another piece pressing against it, an eccentric surface used to give variable movement to the valves of an engine.

From Cassell's Technical Educator, 1879, comes: 'CAMS are variously formed plates, or grooves, by means of which a circular may be converted into a reciprocating motion'. CAMS are used in machines where a uniform revolving motion is employed to actuate any kind of non-uniform alternating motion. The original method was by cogs and teeth, fixed or cut at certain points in the circumference of a wheel but a CAM is now any kind of eccentric heart-shaped or spiral disk.

The word CAM goes back at least to 1777 when it appeared in a patent specification. It comes probably directly from the Dutch and is closely related to COMB. It is also related to Scandinavian words for toothed rim, toothed wheel, and cogwheel. It is said by the Century Dictionary to be a dialect form

Form A. A projection on a revolving shaft designed to give a variable motion to an object.

Form AA. Projection on a revolving shaft to give variable motion to a part pressing against it.

FORM A. 37.	FW	LA	NY	NY	NY	PH	SUM	FORM AA. 9.	NY
wrist-pin	1	2	5	5	20	22	55	wrist-pin	10
tappet	0	2	5	1	9	5	22	tappet	7
lobe	0	9	6	3	16	9	43	lobe	0
CAM	16	40	18	46	89	142	351	CAM	42
camber	1	0	1	1	3	11	17	camber	0
unmarked	0	1	2	10	3	11	27	unmarked	4
total	18	54	37	66	140	200	515	total	63

of COMB, which goes back to the Anglo-Saxon *camb*. The word COG goes back much further, perhaps to as early as 1250. The term COG is used most often today for one of a series of teeth or projections on the circumference of a wheel which engage with corresponding projections on another wheel.

To the question: 'A projection on a revolving shaft designed to give a variable motion to an object', the correct answer CAM is marked by 351 persons in a population of 515; but WRIST-PIN is marked by 55, the most frequently marked mislead. Both a WRIST-PIN and a CAM are projections designed to give a variable motion, each is a device used to convert a regular rotary motion into a reciprocating or back-and-forth motion. A WRIST-PIN projects from the side of a wheel and actuates a connecting rod the other end of which is attached to the part which moves back and forth. A CAM is a projection on the edge of a wheel which by direct pressure moves another part back and forth.

59. *HELICOPTER* (*hĕl'-ĭ-kŏp-ter*) *n.* A heavier-than-air craft
lifted by horizontally rotated vanes, a flying machine whose
supporting surfaces are rotated mechanically.

A HELICOPTER is capable of vertical flight, of lifting itself
straight up. There is no propeller, the rotors supplying the
horizontal motion. As early as 1796 Sir George Cayley made
toy HELICOPTERS or machines with directly lifting screws and
no wings.

The word HELICOPTER comes from the Latin *helix*, a kind of
ivy, also a volute in architecture. This Latin word is the direct
source of the English HELIX (*hē'-lĭks*), a spiral line like a screw

Form A. Type of rotor plane whose support in air is normally
derived from airfoils mechanically rotated about an approximately vertical axis.

Form AA. Plane supported by vanes turned by power around a
vertical axis.

FORM A. 6.	FW	LA	NY	NY	NY	PH	SUM	FORM AA. 5.	NY
dirigible	0	0	0	1	3	5	9	dirigible	1
autogiro	1	7	9	14	14	37	82	autogiro	7
ornithopter	0	0	0	1	1	3	5	sesquiplane	0
HELICOPTER	17	47	26	48	120	147	405	HELICOPTER	52
gyroplane	0	0	2	2	2	6	12	gyroplane	3
unmarked	0	0	0	0	0	2	2	unmarked	0
total	18	54	37	66	140	200	515	total	63

thread, a corkscrew, or the wire in a coil, a spiral which gradually rises in the center. The Latin *helix* comes in turn from the
Greek ἕλιξ (helix), ἕλικος (helikos), with the ASPER or rough
breathing over the *e* which becomes HE in English, anything
which is spiral in shape, a twist, whirl, convolution, also the
tendril of a vine, and the smaller scroll under the flowers in a
Corinthian capital, called a VOLUTE.

To the question: 'Type of rotor plane whose support in air is
normally derived from airfoils mechanically rotated about an
approximately vertical axis', 405 persons out of 515 answer
HELICOPTER, but 82 answer AUTOGIRO, the only frequently
marked mislead. Although GYROPLANE, GYROSCOPE, and the col-
loquial GYRO, all have Y, AUTOGIRO is correct with I, for this is

the name of the particular machine designed by Sr. de la Cierva in Spain, about 1920, and both the Italians and the Spaniards spell GYRO with I, *giro*, meaning circuit, a round. GIRO, with I, has been used by both George Eliot and Motley for a tour, a circuit in a foreign country.

Both the AUTOGIRO and the HELICOPTER are supported by horizontally rotating vanes turning about a vertical axis. Neither have wings. The difference is that in the AUTOGIRO the vanes are free, rotating automatically as a propeller drives the craft forward. In the HELICOPTER the lifting vanes turn under power and there is no propeller.

60. *PHOTOMETER* (*fō-tŏm'-ē-ter*) *n.* An instrument for measuring intensity of illumination by comparing the brightness of one light source with that of another of the same color, usually the brightness of an unknown with a known standard.

To the question: 'Instrument for comparing the candle-power of two sources', 444 persons out of 537 answer PHOTOMETER; but 39 answer STEREOSCOPE, and another 39 ELECTROPHORUS. These are also the two most frequently marked misleads in seven out of the nine small populations tabulated separately for different cities. In general, very small samplings, even twenty persons, give an indication of the most and of the least frequently marked misleads.

PHOTOMETER is one more technical term which those who score high in the English literary vocabulary mark correctly 39 times out of 40, whereas among those who score low in English vocabulary it is marked correctly only 23 times out of 40, 8 of this group choosing STEREOSCOPE.

In the word STEREOSCOPE (*stĕr'-ē-ō-skōp*) the last syllable comes from the Greek σκοπεῖν (skopein), to view, see, look at, from the same source as TELESCOPE, literally distant view, and MICROSCOPE, minute view. The STEREOSCOPE is an instrument for obtaining a single image from two photographs taken from positions as far apart as the distance between the two eyes, so that the combined impression is that of seeing a solid object. The books of Mr. Newman, the well-known philosophical instrument maker, supply evidence of his having constructed

STEREOSCOPES for Sir Charles Wheatstone (*hwēt'-stōn*), the inventor of the instrument, in the year 1832. In 1838 Professor Wheatstone said: 'I propose that it be called a STEREOSCOPE to indicate its property of representing solid figures'; for the first part of the word comes from the Greek στερεός (stereos), solid. Both the STEREOSCOPE and the PHOTOMETER involve the bringing together of light from two sources, the STEREOSCOPE two photographs, the PHOTOMETER two lights of different intensities.

The last half of the word PHOTOMETER comes from the Greek μέτρον (metron), which may mean measure, as in PERIMETER (23), the measure around, and DIAMETER, the measure across, or more often today the measuring instrument, as: INTERFEROM-

Instrument for comparing the candle-power of two sources.

FORM E. 6.	BO	FW	LA	NY	NY	NY	NY	PH	TU	SUM
camera	0	1	0	0	0	1	3	2	0	7
PHOTOMETER	25	32	30	16	19	33	174	90	25	444
electric eye	0	0	1	0	1	0	6	0	0	8
electrophorus	2	7	0	2	0	1	21	5	1	39
stereoscope	1	10	2	2	0	5	14	3	2	39
unmarked	0	0	0	0	0	0	0	0	0	0
total	28	50	33	20	20	40	218	100	28	537

ETER, an instrument for measuring the interference of beams of light; SPECTROMETER, an instrument for measuring spectrum lines; and the simple METER. The first part of PHOTOMETER comes from the Greek φῶς (phos), φωτίς (photis), light, from the same source as the word PHOTOGRAPHY.

While the unaided eye distinguishes the radiations from a 25-watt electric light bulb and from a 100-watt, even from a 40-watt and a 60-watt, it cannot evaluate this quantitatively, nor can it recognize finer gradations. But when two sources of light illumine adjoining surfaces, or contiguous parts of the same surface, the eye detects minute differences. This is the principle of the PHOTOMETER.

In the diffusion type of PHOTOMETER, designed by Joly, a pair of paraffin blocks, separated by a thin sheet of tin-foil so that light from one cannot penetrate the other, are placed between two lights to be compared. Viewed at right angles to this line, one of the two blocks may seem darker than the other. By moving the pair of paraffin blocks away from the brighter light, toward the dimmer, the two blocks may be equally illuminated. At this point the relative distances of the two lights lead to a quantitative evaluation of their relative brightness, for intensity varies inversely as the square of the distance.

In the LUMMER-BRODHUN PHOTOMETER, used for more precise work, a white plaster disk with a matt surface replaces the paraffin. By means of mirrors and prisms one side of this plaster disk is seen as a circle, lighted by one light, and the other side as

Instrument for comparing the candle-power of two sources.

FORM E. 6.   ENGLISH VOCABULARY

	HIGH	LOW
camera	0	2
PHOTOMETER	39	23
electric eye	0	0
electrophorus	0	6
stereoscope	1	8
unmarked	0	1
total	40	40

background, lighted by the other light. By moving the PHOTOMETER HEAD, which carries the white plaster disk, toward one light source and away from the other the circle can be made to blend perfectly into the background.

61. *SPECTROSCOPE* (*spĕk′-trō-skōp*) *n*. An instrument for dispersing light of different colors; the essential part is either a prism or diffraction grating.

SPECTRO- comes from the Latin *spectrum*, a vision, apparition, image. As used in physics the SPECTRUM is the continuous band of light showing the successive prismatic colors or isolated lines or bands of color.

To the question: 'The common optical instrument for forming and viewing spectra', 79 per cent of 2234 persons answer SPECTROSCOPE; but 6 per cent answer MICROSCOPE, and practically the same number POLARISCOPE. All three words end in -SCOPE, the Greek word σκοπεῖν (skopein), written in Roman letters, and meaning to see, look at, view. The Greek noun σκοπός (skopos) designated a spy, a watcher. The English SCOPE, as: 'Of wide SCOPE', means outlook, view. All three instruments, the SPECTROSCOPE, the MICROSCOPE, and the POLARISCOPE, are for viewing.

The differentiation of the terms SPECTROSCOPE and MICROSCOPE depends as much upon a knowledge of Greek as upon science. A MICROSCOPE, from the Greek μικρός (mikros), small, is an instrument with which one looks at small things. From the same Greek μικρός (mikros), small, little, come MICROBE, a minute living organism, a combination of μικρός (mikros) and

Common optical instrument for separating and viewing the radiations from a luminous body.

FORM C. 6.	NY	FORM CA. 2.	BO	NY HIGH	NY NEXT	NY REST	NY MISC.	SUM
spectro-		spectro-						
photometer	12	photometer	2	1	7	105	13	128
refractometer	5	photosphere	0	0	1	84	0	85
microscope	12	microscope	3	1	2	118	17	141
polariscope	3	polariscope	7	3	5	100	4	119
SPECTRO-								
SCOPE	368	SPECTROSCOPE	88	395	385	693	200	1761
unmarked	0	unmarked	0	0	0	0	0	0
total	400	total	100	400	400	1100	234	2234

βίος (bios), life; also MICROMETER, an instrument for measuring very small distances; and MICROPHONE, by derivation a little voice, the mouthpiece into which a small sound enters before being amplified. A MICROSCOPE is for viewing small objects; a SPECTROSCOPE is for viewing SPECTRA, primarily for looking at light separated into its different wave lengths.

The SPECTROSCOPE is used by astro-physicists in determining the chemical composition of a star by recognizing wave lengths of light known to be emitted only by some specific substance. It is also used in measuring the motion of a star to or from the observer by the shift of a known line toward one end of the spectrum or the other. With a star moving toward the observer, wave lengths from known substances are shortened; with a star moving away, wave lengths are lengthened.

62. *TRANSFORMER* (trăns-fŏr'-mer) n. Stationary apparatus for raising or lowering electrical potential, a voltage changer.

The word TRANSFORMER comes from the Latin *trans,* over, and *formare,* to form, shape. From the Latin *trans-,* over, come a multitude of English words. To TRANSPORT, from *trans-,* over, and *portare,* to carry, means to carry over, to carry across from one place to another. To TRANSCRIBE, from *trans-,* over, and *scribere,* to write, means to write once again, copy, sometimes more specifically to type from shorthand notes. To TRANSCEND, from *trans-* and *scandere,* to climb, mount, was once literally to climb over, but the word is now used only figuratively to mean surpass, excel, exceed, go beyond. Finally TRANSIENT, from *trans-* and *ire,* to go, now means going by quickly, and therefore momentary, fleeting, passing away quickly.

The verb to TRANSFORM means to form over again, reshape, change, alter, metamorphose. The noun TRANSFORMATION is a change in form, alteration in appearance. A TRANSFORMER is by derivation anything which changes something into something else. The scientific term TRANSFORMER designates a contrivance for altering electricity, with no change in the total amount present.

To the question: 'Stationary apparatus for raising or lowering voltage', 76 per cent of 2234 examinees answer TRANSFORMER, the correct answer; while 6 per cent of examinees answer RECTIFIER and another 6 per cent CONDENSER. In the earlier study of form C, TRANSFORMER was marked correctly by 91 per cent of what appears to have been a higher vocabulary group; but the same misleads, RECTIFIER and CONDENSER, were popular. Among the 400 New York persons who score highest in the physics vocabulary test as a whole out of a total population of 1900, marked HIGH in the table, nearly all, 389, answer TRANSFORMER, and only 2 CONDENSER and 2 RECTIFIER. It is only the 1100 who score lowest in the physics test, called REST in the table, who mark these two misleads in quantity. Both a RECTIFIER and a TRANSFORMER are stationary apparatus, without moving parts. Both are used with alternating currents only. A RECTIFIER changes alternating current to direct by allowing the current to flow in one direction only. A TRANSFORMER changes not one kind of current to another but one strength of current to another strength. Leaving the product of VOLTS times AMPERES always the same, except for heat losses, a TRANSFORMER increases the voltage and lowers the current, or vice versa.

CONDENSER, an equally attractive mislead, is also a stationary electrical device which contains no moving parts. A CONDENSER stores a charge. It consists basically of two metal plates, separated by a sheet of glass or any nonconductor. When the metal plates are charged simultaneously, one positively and the

Stationary apparatus for raising or lowering voltage.

FORM C. I I. NY		FORM CA. 3. BO		NY HIGH	NY NEXT	NY REST	NY MISC.	SUM
motor-		motor-						
generator	8	generator	0	0	8	109	5	122
detector tube	2	booster	0	7	8	97	12	124
rectifier	9	rectifier	6	2	7	120	9	144
condenser	14	condenser	3	2	9	123	4	141
TRANS-								
FORMER	366	TRANSFORMER	91	389	368	651	203	1702
unmarked	1	unmarked	0	0	0	0	1	1
total	400	total	100	400	400	1100	234	2234

other negatively, the CONDENSER retains the charge for an appreciable period, but can be discharged at any moment by connecting the two plates. Although CONDENSERS play important parts in many alternating-current circuits, their simplest use is with direct currents.

A TRANSFORMER operates only with an alternating current. It consists of two separate coils of wire, both wound around the same common core or center of soft iron. An alternating current sent through one of the two coils produces an alternating current in the other. The voltage in one coil multiplied by the amperage equals the voltage in the other coil multiplied by its amperage. The voltages passing through the two coils have the same ratio to each other as the number of turns of wire in the two coils. Thus, should one coil have ten times as many turns of wire as the other, the voltage in that coil would be ten times that in the other.

Tiny TRANSFORMERS with coils less than an inch in diameter may reduce the voltage in a public service line, enabling it to operate the doorbell in a private house. Other TRANSFORMERS, ten to twelve feet in height and oval in section, may be seen out of doors, standing in groups and used to lower the voltage of electricity which has been brought from afar. Since electricity of high voltage and low amperage travels through small wires without heating them, power can be sent great distances in this form and then converted, TRANSFORMED, into low voltage and high amperage and so used. Partly because of the great usefulness of the TRANSFORMER, alternating current electricity has gradually replaced direct current.

63. *HUM* (*hŭm*) *n*. A low continuous sound made by a bee or by another insect or by a spinning top or by a machine in motion.

The verb to HUM has been known since nearly 1300. A HUM is labial-nasal and distinguished from a BUZZ, which is sibilant.

In radio, the word HUM is applied to alternating currents which appear in the output of an amplifier. In audio-frequency

The results of insufficient power supply filtering.

FORM A. 20.	NY	NY	NY	SUM
voltage-drop	1	5	15	21
reinforcement	1	0	2	3
HUM	27	24	114	165
frequency deviation	1	6	13	20
side-bands	5	5	3	13
unmarked	2	0	0	2
total	37	40	147	224

amplifiers the causes of HUM are stray electrostatic and magnetic fields, alternating current in the filaments and in the heaters of the tubes, and poorly filtered power supply systems.

To the question: 'The results of insufficient power supply filtering', 165 persons out of 224 mark the correct answer HUM. Others scatter more or less evenly among three other misleads; while only 3 answer REINFORCEMENT.

64. *WEIGHT OF WATER* (*wāt ŏv waw'-ter*). One gram
    per cubic centimeter, one kilogram per liter, 62.4 pounds
per cubic foot, or approximately 1000 ounces per cubic foot.
The noun WEIGHT and the corresponding verb to WEIGH go
directly back to Anglo-Saxon. To WEIGH originally meant to
lift, raise, as: 'To WEIGH anchor'. The noun WEIGHT, heaviness,
ponderosity, is the downward force of a body due to gravity.
The word might have been spelt *wight* to parallel NIGHT and
SIGHT, but is always spelt WEIGHT to agree with the verb.

The word WATER is also of Anglo-Saxon origin, and defined
by one dictionary as a transparent, inodorous, tasteless fluid.
The chemical formula is H_2O.

Several items of this type which are not vocabulary have
found their way into the vocabulary tests, and have been included here to show where a knowledge of such constants falls
in relation to words. To the question: 'Weight of one cubic

Weight of one cubic foot of water.

FORM E. 19.	BO	FW	LA	NY	NY	NY	NY	PH	TU	SUM
32 lbs.	2	5	2	2	2	4	32	4	1	54
80 cm.	0	1	0	1	0	0	1	2	0	5
62.4 lbs.	22	39	26	14	18	34	165	90	24	432
12.7 lbs.	2	5	4	2	0	0	14	4	3	34
5.3 lbs.	0	0	1	1	0	1	6	0	0	9
unmarked	2	0	0	0	0	1	0	0	0	3
total	28	50	33	20	20	40	218	100	28	537

foot of water', 432 persons out of 537 answer correctly 62.4
pounds; while 54 answer 32 lbs. The figure 32 feet per second
per second is the acceleration of gravity, one of the commonly
used figures in physics.

In the metric system, based on the WEIGHT OF WATER, there
is little trouble in learning and remembering the figures. One
cubic centimeter is one gram. One cubic decimeter, 1000 cubic
centimeters, is one kilogram. Nearly three decimeters, 2.8,
equal a foot; and 2.8 cubed is 26. As there are 26 cubic decimeters in a cubic foot, and a decimeter of water weighs a
kilogram, a cubic foot of water weighs 26 kilograms. A kilogram is about 2.2 pounds; so that 26 kilograms is 62.4 pounds.

65. *FLUORESCENCE* (*floo-ō-rĕs'-sĕns*) *n.* Luminescence observable only so long as the stimulus responsible for it is maintained.

FLUORESCENCE is the process of absorbing radiant energy and then re-radiating a part of it in longer wave lengths. From Sir George Gabriel Stokes, writing in 1852, comes: 'I am almost inclined to coin a word and call the appearance FLUORESCENCE from FLUOR-SPAR, as the analagous term OPALESCENCE is derived from the name of a mineral'. FLUOR-SPAR frequently exhibits

Immediate re-radiation by some substances of absorbed radiant energy.

FORM F. 8.	BO	FORM EA. 30.	BO
radium emanation	1	radium emanation	8
canal rays	0	canal rays	1
phosphorescence	4	phosphorescence	6
positive rays	0	positive rays	0
FLUORESCENCE	6	FLUORESCENCE	16
unmarked	0	unmarked	0
total	11	total	31

pure bright tints of yellow, green, blue, and red, which are not mineral pigments. Professor Stokes was a little older than Clerk Maxwell and Lord Kelvin, all of whom were at Cambridge at the same time. From Ure's Dictionary of the Arts a few years later, 1867, comes: 'Pennsylvanian petroleum is dark colored, with a peculiar greenish lustre or FLUORESCENCE'.

To the question: 'Immediate re-radiation by some substances of absorbed radiant energy', 22 persons out of 42 answer FLUORESCENCE; but 10 answer PHOSPHORESCENCE. The word PHOSPHORESCENCE comes from the chemical element PHOSPHORUS, although the glowing of PHOSPHORUS, which led to the word, is now thought due to slow oxidation and not to PHOSPHORESCENCE. PHOSPHORESCENCE is delayed FLUORESCENCE. It is a form of luminescence in which the emission of light continues after the exciting stimulus has ceased. FLUORESCENCE is the same sort of luminescence which ceases instantly with the exciting stimulus. The radiation from substances bombarded by X rays, though it is not visible, is also called FLUORESCENCE.

According to Stokes' law the exciting primary radiation must be of shorter wave length, or contain shorter, than the wave length of the FLUORESCENT radiation. Red light, of long wave length, cannot excite blue-green FLUORESCENCE.

66. *VERTEX* (*ver'-tĕks*) *n.* The point of any angle, point of a figure most distant from the center, any convex angle of a polygon. The plural may be VERTICES (*ver'-tĭ-sēz*) or VERTEXES (*ver'-tĕk-sĕz*).

The public seems to distinguish between VERTEX and APEX, for to the question: 'The point of intersection of two straight lines forming an angle', 403 persons out of 525 answer VERTEX and only 87 APEX. Dictionaries define the two almost inter-

The point of intersection of two straight lines forming an angle.

FORM C. 20.	CH	FORM CA. 6.	CH	LA	NY	NY	PH	SUM
center	0	center	1	0	1	2	2	6
VERTEX	57	VERTEX	33	29	77	206	58	403
pole	0	pole	1	1	2	2	2	8
apex	9	apex	5	6	13	53	10	87
vortex	1	vortex	0	1	4	11	2	18
unmarked	1	unmarked	0	0	0	3	0	3
total	68	total	40	37	97	277	74	525

changeably, beginning as far back as John Harris, 1704: 'VERTEX of a Cone, Pyramid, Conick Section, &, is the Point of the upper Extremety of the Axis, or the Top of the Figure. So the VERTEX of an Angle, is the Angular point'. Thus Harris uses VERTEX of a solid.

Of APEX the Century Dictionary says: 'From the Latin *apex, apicis*, point, tip, summit, from *apere*, to fit. The angular point of a cone or conic section, the angular point of a triangle opposite the base', using APEX of both a solid and plane figure. The Oxford New English Dictionary gives under APEX: 'The VERTEX of a triangle or cone'; while Cassell's Technical Educator, 1879, says: 'The APEX of this triangle'.

The derivation does not help for VERTEX comes from the Latin *vertex, verticis*, whirl, whirlpool, eddy, vortex, top of the head, pole of the heavens, highest point, from *vertere*, to turn. From *vertex*, meaning highest point, comes VERTICAL, upright, perpendicular to the horizon, the line which drawn up from the horizon would go through the VERTEX or zenith.

Edward Phillips, in the New World of Words, says: 'APEX, principally in a Geometrical signification, the top of a Conical figure, which ends and sharpens into a point'. APEX seems to be

FORM CB. 7.	NY
center	5
VERTEX	60
pole	0
apex	13
vortex	8
unmarked	0
total	86

used most frequently for the point of a solid figure, a cone or pyramid; and VERTEX for the point of a two-dimensional figure, as an angle or triangle.

67. *SUBSCRIPT* (*sŭb'-skrĭpt*) *n.* Something written underneath, printed beneath.

The noun SUBSCRIPT comes from the Latin *subscriptus*, the past participle of *subscribere*, to write underneath, a combination of the Latin *sub*, under, and *scribere*, to write. SUB-, from the Latin *sub*, under, appears in SUBWAY, under the way, under the street; in SUBTERRANEAN, under the TERRAIN, under the ground; and in SUBNORMAL, under NORMAL, below normal, less than normal. The Latin verb *scribere*, to write, appears in a host of English words, such as SCRIBBLE, to write over and over, the frequentative of the rare and more elegant verb to SCRIBE, to write carefully; also DESCRIBE, literally to write from, often to draw from observations of nature; also ASCRIBE, TRANSCRIBE, and INSCRIBE, to cut into, already discussed under CONCENTRIC (31). To SUBSCRIBE is to write beneath; and from this in literature to sign with one's own hand and so promise, give consent. From *scriptus*, written, the past participle of *scribere*, come MANUSCRIPT, something written by hand, *manus;* TRANSCRIPT, a copy; CONSCRIPT, by derivation one whose name has been written with others; and SUBSCRIPT, something written below, underneath.

To the question: 'The figure 1 in x_1', 80 persons out of 132 answer correctly SUBSCRIPT; but 25 answer COEFFICIENT, and 14 EXPONENT. A COEFFICIENT is a figure, usually a known number, which multiplies another symbol and is ordinarily written before it. The figure 3 in $3x$ is the COEFFICIENT. In the expression 3 apples, 3 is the COEFFICIENT. Reread COEFFICIENT OF FRICTION (54). An EXPONENT is written above and to the right

The figure 1 in x_1.

FORM A. 47.	BO	NY	SUM	FORM AA. 16.	NY
SUBSCRIPT	16	30	46	SUBSCRIPT	80
coefficient	0	6	6	coefficient	25
exponent	1	4	5	exponent	14
parameter	0	0	0	superscript	4
coordinate	1	1	2	coordinate	9
unmarked	2	0	2	unmarked	0
total	20	41	61	total	132

of another number or symbol, as the figure 3 in x^3, which signifies that x is to be multiplied by itself three times, x times x times x. Reread EXPONENT (42). A SUBSCRIPT rarely indicates a mathematical process. It is used when a mathematician begins to run out of letters, or when he wants to show that several equations involve the same variable but with different values in each. But the word SUBSCRIPT is taken for granted by many textbooks and not defined.

68. *DIMENSION* (dĭ-mĕn'-shŏn) *n.* Measurable extent of any kind, magnitude, size.

DIMENSION comes from the Latin *dimension, dimensionem,* from the verb *dimetiri,* to measure out, a combination of *di* and *metiri,* to measure.

To the question: 'The length, breadth, or thickness of a geometric figure', 64 persons out of 86 answer DIMENSION; but 16 answer VOLUME. This seems a misreading of the question; for the word VOLUME is number 14 in this book and so comparatively easy; length, breadth, and thickness, might be VOL-

UME; but the word DIMENSION is extension in one direction usually with the idea of measurable extensions also in other directions.

From Billingsley's translation of Euclid, 1570, comes: 'There pertaine to quantitie three DIMENSIONS, length, bredth, and thicknes'. And still earlier, about 1400, from the Pylgremage

The length, breadth, or thickness of a geometric figure.

FORM CB. 10.

DIMENSION	64
eccentricity	2
increment	1
volume	16
shape	3
unmarked	0
total	86

of the Sowle, printed by William Caxton in 1483: 'Ther is no-body parfit withouten thre dymensions, that is breede, lengthe, and depnesse'.

69. *MAXIMUM* (*măks'-ĭ-mŭm*) *n*. In mathematics, the value of a changing quantity when it stops growing larger and begins to grow smaller. The plural follows the Latin MAXIMA. In literature the word MAXIMUM means utmost value, greatest extent, limit. But in mathematics the word is used for a turn-ing point at the top. Prices which have been going up reach a MAXIMUM if they start down again even though later they rise still higher.

The word MAXIMUM comes from the Latin *maximum*, the neuter of *maximus*, greatest. This is the superlative of *magnus*, great, the source of the word MAGNITUDE, largeness, greatness, size.

To the question: 'A value which a variable may not exceed', 89 persons out of 132 answer MAXIMUM. MAXIMUM seems an easier word than its position here, placed by the number who mark it correctly. Also MINIMUM, the smallest amount, the opposite of MAXIMUM, a type of mislead frequently marked by those who are doubtful of a meaning, is in this case chosen by only 5 persons, the least frequently marked. Perhaps the definition is awkward, for it is more a definition of LIMIT than MAXIMUM, and this no doubt leads 20 persons to answer DIFFERENTIAL. A DIFFERENTIAL is an infinitesimal difference be-

A value which a variable may not exceed.

FORM A. 2.	BO	NY	SUM	FORM AA. 17.	NY
sum	2	2	4	sum	6
product	1	4	5	product	11
differential	0	4	4	differential	20
minimum	0	2	2	minimum	5
MAXIMUM	16	29	45	MAXIMUM	89
unmarked	1	0	1	unmarked	1
total	20	41	61	total	132

tween two values of a variable. But the ratio of two DIFFERENTIALS is the limit which the ratio of two quantities approaches. A MAXIMUM is a height, peak, a value reached by a quantity before it turns down.

70. *QUADRILATERAL* (*kwŏd-rĭ-lăt′-ē-răl*) *n.* The general term for any four-sided plane figure including the square, the rhombus, and the trapezoid. Read also PARALLELOGRAM (71). The word QUADRILATERAL comes from the Latin *quadrilaterus*,

Any four-sided plane figure.

FORM B. 20.	NY	MISC.	SUM
trapezium	3	19	22
QUADRILATERAL	36	225	261
quadrant	3	15	18
quadratic	1	9	10
rhomboid	5	23	28
unmarked	0	18	18
total	48	309	357

four sided, from *quattuor*, four, which becomes *quadri-*, and *latus*, side, flank. From *latus, lateris*, side, come the adjective LATERAL, pertaining to the side, toward the side, as: 'LATERAL motion'; BILATERAL, two sided; COLLATERAL, at the side, and so secondary, subordinate, accompanying, and from this strengthening, confirming, aiding; as well as LATITUDE, distance measured each side of the equator.

Despite the present wording of the question: 'Any four-sided plane figure', 261 persons out of 357 answer as intended, QUADRILATERAL; and only 28 answer RHOMBOID, which is one of the four-sided plane figures. RHOMBOID is not the general term, but a four-sided figure whose opposite sides are equal and parallel, but whose four sides are not equal, whose opposite angles are equal, but whose four angles are not equal. QUADRILATERAL is the general term for any four-sided plane figure.

71. *PARALLELOGRAM* (*pă-răl-lĕl'-ō-grăm*) *n.* A four-sided figure with its opposite sides parallel, a plane rectilinear figure of four sides whose opposite sides are parallel. Reread QUADRILATERAL (70).

The word PARALLELOGRAM and the corresponding French *parallélogramme* come from the Latin *parallelogrammum*. This in turn comes from the Greek παραλληλόγραμμον (parallelogrammon), a combination of παράλληλος (parallelos), parallel,

Form A. Any four-sided plane figure whose opposite sides are parallel.
Form AA. The general term for any four-sided plane figure whose opposite sides are parallel.

FORM A. 12.	BO	NY	SUM	FORM AA. 11.	NY
rhombus	1	3	4	rhombus	5
trapezium	2	1	3	trapezium	1
square	1	1	2	quadrilateral	8
rectangle	3	3	6	rectangle	18
PARALLELOGRAM	13	33	46	PARALLELOGRAM	100
unmarked	0	0	0	unmarked	0
total	20	41	61	total	132

and γράμμα (gramma), line. The English PARALLEL and the French *parallèle* go back through the Latin *parallelus*, to the Greek παράλληλος (parallelos), beside one another, a combination of παρά (para), beside, and ἄλλος (allos), another, with a second ἄλλος (allos), translated as beside one another or another beside another.

To the original question: 'Any four-sided plane figure whose opposite sides are parallel', 46 persons out of 61 answer PARALLELOGRAM, while 6 answer RECTANGLE, and 4 RHOMBUS. Both a RECTANGLE and a RHOMBUS are four-sided figures whose opposite sides are parallel; both are specialized forms of the PARALLELOGRAM, and as such correct answers to the question as worded. A RECTANGLE is a four-sided figure whose opposite sides are parallel and all of whose angles are right angles. A RHOMBUS is a four-sided figure whose opposite sides are parallel and all of whose sides are of equal length. PARALLELOGRAM is the general term for any four-sided figure whose opposite sides are parallel.

With the revised wording of the question: 'The general term for any four-sided plane figure whose opposite sides are parallel', 100 persons out of 132 mark the correct answer PARALLELOGRAM; while 18 still mark RECTANGLE, even a larger percentage than before, and 8 mark the new mislead QUADRILATERAL. A QUADRILATERAL is any four-sided figure. A PARALLELOGRAM is a QUADRILATERAL with opposite sides parallel.

72. *WORKING* (*wer'-kĭng*) *pa. adj.* Connected with the carrying on of some operation, usual, customary, ordinary, operating.

The Anglo-Saxon ending -ING was originally added to verbs to make the corresponding abstract noun of action. WORKING is used occasionally attributively in such combinations as WORKING LOAD and WORKING VOLTAGE.

To the question: 'The voltage rating of a condenser for a voltage which it will withstand continuously', 102 persons out of 147 answer WORKING; while 20 answer OUTPUT, and 18 MAXIMUM. MAXIMUM means greatest possible. The confusion may be doubt about the meaning of MAXIMUM, word 69 in this book, and so of the same difficulty as this question. Or it may be the definition of WORKING LOAD given by one dictionary: 'The MAXIMUM load that a member of a machine or other structure is designed to bear'. Most machines and structures are designed to bear greater loads than anticipated in ordinary operation. The WORKING LOAD is often no more than half the MAXIMUM which a machine is designed to withstand for a moment. A satisfactory paper condenser or capacitor must withstand a single application of twice its WORKING VOLTAGE; and even this is seldom the MAXIMUM.

A table in the Electrical Engineer's Handbook edited by Harold Pender tabulates the MAXIMUM WORKING VOLTAGE for various paper condensers, and this association of the two words

The voltage rating of a condenser for a voltage which it will withstand continuously.

FORM A. 24.	NY
maximum	18
minimum	5
WORKING	102
output	20
ripple	2
unmarked	0
total	147

may add to their confusion. The phrase WORKING VOLTAGE implies the greatest voltage at which the condenser can be operated safely over a long period. This is not the greatest or MAXIMUM voltage which it will stand for an instant.

73. *CEILING* (*sē'-lĭng*) *n*. The distance up from the ground to the lower surface of the clouds when the sky is more than half covered.

The noun CEILING comes from the verb to CEIL, which originally meant to supply with a canopy or with hangings overhead. This goes back to an Early English word which meant a canopy; and the noun CEILING in English first meant canopy, hangings overhead. But the verb was early confused with another verb which meant to line a room with carved wood. From these two together comes the modern meaning of CEILING, the upper surface of a room, the overhead surface. It is this meaning which aviation has taken when it uses the word CEILING, the distance up to the underside of the clouds above, the overhead surface of the visible world.

To the question: 'The vertical distance from the ground to the lower limits of the cloud base', 366 persons out of 515 answer correctly CEILING; but 64 answer SERVICE CEILING, and another 35 VISIBILITY. SERVICE CEILING is a characteristic of the airplane and not of the weather. It is the height above sea level at which a particular airplane is unable to climb, because of the thinness of the air, faster than 100 feet per minute under standard air conditions.

CEILING, when that word is unmodified, and VISIBILITY are both weather conditions. VISIBILITY (*vĭ-zĭ-bĭl'-ĭ-tē*) is horizontal, toward the horizon. It is the greatest distance at which prominent objects, such as mountains and buildings, can be seen by the normal eye unaided by binoculars or other optical devices. It is reported in miles or fractions of a mile. CEILING is the

Form A. The vertical distance from the ground to the lower limits of the cloud base.
Form AA. Height from the ground to the lower limits of the cloud base.

FORM A. 27.	FW	LA	NY	NY	NY	PH	SUM	FORM AA. 8.	NY
altitude	0	2	1	2	8	11	24	altitude	3
CEILING	17	38	27	45	104	135	366	CEILING	48
absolute								absolute	
ceiling	0	2	2	2	2	6	14	ceiling	4
service ceiling	1	6	3	12	13	29	64	service ceiling	5
visibility	0	6	3	1	13	12	35	visibility	3
unmarked	0	0	1	4	0	7	12	unmarked	0
total	18	54	37	66	140	200	515	total	63

distance up from the ground to the bottom of an overcast or broken clouds. OVERCAST is the technical term for clouds which cover more than nine tenths of the sky; BROKEN CLOUDS cover more than five tenths but not more than nine tenths. When more than one tenth is covered but less than five tenths, clouds are called SCATTERED and are not a CEILING. When less than a tenth is covered the sky is called CLEAR. To form a CEILING more than half the sky must be covered by clouds. The CEILING is then the distance up from the ground to the underneath surface of these clouds.

74. *PRESSURE* (*prĕsh'-shŭr*) *n.* Pounds per square inch,
grams per square centimeter, dynes per square centimeter,
force per unit area. Read also ATMOSPHERE (75).
The technical application of this word in physics is only one
of its uses. In literature, PRESSURE is used in such a phrase as:
'To put PRESSURE on a group to make it act'. In 1656 Thomas
Hobbes, an English philosopher, wrote: 'When two bodies
having opposite endeavours, press one another, the endeavour
of either of them is that which we call PRESSURE, and is mutual
when their PRESSURES are opposite'.

The English ending -URE (*ūr*) comes from the Latin -*ura*.
This was added to Latin verbs to make the feminine form of
the future participle. This in turn became a feminine noun to
designate the result of the action of the verb. Among the verbs
of which the future participles have become nouns used today
is the Latin verb *scribere*, which means to write. From this
came the future participle and the noun *scriptura;* and from this
the English word SCRIPTURE, by derivation anything written.
Spelt with a capital and often in the plural, the SCRIPTURES,

Pounds per square inch.

FORM C. 2.	NY	FORM CA. I.	BO	NY	NY	NY	NY	SUM
force	14	force	7	16	19	117	14	173
mass	7	mass	2	2	11	95	7	117
strain	4	strain	2	1	1	88	2	94
PRESSURE	374	PRESSURE	83	378	351	655	187	1654
		specific						
impulse	0	weight	6	3	18	145	24	196
unmarked	1	unmarked	0	0	0	0	0	0
total	400	total	100	400	400	1100	234	2234

the word means the writings of the Old and of the New Testa-
ments, the Bible. The Latin verb *aperire* means to open. The
future participle and the corresponding noun, *apertura*, an
opening, hole, becomes in English APERTURE, an opening, hole.
The Latin verb *texere* means to weave. From this comes the
future participle and noun *textura*, and the English TEXTURE, a
weaving, something woven, a cloth, fabric, or now more frequently the way something is woven, the kind of weave.

The Latin verb *pressare* meant to press, crowd, jam. It is the frequentative formed from the past participle *pressus* of the more familiar verb *premere*, to press. The future participle and so the corresponding noun was *pressura*, a pressure, burden, load. From this comes the English noun PRESSURE. From each of these Latin verbs come many English words. From *premere*, to press, come not only PRESSURE and the verb to PRESS but also the verbs to COMPRESS, to press together, push together, condense, make smaller, consolidate, to DEPRESS, to press down, push down, to IMPRESS, to press into so as to leave a mark, to REPRESS, to push back, and to OPPRESS, used figuratively to mean press down with burdens, as: 'To OPPRESS with heavy taxes'.

To the question: 'Pounds per square inch', 74 per cent of 2234 persons answer PRESSURE; but 9 per cent answer SPECIFIC WEIGHT, now the most frequently marked mislead, added as a result of the first study, and 8 per cent FORCE. SPECIFIC WEIGHT is weight per unit volume. Pounds per cubic inch would be SPECIFIC WEIGHT. But the definition asks for pounds per square inch, PRESSURE on a flat surface.

The word FORCE, the second most frequently marked mislead, comes from the Latin *fortis*, strong, powerful. From the same Latin source come also the two nouns FORT and FORTRESS, both by derivation strong places. The word FORCE is used in literature to mean might, vigor, both mental and physical. In science FORCE is the total PRESSURE needed to support a weight against the pull of gravity, to compress an elastic body, or to move a mass. PRESSURE is the total FORCE divided by the area over which the FORCE acts. PRESSURE is the FORCE exerted on any unit area. In the form of an equation:

$$\text{PRESSURE} = \frac{\text{FORCE}}{\text{AREA}}$$

The metric system expresses FORCE in grams or dynes; the English system, in pounds or poundals. The metric system expresses PRESSURE in grams per square centimeter or dynes per square centimeter; the English system, in pounds per square foot or pounds per square inch.

75. *ATMOSPHERE* (*ăt'-mŏs-svēr*) *n.* A pressure of about 15
    pounds on the square inch, more exactly 14.7 pounds. Re-
read PRESSURE (74).

The word ATMOSPHERE comes through the French from the
Greek ἀτμός (atmos), vapor, and σφαῖρα (sphaira), ball, sphere.
Apart from its figurative use, as: 'Genius can only breathe
freely in an atmosphere of freedom', from Liberty by John
Stuart Mill, 1859, ATMOSPHERE is used in two ways in the
sciences. It may designate the mass of air enveloping the earth;
or the pressure of this mass at the surface of the earth. Writing
in 1867, in Astronomy without Mathematics, Edmund Beckett

One atmosphere.

FORM E. 14.	BO	FW	LA	NY	NY	NY	NY	PH	TU	SUM
32 lb./in.²	1	9	3	5	2	3	39	6	1	69
14.7 LB./IN.²	23	34	29	13	17	34	159	93	26	428
1 lb./in.²	2	1	0	0	0	1	6	0	0	10
30 lb./ft.²	0	2	0	1	1	1	8	0	0	13
2.3 lb./in.²	0	3	0	1	0	1	3	1	0	9
unmarked	2	1	1	0	0	0	3	0	1	8
total	28	50	33	20	20	40	218	100	28	537

Denison says: 'The earth's atmosphere decreases so rapidly in
density, that half its mass is within 3½ miles above the sea; and
at 80 miles high there can be practically no atmosphere'. More
than a hundred years earlier Ephraim Chambers, in his great
Cyclopaedia, says: 'Among some of the more accurate writers,
the ATMOSPHERE is restrained to that part of the air next the
earth, which receives vapours and exhalations; and is terminated by the refraction of the sun's light'.

The pressure of the ATMOSPHERE is the weight of a column
of air extending up to its top. This balances a column of water
34 feet in height, or about 1030 centimeters, or a column of
mercury 76 centimeters in height. Since a cubic centimeter of
water weighs a gram, 1030 cubic centimeters, piled on top of
one another, weigh 1030 grams; making the pressure of 1030
centimeters of water 1030 grams per square centimeter. Or
using mercury, a cubic centimeter of mercury weighs 13.55
grams, so that 76 cubic centimeters weigh 1030 grams. Chang-

ing this to pounds per square inch instead of grams per square centimeter gives approximately 14.6 or 14.7 pounds per square inch pressure.

To the question: 'One atmosphere', 428 persons out of 537 answer 14.7 pounds to the square inch; but 69 answer 32 pounds to the square inch, the same figure which was the most popular wrong answer to the weight of a cubic foot of water, the acceleration of gravity, 32 feet per second per second. Both the acceleration of gravity and the pressure of the atmosphere are constants of frequent appearance associated with the earth. Both belong to the British system of units.

Atmospheric pressure varies from place to place on the earth's surface, and may change from day to day with the weather as much under extreme conditions as two centimeters of mercury either way. In climbing a mountain or rising in a plane the pressure drops about one inch of mercury in the first thousand feet. The accepted standard pressure is that exerted by 76 centimeters of mercury, or 29.29 inches of mercury, at 0 degrees centigrade, at 45 degrees latitude, and at mean sea level.

76. *RHEOSTAT* (*rē'-ō-stăt*) *n.* A variable resistance for limiting the current in a circuit.

RHEOSTAT comes from the Greek ῥεῖν (rhein), to flow, and στατός (statos), the verbal adjective of ἱστάναι (histanai), to stand. The term was coined by Sir Charles Wheatstone, the inventor for whom the Wheatstone bridge is named. In 1843 Wheatstone wrote: 'As the principal use of this instrument is to adjust or regulate the circuit so that any constant degree of force may be obtained I have called it a RHEOSTAT'. This definition appears in the Encyclopaedic Dictionary of 1882 to 1888; but was changed in the Century Dictionary of 1891 to read: 'An instrument for regulating and adjusting a circuit so that any required degree of resistance may be maintained; a resistance-coil'.

Using the original Wheatstone definition: 'Instrument for regulating or adjusting a circuit so that any required degree of force may be maintained', 373 persons out of 515, or 72 per cent, answer RHEOSTAT; but 93, or 18 per cent, answer TRANS-

FORMER. With a simpler definition: 'Instrument for adjusting the resistance in an electric circuit', the mislead TRANSFORMER is marked by only 5 persons out of 63 whose scores have been tabulated, or by 8 per cent, instead of 18; but the term has become more difficult due to the new mislead CONDENSER, and is now marked correctly by only 59 per cent.

The word TRANSFORMER (62) comes from the French *transformateur*, a term invented by Hospitalier in 1882 and used in his Modern Applications of Electricity: 'We designate by the term ELECTRIC TRANSFORMERS apparatus in which electricity is no longer produced directly, but is transformed and changes its properties'. A TRANSFORMER consists of two separate coils, wound together so that current in one of the two coils induces

Form A. Instrument for regulating or adjusting a circuit so that any required degree of force may be maintained.
Form AA. Instrument for adjusting the resistance in an electric circuit.

FORM A. 8.	FW	LA	NY	NY	NY	PH	SUM	FORM AA. 7.	NY
transformer	0	4	12	14	26	37	93	transformer	5
cathode	0	1	1	2	3	2	9	cathode	3
filament	0	0	1	2	1	0	4	condenser	9
magneto	0	1	2	2	15	11	31	magneto	9
RHEOSTAT	18	48	20	44	95	148	373	RHEOSTAT	37
unmarked	0	0	1	2	0	2	5	unmarked	0
total	18	54	37	66	140	200	515	total	63

current in the other. A TRANSFORMER is used to change current to potential, to transform amperes, which might overheat a small wire, to volts; and, with the Wheatstone definition of RHEOSTAT, TRANSFORMER is probably a justified answer, for it regulates the potential in a circuit. A RHEOSTAT is a resistance coil, parts of which can be used or cut out, which blocks the flow of current with no effect on the voltage.

77. *HORSEPOWER* (*hōrs'-pow-er*) *n*. A popular unit for expressing rate of doing work, 550 foot-pounds per second, 33,000 foot-pounds per minute, 746 watts.
To the question: 'One HORSEPOWER', 414 persons out of 537

answer correctly 550 ft.-lbs/sec., while 48 answer 3000 ft.-lbs/min.; 33,000 foot-pounds per minute would be correct, but not 3000.

The term HORSEPOWER seems to have been first used by Thomas Savery as early as 1700; though James Watt was the first to give it definite value in 1783, when his engines, produced by the firm of Boulton and Watt, had largely replaced the earlier engines of Newcomen for pumping water from the coal mines in Cornwall, and just after his third patent of 1782 which changed his earlier single-acting engine to double-acting, introducing steam alternately at each end of the cylinder.

In 1806, Olinthus G. Gregory, in A Treatise on Mechanics, wrote: 'The usual method of estimating the effects of engines by what are called "horse powers"', writing the expression as two separate words. By 1881 the Encyclopaedia Britannica hyphenated the pair, HORSE-POWER; and in 1901 the Oxford New English Dictionary still used the hyphen. But with use

One horsepower.

FORM E. 10.	BO	FW	LA	NY	NY	NY	NY	PH	TU	SUM
3000 ft.-lb./min.	1	5	1	1	2	4	25	8	1	48
550 FT.-LB./SEC.	23	38	26	14	17	34	158	79	25	414
356 watts	0	2	3	2	1	2	14	6	1	31
221 ft.-lb./sec.	2	0	2	1	0	0	13	2	0	20
1100 ft.-lb./sec.	2	5	1	2	0	0	8	4	1	23
unmarked	0	0	0	0	0	0	0	1	0	1
total	28	50	33	20	20	40	218	100	28	537

and general acceptance terms coined by joining two previous shorter ones gradually become single words without the connecting line. Professor Frederick A. Saunders of Harvard University, in his Survey of Physics of 1930, was one of the last authorities to use the hyphen in a textbook; since then almost without exception the word has appeared as HORSEPOWER.

HORSEPOWER is a unit of power, not of work, for the same amount of work may be done quickly or slowly. Total work done over a period of time divided by the number of minutes gives the work done per minute. An engine is said to develop one HORSEPOWER when it does 33,000 foot-pounds of work per minute, or 550 foot-pounds per second; that is when it can lift 33,000 pounds one foot per minute. It is said that one HORSE-POWER is more than can be expected of an average horse working steadily; only a heavy Norman dray horse can do it for a short time. One tenth of a HORSEPOWER is about one man-power.

78. *RECTIFIER* (*rĕk'-tĭ-fī-er*) *n*. An electronic valve which allows only one half of an alternating current voltage wave to pass, kenetron or kenotron, thermionic valve, usually an electron tube which allows electrons to flow in one direction only.

The word RECTIFIER comes from the Latin adjective *rectus*, straight, and *facere*, to make. This last appears as -FY at the end of the verb to RECTIFY, just as it does at the end of AMPLIFY (21), a combination of *amplus*, large, ample, and the same

A device, used in radio, for the purpose of allowing the flow of current in one direction only.

FORM E. 30.	BO	FW	LA	NY	NY	NY	NY	PH	TU	SUM
switch	0	1	0	1	0	4	6	3	1	16
audio	1	0	1	0	0	0	2	2	0	6
RECTIFIER	20	35	31	15	18	30	171	86	25	431
fuse	0	3	1	1	0	1	7	0	0	13
transmitter	4	9	0	3	2	4	29	8	2	61
unmarked	3	2	0	0	0	1	3	1	0	10
total	28	50	33	20	20	40	218	100	28	537

facere, to make, as well as in MAGNIFY, from *magnus*, great, and NULLIFY, from *nullus*, none, and *facere*, to make. From the Latin adjective *rectus*, which may mean both straight and right, come RECTITUDE, straightness of character, rightness, uprightness, and RECTANGULAR, right angled.

A RECTIFIER is any device which allows current to flow more easily in one direction than another. A film of copper oxide on metallic copper allows electrons to flow from the metal through the oxide film, but does not admit electrons from the outside. With a plate of aluminum and a plate of lead dipped in a solution such as borax, electrons escape from the aluminum but not from the lead, current flowing in one direction but not the other.

Or a RECTIFIER may be a tube in which electrons carry a current from a hot terminal to a cold one, but in which they cannot move in the reverse direction, away from the cold terminal. In the TUNGAR RECTIFIER the heated filament is tungsten and the tube contains the inert gas argon, TUNGAR standing for TUNGSTEN-ARGON.

To the question: 'A device, used in radio, for the purpose of allowing the flow of current in one direction only', 431 out of 537 persons mark RECTIFIER; but 61 mark TRANSMITTER. This is also the most frequently marked mislead in six of the eight small populations. It is also the most frequently marked mislead

FORM E. 30.   ENGLISH VOCABULARY

	HIGH	LOW
switch	0	2
audio	3	2
RECTIFIER	37	27
fuse	0	1
transmitter	0	8
unmarked	0	0
total	40	40

in the low English vocabulary group where it is marked by 8 out of 40; but by none of the 40 who score high in English literary vocabulary. A radio TRANSMITTER is a combination of an OSCILLATOR, voltage amplifiers, power amplifiers, modulating equipment, and power supply apparatus.

To the same question the second most frequently marked mislead, chosen by 16 persons out of 537, is SWITCH. The word SWITCH comes from Dutch. The original meaning was whip, flexible twig, easily bent rod. From this the word came to be used for a railway switch, which shifts trains from one track to another; and then for an electric switch, a device for closing or breaking an electric circuit. A SWITCH when closed allows a current to flow, as stated in the question, but not necessarily in one direction only, the essential characteristic of a RECTIFIER. A RECTIFIER is used in charging a battery from an alternating current supply or in furnishing direct current for electrolytic cells or to excite field coils.

79. *SHUNT* (*shŭnt*) *n.* A conductor, usually of relatively low
   resistance, in parallel with a part of an electric circuit, an
electrical by-pass introduced to diminish the current flowing
through the main circuit or to furnish current to excite field
coils. The verb to SHUNT is to divert a portion of an electric
current.

SHUNT goes back through Middle English to an Anglo-
Saxon word which meant to hasten. In railroading, a SHUNT is
a turning off to a siding or short lines of rails so that the main
line is kept clear.

To the question: 'An electric current conductor in parallel
with part of a circuit', the popular mislead is INDUCTION COIL.
An INDUCTION COIL consists of two windings on the same core,
each a part of a separate circuit, one a few turns of heavy wire,
the other many turns of light wire. The two windings are not
connected. A continuous current in either circuit does not
affect the other. It is only the making and breaking of current
in one of the windings which causes an electromotive force in
the other. An INDUCTION COIL is an apparatus consisting of two
juxtaposed electric circuits, such that variations of current in
one circuit affect the electromotive force in the other.

A SHUNT joins two points in an electric circuit, it forms a
by-path through which a part of the current passes depending
upon the relative resistance of the SHUNT and of that part of
the circuit which the SHUNT cuts off.

80. *SCALENE* (*skā-lēn'*) *adj.* Applied to a triangle with no
   equal sides. Reread ISOSCELES (34).
The word SCALENE goes back through the French *scalene*
and the Latin *scalenus*, to the Greek σκαληνός (skalenos), uneven, unequal, odd, slanting, oblique. The original phrase was
τρίγωνον σκαληνόν (trigonon skalenon), triangle scalene. The
Greek adjective comes from σκελλός (skellos), crooked legged,
from σκέλος (skelos), a leg. A SCALENE triangle has all three
sides unequal.

To the question: 'Any triangle with unequal sides', 98 persons out of 132 answer SCALENE; while 21 answer ISOSCELES,
the popular mislead also in the smaller groups studied. The
adjective ISOSCELES (34) is applied to a triangle when two of

its sides are equal. A cone or a cylinder is sometimes said to be SCALENE when its axis is not at right angles to the base; but the adjective OBLIQUE is more correct and more frequently used.

Any triangle with unequal sides.

FORM A. 37.	BO	NY	SUM	FORM AA. 7.	NY
isosceles	4	3	7	isosceles	21
SCALENE	14	36	50	SCALENE	98
right	0	1	1	right	2
equilateral	1	0	1	equilateral	5
spherical	0	1	1	truncated	6
unmarked	1	0	1	unmarked	0
total	20	41	61	total	132

An EQUILATERAL triangle has all three sides of the same length. An ISOSCELES triangle has only two sides alike, of the same length. A SCALENE triangle has no two sides of the same length.

81. *LINEAR* (*lin'-ē-ahr*) *adj.* In mathematics, pertaining to a line, involving one dimension only, of the first degree.
The adjective LINEAR comes from the Latin *linearis*, pertaining to a line, from *linea*, a linen thread, string, line, from *linum*, flax, linen. From *linea* comes DELINEATE, to draw in outline. The Latin suffix -*aris*, which becomes -AR in English, is a variation of the more common -*alis*, with the accusative -*alem*, or -AL in English. Both endings -*alis* and -*aris* mean of the kind of, pertaining to. They are added to nouns to make the corresponding adjectives. From *manus*, hand, comes the Latin *manualis*, or in English MANUAL, done by hand. When the stem of the noun ends in L the Latin ending becomes -*aris*, and the English ending -AR. Thus the Latin *stella*, star, becomes *stellaris*, or in English STELLAR. The Latin *polus*, pole, becomes the adjective *polaris*, and in English POLAR. The Latin *linea* became even in Latin both *linealis* and *linearis*, and in English is both LINEAL and LINEAR. The distinction between the two is largely custom. LINEAL means a bit more simply pertaining to a line, extending in a straight line. LINEAR is used in most phrases such as LINEAR EQUATIONS.

A LINEAR EQUATION is an equation of the first degree; that is contains no squares (12), or cubes, or higher powers of the variable. When plotted graphically every LINEAR EQUATION is a straight line. John Harris says: 'LINEAR PROBLEM, in mathematicks, is such an one as can be solved Geometrically by the

Form c. Item 18. An equation expressed in variables no one of which exceeds the first power.

Form CA. Item 10. An algebraic equation which is of the first degree in its variables.

Form CB. Item 9. An algebraic equation of the first degree, with no squares, or cubes, or higher powers.

FORM C. 18.	CH	FORM CA. 10.	CH	LA	NY	NY	PH	SUM
LINEAR	44	LINEAR	30	31	68	182	57	368
curvilinear	5	curvilinear	0	0	0	14	0	14
quadratic	7	quadratic	7	3	19	28	11	68
determinant	3	determinant	1	3	7	20	1	32
logarithmic	9	logarithmic	1	0	3	32	3	39
unmarked	0	unmarked	1	0	0	1	2	4
total	68	total	40	37	97	277	74	525

FORM CB. 9.	NY
LINEAR	75
simultaneous	5
quadratic	3
indeterminate	1
logarithmic	1
unmarked	1
total	86

Intersection of two Right Lines; as to measure an inaccessible Height by means of two unequal Sticks or Staves. This is also called a Simple problem, and is capable but of one Solution.' Such LINEAR EQUATIONS contain two variables, but no squares or cubes or products.

To the question as it read in the original form c: 'An equation expressed in variables no one of which exceeds the first power', 65 per cent answered correctly LINEAR; but the word POWER is number 212 in this book and so too difficult for this question.

In the revised form CA the question was changed: 'An algebraic equation which is of the first degree in its variables'. This was answered correctly by 70 per cent. But in an effort to word the question still more simply, it was changed again in form CB to read: 'An algebraic equation of the first degree, with no squares, or cubes, or higher powers'. To this 87 per cent answer correctly LINEAR.

In form CA, where the largest sampling has been tabulated, QUADRATIC, somewhat popular in all forms, has been chosen by 68 out of 525 persons. The word QUADRATIC comes from the adjective QUADRATE, having four equal and parallel sides and so square. This comes from the Latin *quadratus*, square, the past participle of *quadrare*, to make four-cornered, square, from *quadra*, a square, and this from *quattuor*, four. A QUADRATIC equation involves the square of the unknown quantity, includes a variable of the second degree, is an equation of two dimensions. In algebra the general form of a QUADRATIC equation is:

$$ax^2 + bx + c = o.$$

To such an equation there are two solutions; while there is only a single solution to a LINEAR equation.

82. *ADJACENT* (ăd-jā'-sĕnt) *adj.* In geometry, of angles, having the same vertex (66) and a common side between them. In literature, lying near, adjoining, bordering but not necessarily touching though this is by no means precluded.

The word ADJACENT comes from the Latin *adjacentem*, the present participle of *adjacere*, to lie. This is a combination of *ad*, to, and *jacere*. There are two Latin verbs *jacere*, spelt alike. One means to throw, cast, and is the source of EJECT, to throw out, and INJECT, by derivation to throw into. The other *jacere* means to lie, perhaps originally to be thrown down and so to lie where thrown.

To the question: 'Lying close to', 46 persons out of 61 answer ADJACENT, and 7 CONTIGUOUS. The word CONTIGUOUS comes from the Latin *contiguus*, touching, from *contingere*, to touch. This is a combination of *con-*, together, and *tangere*, to touch, the source of the English TANGIBLE, capable of being touched, as well as CONTACT, touch, and CONTAGION (kŏn-tā'-jŏn), by derivation the communication of a disease by touch. CON-

TIGUOUS really ought to mean touching. By derivation there is no question but what CONTIGUOUS angles should touch; and Ephraim Chambers in his Cyclopaedia of 1727 says: 'CON-TIGUOUS angles are such as have one leg in common to each angle'.

The Century Dictionary says: 'ADJACENT or CONTIGUOUS angles', making no distinction between the two, 'are such as have the vertex and one leg common to both angles, both together being equal to two right angles'. In his Course of Mathe-

Lying close to.

FORM A. 3.	BO	NY	SUM	FORM AA. 15.	NY
ADJACENT	16	30	46	ADJACENT	25
congruent	0	1	1	complementary	82
contiguous	0	7	7	contiguous	6
coincident	1	1	2	corresponding	12
tangent	3	1	4	tangent	3
unmarked	0	1	1	unmarked	4
total	20	41	61	total	132

matics, published in 1827, Hutton says: 'The sum of two ADJACENT angles is equal to two right angles'. The Oxford New English Dictionary defines ADJACENT angles as the angles which one straight line makes with another upon which it stands'.

The definition used in form A: 'Lying close to', might be interpreted as near but not touching, and so ADJACENT as correctly used in literature. To experiment with what seems to be more precise, the definition has been changed in form AA to read: 'Of two angles with a common side which add to two right angles'. With this 82 persons out of 132 answer COMPLE-MENTARY; and only 25 ADJACENT. COMPLEMENTARY is used of two angles which add to 90 degrees, to one right angle, and is not correct; but ADJACENT, adding to 180 degrees, is apparently so little known that most persons mark COMPLEMENTARY.

83. *SUBTRAHEND* (sŭb-tră-hĕnd') *n*. In mathematics: the figure or quantity which is to be subtracted or taken away. From Samuel Jeake, Arithmetic, 1674, comes: 'The number to be subtracted, called the SUBTRAHEND'. The word comes

from the Latin *subtrahendus*, the gerund of *subtrahere*, a combination of *sub*, and *trahere*, to draw, carry. To SUBTRACT is to withdraw, take away. The SUBTRAHEND is the quantity withdrawn. From Robert Recorde, an English mathematician who lived from 1510 to 1558, in his Ground of Artes, comes: 'Subtraction diminisheth a grosse sum by withdrawing of other from it, so that subtraction or REBATION is nothing else but an arte to withdraw and abate one sum from another, that the remainer may appeare'.

To the question: 'Quantity to be subtracted from another quantity', 280 persons out of 357 answer correctly SUBTRAHEND; while 57 answer MINUEND, the only frequently marked mislead. The MINUEND is the quantity from which another quantity is to be subtracted. The word MINUEND comes from the Latin

Quantity to be subtracted from another quantity.

FORM B. 5.	NY	MISC.	SUM
SUBTRAHEND	36	244	280
minuend	8	49	57
remainder	2	0	2
difference	2	15	17
integer	0	0	0
unmarked	0	1	1
total	48	309	357

minuendus, the future participle of *minuere*, to lessen, diminish. From William Jones, 1706, comes: 'The greater of the given numbers is called the MINUEND'. And from 1892, Barnard Smith and Hudson, Arithmetic for Schools: 'The smaller number is called the SUBTRAHEND. The greater is called the MINUEND.'

84. *SPHERE* (*sfēr*) *n*. A solid figure generated by the revolution of a semicircle about its diameter. This is Euclid's definition.

From an Encyclopaedia printed by Thomas Dobson in Philadelphia in 1798 comes: 'EUCLID of Alexandria, the celebrated mathematician, flourished in the reign of Ptolemy Lagus, about 277 B.C. He reduced all the fundamental principles of pure mathematics, which had been delivered down by Thales,

Pythagoras, Eudoxus, and other mathematicians, before him, into regularity and order, and added many others of his own discovering; on which account he is said to be the first who reduced arithmetic and geometry into the form of a science. He likewise applied himself to the study of mixed mathematics, and especially to astronomy, in which he also excelled. The most celebrated of his works is his Elements of Geometry, of which there have been a great number of editions in all languages.'

The word SPHERE goes back through the Latin *sphaera*, to the Greek σφαῖρα (sphaira), a ball, globe, sphere, a playing ball, also the earth. The idea of the earth as a SPHERE appeared perhaps first in the Phaedon (*fē'-dŏn*), a dialogue of Plato purporting to be the last conversation of Socrates, with an account of his death. From the same source come the adjective

Figure produced by revolving a circle around its diameter as an axis.

FORM B. 43.	NY	MISC.	SUM
cycloid	0	19	19
great circle	4	21	25
paraboloid	3	18	21
hypocycloid	1	13	14
SPHERE	36	205	241
unmarked	4	33	37
total	48	309	357

SPHERICAL, round, like a sphere, SPHEROID, by derivation in the form of a sphere, actually in geometry the figure made by the revolution of an ellipse about either of its axes.

To the question: 'Figure produced by revolving a circle around its diameter as an axis', 241 persons out of 357 answer SPHERE; while 25 answer GREAT CIRCLE. A GREAT CIRCLE is a line on the surface of a SPHERE. Any GREAT CIRCLE revolved about any line through its center generates the sphere of which it is a great circle. From Nathan Bailey, English dictionary of 1721: 'A SPHERE, any solid, round Body, conceived (according to the Rules of Geometry) to be formed by the Circumvolution of a Semi-Circle round about its Diameter'.

85. *NEWTON'S THIRD LAW OF MOTION* (*nū'-tŏn*).

To every action there is an equal and opposite reaction.

Sir Isaac Newton published his now famous three laws of motion in 1687 in Latin in his Philosophiae Naturalis Principia Mathematica (Mathematical Principles of Natural Philosophy), called for short Principia (*prĭn-sĭp'-ĭ-ah*). They are:

First: A body at rest remains at rest, or a body in motion continues in motion in a straight line with constant velocity, unless acted upon by some external force. This first law is called also LAW OF INERTIA. It is qualitative, and cannot be verified experimentally.

Second: Change of momentum is proportional to the force that produces it, and takes place in the direction of the force. This second law is really a definition of force. It says:

$$\text{FORCE} = \text{MASS} \times \text{ACCELERATION}.$$

Third: To every action there is an equal and opposite reaction.

The first two of the three laws now universally called NEWTON'S were formulated by GALILEO, who died in January, 1642, the year in which Newton was born. Newton himself gives credit to Galileo. The third law is unquestionably Newton's contribution. Although called LAWS in nearly every textbook, these statements were made originally more as axioms.

In discussing Newton's third law Frederick A. Saunders says that it is impossible to pull a loose piece of thread across a smooth table top with a fifty-pound pull; there is nothing to hold it back. The exertion of force demands a reaction to that force; to every action there is an equal and opposite reaction.

In answer to the question: 'Law stating that to every action there is an equal and opposite reaction', 76 per cent of students answer correctly NEWTON'S; but 15 per cent answer LAW OF MOMENTS. Newton's laws can be restated as laws of rotation instead of laws of translation. When they are, LAW OF MOMENTS is the name sometimes given to Newton's second law.

Despite the drop in the percentage of correct answers from 95 per cent in form AB to 76 per cent in form DA, this item has held its place in four studies as one of the easiest. The drop in correct answers seems due in part to a difference in the populations which have taken the four forms and in part to the insertion of a new mislead in form DA, LAW OF MOMENTS, which has attracted 15 per cent of students, becoming the most

Law stating that to every action there is an equal and opposite reaction.

FORM AB. 3.	%	FORM D. 2.	NY	%
Tycho Brahe's	0	Tycho Brahe's	10	2.9
Einstein's theory	0	Einstein's theory	4	1.1
NEWTON's	95	NEWTON's	279	79.7
Lenz's	4	Lenz's	27	7.7
Kepler's	1	Kepler's	28	8.0
unmarked	0	unmarked	2	0.6
total	100	total	350	100.0

FORM DA. 1.	NY	FORM DB. 1.	NY
Tycho Brahe's	1	Galileo's	8
law of moments	15	law of moments	13
NEWTON's	76	NEWTON's	55
Lenz's	6	Lenz's	8
Kepler's	2	law of inertia	22
unmarked	0	unmarked	0
total	100	total	106

frequently marked mislead, in place of EINSTEIN'S THEORY which attracted practically no one in the earlier forms. In form DB, the new mislead LAW OF INERTIA attracts 21 per cent, leaving only 52 per cent marking the correct answer.

86. MUTUAL INDUCTANCE (mū'-tū-ăl ĭn-dŭk'-tăns).

Change of flux-linkages produced in one coil by a unit change of current in another, flux-linkages in one circuit per ampere in the other.

The INDUCTANCE of a circuit is electromagnetic inertia. INDUCTANCE opposes any change in current flow. At the closing of a switch a current of electricity in a coil of wire around a soft iron core does not instantly flow at its full. In starting to flow, current builds a magnetic field. The growth of this magnetic field induces voltage in the coil which opposes the flow of current. When the switch is opened and current no longer flows the dying away of the magnetic field induces voltage which upholds the current so that the current does not stop instantly with the opening of the switch.

MUTUAL INDUCTANCE is INDUCTANCE produced in one circuit by a change of current in another circuit, it is the flux-linkages

Flux linkages in one circuit per ampere in the other.

FORM BA. 19.	%	FORM D.	NY	%
MUTUAL				
INDUCTANCE	58	MUTUAL INDUCTANCE	213	60.9
impedance	10	impedance	36	10.3
reactive factor	12	reactive factor	37	10.6
reluctance	5	reluctance	20	5.7
permeance	13	permeance	24	6.8
unmarked	2	unmarked	20	5.7
total	100	total	350	100.0

FORM DA. 10.	NY	FORM DB. 6.	NY
MUTUAL			
INDUCTANCE	70	MUTUAL INDUCTANCE	46
impedance	9	impedance	22
reactive factor	10	reactive factor	16
mutual reluctance	4	mutual reluctance	10
permeance	7	permeance	7
unmarked	0	unmarked	5
total	100	total	106

in one circuit per ampere in another, a change of current in one circuit producing an electromotive force in another.

To the question: 'The linkages of flux with a coil due to a one ampere current flowing in a second coil', 70 per cent of students answer correctly MUTUAL INDUCTANCE. The remaining 30 per cent divide among the other four choices: IMPEDANCE, REACTIVE FACTOR, MUTUAL RELUCTANCE, and PERMEANCE. This does not mean that 70 per cent of students know the meaning of MUTUAL INDUCTANCE; for the student who has no idea of the meaning must guess, and mark one of the five choices. If he has no idea of the meaning there is as much

chance of his marking MUTUAL INDUCTANCE by luck as there is
of his marking any of the other choices. Therefore with 30
per cent marking four wrong choices, 7½ per cent marking
each, 7½ per cent probably mark MUTUAL INDUCTANCE by pure
luck not knowing it is correct. Correcting for luck MUTUAL
INDUCTANCE is probably known to 70—7½ or 62½ per cent.

87. *AXIS* (ăk'-sĭs) *n*. Any line in a regular figure which divides
      it into two symmetrical parts, which joins opposite angles
or opposite sides.
The word AXIS comes from the Latin *axis*, a word which means
axis, axle, and the pole of the earth. Today the word AXLE

A straight line about which a geometric figure revolves.

FORM A. I.	BO	NY	SUM	FORM AA.	NY
center	1	4	5	center	5
radius	2	4	6	radius	23
polar coordinate	2	3	5	polar coordinate	3
AXIS	15	27	42	AXIS	95
diagonal	0	2	2	diagonal	5
unmarked	0	1	1	unmarked	1
total	20	41	61	total	132

means an actual pin or spindle on which a wheel turns; while
an AXIS is more often an imaginary line about which anything
revolves or may be thought of as revolving, as: 'The AXIS of
the earth'. Or in a plane figure the AXIS is the line which divides
it in half, about which it is symmetrical.

   To the question: 'A straight line about which a geometric
figure revolves', 95 persons out of 132 answer AXIS; while 23
answer RADIUS. Although the DIAMETER of a circle is an AXIS
about which it might revolve, the RADIUS is only half the DIAM-
ETER, a line from the center to the edge. The word RADIUS
(17) comes from the Latin *radius*, the spoke of a wheel. This
may in some vague way suggest revolve.

   Charles Hutton, in his Mathematical and Philosophical Dictionary of 1796, says: 'Axis, more generally a right line conceived to be drawn from the vertex of a figure to the middle
of the base'. Still from Hutton: 'The ellipse and hyperbole have

each two AXES, but the parabola has only one and that infinite in length'. In a curve such as the parabola the AXIS is a straight line which bisects parallel chords. From the Builder's Dictionary of 1734 comes: 'AXIS of a conic section, is a quiescent right line passing through the middle of the figure and cutting all the ordinates at right angles'.

88. *ION* (*ī'-ŏn*) *n.* A carrier of an electrical charge, part of a molecule which is charged electrically, an atom or a part of a molecule which is either positively or negatively

Either part of a molecule of electrolyte broken down by an electric current.

FORM BA. 13.	%	FORM D.	NY	%
cation	12	cation	32	9.2
anion	10	anion	30	8.6
thermion	1	deuton	20	5.7
ION	73	ION	249	71.1
diatom	3	diatom	16	4.6
unmarked	1	unmarked	3	0.8
total	100	total	350	100.0

FORM DA. 3.	%	FORM DB. 3.	NY
cation	5½	cation	2
anion	12	ION	85
deuton	2	deuteron	8
ION	72	anion	6
nucleus	6½	nucleus	5
unmarked	2	unmarked	0
total	100	total	106

charged because it has lost or gained one or more electrons the number in the case of an atom equaling the valence of the chemical element. Reread ELECTROLYSIS (50).

The word ION, one of those coined by Michael Faraday, comes from the Greek ἰόν (ion), the neuter of ἰόν (ion), the present participle of ἰέναι (ienai), to go. This Greek word comes from the same root as the more familiar Latin *ire*, to go. From the same source comes the English ITINERANT which, as an adjective, in the phrase: 'An ITINERANT preacher', means wandering, strolling, moving from place to place. An ION is a wanderer.

In ELECTROLYSIS (50), electricity is carried by two oppositely moving streams of charged particles. These carriers of electricity are IONS. A salt such as sodium chloride (NaCl) breaks in ELECTROLYSIS into two IONS, a sodium ION (Na^+) with a positive charge, which means that it moves toward the negative pole, and a chlorine ION (Cl^-) with a negative charge, which in consequence moves toward the positive pole. In the same manner, when a current of electricity passes through a solution of sulphuric acid, H_2SO_4, positively charged hydrogen particles, called IONS, and symbolized by H^+, move toward the cathode, while negatively charged sulphate particles, also called IONS, and symbolized by SO_4^{--}, each with two negative charges, move toward the anode.

To the question: 'Either of the two constituents into which a molecule of electrolyte is separated by the passage of an electric current', 72 per cent of those whose scores have been tabulated for form DA answer correctly ION; but 12 per cent answer ANION. The word ANION comes from the Greek ἀνά (ana), up, plus the same ἰών (ion), going, the source of ION. In Faraday's own words: 'I propose to distinguish such bodies by calling those ANIONS which go to the ANODE of the decomposing body'. An ANION is specifically an electro-negative ION which, in electro-chemical decompositions, moves toward the positive pole. The term ION is more general including both negative and positive carriers.

89. *DRIFT ANGLE* (*drĭft ăng'-gl*). Angle to the right or left measured from the fore and aft line of the aircraft to a line drawn through consecutive points on the ground over which the craft has passed, angle either to the port or to the starboard between the direction an airplane is headed and its ground course, the horizontal angular difference between the longitudinal axis of a plane and its forward flight path over the ground. Called also ANGLE OF DRIFT.

To the question: 'The angle between the direction in which the aircraft is pointed and the direction in which it is actually moving', 328 persons out of 515 answer correctly DRIFT ANGLE; but 91 answer WIND-CORRECTION ANGLE and 59 FLIGHT-PATH ANGLE; the popular misleads also in the revised form AA. The FLIGHT-PATH ANGLE is a vertical angle, up from the ground. It

Form A. The angle between the direction in which the aircraft is pointing and the direction in which it is actually moving.
Form AA. Angle between the direction an aircraft is pointing and its course over the ground.

FORM A. 11.	FW	LA	NY	NY	NY	PH	SUM	FORM AA. 12.	NY
angle of pitch	0	1	3	1	12	8	25	pitch	3
DRIFT ANGLE	12	38	26	42	84	126	328	DRIFT	25
flight-path angle	1	5	5	4	18	26	59	flight path	17
trim angle	0	1	0	2	2	5	10	back bearing	1
wind-correction angle	5	9	2	16	24	35	91	wind correction	17
unmarked	0	0	1	1	0	0	2	unmarked	0
total	18	54	37	66	140	200	515	total	63

is the angle between the path of flight of the aircraft and the horizontal, between the path of a rising or descending plane and the level earth beneath. The FLIGHT-PATH ANGLE is vertical; the DRIFT ANGLE horizontal.

The WIND-CORRECTION ANGLE or DRIFT-CORRECTION ANGLE, the most frequently marked mislead, is the angle an aircraft must head into the wind to make good a desired course on the ground. Like the ANGLE OF DRIFT it is horizontal. It is the angle between the course a pilot wishes to fly and the direction in which he must head the airplane in order to counteract the drift and remain on his course. Given the direction in which an aircraft is heading, that is the direction of its fore-and-aft line, and the direction of its motion over the ground, the difference between the two is the ANGLE OF DRIFT or DRIFT ANGLE. Given the direction of the point which the pilot wants to reach and the air speed he expects to make, given the direction of the wind and its speed, he can then compute the WIND-CORRECTION ANGLE. This he can then or later compare with his angle of drift or DRIFT ANGLE, the horizontal angle he is actually making between the longitudinal axis of his aircraft and its path relative to the ground, the angular difference between the heading and the track.

90. *POLARIZE* (*pō'-lahr-īz*) *v.* To eliminate all transverse vibrations except those in one plane.

The words POLARIZATION and POLARIZE were coined in 1811 by Etienne Louis Malus (*mah-lūs'*), a French military engineer; except that in French both words are spelt with an s instead of z, *polarisation*. In Nicholson's Journal, 1812, the first English journal on natural philosophy, begun by William Nicholson in 1797, there appeared: 'By giving to these sides of the vertical ray the name of POLES, Malus has given the name of POLARIZATION to that modification which imparts properties to light which are relative to these poles'.

The Oxford New English Dictionary comments: 'This unfortunately assumed a sense of pole quite different from its use in astronomy, geography, and magnetism, with the consequence that POLARIZATION as applied to light and radiant heat has nothing in common with magnetic or electric polarization'.

To the question: 'A transverse vibration in one plane', the only popular misconception is ECHO. This word comes from the Greek ἠχώ (echo), from ἠχή (eche), sound. ECHO refers specifically to sound reflected back from some surface. As sound pulsations move ahead they do not at the same time undulate up and down or sideways but instead push back and forth in the direction of their motion. Sound pulses cannot therefore be polarized. The word ECHO is not used of light, though light is reflected from a surface in much the same way, and is POLARIZED when thus reflected.

The Harmsworth Encyclopaedia of 1906 says: 'The doubly refracted rays have what Newton called SIDES; and it is this sidedness or laterality which is known as POLARIZATION'. Thomas Young in his Course of Lectures on Natural Philosophy and the Mechanical Arts published in 1845 says: 'Light which consists of vibrations in one direction only is termed POLARIZED light'. Sir David Brewster in his Optics says: 'These two beams are said to be POLARIZED because they have sides or poles of different properties'.

91. *DECIBEL* (*dĕs'-ĭ-bĕl*) *n.* The logarithm of a ratio, the electrical or mechanical power, expressed in watts, used to produce a sound divided by the power used to produce another weaker sound, a power-interval unit corresponding to the power ratio $10^{1/10}$ or 1.259 used to express acoustic sensation level differences, equal to 1/10th of a BEL.

DECI-, meaning one tenth, is short for *decimi-*, from the Latin *decimus*, tenth, the source of the English DECIMAL. DECI- occurs also in DECIMETER, a tenth of a meter; and in DECIGRAM, a tenth of a gram. A DECIBEL is a tenth of a BEL. A BEL, named for Alexander Graham Bell, the inventor of the telephone, is the measure, or an indication, of the increase in sound due to a

The ratio required to make a just noticeable difference in sound intensity.

FORM A. 19.	NY	NY	NY	SUM
DECIBEL	24	28	114	166
choke	0	0	5	5
half-note	4	10	15	29
monitor	6	1	10	17
henry	1	1	3	5
unmarked	2	0	0	2
total	37	40	147	224

ten-fold increase in the power used to produce the sound; it is actually a logarithm, the logarithm to the base 10, the common logarithm, of the ratio of two powers. An increase of ten-fold in the power used to produce a sound is an increase of one BEL, the logarithm of 10. An increase of a hundred fold in the power used to produce a sound, ten squared, is an increase in sound of two BELS.

The response of the human ear to sounds of different intensity is logarithmic. Squaring the power doubles the impression of the sound on the human ear as measured in BELS; cubing the power increases the impression of the sound three times, or by three BELS. Increasing the power by the square root of ten, or by 3.15, makes a sound which is just half as loud as if the power used were increased ten times, or half a BEL. Increasing the power used by the tenth root of ten, or by 1.259, makes a sound one tenth as loud as if it were increased ten times, or makes a sound one DECIBEL louder, one tenth of a BEL. As the BEL is too large for most purposes the DECIBEL is used. Both the DECIBEL and the BEL are relative units and do not specify any definite amount of sound, power, current, or voltage.

To the question: 'The ratio required to make a just noticeable difference in sound intensity', 166 persons out of 224 answer DECIBEL; but 29 answer HALF-NOTE. A HALF-NOTE difference signifies a difference in pitch, not in sound intensity. Pitch depends on wave frequency or wave length. Loudness depends on wave height, AMPLITUDE, or AMPLIFICATION. The operating characteristics of an audio amplifier are generally expressed in terms of its gain in volume. The unit is based on the ability of the human ear to respond. The smallest change in sound intensity which a keen human ear can detect is said to be about one DECIBEL, though some hear no changes under two or three DECIBELS. It is also said that the human ear hears an increase of 25 per cent in loudness. This applies at all levels of loudness or intensity. It happens that the DECIBEL, one tenth of a BEL, represents a gain in power of 1.26, an increase in power of 26 per cent. This is very nearly the lowest change in loudness which can be heard.

92. ARCHIMEDES' PRINCIPLE (ahr-kĭ-mē'-dēz prĭn'-sĭ-pl).

A body in a liquid is buoyed up by a force equal to the weight of the displaced liquid.
A PRINCIPLE is a basic general truth, comprehending many subordinate truths, in contrast to a LAW, a statement in words. Thus James McCosh says: 'To enunciate precisely the general LAW which is the expression of a PRINCIPLE'. As Archimedes' words have not survived his discovery is not a LAW; but it is fundamental, accepted as true, and so is honored by the term PRINCIPLE.

Hiero, king of Syracuse where Archimedes was born and died, is said to have ordered a crown of pure gold. By weighing the crown immersed in water and weighing it in the air, and subtracting the first from the second, Archimedes obtained the weight of the water displaced. Were the crown pure gold it should have weighed in air 19.3 times its weight in water, the specific gravity of gold. Were the crown pure silver it should have weighed in air 10.5 times the weight of the water displaced, the specific gravity of silver. It weighed between the two, showing that it was not pure gold.

Archimedes lived from 287 B.C. to 212 B.C. In Greek letters his name is spelt 'Αρχιμήδης. His greatest contributions were to

A body placed in a liquid is buoyed up by a force equal to the weight of the displaced liquid.

FORM E. 5.	BO	FW	LA	NY	NY	NY	NY	PH	TU	SUM
Bernoulli's principle	4	11	3	2	1	2	15	14	5	57
Peltier effect	1	0	0	0	0	0	6	1	0	8
Doppler effect	0	1	0	0	0	1	1	0	1	4
ARCHIMEDES' PRINCIPLE	23	37	30	17	18	36	189	84	22	456
conservation principle	0	1	0	1	1	1	7	1	0	12
unmarked	0	0	0	0	0	0	0	0	0	0
total	28	50	33	20	20	40	218	100	28	537

pure geometry; but he is best known by his applications of mathematics to mechanics.

To the question: 'A body placed in a liquid is buoyed up by a force equal to the weight of the displaced liquid', 456 persons out of 537 answer ARCHIMEDES' PRINCIPLE; but 57 answer BERNOULLI'S PRINCIPLE. This is also the most frequently marked mislead in seven out of the eight small populations tabulated separately, strengthening the impression that even small populations surprisingly often indicate the popular misconception.

Daniel Bernoulli (*bār-nool-lyē′*), also spelt BERNOUILLI, 1700 to 1782, was a member of a Dutch-Swiss family distinguished for several generations by its scientific attainments. Bernoulli started as a physician, then became professor of mathematics, then of anatomy in 1733 at the University of Basel in Switzerland, then professor of botany, and finally in 1750 professor of experimental and speculative philosophy. His work on hydrodynamics laid the foundation for the kinetic theory of gases. When a liquid flows through a pipe and meets a constricted section, smaller in diameter or smaller in cross section, the pressure in this section of the pipe is less than in the preceding larger section. The same amount of fluid must flow through the small section as through the large one, if the flow continues. It must therefore flow faster in the constricted section. To do this it must be accelerated in passing from the large to the narrow section. This demands greater pressure in the large section than in the smaller one. This is Bernoulli's principle.

The confusion of BERNOULLI with ARCHIMEDES is not apparently mere chance guess from complete ignorance, for of the 40 persons very low in English vocabulary not one marks BERNOULLI. It is only the middle group who know enough to realize that both ARCHIMEDES' PRINCIPLE and BERNOULLI's deal with hydrodynamics, and yet do not know enough to separate

FORM E. 5.	ENGLISH VOCABULARY	
	HIGH	LOW
Bernoulli's principle	1	0
Peltier effect	0	0
Doppler effect	0	1
ARCHIMEDES' PRINCIPLE	39	38
conservation principle	0	0
unmarked	0	1
total	40	40

them; for at the top only one very high in English vocabulary marks BERNOULLI. The Laboratory believes that when a confusion of this type occurs with practically every group studied, and in every city where it tests, the confusion, instead of being avoided, should be used as a natural and apparently necessary step in the learning process.

The third edition of the Encyclopaedia Britannica, in 18 volumes and printed in Edinburgh, appeared in 1797. A year later a work of similar size, called merely Encyclopaedia, appeared in Philadelphia. From this comes the following article: ARCHIMEDES, a celebrated geometrician, born at Syracufe in the ifland of Sicily, and related to Hiero king of Syracufe. He was remarkable for his extraordinary application to mechanical ſtudies; in which he uſed to be ſo much engaged, that his ſervants were often obliged to take him from thence by force. He had ſuch a ſurpriſing invention in mechanics, that he affirmed to Hiero, if he had another earth, whereon to plant his machines, he could move this which we inhabit. He is ſaid to have formed a glaſs ſphere, of the moſt ſurpriſing workmanſhip, wherein the motions of the heavenly bodies were repreſented. He diſcovered the exact quantity of the ſilver which a goldſmith had mixed with the gold in a crown he had made for the king; he had the hint of this diſcovery from his perceiving the water riſe up the ſides of the bath as he went into it, and was filled with ſuch joy, that he ran naked out of the bath, crying: εὕρηκα (eureka), εὕρηκα (eureka), "I have found it! I have found it!" By the invention of machines, he, for a long time, defended Syracuſe on its being beſieged by Marcellus. On the city's being taken, that general commanded his ſoldiers to have a particular regard to the ſafety of this truly great man; but his care was ineffectual. "What gave Marcellus the greateſt concern (ſays Plutarch), was the unhappy Archimedes, who was at that time in his muſaeum, and his mind, as well as his eyes, ſo fixed and intent upon ſome geometrical figures, that he neither heard the noiſe and hurry of the Romans, nor perceived the city was taken. In this depth of ſtudy and contemplation, a ſoldier came ſuddenly upon him, and commanded him to follow him to Marcellus; which he refuſed to do till he had finiſhed his problem, the ſoldier, in a rage, drew his ſword, and ran him through the body." Others have related the circumſtances of his death in a ſomewhat different manner. It however happened 208 years before the Chriſtian era. Cicero, when he was quaeſtor in Italy, diſcovered his tomb, on which was carved a cylinder and ſphere. Some of the works of this great mathematician are loſt, but others are preſerved. His pieces which remain are, 1. Two books on the Sphere and Cylinder. 2. The Dimenſions of a Circle. 3. Of Centers of Gravity, or Aequiponderants. 4. Of Spheroids and Conoids. 5. Of Spiral Lines. 6. The Quadrature of a Parabola. 7. Of the Number of the Sand. 8. Of Bodies that float on Fluids. The beſt edition of theſe is that publiſhed in London in 1675, 4to.

93. *ANEROID BAROMETER* (ăn'-ĕ-roid bă-rŏm'-ĕ-tĕr) *n.*
A metal box designed to indicate atmospheric pressure on its cover by moving a pointer. Reread ATMOSPHERE (75).

The Italian mathematician Evangelista Torricelli, who went to Florence in 1641 to meet Galileo Galilei, remained with him as his secretary until his death three months later. Torricelli then became professor of mathematics in the Florentine Academy, and there in 1643 built the first BAROMETER. He filled with mercury a glass tube 80 or more centimeters high, sealed

An evacuated metal box actuating a pointer which indicates atmospheric pressure.

FORM C. 4.	NY	FORM CA. 5.	BO	NY HIGH	NY NEXT	NY REST	NY MISC.	NY SUM
electroscope	2	barograph	6	17	40	157	14	234
Bourdon gauge	26	Bourdon gage	1	4	11	100	9	125
manometer	8	manometer	1	1	4	94	5	105
hygrometer	6	hygrometer	4	0	0	98	11	113
ANEROID BAROMETER	357	ANEROID BAROMETER	88	378	345	651	195	1657
unmarked	1	unmarked	0	0	0	0	0	0
total	400	total	100	400	400	1100	234	2234

at the bottom end. This he turned upside down and left with the open end at the bottom resting in a bowl of mercury. Under such conditions the mercury in the tube drops down from the top, if the tube is long enough, leaving a vacuum at the closed end. The height of the column of mercury, above the surface of the mercury in the bowl at the bottom, equals the atmospheric pressure.

Standard atmospheric pressure at a temperature of zero degrees centigrade sustains a column of mercury 76 centimeters in height, sometimes called a pressure of one atmosphere.

In contradistinction to this early form of BAROMETER the ANEROID BAROMETER contains no mercury, no liquid. The word ANEROID comes from the Greek νηρός (neros), wet, liquid. A NEREID (nē'-rē-ĭd), in Greek mythology, was a sea nymph who rode a sea monster and helped voyagers. The Greek negative

or privative A at the beginning of ANEROID occurs also in AMOR-
PHOUS, without form, formless; in ACHROMATIC, not chromatic,
not colored, without color; and in ATYPICAL, not typical, unrep-
resentative. ANEROID means not wet, without liquid.

To the question: 'An evacuated metal box actuating a pointer
which indicates atmospheric pressure', 74 per cent of 2234
persons answer ANEROID BAROMETER; while 11 per cent answer
BAROGRAPH. In the earlier study of form C, based on 400 persons
and without the mislead BAROGRAPH which was inserted later,
89 per cent answer ANEROID BAROMETER; and 6 per cent BOURDON
GAGE, the most frequently marked mislead. A BAROGRAPH, the
new mislead, is a recording BAROMETER.

Both an ANEROID BAROMETER and a BOURDON GAGE measure
pressures and neither instrument uses mercury or other liquid.
A BOURDON GAGE (boor'-don gädj) is a flat metal tube bent
like the circumference of a circle into a nearly complete ring.
One end is sealed and the other open to admit vapor under
pressure. An increase in the pressure of this vapor, by tending
to straighten the tube, moves an indicating needle. A BOURDON
GAGE measures only high pressures such as those of steam boilers
and ordinarily reads zero at a pressure of one atmosphere.
BAROMETERS are not built for high pressures but for those of
about one atmosphere.

An ANEROID BAROMETER is a circular, disk-shaped metal box,
sometimes no larger than a man's watch. The top is of thin
metal, with circular corrugations so that the center of the
top depresses easily. This center is supported inside by a spring,
the air is exhausted, and the box permanently sealed. An increase in atmospheric pressure pushes down the top of the box.
This moves a needle which indicates the change.

94. *PISTON DISPLACEMENT* (pĭs'-tŏn dĭs-plās'-mĕnt). The
volume of a cylinder between the extreme positions of the
piston, the space covered by one stroke of the piston, area of
the cross section of a cylinder multiplied by the distance the
piston travels.

PISTON DISPLACEMENT is usually stated in cubic inches. As
the area of a circle is πr^2, the area of the cross section of the
cylinder is 3.1416 times half the diameter or bore in inches

squared. This multiplied by the travel of the piston is the DISPLACEMENT. In a so-called SQUARE engine the diameter or bore and the stroke are approximately equal.

The total PISTON DISPLACEMENT of an engine is the PISTON DISPLACEMENT of each cylinder multiplied by the number of cylinders. With other factors constant, the greater the piston displacement the greater the maximum horsepower of the engine. But if the piston travel, the length of the stroke, is too

Form A. The volume of gas displaced during one stroke of a piston.

Form AA. Volume of cylinder between top and bottom of stroke.

FORM A. 44.	FW	LA	NY	NY	NY	PH	SUM	FORM AA. 11. NY	
PISTON DISPLACEMENT	15	43	25	31	97	122	333	PISTON DISPLACEMENT	50
valve overlap	1	2	0	0	3	4	10	bore	5
mechanical efficiency	0	0	2	2	8	10	22	mechanical efficiency	0
volumetric efficiency	2	5	5	16	19	33	80	volumetric efficiency	6
gassing factor	0	2	3	5	11	16	37	gassing factor	2
unmarked	0	2	2	12	2	15	33	unmarked	0
total	18	54	37	66	140	200	515	total	63

long the connecting rod moves through too great an angle. And if the bore, the second most frequently marked mislead in the revised form AA, or diameter of the cylinder is too great, fuel seems to be wasted. Increased displacement is obtained by adding cylinders.

To the question: 'The volume of gas displaced during one stroke of the piston', 333 persons out of 515 answer PISTON DISPLACEMENT, but 80 persons or 16 per cent answer VOLUMETRIC EFFICIENCY, the most frequently marked mislead and almost justified by the present wording; for VOLUMETRIC EFFICIENCY is the volume of the gas actually displaced by one stroke of the piston divided by the volume of the space through which the piston moves, more exactly it is the volume of the charge at atmospheric pressure divided by the PISTON DISPLACE-

MENT. The gas displaced by one stroke of the piston is equal to the piston displacement only when the volumetric efficiency is 1.00. Some of the factors which reduce the volume of gas actually displaced are: improper timing of the valves, fuel lines which are too small or have too many bends, and incomplete scavenging on the previous exhaust stroke and so a space already partly filled.

PISTON DISPLACEMENT is not the gas displaced but the volume of the space in the cylinder between the piston at the bottom of its stroke and at the top. With the new wording in the revised form AA: 'Volume of cylinder between top and bottom of stroke', only 6 persons in 63, or 10 per cent instead of 16, mark the mislead VOLUMETRIC EFFICIENCY, in place of the correct answer PISTON DISPLACEMENT.

95. *INDUCED DRAG* (ĭn-dŭst' drăg). That part of the resistance to the forward motion of an aircraft which is caused by the lift primarily of the wings, resistance which would be encountered if the air had no viscosity.

The verb INDUCE comes from the Latin *inducere*, a combination of *in*, and *ducere*, to lead. In literature to INDUCE means to lead by persuasion, prevail upon, incite, influence, bring

Form A. Drag induced by lift.
Form AA. Resistance to forward motion caused by lift.

FORM A. 22.	FW	LA	NY	NY	NY	PH	SUM	FORM AA. 13.	NY
parasite drag	2	7	6	8	23	41	87	parasite drag	10
								interference	
damping	1	0	1	4	3	7	16	drag	11
								beam	
deceleration	1	1	2	4	13	4	25	component	1
profile drag	2	7	5	6	16	16	52	profile drag	7
INDUCED DRAG	12	39	22	39	84	125	321	INDUCED DRAG	34
unmarked	0	0	1	5	1	7	14	unmarked	0
total		18	54	37	66	140	200	515	total	63

about. James Russell Lowell says: 'Solitude INDUCED reflection', brought it about, produced it. The INDUCED DRAG is that part of the drag produced by the lift of the moving airplane.

To the definition: 'Drag induced by lift', 321 persons out of 515 answer correctly INDUCED DRAG; but 87 answer PARASITE DRAG. The PARASITE DRAG is the entire drag of the airplane except for the INDUCED DRAG. The PARASITE DRAG includes skin friction and form drag dependent on the shapes of the parts moving through the air. In the revised form AA, where the question has been changed to read: 'Resistance to forward motion caused by lift', INTERFERENCE DRAG, which replaces DAMPING in the earlier form A, is now the most popular. INTERFERENCE DRAG is caused by the interference of the airflow around two objects which are close together. The INDUCED DRAG is the unavoidable drag which always accompanies lift.

96. *CHANNEL* (*chăn'-nĕl*) *n.* The band of radio frequencies
    assigned to a transmitting station. Reread BAND (37).
The word CHANNEL goes back through Middle English to the Latin *canalis*, a water-pipe, canal. From this the first meaning of the word in English was the bed of a stream, the course in which water flows. From this CHANNEL came to mean the deeper part of a river, safest for navigation, and so the course which ought to be followed by a ship. Radio has extended this last use.

A group of radio frequencies which a modulated signal may occupy.

FORM A. 28.	NY	NY	NY	SUM
multiple	2	2	8	12
side frequencies	10	12	34	56
grid	1	0	3	4
variable	1	2	7	10
CHANNEL	19	23	94	136
unmarked	4	1	1	6
total	37	40	147	224

To the question: 'A group of radio frequencies which a modulated signal may occupy', 136 persons out of 224 answer CHANNEL; while 56 answer SIDE FREQUENCIES. The amplitude or width of the carrier wave is constant, its frequency is also constant at the center of the CHANNEL. The SIDE FREQUENCIES or SIDE-BAND FREQUENCIES are on each side of the CARRIER (57) frequency and are those frequencies into which the carrier frequency is taken by modulation. SIDE FREQUENCIES is a correct answer to one interpretation. The question has been changed to read: 'A group of radio frequencies assigned to a station'.

97. *VARIABLE CONDENSER* (*vă'-rĭ-ā-bl kŏn-dĕn'-ser*). A condenser the capacitance of which can be changed. Called also a VARIABLE CAPACITOR.

The tuning of a radio receiver can be accomplished by varying either the inductance of the tuning circuit or its capacitance. The usual method is to vary the capacitance by means of a VARIABLE CONDENSER. This consists of two sets of plates, a

Instrument for changing the rate of oscillation of an electric circuit.

FORM E. 32.	BO	FW	LA	NY	NY	NY	NY	PH	TU	SUM
VARIABLE CONDENSER	20	33	25	13	18	30	153	80	20	392
dynamo	2	6	2	3	1	0	12	0	0	26
diaphragm	3	2	1	0	0	1	8	3	2	20
armature	0	4	2	2	0	7	26	7	1	49
filter	0	5	3	2	1	1	15	10	5	42
unmarked	3	0	0	0	0	1	4	0	0	8
total	28	50	33	20	20	40	218	100	28	537

rotating set and a stationary set. The rotating plates, all parallel to one another and mounted perpendicular to their axis, swing in between the parallel stationary plates. Capacitance depends on the area of the plates which are in mesh and on the air spaces between the plates. The thickness of the plates has no effect.

To the question: 'Instrument for changing the rate of oscillation of an electric circuit', 392 persons out of 537 answer correctly VARIABLE CONDENSER. The remainder divide nearly evenly among the four misleads. This is one of the few items where those who score high in English vocabulary and those who score low mark the correct answer equally often.

Three types of VARIABLE CONDENSERS are used in tuning. With the STRAIGHT-LINE-CAPACITY type the capacitance of the condenser increases in direct ratio with the amount of rotation of the movable plates. When these are one quarter in mesh the capacity of the condenser is one quarter of its maximum. With this type of condenser the upper half of the frequency band, 1100 to 1600 kilocycles, is crowded together in approximately one eighth of the dial, making it difficult to separate adjacent stations. This is because the resonant frequency does not vary directly with the capacitance.

In the STRAIGHT-LINE-WAVE-LENGTH type the rotating plates are not half circles, as in the preceding, but reduced in area on the side which first enters into mesh. With this type of VARIABLE CONDENSER the capacitance increases slowly at first and faster as the plates go further into mesh. With this type the wave length of the tuned circuit increases directly with the amount

FORM E. 32.	ENGLISH VOCABULARY	
	HIGH	LOW
VARIABLE CONDENSER	29	29
dynamo	1	2
diaphragm	3	2
armature	2	7
filter	5	0
unmarked	0	0
total	40	40

of rotation of the movable plates. This STRAIGHT-LINE-WAVE-LENGTH variable condenser gives better selectivity than the straight-line capacity type; but stations in the upper half of the frequency band, with carrier frequencies greater than 1100 kilocycles, still crowd together in the upper third of the dial.

In the STRAIGHT-LINE-FREQUENCY type the rotating plates are more carefully shaped so that the resultant frequency of the tuned circuit varies directly with the amount of rotation.

In the first VARIABLE CONDENSERS the rotating plates swung through 180 degrees, now often through 270 degrees. There are now more plates with smaller surface area, and often smaller air gaps. Also the stationary plates are now shaped and the rotating plates semicircular. Practically all tuning circuits of radio receivers use VARIABLE CONDENSERS.

98. *ELECTRON* (ē-lĕk'-trŏn) *n.* A negatively charged electrical particle with a mass about one two-thousandth that
of the hydrogen atom.

Starting vague and ill-defined, the word ELECTRON grows
gradually more exact, as language should. Before the Christian
era the Greek ἤλεκτρον (elektron) meant not only amber, but
also pure gold, at one time any substance with miraculous characteristics. Later the Greek word became *electrum* in Latin,
and meant an alloy of gold and silver, and, in the middle ages,
brass, in addition to all of the original meanings. Even in the
first edition of the Century Dictionary, prepared in 1889,
ELECTRON appears as another spelling of ELECTRUM, defined as
amber, gold, or brass. Not until 1891 was the word ELECTRON
used by Dr. G. Johnston Stoney for the natural unit of electricity which must pass through a solution in order to liberate
one atom of hydrogen. In the Scientific Transactions of the
Royal Dublin Society, he declared: 'Attention must be given to
Faraday's law of ELECTROLYSIS, which is equivalent to the
statement that in electrolysis a definite quantity of electricity,
the same in all cases, passes for each chemical bond that is rup-
tured'. Johnston Stoney continues: 'Nature presents us with
a single definite quantity of electricity which is independent of
the particular bodies acted on. This definite quantity of electricity I shall call an ELECTRON'.

Robert Andrews Millikan tried to perpetuate this meaning
and even in the title of his book: Electrons (+ and −),
Protons, Photons, Neutrons, Mesotrons, and Cosmic Rays,
blazoned the fact that he would like the word ELECTRON to denote either positive or negative electricity. But ELECTRON is
used today by most writers only for a definite elementary
quantity of negative electricity, for what Millikan would call
the free negative electron, the smallest existent particle of negative electricity, in mass little more than 1/1840th that of the
lightest atom. This may go back to the original meaning of the
Greek, for amber when rubbed becomes negatively charged.

To the question: 'Particles free to move through a metallic
conductor', 69 per cent of 2234 persons answer ELECTRONS;
while 12 per cent answer IONS. Among the 400 New York cases
who score highest on the physics vocabulary test as a whole

92 per cent answer correctly; 6 per cent answer ION; and few answer otherwise. Both ELECTRONS and IONS carry electrical charges. An ION (88) moves through a solution and carries either a positive or a negative electrical charge. Each of these moving ions is an atom, or group of atoms, which has lost or gained one, two, three, or more unit charges of negative

Particles that are free to move through a metallic conductor.

FORM C. 7.	NY	FORM CA. 6.	BO	NY HIGH	NY NEXT	NY REST	NY MISC.	SUM
atoms	13	atoms	3	0	5	119	7	134
ELECTRONS	333	ELECTRONS	82	367	327	584	182	1542
ions	42	ions	12	25	40	165	22	264
protons	4	molecules	2	2	18	132	17	171
monads	8	monads	0	6	10	100	6	122
unmarked	0	unmarked	1	0	0	0	0	1
total	400	total	100	400	400	1100	234	2234

electricity. Each of these unit charges is called an ELECTRON. An ION possesses a mass as great as that of an atom or even of several atoms; an ELECTRON is only a minute part of an atom, less than a thousandth part of the lightest atom. An ION may be either positive or negative; an ELECTRON, as the word is now used, is always negative. An ION moves through a liquid conductor; an ELECTRON through a metallic one.

99. *MARGIN OF SAFETY* (*mahr'-ĵin ŏv sāf'-tē*). The difference between the maximum load experienced by any working part in actual operation and the load which would cause destructive failure in a strength test.

The FACTOR OF SAFETY, perhaps a more familiar term, is the load which just causes destructive failure in a strength test divided by the maximum load experienced by the part in operation. The FACTOR OF SAFETY is a ratio and is always more than one. The MARGIN OF SAFETY is not a factor, but is the difference between the destructive load and the top operating load.

To the question: 'The difference between the ultimate load and any applied load', 321 persons out of 515 answer correctly MARGIN OF SAFETY, but 86 answer PAY LOAD and 50 USEFUL LOAD.

The PAY LOAD is the passengers and freight, that part of the USEFUL LOAD from which revenue is derived. It is only a part of the maximum load experienced in operation. The USEFUL LOAD includes the PAY LOAD, and in addition the crew, oil and fuel of any sort, ballast, and portable equipment.

In technical terms the LIMIT LOAD, that is the load which may be experienced safely in operation but which should not be exceeded, multiplied by the FACTOR OF SAFETY equals the ULTIMATE

Form A. The difference between the ultimate load and any applied load.
Form AA. The difference between the destructive load and the maximum load in operation.

FORM A. 26.	FW	LA	NY	NY	NY	PH	SUM	FORM AA. 15.	NY
pay load	4	9	8	11	25	29	86	pay load	5
impact									
pressure	0	3	2	0	3	2	10	limit load	7
balance	0	3	4	4	12	12	35	balance	3
useful load	2	4	6	6	11	21	50	useful load	0
MARGIN OF								MARGIN OF	
SAFETY	12	35	15	40	89	130	321	SAFETY	48
unmarked	0	0	2	5	0	6	13	unmarked	0
total	18	54	37	66	140	200	515	total	63

LOAD, the load just below destructive failure in strength tests. The MARGIN OF SAFETY is the difference between the LIMIT LOAD and the ULTIMATE LOAD.

100. *REACTANCE* ($r\bar{e}$-ăk'-tăns) *n*. The reduction of an alternating current by inductance and capacitance but not including resistance. INDUCTIVE REACTANCE is that component of the IMPEDANCE due to inductance; CAPACITIVE REACTANCE, that component due to capacitance. Reread MUTUAL INDUCTANCE (86).

To the test question: 'The combination effect of capacitance and inductance', 153 persons out of 224 answer REACTANCE; while 25 answer RESISTANCE. The word RESISTANCE is used for opposition to the flow of current due to the nature of the material through which the current flows. There is RESISTANCE to both direct and alternating currents. REACTANCE does not occur with direct currents. It is opposition to the flow of an alternating current due to the magnetic field set up by the current.

REACTANCE is of two kinds. An alternating current, flowing through a wire, builds up a magnetic field which opposes the flow of current in adjacent wires of the same coil. This sort of REACTANCE is called INDUCTIVE REACTANCE. INDUCTIVE REACTANCE is expressed in ohms much like resistance to a direct current. A

FORM A. 29.	NY	NY	NY	SUM
REACTANCE	20	26	107	153
resistance	7	2	16	25
resilience	2	4	10	16
ampere	2	3	6	11
voltage	0	4	6	10
unmarked	6	1	2	9
total	37	40	147	224

condenser in an alternating-current circuit reduces the current by its CAPACITANCE. This sort of REACTANCE is called CAPACITIVE REACTANCE. The combination of INDUCTIVE REACTANCE and CAPACITIVE REACTANCE are together called REACTANCE. REACTANCE does not include RESISTANCE to the flow of the current caused by the material.

101. *NICOL PRISM* (*nĭk'-ŏl prĭz'-m*). A device for polarizing light, a crystal of Iceland spar cut diagonally and cemented together again with Canada balsam so that the ordinary component of a beam of light is eliminated by total reflection from the Canada balsam while the extraordinary component passes through. A NICOL PRISM is so well known that it is sometimes called merely a Nicol, spelt with a capital, or more correctly NICOL with a small letter. Reread POLARIZE (90).

William Nicol, 1768 to 1851, was a Scottish physicist who acquired great skill in working glass and crystal surfaces. He devised his prism in 1828, twelve years after Biot's discovery of the double refraction of TOURMALINE in 1816. NICOL'S PRISM is primarily a crystal of Iceland spar or as it is sometimes called DOUBLE-REFRACTING SPAR, a transparent colorless variety of

CALCITE (kăl'-sĭt), a native calcium carbonate or carbonate of lime. A beam of light entering the end of an ICELAND-SPAR crystal divides into two slightly divergent beams, one polarized up and down, the other across. Nicol based his prism on the index of refraction of Canada balsam, 1.55, which is intermediate between the two indices of ICELAND SPAR or calcite, 1.66 and 1.49. By cutting an ICELAND-SPAR crystal at exactly the right angle and then fastening the two pieces together again with Canada balsam, one of the two beams into which calcite separates light continues through the Canada balsam while the other is reflected. The difference between the two indices of ICELAND SPAR is just great enough so that the beam which is polarized across can be reflected down and away by the Canada balsam and the other, polarized up and down, allowed to pass through. This was Nicol's discovery.

To the question: 'Two pieces of calcite crystal cemented together with Canada balsam', the popular mislead is TOURMALINE. Both TOURMALINE and a NICOL PRISM polarize light, for a section of TOURMALINE crystal, cut parallel to the axis, polarizes light much as does a NICOL PRISM. But TOURMALINE is usually colored green or red, and so is not ideal. TOURMALINES vary in composition depending on the country from which they come and the conditions under which they are found; for TOURMALINE has no definite chemical formula. Most TOURMALINES contain in the neighborhood of 38 per cent of silica, but vary from 30 to 40 per cent of alumina, and some magnesia. The Encyclopaedic Dictionary, Cassell, says: 'Though now largely superseded by NICOL's prisms, TOURMALINE sections are still convenient for some purposes, in spite of their color, owing to their large angular field of vision'.

102. *FARAD* (fă'-răd) n. The capacitance of a condenser which, when charged with one coulomb of electricity, has a potential difference of one volt between the plates. Reread VARIABLE CONDENSER (97).

The capacitance of any body depends on its size and shape, and on the surrounding medium. The influence of the medium on the effect of one charge on another was discovered in 1773 by Henry Cavendish, who seems to have had the first clear idea of the capacitance of a conductor and of measuring it. But his knowledge was lost to the world through his failure to publish it, until finally a hundred years later, in 1879, his manuscripts were published by Maxwell. Meanwhile Michael Faraday, in 1837, had rediscovered the effect of the medium on the capacitance of conductors; and the unit of capacitance is in consequence called a FARAD.

Michael Faraday was the son of a blacksmith who moved from Yorkshire to London before Michael was born in 1791. In 1804 the son served as errand boy at a bookbindery near his home, and the following year was appriticed to the bookbinder, working with him to the age of 22. Then he heard four lectures by Sir Humphrey Davy delivered at the Royal Institu-

Unit of capacitance.

FORM AB. 10.	NY	FORM D. 7.	NY	%
FARAD	85	FARAD	215	61.5
henry	6	henry	33	9.4
gauss	4	gauss	52	14.8
weber	2	weber	22	6.3
maxwell	3	maxwell	16	4.6
unmarked	0	unmarked	12	3.4
total	100	total	350	100.0

FORM DA. 9.	NY	FORM DB. 2.	NY
FARAD	72	FARAD	49
henry	16	henry	18
gauss	6	gauss	18
weber	2	gilbert	11
maxwell	4	maxwell	7
unmarked	0	unmarked	3
total	100	total	106

tion. 'My desire', he said later, 'to escape from trade, which I thought vicious and selfish, and to enter into the service of science, which I imagined made its pursuers amiable and liberal, induced me at last to make the bold and simple step of writing to Sir H. Davy, expressing my wishes, and a hope that if an opportunity came in his way he would favour my views; at the same time I sent the notes I had taken of his lectures'. Davy replied: 'I am far from displeased with the proof you have given me of your confidence'. As a result he became assistant to Davy in experiments and writing. Six months later he left England with Davy and his wife to tour France, Italy, and Switzerland, for a year and a half, even though France and England were at war when they started. Though it is sometimes said that Faraday acted at times almost as a servant to the Davys on this trip, it was certainly Humphrey Davy who gave Faraday his great opportunity in the sciences.

'A unit of capacitance' is thought correctly by 72 per cent of students to be the FARAD; but it is thought by another 16 per cent to be the HENRY. In the decade which followed 1830, Joseph Henry, 1797 to 1878, and Michael Faraday, born six years earlier, 1791 to 1867, were both experimenting independently with induced currents, Henry at Albany Academy, Albany, New York, and Faraday at the Royal Institution in London. Today the HENRY is a unit of inductance; the FARAD a unit of capacitance.

For an isolated sphere in free space the capacitance equals the radius. Thus the capacitance of a sphere of one centimeter radius is one electrostatic unit of capacitance. For any isolated body the potential is proportional to the charge. The capacitance equals numerically the charge required to give it unit potential. Capacitance is the ratio of the charge on a condenser to the potential difference between the terminals. The FARAD is the capacity of a condenser which requires one coulomb to charge it to a potential difference of one volt. Because the FARAD is so large, 9×10^{11} electrostatic units of capacitance, the MICROFARAD, one millionth of a FARAD, is ordinarily used.

103. *SINE* (sīn) *n.* The height of a right-angle triangle divided by the hypotenuse (29), or the side opposite the angle in question divided by the side opposite the right angle.
Originally the SINE, like other trigonometric functions, was not a ratio as it is today but a length associated with a circle, half the length of the chord drawn between the ends of two radii separated by twice the angle, or the length of a perpendicular dropped from one side of an angle to the other. More

fully, start with an angle at the center of a circle made between
two radii, two lines from the center of the circle and drawn out
cutting the edge. Starting at the point where the upper of these
two lines cuts the circle drop a line perpendicular to the other
line. The length of this up-and-down line was originally called

a Function of the angle A obtained by dividing
the length of side a by the length of side h.

FORM A. 20.	BO	NY	SUM	FORM AA. 20.	NY
tangent	2	4	6	tangent	15
SINE	13	27	40	SINE	75
cosine	3	3	6	cosine	22
cotangent	0	3	3	cotangent	6
secant	1	3	4	secant	13
unmarked	1	1	2	unmarked	1
total	20	41	61	total	132

the SINE. The radius of the circle was always unity; so that the
SINE divided by unity gave the same numerical value for the
SINE of an angle which is used today. The use of the SINE defined as half the chord dates back before Ptolemy to Hipparchus.

The word SINE goes back to the Latin *sinus*, a bend, curve,
fold, coil, the hanging fold of the upper part of the toga, used
to translate, really to describe, the Arabic word or symbol
for SINE, thought to look like the folds of a toga.

To the question: ' a Function of the angle A ob-

tained by dividing the length of side a by the length of side h',
75 persons out of 132 answer SINE, while 22 answer COSINE, and
15 TANGENT. The SINE was the first of the trigonometric functions to be discovered, and is today the most familiar, for it is
marked correctly by 57 per cent, compared with 14 who mark
COTANGENT correctly in a later item. This agrees with the finding that technical terms of the same type are familiar today in
proportion to their age; the older a technical term the larger
the percentage of persons who mark it correctly.

104. *CONSTANT* (kŏn'-stănt) *n*. In mathematics, a quantity invariable through a study, a value fixed while others change, a figure which under certain conditions does not alter. The word CONSTANT comes from the Latin *constans, constantis*, steady, firm, constant, the present participle of *constare*, to stand together, stand firm, endure, be established, settled. This is a combination of *com-*, together, and *stare*, to stand. The adjective CONSTANT means fixed, standing firm, persevering, stable, steady, immovable, unshaken, steadfast, and goes back at least to Ephraim Chambers, who says: 'CONSTANT quantity, in geometry, that which remains the same, while others increase or decrease'. The noun CONSTANT, used primarily in mathematics and physics, did not appear until nearly a hundred years later. A CONSTANT is something not subject to change, opposed to a VARIABLE, something which changes.

To the question: 'The figure ½ in the formula for the area of a triangle, h = ½ba', 231 persons out of 357 answer CONSTANT; while 35 answer BETA COEFFICIENT, and 28 FUNCTION. A FUNCTION is the expression of a variable which depends for its value

The figure ½ in the formula for the area of a triangle, h = ½ ba.

FORM B. 44.	NY	MISC.	SUM
variable	1	5	6
function	4	24	28
ABSOLUTE CONSTANT	35	196	231
beta coefficient	1	34	35
improper fraction	2	16	18
unmarked	5	34	39
total	48	309	357

upon another variable. The expression of a FUNCTION may contain a CONSTANT, but a FUNCTION is primarily a variable. Thus one speaks of one thing being the FUNCTION of another, meaning that it varies as the other varies. The area of a triangle is a FUNCTION of its base and altitude.

In physics, the word COEFFICIENT is used for a constant fixed for one substance, but which differs with other substances. In mathematics, a CONSTANT is a quantity which does not vary throughout an investigation, a quantity assumed to be invariable in some discussion. An ABSOLUTE CONSTANT remains the same under all conditions, as the value of π, the ratio of the diameter to the circumference of a circle, or ½ in the area of a triangle.

105. $\sqrt{}$ The *RADICAL* (răd'-ĭ-kl) sign; also called RADICAL.

Both Michael Stifel, a German mathematician, 1550, and Simon Stevin of Bruges, 1548 to 1620, used the RADICAL sign. Before that time ROOT had been indicated by the letter R. Stifel

$\sqrt{}$.

FORM C. 21.	CH	FORM CA. 11.	CH	LA	NY	NY	PH	SUM
square	24	square	7	4	33	76	15	135
irrational	4	irrational	0	1	2	10	1	14
power	1	power	4	2	3	11	3	23
RADICAL	38	RADICAL	28	26	56	169	53	332
exponential	1	exponential	0	4	3	9	1	17
unmarked	0	unmarked	1	0	0	2	1	4
total	68	total	40	37	97	277	74	525

also used the symbol + for addition, instead of the word PLUS or the letter p; and the symbol — for subtraction in place of the word MINUS or the letter m.

To the question: '$\sqrt{}$', 332 persons out of 525 answer correctly RADICAL; but 135 answer SQUARE. The SQUARE (12) of a

FORM CB. 12.	NY
square	18
irrational	1
power	4
RADICAL	63
inflection	0
unmarked	0
total	86

number is the number multiplied by itself. The SQUARE of 4 is 16. The SQUARE ROOT is a number which multiplied by itself gives the original number. The SQUARE ROOT of 4 is 2. In species the SQUARE of a is written a^2; the SQUARE ROOT of a is written $\sqrt{a}$.

It has been said by some that the RADICAL sign is a modified letter r, the initial letter of the Latin word *radix, radicis*, root. To designate the particular root, a number is written over the sign, 3 for cube root, $\sqrt[3]{a}$; 4 for fourth root, $\sqrt[4]{a}$. In the case of square root, the number 2 is usually omitted but understood; and this no doubt leads to the marking of the mislead SQUARE.

106. *WAVE-LENGTH* (*wāv'-lĕngth*) *n.* Distance from the crest of one wave to the crest of the next, or from the bottom of one wave to the bottom of the next, distance from any point on a wave to the corresponding point on the next.

The noun WAVE, in its modern sense, first appeared in the 16th century, about 1525, when it quickly replaced, by popular con-

Distance in wave motion between two points in the same phase.

FORM AB. 16.	NY	FORM D. 12.	NY	%
frequency	4	frequency	60	17.1
WAVE-LENGTH	78	WAVE-LENGTH	235	67.2
amplitude	9	amplitude	35	10.0
period	4	period	16	4.6
displacement	5	displacement	3	0.8
unmarked	0	unmarked	1	0.3
total	100	total	350	100.0

FORM DA. 5.	NY	FORM DB. 7.	NY
frequency	15	frequency	13
WAVE-LENGTH	69	WAVE-LENGTH	63
amplitude	3	amplitude	18
period	2	period	6
cycle	11	cycle	6
unmarked	0	unmarked	0
total	100	total	106

sent, an earlier WAW, which dates back to 1200 and Anglo-Saxon.

With the definition: 'Distance in wave motion between two points in the same phase', the popular mislead is FREQUENCY, marked by 12 per cent in one study, by 15 per cent in another, and by 17 per cent in a third. The confusing word in the definition may be PHASE; for the term WAVE-LENGTH seems easier than indicated by the number of persons who mark wrong answers; and the mislead FREQUENCY is easier, word 51 of this book. FREQUENCY is the number of waves per second which pass a given point. FREQUENCY is the reciprocal of WAVE-LENGTH. At a given speed, the longer the waves the fewer pass by. The shorter the waves the greater their frequency.

Joseph Fraunhofer, 1787 to 1826, was the first to measure WAVE-LENGTHS of light, obtaining the WAVE-LENGTH of the bright yellow sodium D line with extraordinary accuracy as 0.0005888 millimeters.

107. *VOLTMETER* (*vōlt'-mē-ter*) *n.* A commercial instrument for measuring difference in potential with a scale reading in volts.

In his article in the Encyclopaedia Britannica J. A. Fleming, originator of the Fleming valve, a two-electrode vacuum tube, says: 'VOLTMETER, an instrument for measuring difference of electric potential in terms of the unit called a VOLT. The VOLT is defined to be the difference of potential which acting between the terminals of a resistance of one ohm sends through it a continuous current of one ampere. A VOLTMETER is therefore one form of ELECTROMETER, but the term is generally employed to describe the instrument which indicates, on a scale, not merely in arbitrary units but directly in volts'.

A VOLTMETER is connected in parallel with that part of the circuit where the fall of potential is to be measured, and must have a high resistance.

To the question: 'An instrument which measures difference in potential', 68 per cent answer VOLTMETER, but 14 per cent answer AMMETER. In the same article on VOLTMETERS Fleming says: 'The instrument then becomes an AMMETER of high resistance, and may take any of the forms of practically used AMMETERS'. The scale of an AMMETER is marked in AMPERES; the scale of a VOLTMETER in VOLTS. An AMMETER indicates current flowing; a VOLTMETER indicates potential difference.

An AMMETER is inserted directly in the circuit (9), the full current going through the AMMETER; a VOLTMETER is connected across the circuit as a shunt (79). The resistance of the

AMMETER is very low so as not to disturb the current flowing in the circuit; the resistance of the VOLTMETER is very high so as to take almost no current through it from the circuit.

The usual type of AMMETER or VOLTMETER is essentially a D'Arsonval galvanometer whose coil is restored by a spring rather than by a twisted suspension. It is calibrated to read

An instrument to measure difference in potential.

FORM AB. 7.	NY	FORM D. 4.	NY	%
ammeter	8	ammeter	41	11.5
megger	0	ohmmeter	30	8.6
frequency meter	2	frequency meter	36	10.3
wattmeter	2	wattmeter	12	3.4
VOLTMETER	88	VOLTMETER	227	65.1
unmarked	0	unmarked	4	1.1
total	100	total	350	100.0

FORM DA. 8.	NY	FORM DB. 8.	NY
ammeter	14	ammeter	20
ohmmeter	9	ohmmeter	13
frequency meter	6	frequency meter	10
wattmeter	3	wattmeter	4
VOLTMETER	68	VOLTMETER	59
unmarked	0	unmarked	0
total	100	total	106

directly either the current which flows through it, or that current multiplied by the resistance of the instrument, that is its own fall of potential.

108. *RECIPROCAL* (rē-sǐp'-rō-kǎl) *n.* In mathematics, an inverse relation, a function or expression so related to another that their product is unity, the quotient obtained by dividing unity by any quantity. Reread INVERSE PROPORTION (46).

The RECIPROCAL of 3 is ⅓. The RECIPROCAL of a fraction is the fraction inverted. From the 3d edition of the Encyclopaedia, 1797, comes: 'Likewise 1/x is said to be the RECIPROCAL of x, which is again the RECIPROCAL of 1/x'.

The word RECIPROCAL comes from the Latin *reciprocus*, re-turning, alternating, a combination of *re-*, back, plus the adjective ending *-cus*, and *pro*, forward, plus again the adjective ending *-cus*. This derivation, back and forth, is clear for the word RECIPROCATING in machines, as: 'RECIPROCATING motion', meaning back and forth.

To the question: '1/n', 227 persons out of 357 answer RECIPROCAL OF N; while 33 answer TRANSPOSE; and 29 N-FACTORIAL. A FACTORIAL is a continued product, in which every factor is

$1/n.$

FORM B. 26.	NY	MISC.	SUM
n-factorial	6	23	29
RECIPROCAL OF N	39	188	227
transpose	0	33	33
radical	0	20	20
irrational	3	15	18
unmarked	0	30	30
total	48	309	357

derived from the preceding by increasing the variable by unity. FACTORIAL 3 is $1 \times 2 \times 3 = 6$. The RECIPROCAL of 3 is $\frac{1}{3}$. FACTORIAL 4 is $1 \times 2 \times 3 \times 4 = 24$; the RECIPROCAL of 4, $\frac{1}{4}$.

109. *CATHODE RAYS* (kăth'-ōd rāz). Stream of tiny negatively charged particles which shoot off from the cathode at right angles to its surface in a vacuum tube, rays of electrons which move with a velocity about one tenth that of light or 30,000 kilometers per second. Reread ELECTRON (98).

The word CATHODE was first used by Faraday in 1834 in his study of electrolysis, long before CATHODE RAYS were known. These were discovered, according to J. J. Thomson, by Plücker in 1859; though Rutherford says Varley noticed them first. They were not investigated in detail until Crookes and Hittorf. The fact that they are negatively charged particles was first successfully demonstrated in 1897 by J. J. Thomson who called them CORPUSCLES, literally small bodies, the diminutive of the Latin *corpus*, body.

Each CATHODE particle has a mass about 1/1840th that of the lightest atom, the hydrogen atom, and a negative electrical charge the same as a hydrogen ion in electrolysis. Read Sir J. J. Thomson's Conductivity of Electricity through Gases.

To the question: 'Stream of electrons set in rapid motion by an electric field', 70 per cent of students answer correctly CATHODE RAYS; but 17 per cent, nearly one in five, answer

Stream of rapidly moving particles set in motion by an electric field.

FORM AB. 28.	NY	FORM D. 22.	NY	%
CATHODE RAY	62	CATHODE RAY	149	42.6
X ray	30	X ray	109	31.2
gamma ray	2	gamma ray	24	6.8
beta ray	1	ultra-violet light	26	7.4
thermion	5	thermion	28	8.0
unmarked	0	unmarked	14	4.0
total	100	total	350	100.0

FORM DA. 27.	NY	FORM DB. 5.	NY
CATHODE RAY	70	CATHODE RAYS	32
X ray	17	X rays	11
gamma ray	4	gamma rays	40
ultra-violet light	3	ultra-violet light	12
thermion	3	Röntgen rays	11
unmarked	3	unmarked	0
total	100	total	106

X RAYS. X RAYS are not particles but an undulation which travels with the speed of light, a transverse wave motion, like light in almost every way except that X RAYS are of much shorter wave-length and for this reason penetrate matter.

CATHODE RAYS are not undulations or vibrations, but streams of particles which never move with the speed of light but with from one tenth to one third of its speed. Any object bombarded by CATHODE particles gives off X-RAY vibrations. An X-ray tube is designed to shoot electrons, CATHODE RAYS, from the cathode, the negative pole. These strike a small metal target, and this gives off X-RAY vibrations.

110. *BLACK BODY* (*blăk bŏ'-dē*). A theoretical body which
absorbs all of the radiation falling upon it and reflects
none, surface with 100 per cent absorptivity and zero re-
flectivity.

Black velvet or a surface coated with lamp black or bismuth
black is nearly an ideal BLACK BODY. A perfectly BLACK BODY
when illuminated would appear absolutely black and would be

Theoretical surface which absorbs all of the radiation falling
on it.

FORM BA. 9.	NY		FORM D. 11.	NY	%
perfect reflector	6		perfect reflector	17	4.9
BLACK BODY	80		BLACK BODY	277	79.1
transparent body	3		transparent body	10	2.9
white body	4		white body	12	3.4
translucent body	6		translucent body	30	8.6
unmarked	0		unmarked	4	1.1
total	100		total	350	100.0

FORM DA. 2.	NY		FORM DB. 4.	NY
perfect reflector	4		reflector	0
BLACK BODY	70		BLACK BODY	70
absorber	19		absorber	26
white body	2		mirror	1
translucent body	5		translucent body	8
unmarked	0		unmarked	1
total	100		total	106

invisible except for covering objects behind it. In addition such
a perfectly BLACK BODY would absorb all sorts of radiation, including heat waves and X rays as well as light.

Just as a BLACK BODY absorbs more radiation than other surfaces, so when heated it emits more. In 1879 the Austrian
physicist J. Stefan formulated a law connecting the heat radiated by a BLACK BODY with its absolute temperature; the heat
emitted is proportional to the fourth power of the BLACK BODY's
absolute temperature. The spectral energy distribution is given
by Wien's law in terms of temperature and the wave length of
the light emitted and by Planck's equation.

To the question: 'A theoretical body which absorbs all incident radiation', 70 per cent of students answer correctly BLACK BODY, but 19 per cent answer ABSORBER. Joseph Norman Lockyer, an English astronomer, used the word ABSORBER in connection with spectrum analysis: 'Let us study the effect of using sodium vapour as the medium—not as a source of light, but as an ABSORBER'. The verb to ABSORB comes from the Latin *absorbere*, to swallow, a combination of *ab*, away, and *sorbere*, to suck up; but the noun ABSORBER is rarely used technically, and when it appears refers to an actual and often partial absorber and not to a theoretical body. In the 1940 form DA, this mislead ABSORBER replaced TRANSPARENT BODY, used in the original 1929 form BA and retained in the 1934 form D.

For experimental purposes the nearest approach to a perfect BLACK BODY is a nearly completely enclosed cavity with only a single very small opening. Radiation which enters a tiny hole is almost entirely trapped by multiple reflection from the walls, so that the opening appears intensely black; while the radiation which escapes from such an enclosure when uniformly heated resembles perfect BLACK-BODY radiation.

111. *PARABOLA* (*pă-răb'-ō-lah*) *n.* One of the three conic sections between the more open hyperbola and the closed ellipse.

From John Harris, Lexicon Technicum, 1704, the first great technical dictionary, a quarter of a century before Ephraim Chambers' much larger Cyclopaedia of 1728 and half a century before Dr. Johnson's Dictionary of 1755, comes: 'PARABOLA, is a conic section arising from a Cone's being cut by a plane parallel to one of its Sides, or parallel to a plane that touches one Side of the Cone'.

To the question: 'The curve whose equation is: $y = ax^2 + b$', 317 persons out of 525 answer PARABOLA; 75 HYPERBOLA, the most frequently marked mislead; and 71 ELLIPSE. A CIRCLE, the least frequently marked mislead, arises when a cone is cut by a plane parallel to the base of the cone. An ELLIPSE arises when a cone is cut by a plane not parallel to the base but not tipped enough to be parallel to the side of the cone, a plane which still cuts both sides of the cone. The HYPERBOLA arises when a cone is cut by a plane tipped still more than the plane parallel to the side, tipped enough so that it cuts only one side of the cone. The formula for the HYPERBOLA is:

$$\frac{x^2}{a^2} - \frac{y^2}{b^2} = 1$$

Ephraim Chambers says: 'PARABOLA, in geometry, a figure ariſing from the ſection of a cone, when cut by a plane parallel to one of its ſides.

'From the ſame point of a cone, therefore, only one parabola can be drawn; all the other ſections within thoſe parallels being ellipſes; and all without them hyperbolas'.

The English PARABOLA, the French *parabole*, and the Spanish *parabola*, all come from the Greek παραβολή (parabola), a word invented by Apollonius of Perga, about the 3d century B.C.,

The curve whose equation is: $y = ax^2 + b$.

FORM C. 5.	CH	FORM CA. 16.	CH	LA	NY	NY	PH	SUM
PARABOLA	31	PARABOLA	21	25	60	157	54	317
hyperbola	18	hyperbola	6	4	16	38	11	75
ellipse	8	ellipse	6	5	10	45	5	71
circle	0	circle	1	1	8	12	1	23
logarithmic	10	logarithmic	6	1	3	22	1	33
unmarked	1	unmarked	0	1	0	3	2	6
total	68	total	40	37	97	277	74	525

FORM CB. 13.	NY
PARABOLA	45
hyperbola	20
ellipse	14
limacon	1
logarithmic	4
unmarked	2
total	86

and used in his work on the conic sections. This comes in turn from the verb παραβάλλειν (paraballein), to throw beside, a combination of παρά (para), beside, and βάλλειν (ballein), to throw. From the Greek verb βάλλειν (ballein), to throw, comes

BALLISTA, a machine for hurling stones, catapult, and from this the modern term BALLISTICS, the science of projectiles, study of missiles. Chambers says: 'Wolfius defines the PARABOLA to be a curve wherein ax = y^2, that is, the fquare of the femi-ordinate is equal to the rectangle of the abfciffe, and given a right line called the parameter of the axis, or latus rectum; whence its name from παραβάλλειν (paraballein), to equal'.

112. *PYTHAGORAS* (*pĭ-thăg'-ō-răs*). The theorem of PY-THAGORAS is that in a right-angled triangle the square of the hypotenuse (29) is equal to the sum of the squares on the other two sides.

To the question: 'Man accredited with having first stated the relationship between the squares of the two legs of a right triangle and the square of the hypotenuse', 98 persons out of 132, whose test scores have been tabulated for form AA, answer PYTHAGORAS; while 17 answer ARCHIMEDES and 11 EUCLID. AR-CHIMEDES' greatest contributions were to the field of geometry; but he is best known for his principle which states that a

Man accredited with having first stated the relationship be-tween the squares of the two legs of a right triangle and the square of the hypotenuse.

FORM A. 34.	BO	NY	SUM	FORM AA.	NY
Euclid	1	10	11	Euclid	11
Democritus	0	0	0	Thales	4
PYTHAGORUS	15	28	43	PYTHAGORUS	98
Archimedes	3	3	6	Archimedes	17
Anaxagorus	0	0	0	Anaxagorus	1
unmarked	1	0	1	unmarked	1
total	20	41	61	total	132

floating body is buoyed up by a force equal to the weight of the liquid it displaces. EUCLID taught at the University at Alex-andria in Egypt about 300 B.C. He is the author of the great textbook of geometry known as the Elements. PYTHAGORAS, who lived nearly three hundred years earlier, was born about 580 B.C. He is believed to have constructed the regular pen-tagon, and the five regular polyhedrons. He is also said to have known that six equilateral triangles can be placed about a point, as well as four squares, and three hexagons, and no other regular polygons. But he is best known by the theorem which always bears his name, that the area of a square on the hypotenuse of a right-angled triangle is the same as the sum of the areas of the squares on the other two sides. This relationship was known for special cases before PYTHAGORUS; but he is thought to have been the first to prove it, although the proof in most textbooks of geometry today is attributed to EUCLID.

113. *MANTISSA* (*măn-tĭs'-sah*) *n.* The decimal part of a logarithm, the figures in a logarithm which are to the right of the decimal point.
The Encyclopaedic Dictionary, started with Robert Hunter as editor but finished by the publisher Cassell because Hunter

The decimal part of a logarithm.

FORM B. 40.	NY	MISC.	SUM
MANTISSA	36	192	228
characteristic	7	40	47
antilog	1	19	20
e	0	6	6
log	1	18	19
unmarked	3	34	37
total	48	309	357

was slow, says: 'The logarithm of 900 being 2.95424, the part .95424 is the MANTISSA'.

The word MANTISSA was introduced by Henry Briggs, professor of geometry at Gresham College, London, 1596 to 1620, and Savilian professor of astronomy at Oxford, 1620 to 1631, and a friend of Napier until his death in 1617. MANTISSA applies only to Briggsian logarithms, where the MANTISSA is the same for any specific number no matter where its decimal point. Thus for the numbers 9, 90, and 900, the MANTISSA is the same. This is because the base of Briggsian or common logarithms is 10; they are exponents of the base 10. This is not true for the original Napierian logarithms, now called NATURAL logarithms, exponents of a base e, 2.71828...

The word MANTISSA comes from the Latin *mantissa*, originally a makeweight, a useless something put into a scale to add weight; and so an addition. The MANTISSA is so called as being additional to the characteristic or integral part. The word is said to be of Etruscan origin, from ancient Italy.

To the question: 'The decimal part of a logarithm', 228 persons out of 357 answer MANTISSA; and 47 CHARACTERISTIC. The CHARACTERISTIC of a common logarithm is the number in front of the decimal, the integer part of the logarithm, to the left of the decimal point. The CHARACTERISTIC is not shown in a logarithm table, but is always one less than the number of figures to the left of the decimal point in the original number. Only the MANTISSA, the decimal part of the logarithm, is looked up in a logarithm table.

114. *SLOT* (*slŏt*) *n*. An air passage near the leading edge of a wing to improve the airflow over the upper surface at high angles of attack, a passage in the nose of a wing back of the leading edge.

During a steep climb, with the wing at a sharp angle to the advancing airstream, the air is turbulent in the low-pressure

Form A. The nozzle-shaped passage through a wing whose primary object is to improve the flow conditions at high angles of attack.

Form AA. Air passage through a wing to improve air flow at high angles of attack.

FORM A. 25.	FW	LA	NY	NY	NY	PH	SUM	FORM AA. 20.	NY
spoiler	2	8	6	6	13	23	58	spoiler	9
sponson	0	2	1	5	6	16	30	sponson	0
float chamber	1	1	9	9	28	20	68	float chamber	9
SLOT	13	33	14	37	66	109	272	SLOT	26
frise aileron	2	10	5	4	25	25	71	frise aileron	19
unmarked	0	0	2	5	2	7	16	unmarked	0
total	18	54	37	66	140	200	515	total	63

region above the wing and opening a narrow SLOT toward the forward edge of the wing allows an airstream to pass through and does away with the turbulence.

There are two types of SLOTS, the fixed and the automatic. The fixed slot varies in its operation with the angle of attack. The automatic slot is formed by moving the nose portion of the wing forward. This movable auxiliary airfoil, called the SLAT, is attached to the leading edge of the wing. When the SLOT is closed the SLAT falls within the original contour of the main wing.

To the question: 'The nozzle-shaped passage through a wing whose primary object is to improve the flow conditions at high angles of attack', 272 persons out of 515 mark the correct answer, SLOT; 71 mark FRISE AILERON; 68, FLOAT CHAMBER; and 58 SPOILER. In its effect the SPOILER is the opposite of the SLOT. It is a small hinged plate projecting above the upper forward surface of the wing. By disturbing or spoiling the smooth airflow it increases the drag.

The FRISE AILERON is at the trailing edge of the wing; the SLOT, at the forward edge. Normally the lower surface of the FRISE AILERON is level with the lower surface of the wing and really a part of it. When the trailing edge of the aileron is raised the forward edge turns down below the lower surface of the wing and so creates drag. Like the SPOILER, the FRISE AILERON is opposite in effect to the SLOT.

115. *SHIELDING* (shēl'-dĭng) *n.* A metallic shell enclosing wiring or apparatus, an iron box around an object either to keep lines of force out of the air space inside or to keep lines of force from escaping out of the box.

Lines of force flow through iron in preference to air. Therefore, by enclosing an air space in an iron box, lines of force flow through the iron around the air space instead of going through the air space inside. This protects a measuring instrument inside the box from outside influences.

The word SHIELD goes back to the Anglo-Saxon word for SHIELD, carried on the arm of a warrior for protection in battle.

To the question: 'Construction which reduces coupling by circuits near each other', 161 persons out of 224 answer SHIELDING, while 28 answer TWO-CONDUCTOR LINE. The word COUPLING is too difficult to appear in the question, especially as the same word occurs as one of the five choices.

Magnetic and electrostatic fields can be confined to restricted spaces, or can be prevented from entering a particular space, by suitable shields. Stray electrostatic lines of force are short circuited by the conducting material and grounded. When a magnetic field passes through a shield an electromotive force is induced and a current flows in the shield. Magnetic flux, penetrating a conducting material, produces eddy currents

Construction which reduces coupling by circuits near each other.

FORM A. 12.	NY	NY	NY	SUM
two-conductor line	6	9	13	28
tube	2	1	12	15
SHIELDING	25	26	110	161
chassis	4	0	5	9
coupling	0	4	7	11
unmarked	0	0	0	0
total	37	40	147	224

which oppose further penetration. Magnetic fields at radio frequencies are best controlled by such good conductors as copper and aluminum. Such shields must completely enclose the space; and the joints should overlap and be soldered to minimize resistance to eddy currents. Also the thickness should be several times the skin depth of the current.

The thicker the shell the better the shielding. In aircraft, generators, magnetos, and motors have their own metallic frames which enclose them, except for points where leads are brought out and inspection holes are provided for servicing and changing brushes. These break the shielding. Covers should be secured with good contact and the contact surfaces kept clean, for a metal cover making a poor metallic contact allows leakage, causing a disturbing radio-interference field.

116. *INERTIA* (*ĭ-nĕr′-shah*) *n.* The tendency to resist a change in velocity, continuance without change.
Johann Kepler introduced the term INERTIA into physics; and Isaac Newton, born in 1642, twelve years after Kepler's death, used the Latin word *inertia* in his Principia: 'Materiae vis insita

est potentia resistendi neque differt quicquam ab INERTIA Massae'. Edward Phillips, in his New World of Words, a dictionary of difficult terms, defines INERTITUDE in 1678; but not until the 1706 edition does INERTIA appear: '*Vis insita Materiae* or *Vis Inertiae*, is the bare Power of Resistance only, by which every Body endeavours to continue in that State in which it is, either of Rest or Motion'.

The noun INERTIA parallels the adjective INERT, lifeless, without force, having no power to act. INERT comes from the Latin *in*, not, without, and *ars, artis*, art, and by derivation means without art, unskilled. Today the adjective INERT is used in literature to mean lifeless, inactive, lazy, indolent, as: 'An INERT

The tendency to resist a change of velocity.

FORM C. 8.	NY	FORM CA. 9.	BO	NY HIGH	NY NEXT	NY REST	NY MISC.	SUM
rigidity	9	rigidity	2	0	8	136	11	157
friction	49	friction	8	17	45	198	42	310
weight	3	mass	2	0	5	90	1	98
INERTIA	301	INERTIA	79	380	330	503	170	1462
retardation	38	retardation	8	3	12	173	10	206
unmarked	0	unmarked	1	0	0	0	0	1
total	400	total	100	400	400	1100	234	2234

mass'. In literature INERTIA implies a disinclination to act, sluggishness, slothfulness, lifelessness, laziness. In physics the word designates the property of matter which causes a stationary body to remain stationary, or a moving body to continue moving without change of direction or velocity unless acted upon by some external force.

The termination -IA is the nominative ending of both Greek and Latin feminine nouns of the first declension. Usually this -*ia* changes in English to Y, the Latin *injuria*, wrong, harm, injury, becoming in English INJURY. But occasionally the English noun retains the Latin ending. The English MILITIA, body of soldiers, soldiery, is the Latin word *militia*, unchanged in form or meaning. The English MANIA, madness, excitement, insanity, is the Latin *mania*, madness, frenzy, which in turn comes directly from the Greek μανία (mania), madness.

To the question: 'The tendency to resist a change of velocity', 65 per cent answer INERTIA; while 14 per cent answer FRICTION, and another 9 per cent RETARDATION. In the earlier study of form C of the physics vocabulary test, based on 400 persons, 75 per cent answered INERTIA; 12 per cent FRICTION, and 10 per cent RETARDATION. RETARDATION is the general term for the slowing down of something already in motion, the process of delaying. RETARDATION is the opposite of ACCELERATION. It is the noun formed from the verb RETARD. In literature to RETARD is to slow down, delay, impede, hinder, make slower. The word is used specifically of slowing down something already moving. INERTIA is in effect the opposite of RETARDATION, for while INERTIA keeps a stationary body from moving, once the body is set in motion INERTIA makes it continue to move without slowing down.

FRICTION (54) is a rubbing against something. This rubbing causes RETARDATION. FRICTION always tends to bring a body to rest, to reduce velocity to zero. If a body is at rest both FRICTION and INERTIA resist any attempt to move it. If, however, a body is in motion, FRICTION tends to slow it down and ultimately to bring it to rest; whereas INERTIA makes it continue to move in the same direction at the same velocity. INERTIA is that inherent property of matter by which it tends to resist change.

117. *SPEED* (*spēd*) *n.* Distance per unit time, velocity, miles per hour, feet per second, centimeters per second. Reread SPEED OF LIGHT (19).

The word SPEED comes from Anglo-Saxon and originally meant success, wealth, riches. To wish a man good SPEED is to wish him success. But this meaning has almost disappeared; and SPEED today means rate of moving, rapidity of progress.

To the question: 'Distance per unit time', 64 per cent answer SPEED; but 15 per cent answer ACCELERATION. In the earlier study, based on 400 persons, 73 per cent answered SPEED; and 16 per cent ACCELERATION. SPEED is the simpler concept. Assuming no change of SPEED during a given period, speed equals distance traveled, designated in any linear unit, divided by the time consumed. A SPEEDOMETER indicates SPEED, shows how fast an automobile is moving.

ACCELERATION is from the Latin *ad*, to, and the verb *celerare*, to hasten. This comes in turn from the Latin adjective *celer*, quick, the source of the English noun CELERITY (*sĕ-lĕ'-rĭ-tē*),

Distance per unit time.

FORM C. 40.	NY	FORM CA. 11.	BO	NY HIGH	NY NEXT	NY REST	NY MISC.	SUM
displacement	5	momentum	3	9	13	148	8	181
motion	16	motion	1	4	9	110	11	135
acceleration	63	acceleration	6	18	56	212	37	329
SPEED	293	SPEED	83	368	314	495	171	1431
feet	6	feet	6	1	8	135	7	157
unmarked	17	unmarked	1	0	0	0	0	1
total	400	total	100	400	400	1100	234	2234

quickness, swiftness, rapidity, speed, a literary word, not scientific. To ACCELERATE (*ăk-sĕl'-ĕ-rāt*) is to hasten, make quicker, cause to move faster. In physics ACCELERATION is rate of change of SPEED. If the ACCELERATION be constant:

$$\text{ACCELERATION} = \frac{\text{FINAL SPEED} - \text{INITIAL SPEED}}{\text{TIME}}.$$

One speaks of an acceleration of 5 feet per second in one second, or of 5 feet per second per second, sometimes written as:

$$5 \frac{\text{ft}}{\text{sec}^2}.$$

SPEED and VELOCITY are practically synonymous. Wherever textbooks differentiate, VELOCITY specifies not only SPEED, not only how fast, but also direction. VELOCITY is both rate of motion and the direction of that motion. SPEED is merely rate of motion. The formula for SPEED is:

$$\text{SPEED} = \frac{\text{DISTANCE}}{\text{TIME}}.$$

SPEED as applied to an automobile, train, or airplane, is expressed in miles per hour; SPEED as applied to a boat is KNOTS, a unit of speed, one nautical mile per hour. SPEED in physics is usually feet per second or centimeters per second.

118. *COMMUTATOR RIPPLE* (kŏm'-mū-tā-tor rĭp'-pl).
Slight fluctuations in the direct current from a generator.
Reread GENERATOR (2).

As a single coil of wire rotates in a magnetic field there is an
instant when the plane of the coil is at right angles to the magnetic field, when the wires of the coil move parallel to the
magnetic lines and so cut no lines. At this point no current is

Traces of pulsation in a direct-current generator.

FORM E. 41.	BO	FW	LA	NY	NY	NY	NY	PH	TU	SUM
compressibility	1	2	1	2	0	1	4	4	4	19
constrained motion	3	6	1	1	0	1	13	2	1	28
damping	1	3	2	2	2	3	17	8	0	38
drag	3	5	1	5	2	4	22	3	1	46
COMMUTATOR										
RIPPLE	17	32	28	10	16	28	158	82	22	393
unmarked	3	2	0	0	0	3	4	1	0	13
total	28	50	33	20	20	40	218	100	28	537

produced in the coil. A quarter of a turn later the rotating coil
cuts the largest number of magnetic lines. Another quarter of a
turn further on the single rotating coil again cuts no magnetic
lines and the generated current is again zero.

With two coils at right angles, rotating on the same axis, the
maximum current from one coincides with the zero current

FORM E. 41.	ENGLISH VOCABULARY	
	HIGH	LOW
compressibility	1	3
constrained motion	2	3
damping	2	2
drag	0	7
COMMUTATOR RIPPLE	34	25
unmarked	0	0
total	39	40

from the other. In this instance the current never drops to zero
but still fluctuates widely. If the number of coils be further
increased the maximum current from each can be made to

coincide with the lowest current from the others. The function of the COMMUTATOR is to pick current from one coil after another, each at the right moment; for the word COMMUTATOR comes from the Latin *commutare*, to change, also exchange, a combination of *com-*, which in this case intensifies the meaning, and *mutare*, to change. From *mutare* come MUTABLE, changeable, capable of being altered, and MUTATION, a word used in biology for a sudden change.

With any finite number of coils rotating on the same axis in a magnetic field, the current from each drops slightly before it is cut off by the commutator and taken up from the next coil. This causes a slight up and down in electromotive force as the current shifts from each successive coil to the next as the armature turns. The series of maxima do not hold the current at a steady maximum. This up and down in the electromotive force is called the COMMUTATOR RIPPLE.

To the question: 'Traces of pulsation in a direct-current generator', 393 out of 537 answer correctly COMMUTATOR RIPPLE, with the others scattering.

119. *MEAN FREE PATH* (*mēn frē păth*). The average distance which each molecule of a gas travels before it hits another in the process of thermal agitation.
According to the kinetic theory the molecules of a gas dart

Average distance particles of a gas travel between collisions.

FORM E. 42.	BO	FW	LA	NY	NY	NY	NY	PH	TU	SUM
MEAN-FREE-PATH	18	28	27	10	15	20	132	73	22	345
fundamental-vibration	3	1	2	2	3	3	28	7	0	49
integral-invariants	2	7	0	2	0	6	19	10	3	49
orbit	1	7	2	5	2	4	29	8	2	60
least-action	1	6	2	1	0	3	6	1	1	21
unmarked	3	1	0	0	0	4	4	1	0	13
total	28	50	33	20	20	40	218	100	28	537

about in all directions with speeds which exceed those of rifle bullets, 1 to 7 miles per second where the speed of a rifle bullet may be as low as half a mile a second. The impact of these molecules against the walls of the containing vessel causes pressure which can be measured in the laboratory.

In a solid the MEAN FREE PATH is short, the molecules resembling, physicists say, people in a densely packed crowd, each molecule restricted by others near it. In a liquid the MEAN

FORM E. 42.   ENGLISH VOCABULARY

	HIGH	LOW
MEAN-FREE-PATH	36	18
fundamental-vibration	2	2
integral-invariants	0	10
orbit	0	6
least-action	2	4
unmarked	0	0
total	40	40

FREE PATH is longer, the molecules wandering through the entire mass, according to Robeson in his Physics, like dancers in a crowded ballroom.

On the assumption that in water, a liquid, the molecules are tightly packed, it is possible to compute their freedom of motion in steam, the corresponding gas which, at the same temperature and pressure, is some 1240 times the volume of water. According to Maxwell the MEAN FREE PATH of a molecule of a gas is about 1000 Ångström units. This is several hundred molecule diameters. In tenth-meters, that is one 10,000,000,000th or 10^{-10} part of a meter, the MEAN FREE PATH as given by Maxwell is:

hydrogen	965
oxygen	560
carbon monoxide	482
carbon dioxide	379

To the question: 'Average distance particles of a gas travel between collisions', 345 persons out of 537 answer MEAN FREE PATH, the others scattering almost evenly among the four misleads. In the small separate study of 40 persons high in English vocabulary, scoring above 206 on the general scale, compared with 40 persons low in English vocabulary, scoring below 114 on the general scale, 10 of the latter, 25 per cent, choose INTEGRAL INVARIANTS. One dictionary defines an INVARIANT as a function of the coefficients of a quantic such that, if the quantic is linearly transformed, the same function of the new coefficients is equal to the first function multiplied by some power of the modulus of transformation, a definition difficult enough for anyone to understand, and quite impossible for one who scores low in English vocabulary. John Buchan, who later became Lord Tweedsmuir, quotes Lord Rutherford as saying that no conclusion which he had ever reached was of any use to him until he could put it into plain English, into language understood by the ordinary man.

Just as the kinetic theory, by starting with the assumption of random moving molecules, arrives at the MEAN FREE PATH of different types of molecules under different conditions, so the Human Engineering Laboratory believes that it can start with a sufficient number of individually moving human beings and arrive at general laws for different types of persons under different conditions.

120. *COSINE* (kō'-sīn) *n*. The base of a right-angled triangle divided by the hypotenuse, half the chord of double the complement of the arc of a circle. Reread SINE (103).
The first syllable, CO-, in the word COSINE, stands for complement. The COSINE of an angle is the SINE of the complement of the angle, that is the SINE of 90 degrees minus the angle. In a right triangle, the two acute angles are complementary, add to ninety degrees. The base divided by the hypotenuse is the SINE of the top angle. Although the Oxford New English Dictionary says that the Latin *cosecans* was used by George Joachim, called Rheticusa, a German astronomer, in his great treatise Opus Palatinum de Triangulis, published as early as 1596, the words COSINE and COTANGENT, for the SINE and TANGENT of the complementary angle, seem not to have been used until 1620 by an English mathematician, Edmund Gunter. Of Welsh extraction, Gunter started as a preacher, but in 1619, at the age of 38, became professor of astronomy in London. In 1620 he published his Canon Triangulorum, a table of logarith-

mic sines and tangents, to 7 decimal places, for every degree and minute of the quadrant.

To the question: ' Function of the angle A obtained by dividing the length of line b by the length of line h', 217 persons out of 357 answer correctly COSINE; but 39 answer SINE. The word SINE comes from the Latin *sinus*. This is a translation of an earlier Arabic word which even then was used in geometry. The SINE is perhaps the easiest of these trigonometric functions to remember. Chambers defines the SINE,

Function of the angle A obtained by dividing the length of line b by the length of line h.

FORM B. 23.	NY	MISC.	SUM
sine	8	31	39
COSINE	32	185	217
cosecant	2	19	21
tangent	5	36	41
coversine	1	12	13
unmarked	0	26	26
total	48	309	357

which was in those days more often called the RIGHT SINE, as: 'A right line drawn from one extremity of an arch, perpendicular to the radius drawn from the other extremity: or, the SINE is half the chord of twice the arch'; for the trigonometric functions were in those days lengths of lines defined in such a way that the radius of the circle by which they might be divided was unity.

Starting with an angle at the center of a circle, which intercepts or embraces an arc of the circle, double the arc, draw the chord from one end of this doubled arc to the other, and half this chord is the SINE of the angle. The COSINE is then the SINE of the complement of this angle; or it is half the chord drawn perpendicular to the other chord, half the chord of twice the complement to the first arc.

121. *TRIANGULATION* (*trī-ăng-gū-lā'-shŏn*) *n*. Measuring
the angles of a net-work of triangles laid out from a base-
line the length of which has been accurately measured.
From the Imperial Dictionary, first edition, 1850, comes:
'TRIANGULATION, the net-work of triangles with which the
face of a country is covered in a trigonometrical survey'. The
Imperial Dictionary, edited by John Ogilvie (*ō'-gl-vē*) and

Measurement of distance by trigonometric functions.

FORM C. 31.	CH	FORM CA. 18.	CH	LA	NY	NY	PH	SUM
vector analysis	6	vector analysis	7	3	10	30	9	59
orientation	2	orientation	4	3	4	15	3	29
TRIANGULATION	47	TRIANGULATION	21	24	60	181	46	332
Cartesian		Cartesian						
coordinates	6	coordinates	3	0	5	34	2	44
quadration								
method	7	polar coordinates	5	6	18	11	10	50
unmarked	0	unmarked	0	1	0	6	4	11
total	68	total	40	37	97	277	74	525

FORM CB. 16.	NY
vector analysis	13
orientation	5
TRIANGULATION	37
topography	17
polar coordinates	13
unmarked	1
total	86

published in Scotland, states on its title page that it is based on
Webster's Dictionary first published in America in 1828. The
Century Dictionary, also American, states in its introduction
that it in turn is based on Ogilvie. The order of these great
dictionaries is therefore: Webster, 1828; Imperial, 1850; and
Century, 1891. The original Noah Webster dictionary was
bound in two volumes; the Imperial in two volumes of the same
size, with a third thinner volume of plates. The second edition
of the Imperial was rebound in four volumes. The Century was
six heavy volumes, with cuts throughout the text.

The noun TRIANGULATION is the verb to TRIANGULATE plus the ending -ION. TRIANGULATE, to divide into triangles, comes in turn from the Latin *tres*, *tri*-, three, and *angulus*, angle. The ending -ION is a common Latin suffix added to form usually abstract feminine nouns from verbs, as: *opinion* from the Latin *opinare*, the source of the English OPINION and the verb to OPINE, to think.

The Oxford New English Dictionary says that the Latin noun *triangulation* was used by Peter Abelard, the notable French scholar who lived from 1079 to 1142. But the application of the word to surveying comes much later. Blackwood's Edinburgh Magazine, founded in 1817, says: 'The English TRIANGULATION, begun by General Roy'. William Roy, 1726 to 1790, was a British surveyor, born in Scotland, who measured the distance between the Greenwich and Paris observatories.

To the question: 'Measurement of distance by trigonometric functions', 332 persons out of 525 answer correctly TRIANGULATION; but 50 answer POLAR COORDINATES, and 59 VECTOR ANALYSIS. POLAR COORDINATES, VECTOR ANALYSIS, and TRIANGULATION, all deal with directions and distances. In POLAR COORDINATES the position of a point is placed by knowing its distance from the origin and its direction. In TRIANGULATION the distance of a point is found by knowing the length of a base line and the direction of the point from each end of the base. A VECTOR is a line of known length and direction. In physics VECTOR ANALYSIS is used in combining two or more forces where their directions and magnitudes are known. In TRIANGULATION the length of a base line is carefully measured; and the essence of TRIANGULATION is measuring the length of only this one line and determining distances by measuring the angles or directions of lines from the ends of this line and so being able to compute the distance of the point at which these two lines cross.

TRIANGULATION and the corresponding verb to TRIANGULATE are surveying terms. From 1826 comes: 'Slieve Snaght, the highest hill of Innishowen, forms an important point in the TRIANGULATION, which connects the North of Ireland with the western islands of Scotland'. In The Geology and Geography of Great Briton, 1863, Sir Andrew C. Ramsay mentions: 'The TRIANGULATION of Scotland for the Ordinance Survey'.

122. *NACELLE* (*nă-sĕl'*) *n.* An enclosed shelter for personnel or for a power plant.

The Oxford New English Dictionary calls NACELLE obsolete and rare in 1890, and gives only one quotation from the Golden Legend, a collection of the lives of the saints, printed by William Caxton in 1483: 'The quene of thys countree wente for to playe on the ryuage of the see and byheld thys lytyl nacelle and the chyld therein'. Here NACELLE means a small boat. The word NACELLE comes directly from the French *nacelle*, and this from the Latin *naucella*, the diminutive of *navis*, ship.

To the question: 'An enclosed shelter for personnel or for a power plant', 273 persons out of 515 answer NACELLE, while 90 answer COCKPIT and another 84 CABIN. Among the 18 tested in Fort Worth, Texas, 14 or 78 per cent answer NACELLE, perhaps because of the local aircraft industry; while in New York

An enclosed shelter for personnel or for a power plant.

FORM A. 24.	FW	LA	NY	NY	NY	PH	SUM	FORM AA. 17.	NY
engine mount	0	1	1	0	3	1	6	cowling	9
hull	1	8	2	8	15	18	52	hull	7
cabin	1	4	6	14	28	31	84	cabin	11
NACELLE	14	33	20	36	60	110	273	NACELLE	14
cockpit	2	7	7	5	34	35	90	cockpit	20
unmarked	0	1	1	3	0	5	10	unmarked	2
total	18	54	37	66	140	200	515	total	63

less than half, 42 per cent, answer correctly. The COCKPIT is a space in the body of an airplane usually for the pilots, or in a small plane for the pilots and passengers. When completely enclosed it is called a CABIN.

In aviation the word NACELLE was first used for the basket suspended from a balloon. Today the word usually refers to the engine NACELLE. In a single-engine airplane there is no NACELLE, the engine being mounted in the fuselage. In a multi-engine airplane there may be a NACELLE built as a separate unit for each engine or built as a part of the primary structure. ENGINE MOUNT, the least frequently marked mislead, is surprisingly close to the right answer when the word NACELLE is used to mean ENGINE NACELLE.

123. *DIODE* (*dī'-ōd*). The simplest radio tube with a cathode and anode and without a grid, a two electrode tube, the basic two-element vacuum tube containing an emitter of electrons, the cathode, and a collector of electrons termed either anode or plate. Reread CATHODE RAYS (109).

The elements are the FILAMENT, the source of electrons, and the PLATE, the metallic element to which the electrons are attracted.

As the word ANODE is a combination of the Greek ἀνά (ana), up, and ὁδός (odos), way, and CATHODE a combination of the Greek κατά (kata), down, and the same ὁδός (odos), way, so DIODE is a combination of the Greek δι- (di-), which stands for δίς (dis), twice, and the same ὁδός (odos), way.

To the question: 'The basic tube', 143 persons out of 224 answer correctly DIODE, while 33 answer ELECTRON. In one sense

The basic tube.

FORM A. 30.	NY	NY	NY	SUM
electron	5	6	22	33
DIODE	22	23	98	143
prong	3	3	5	11
triode	1	4	14	19
pentode	2	4	7	13
unmarked	4	0	1	5
total	37	40	147	224

all such tubes are electronic, but those who know the word DIODE seem to mark it in answer to this question.

Lee de Forest, an American inventor, added a third electrode, the GRID, making a TRIODE, a DIODE with a GRID between the cathode or filament and the anode or plate. The TRIODE is often described under the general heading of Basic Tube Types, and so may justly be called a basic tube. But with the present simple wording of the question fewer persons mark TRIODE than ELECTRON. As many as fifteen to twenty thousand DIODES and TRIODES may be used in an electronic computer.

In a DIODE tube the cathode, the source of electrons, may be a filament or may be indirectly heated. For a given cathode temperature, the current from the cathode to the anode increases at first as the 3/2 power of the plate voltage. With further increase in voltage, all electrons emitted by the cathode go to the anode or plate. At this point still further increase in voltage produces no further increase in current.

The possibility of using such a tube as a rectifier was recognized by J. A. Fleming in London in 1904. Electrons flow from the hot filament to the plate, but not in the opposite direction; for the plate attracts only when positively charged with respect to the filament. Rectifying DIODES are used for rectifying alternating current for charging storage batteries. The charging unit receives alternating current from the line and delivers pulsating direct current.

124. *DELIQUESCENCE* (dĕl-ĭ-kwĕs'-sĕns) *n*. Liquefaction by absorption of moisture from the atmosphere, the property of removing water vapor from the air under ordinary conditions.

Henry Watts, in his Dictionary of Chemistry of 1864, defines DELIQUESCENCE: 'The property which certain very soluble salts and other bodies possess of absorbing moisture from the atmosphere and dissolving therein'. From James Smith, Dictionary of Arts, Sciences, and Manufactures, published in Bos-

Act of becoming liquid gradually by absorbing moisture from the air.

FORM E. 43.	BO	FW	LA	NY	NY	NY	NY	PH	TU	SUM
efflorescence	6	7	5	4	2	7	35	9	6	81
effervescence	5	7	3	1	2	3	30	11	3	65
DELIQUESCENCE	14	31	25	13	16	26	144	78	17	364
fluorescence	0	2	0	0	0	0	1	0	1	4
phosphorescence	0	3	0	2	0	1	5	1	1	13
unmarked	3	0	0	0	0	3	3	1	0	10
total	28	50	33	20	20	40	218	100	28	537

ton in 1854, comes: 'DELIQUESCENCE, the state of a salt which becomes fluid by its absorption of moisture from the atmosphere'. As early as 1704 John Harris wrote in his Lexicon Technicum: 'DELIQUIUM: *Chymicum*, is either a distillation by the force of Fire; or a melting of the Calx, which is suspended in moist cellars, and a Resolution of it into a Lixivious Humour; thus when Salt of Tartar, or any such fix'd Alkali is set in a Cellar or some such cool place in an open Vessel, it will run into a kind of water; which the Chymists call *Oil of Tartar per Deliquium*'. Sulphuric acid, chloride of calcium, and quicklime, all DELIQUESCE.

DELIQUESCENCE and the corresponding verb to DELIQUESCE come from the Latin *deliquescere*, to melt away, dissolve. This in turn is a combination of *de*, down, and *liquescere*, to become liquid, the inceptive of *liquere*, to melt. The ending -ESCE, added to verbs of Latin origin, called INCEPTIVE, inchoative,

FORM E. 43.   ENGLISH VOCABULARY

	HIGH	LOW
efflorescence	2	4
effervescence	0	12
DELIQUESCENCE	38	20
fluorescence	0	1
phosphorescence	0	1
unmarked	0	2
total	40	40

usually suggests beginning to be, coming into existence. The corresponding adjectives end in -ESCENT and the nouns in -ESCENCE. FLUORESCENCE (65) and PHOSPHORESCENCE are lights so faint that they seem to be just beginning or coming into existence.

To the question: 'Act of becoming liquid gradually by absorbing moisture from the air', 364 persons out of 537 answer DELIQUESCENCE; but 81 answer EFFLORESCENCE, and 65 EFFERVESCENCE. EFFERVESCENCE (*ĕf-fer-vĕs'-sĕns*), from the Latin *fervere*, to boil, is by derivation the beginning of boiling. The word is used today for the bubbling, hissing, foaming, of carbonated water. EFFLORESCENCE (*ĕf-flor-ĕs'-sĕns*) is the process of losing water of crystallization. Crystals of neutral carbonate of sodium, $Na_2CO_3 \cdot 10H_2O$, exposed to dry air lose their water of crystallization and crumble to a white power. EFFLORESCENCE, loss of water of crystallization, is almost an opposite of DELIQUESCENCE, the absorption of water.

125. *ISOTHERMAL* (ī-sō-ther'-măl) *adj*. Characterized by no change in temperature, at the same temperature throughout an operation. An ISOTHERMAL process takes place at one temperature.

The word ISOTHERMAL was first used by Alexander von Humboldt. In his book Cosmos he says: 'Our insight into the distribution of heat in the atmosphere has been rendered more clear since the attempt has been made to connect together by lines those places where the mean annual summer and winter temperatures have been ascertained by correct observations.

A constant temperature process.

FORM C. 9.	NY	FORM CA. 7.	BO	NY HIGH	NY NEXT	NY REST	NY MISC.	SUM
isometric	17	isometric	2	8	23	158	20	211
adiabatic	26	adiabatic	8	30	15	124	12	189
isobaric	15	isotherm	8	46	50	172	33	309
isodynamic	12	isodynamic	3	3	12	111	5	134
ISOTHERMAL	326	ISOTHERMAL	79	313	300	535	162	1389
unmarked	4	unmarked	0	0	0	0	2	2
total	400	total	100	400	400	1100	234	2234

The system of ISOTHERMAL, ISOTHERAL (ī-sō-thē'-răl), and ISO-CHIMENAL (ī-sō-kī'-mē-năl) lines, which I first brought into use in 1817 . . .' An ISOTHERAL line joins places on the earth's surface which have the same mean summer temperature; ISO-CHIMENAL, the same mean winter temperature. An ISOTHERMAL line joins places with the same mean annual temperature.

To the question: 'A constant temperature process', 62 per cent of 2234 persons answer ISOTHERMAL; but 14 per cent select ISOTHERM, the new mislead added in form CA. An ISOTHERM, as that word is used in meteorology, is a line drawn on a map through places with the same temperature. ISOTHERM is also the noun which corresponds to the adjective ISOTHERMAL, the correct answer. The difference between the two is syntax, not physics. ISOTHERM should probably not have been used originally and has been removed.

In the previous form C, where the statistics were based on 400 persons, ADIABATIC was the most frequently marked. The words ISOTHERMAL and ADIABATIC (*ăd-ĭ-ă-băt'-ĭk*) are both of Greek origin and both apply to the expansion and contraction of gases. An ADIABATIC process takes place without transference to the surrounding medium of either cold or the heat which is generated. Since in practice complete isolation is virtually impossible to achieve and maintain, most actual ADIABATIC changes go rapidly before the heat and cold developed has opportunity to escape. As the generated heat is not dissipated, an ADIABATIC process occurs at a constantly changing temperature. In this sense ADIABATIC is nearly the opposite of ISOTHERMAL.

The word ISOTHERMAL commences with the Greek ἴσος (isos), equal, alike, already met in ISOSCELES (34), having two legs the same. The adjective THERMAL comes from the Greek θέρμη (therme), heat, already met in THERMODYNAMICS (27), the dynamics of heat. THERMAL means pertaining to heat, characterized by heat. ISOTHERMAL means characterized by equal heat, without change in heat. Since an expanding gas cools and a contracting gas grows hotter, no process is ever perfectly ISOTHERMAL. But a change which occurs in a surrounding medium of uniform temperature and slowly enough so that heat can be absorbed or given off during contraction approaches the ISOTHERMAL and takes place at practically an unchanging temperature.

126. *WATT* (*wŏt*) *n.* Unit of electric power, one joule of work per second, 1/746th of a horsepower, a current of one ampere multiplied by an electromotive force of one volt. Reread HORSEPOWER (77).

A manufacturer and the inventor of the condensing steam engine, James Watt, for whom the WATT is named, hoisted 150 pounds straight up out of a coal pit with a strong dray horse at a rate of 220 feet in one minute. Multiplying weight lifted by the distance, Watt obtained 33,000 foot-pounds of work done in one minute. This he called one HORSEPOWER.

In 1882, sixty-three years after Watt's death in 1819, Sir William Siemens, in his presidential address to the British Association, said: 'The other unit I would suggest adding to the list is that of power. The power conveyed by a current of an Ampere through the difference of potential of a Volt is the unit consistent with the practical system. It might be appropriately called a WATT, in honor of James Watt. A WATT, then, expresses the rate of an Ampere multiplied by a Volt, whilst a horsepower is 746 WATTS, and a *Cheval de Vapeur* 735'.

Five years later, in 1887, in the reports of the same British Association: 'The WATT is defined to be the work done per

Volts ✕ amperes.

FORM AB. 31.	NY	FORM D. 27.	NY	%
coulombs	7	coulombs	54	15.4
ohms	3	ohms	35	10.0
WATTS	60	WATTS	165	47.2
oersteds	13	oersteds	25	7.1
watt-seconds	17	watt-seconds	63	18.0
unmarked	0	unmarked	8	2.3
total	100	total	350	100.0

FORM DA. 25.	NY	FORM DB. 13.	NY
coulombs	13	coulombs	2
ohms	8	ohms	25
WATTS	59	WATTS	69
oersteds	3	joules	5
watt-seconds	14	watt-seconds	3
unmarked	3	unmarked	2
total	100	total	106

second by the ampere passing between two points between which the difference of electrical potential is one volt'.

To the question: 'Volts ✕ amperes', 59 per cent of those who took form DA answer correctly WATTS; but 14 per cent answer WATT-SECONDS. This is a confusion of POWER and WORK. The WATT is electric POWER, as in mechanics the HORSEPOWER is mechanical POWER. The WATT is the work which electricity does per unit time. In mechanics, in the form of an equation:

$$POWER = \frac{WORK}{TIME}, \text{ or}$$

$$POWER \times TIME = WORK.$$

In electricity, the WATT-SECOND, or more frequently the WATT-HOUR, that is the WATT, the unit of POWER, multiplied by the time, expresses the amount of electrical work done. A WATT-HOUR meter, installed in each house by a public service or electric company, integrates and registers the WATTS per second multiplied by the number of seconds, recording the amount of work which the electricity has done for the householder. The WATTHOUR or WATT-SECOND is a unit of work; the WATT, a unit of power.

To the same question: 'Volts $\times$ amperes', another 13 per cent of students answer COULOMB. In mechanics, work equals force times the distance through which the force operates. Thus the equation for power can be rewritten:

$$POWER = \frac{WORK}{TIME} = \frac{FORCE \times DISTANCE}{TIME}.$$

In electricity, the WATT is VOLTS times AMPERES. But time is implicit within the AMPERE; for the AMPERE is one COULOMB per second; so that the equation of the WATT can be rewritten:

$$WATT = VOLTS \times AMPERES = \frac{VOLTS \times COULOMBS}{TIME}.$$

Other ways of expressing the WATT are:

$$\frac{VOLTS^2}{RESISTANCE \text{ in } OHMS} = \text{current in } AMPERES^2 \times RESISTANCE \text{ in}$$

ohms, or one JOULE per second.

The WATT is a metric unit of power, 10^7 ergs of work per second. One KILOWATT, 1000 WATTS, equals approximately 1.34 HORSEPOWER. One HORSEPOWER is equal to about 746 WATTS.

127. *DIGIT* (*dĭj'-ĭt*) *n.* One of the first nine numbers indicated by the fingers in counting; also one of the nine Arabic numerals: 1, 2, 3, 4, 5, 6, 7, 8, 9.
The noun DIGIT comes from the Latin *digitus*, a finger or toe. From the same source comes the adjective DIGITAL (*dĭj'-ĭ-tăl*), pertaining to a finger, through the Latin *digitalis*. From this comes the botanical term DIGITALIS, coined in 1542 by Leonhard Fuchs, a German physician and botanist, born in Bavaria in 1501. DIGITALIS (*dĭj-ĭ-tăl'-ĭs*) is now the technical word for the

popular perennial flower, the FOXGLOVE, where the ending -GLOVE has the same suggestion as FINGER.

To the question: 'A single number, such as 2, 3, or 7', 376 persons out of 525 answer DIGIT; but 101 answer UNIT. In mathematics a UNIT is a number regarded as an indivisible whole and as the base of other numbers. In abstract arithmetic the UNIT is

A single number, such as 2, 3, or 7.

FORM C. 3.	NY	FORM CA. 8.	CH	LA	NY	NY	PH	SUM
prime	4	prime	1	5	7	20	8	41
unit	6	unit	13	5	10	57	16	101
DIGIT	54	DIGIT	25	27	79	197	48	376
factor	4	factor	0	0	1	1	1	3
surd	0	surd	1	0	0	1	0	2
unmarked	0	unmarked	0	0	0	1	1	2
total	68	total	40	37	97	277	74	525

FORM CB. 14	NY
prime	4
unit	19
DIGIT	41
monomial	12
integer	9
unmarked	1
total	86

the least whole number, the numeral ONE represented by the figure 1. Here it is called UNITY. In the sciences a UNIT is any standard quantity by which other quantities of the same kind are measured. In arithmetic there is only one UNIT, the figure 1. There are nine DIGITS.

In this book the word DIGIT is placed in this position in accordance with the statistics for form CA, before additional data were available. In the revised form CB, new misleads, MONOMIAL and INTEGER, replacing FACTOR and SURD, have both proved popular, leaving fewer persons to mark the correct answer, making this item statistically more difficult, shifting it, if the present percentages hold as more data collect, from its present place as word 127 to word 173.

In the revised form CB, UNIT is still the most popular mislead, while MONOMIAL, marked by 12 out of 86 persons, has become second in popularity among the wrong answers. A MONOMIAL is an expression with a single term, a quantity containing one term only and not several added together, much as a BINOMIAL is an expression with two terms connected by a plus or minus sign. The confusion may be the historical term MONAD, which seldom appears in mathematics today, but which in the 17th century meant UNITY.

John Harris, who for a short time held the vicarage of Icklesham in Sussex, England, and later the rectory of St. Thomas, Winchelsea, and who is best known as the editor of the first technical dictionary in English, says: 'DIGITS or MONADES, a term in Arithmetick, signifying an Integer under ten, as 1, 2, 3'. From Thomas Hill, The Arte of Vulgar Arithmeticke, published in 1600: 'Any number which can be written with one figure onely is named a DIGIT; and therefore 1, 2, 3, 4, 5, 6, 7, 8, 9, are onely DIGITS and all the DIGITS that are'.

128. *LOGARITHM* (*lŏg'-ā-rĭth'm*) *n.* The number of times 10 or some other base must be multiplied by itself to give a desired number, the exponent of a base number, an artificial number designed to simplify multiplication and like processes.

Credit for the invention of LOGARITHMS is given unreservedly to John Napier, Baron of Merchiston in Scotland, who announced his discovery in a small quarto volume published in Edinburgh in 1614. The book contains fifty-seven pages of explanatory matter and ninety pages of tables, LOGARITHMS with the base e computed to seven places for the sine of every minute of arc. The work immediately attracted the attention of two eminent English mathematicians: Edward Wright, who before Napier's death in 1617 had translated his work from Latin, in which it was written, into English; and Henry Briggs, who after Napier's death recomputed Napier's LOGARITHMS using the base 10 and who published the first table of common LOGARITHMS, those now most generally used.

The word LOGARITHM was invented by Napier, though he does not explain its literal meaning. The word is a combination of the Greek λόγος (logos), plus ἀριθμός (arithmos), a number, the source of the word ARITHMETIC. The Greek λόγος (logos) originally meant something said, something spoken, and so came to mean word, saying, speech. From this λόγος (logos) came to mean reason, and so finally proportion. It may be in this sense of proportion that Napier thought of it in constructing the word LOGARITHM.

To the question: 'The power to which a fixed base number must be raised to equal another number', 72 persons out of 132 answer LOGARITHM; while 25 answer CHARACTERISTIC, and 17 MANTISSA. A LOGARITHM is made up of two parts: the CHARACTERISTIC to the left of the decimal in the logarithm, and the MANTISSA (113) to the right of the decimal. In common or

The power to which a fixed base number must be raised to equal another number.

FORM A. 14.	BO	NY	SUM	FORM AA. 23.	NY
LOGARITHM	12	23	35	LOGARITHM	72
antilogarithm	1	3	4	antilogarithm	6
e	2	4	6	e	11
mantissa	1	7	8	mantissa	17
characteristic	3	4	7	characteristic	25
unmarked	1	0	1	unmarked	1
total	20	41	61	total	132

Briggsian LOGARITHMS the MANTISSA is the number which is looked up in the logarithm table, it is the part of the logarithm which depends on the number looked up regardless of its decimal place. To obtain the COMMON LOGARITHM, the power to which to raise 10 to equal the desired number, the correct characteristic must be written in front of the MANTISSA.

The principal properties of LOGARITHMS are given by the four equations:

$$\log (MN) = \log M + \log N$$
$$\log (M/N) = \log M - \log N$$
$$\log M^n = n \log M$$
$$\log \sqrt[n]{M} = \frac{1}{n} \log M$$

Interpreting the first of these equations, two or more numbers can be multiplied by looking up their LOGARITHMS in a logarithm table, adding the logarithms, and then looking up the number which corresponds to this logarithmic sum. A table of LOGARITHMS enables a computer to use addition and subtraction instead of the more laborious multiplication and division.

129. *BOYLE'S LAW* (*boilz law*). The volume of a gas varies inversely with the pressure, pressure multiplied by volume is constant provided the temperature is constant.

Doubling the pressure on any enclosed gas lessens the volume to one half; or, if one thinks perhaps of an automobile tire, re-

Law that at constant temperature the volume of a gas varies inversely as the pressure.

FORM AB. 24.	NY	FORM D. 20.	NY	%
Gay-Lussac's law	12	Gay-Lussac's law	39	11.1
Charles' law	15	Charles' law	66	18.9
Dalton's law	3	Dalton's law	19	5.4
Avogadro's law	4	Avogadro's law	26	7.4
BOYLE'S LAW	66	BOYLE'S LAW	193	55.2
unmarked	0	unmarked	7	2.0
total	100	total	350	100.0

FORM DA. 18.	NY	FORM DB. 11.	NY
Gay-Lussac's	12	Gay-Lussac's	9
Charles'	17	Charles'	15
Dalton's	6	Torricelli's	5
Avogadro's	4	Avogadro's	5
BOYLE'S	61	BOYLE'S	72
unmarked	0	unmarked	0
total	100	total	106

ducing the volume increases the pressure, so that compressed gas or air supports a heavy weight, and the more the volume is decreased the greater the pressure it exerts.

For this relationship to hold the temperature must be kept constant. Reducing the volume of a gas by pressure generates heat. This heat must escape so that the conditions are isothermal (125), heat must be withdrawn when the gas is compressed under pressure and supplied when the gas expands.

In addition to constant temperature, isothermal conditions, Boyle's law needs two small corrections when the pressures are great. One correction is explained as due to the size of the molecules. In a gas under ordinary pressure the molecules are free to move, but under great pressures the molecules restrict one another. The other correction, also small, is due to the attraction of molecules for one another. But under ordinary pressures BOYLE'S LAW, found in 1660, is still useful.

The Honorable Robert Boyle, saint and scientist, sometimes called an alchemist because he believed in the transmutation of gold, sometimes the father of chemistry because his Sceptical Chymist contains more authenticated facts than any other chemical treatise of the day, was a contemporary of Newton. Boyle lived from 1627 to 1691, Newton from 1642 to 1727. According to the Encyclopaedia published in Philadelphia in 1798, a year after the completion of the third edition of the Encyclopaedia Britannica, edited in part by Colin Macfarquhar and published in Edinburgh in 1797. 'Robert Boyle was one of the greateſt philoſophers as well as beſt men that England or indeed any other nation has produced, was the ſeventh ſon and the 14th child of Richard, earl of Cork, and born in Ireland, January 25, 1627'.

To the question: 'Law stating that the product of volume and pressure of a gas is constant at constant temperature', 61 per cent of students answer correctly BOYLE'S, but 17 per cent answer CHARLES' and 12 per cent GAY-LUSSAC'S. The same law is called by some CHARLES' LAW and by others GAY-LUSSAC'S because these two men discovered independently, one in 1787 and the other in 1802, the same relation between volume and temperature. Both BOYLE'S LAW and CHARLES' or GAY-LUSSAC'S LAW apply to gases. Both were discovered through an interest in the atmosphere. Both deal with volumes of gases. But the two laws were more than a hundred years apart. During the interval the fahrenheit thermometer scale was devised. CHARLES' LAW, which comes after this discovery, deals with the change of volume with temperature. BOYLE'S LAW, which comes earlier, deals with the change of volume with pressure.

130. *THEOREM* (*thē'-ō-rĕm*) *n.* A universal demonstrable proposition. In his Universal Etymological English Dictionary first published in 1721 N. Bailey says: 'A Mathematical Declaration of certain Properties, Proportions or Equalities, duly inferred from fome Suppofitions about Quantity'. Charles Hutton in A Course of Mathematics, 1806, says: 'A THEOREM is a demonstrative proposition; in which some property is asserted, and the truth of it required to be proved'.

The word THEOREM comes from the Latin *theorema*, parallel to the Greek θεώρημα (theorema), a spectacle, sight, and so something contemplated, principle looked at, from θεωρεῖν (theorein), to look at, view, contemplate.

To the question: 'A general statement which has been proved or can be proved', 75 persons out of 132 answer correctly THEOREM; while 23 answer AXIOM; 17, HYPOTHESIS; and 13, PROPOSITION. An AXIOM cannot be proved. It is a proposition which commends itself to general acceptance, a presumably self-evident principle. An AXIOM is a starting point, almost an

A general statement which has been proved or can be proved.

FORM A. 7.	BO	NY	SUM	FORM AA. 25.	NY
postulate	0	4	4	postulate	4
axiom	4	6	10	axiom	23
THEOREM	14	22	36	THEOREM	75
hypothesis	1	2	3	hypothesis	17
proposition	1	7	8	proposition	13
unmarked	0	0	0	unmarked	0
total	20	41	61	total	132

ASSUMPTION which, at the time it is made, is accepted by everyone as true. The same Charles Hutton says 'A self-evident proposition, requiring no formal demonstration to prove its truth, but received and assented to as soon as mentioned'. Although today an AXIOM is distinguished from a THEOREM, an AXIOM being self-evident, a THEOREM provable, this distinction has not always been made by dictionaries. Edward Phillips, in his dictionary of difficult terms of 1678, says: 'THEOREMATICK, (Greek) belonging to a THEOREME, i. e. An AXIOM, or undoubted truth of any art'. Dr. Samuel Johnson in his dictionary of 1755 follows Edward Phillips: 'THEOREM, a position laid down as an acknowledged truth'.

PROPOSITION marked by only 13 persons out of 132, is nearly synonymous with THEOREM. The Century Dictionary uses them almost interchangeably. It defines CARNOT'S THEOREM as: 'The PROPOSITION that . . .'. The word PROPOSITION comes from the Latin *pro-*, forward, and *positus*, the past participle of *ponere*, to put, place, set. A PROPOSITION should be something proposed, put forward for consideration. An important PROPOSITION of a theoretical nature becomes a THEOREM when it is proved. To be called a THEOREM it should be the statement of a universal truth, and theoretical rather than practical. In the strict sense, a THEOREM must be true. It cannot be self-evident, but should be made evident through reasoning. It should be universal and not a particular proposition.

131. *COEFFICIENT* (*kō-ĕf-fĭsh'-ĕnt*) *n.* A number usually written before an unknown quantity and multiplying it, a constant which multiplies a variable; more generally anything which acts with something else to produce an effect.

The word COEFFICIENT is a combination of CO-, together, and EFFICIENT. The adjective EFFICIENT, already met under EFFI-CIENCY (52), means able to act effectively, capable; of a man or woman it means bringing to bear the requisite knowledge, skill, and industry. In mathematics, the noun EFFICIENT is sometimes used as synonymous with FACTOR, a quantity multiplied by another to produce a third of which it is said to be an EFFICIENT. Things or quantities multiplied together are equally EFFICIENT.

In his Technological Dictionary, first published in two volumes in 1823, seven years after his better known Dictionary of English Synonyms, 1816, George Crabb says: 'COEFFICIENTS (Algeb.) a term first employed by Vieta to denote any known quantity that is multiplied into any of the unknown terms of the equation; thus, in $3a + bx - cx^2$, 3, b, and c are the CO-EFFICIENTS which are thus multiplied into a, x, x^2. When no number is placed 1 is understood to be the COEFFICIENT, as x, which is equivalent to 1x'. Of François Vieta, who lived from 1540 to 1603, the Encyclopaedia Britannica says: 'All that is needed to make his writings look like a modern school algebra is the sign of equality'.

To the question: 'The algebraic constant by which a variable is multiplied', 303 persons out of 525 answer COEFFICIENT; but 107 answer EXPONENT. In algebra an EXPONENT (42) is a number placed above and to the right of another number to denote the power to which the latter is raised, the number of times by which it is to be multiplied by itself. In the expression: a^2,

The algebraic constant by which a variable is multiplied.

FORM C. 46.	CH	FORM CA. 13.	CH	LA	NY	NY	PH	SUM
absolute	6	absolute	4	3	13	23	8	51
radix	1	radix	1	0	1	8	2	12
exponent	20	exponent	12	5	20	58	12	107
factorial	3	factorial	1	3	9	24	3	40
COEFFICIENT	38	COEFFICIENT	20	25	53	157	48	303
unmarked	0	unmarked	2	1	1	7	1	12
total	68	total	40	37	97	277	74	525

FORM CB. 15.	NY
absolute	8
root	9
exponent	19
factorial	3
COEFFICIENT	47
unmarked	0
total	86

which means a $\times$ a, or a times a, 2 is the EXPONENT. Numerically 3^2, where 2 is an EXPONENT, equals 3×3 or 9. In the expression 2a, 2 is a COEFFICIENT, or numerically, if $a = 3$, 2×3 is 6. In the expression: $3ab^2x$, $3ab^2$ is the COEFFICIENT of x; but 3 is also the COEFFICIENT of ab^2. Reread EXPONENT (42) which is so often confused with COEFFICIENT.

132. *CRITICAL TEMPERATURE* (*krĭt'-ĭ-kăl tĕm'-pĕ-rā-tūr*). Temperature below which a gas must be cooled before it can be liquefied, temperature above which a gas cannot be liquefied no matter how great the pressure, a definite tem-

perature at which the liquid and the vapor of a substance are indistinguishable.

For carbon dioxide the CRITICAL TEMPERATURE is 31.1 degrees centigrade, above ordinary room temperature at 20 degrees. Carbon dioxide can therefore be liquefied by pressure alone. As prior to about 1877 similar attempts to liquefy hydrogen, nitrogen, and oxygen had failed, even under as much as 2000 atmospheres' pressure, it was thought that they could not be liquefied. But their CRITICAL TEMPERATURES, above which they cannot be liquefied, are all low, and they had not at the same

Temperature above which a gas cannot be liquefied no matter how great the pressure.

FORM AB. I.	NY	FORM D. I.	NY	%
recalescent	2	recalescence	56	16.0
fusion	0	fusion	26	7.4
CRITICAL	98	CRITICAL	177	50.6
boiling	0	boiling	59	16.9
freezing	0	freezing	26	7.4
unmarked	0	unmarked	6	1.7
total	100	total	350	100.0

FORM DA. 19.	NY	FORM DB. 18.	NY
recalescence	13	recalescence	17
fusion	8	fusion	15
CRITICAL	57	CRITICAL	45
boiling	16	boiling	20
freezing	6	freezing	9
unmarked	0	unmarked	0
total	100	total	106

time been reduced in temperature. For hydrogen (H_2) the CRITICAL TEMPERATURE is one of the lowest, −234.5 degrees centigrade. For nitrogen and air the CRITICAL TEMPERATURES are nearly alike; for nitrogen (N_2) −146 degrees centigrade, and for air −140. The last was finally liquefied by K. P. G. von Linde in 1895. Hydrogen was liquefied in 1898 by Sir James Dewar; and helium in 1908 by H. Kammerlingh Onnes at −268 degrees centigrade, five degrees above absolute zero.

To the question: 'Temperature above which it is impossible to liquefy a gas no matter how great the pressure', 57 per cent of students answer correctly CRITICAL TEMPERATURE; but 16 per cent answer BOILING. At atmospheric pressure HYDROGEN must be cooled below its BOILING POINT at −252 degrees centigrade to be liquefied; but it can be liquefied under pressure at any temperature below −234 degrees centigrade, its CRITICAL TEMPERATURE. At atmospheric pressure helium liquefies at its BOILING POINT, −268.5 degrees, but can be liquefied by pressure under −266 degrees centigrade. The BOILING POINT is the temperature, usually at atmospheric pressure, at which a liquid turns to vapor. Water boils at 100 degrees centigrade, under ordinary atmospheric pressure. Increase this pressure and the water vapor which has formed turns back to water, for pressure raises the boiling point, the point at which liquid turns to vapor. Lift the temperature above this new boiling point and water once more turns to steam. Again increase the pressure and vapor turns back to water. But there comes a temperature, 365 degrees centigrade, where no amount of increased pressure turns steam back to water. This is the CRITICAL TEMPERATURE. Some writers use the term VAPOR for a substance above its boiling point and below its CRITICAL POINT, where there is always some moisture present; and limit the term GAS to a substance above its CRITICAL TEMPERATURE, where no liquid can exist.

133. *CYCLOID* (*sī'-kloid*) *n.* The curve traced by a point on the edge of a wheel rolling on a straight line.

Giles Persone de Roberval, 1602 to 1675, called the curve a TROCHOID. Blaise Pascal, 1623 to 1662, called the same curve a ROULETTE; while Galileo Galilei, 1564 to 1642, called it a CYCLOID. The word CYCLOID comes from the Greek κυκλοειδής (cycloeides), circular, a combination of κύκλος (cyclos), a ring, circle, wheel, disk, orb, and εἶδος (eidos), form, shape, appearance, already met in ANEROID (93), and in SOLENOID (53), by derivation, in the shape or form of a pipe. From the same Greek κύκλος (cyclos), wheel, come TRICYCLE, a three-wheeled vehicle, and CYCLONE, first used in 1848 by H. Piddington, in the Sailor's Horn-book, for all whirling storms such as hurricanes, whirlwinds, African tornados, and water spouts.

To the question: 'Path described by a moving point on the circumference of a circle which is rolled on a straight line', 191 persons out of 357 answer CYCLOID; while 44 answer HYPO-CYCLOID. HYPO-, the first part of this word, comes from the Greek ὑπό (hypo), under. The HYPOCYCLOID is the path described by the same point on the edge of the same wheel which is rolled not on a straight line but on the inside of another circle.

The COMMON CYCLOID is a series of arches. The span of each arch equals the circumference of the rolling wheel, as measured along the base line; while the height of each arch at its mid point is the diameter of the wheel. The length of the curved arch is four times the diameter of the rolling wheel. The area of the CYCLOID is three times the area of the generating circle,

Path described by a moving point on the circumference of a circle which is rolled on a straight line.

FORM B. 24.	NY	MISC.	SUM
epicycloid	3	33	36
rosette	4	15	19
astroid	6	30	36
CYCLOID	27	164	191
hypocycloid	7	37	44
unmarked	1	30	31
total	48	309	357

found first by Galileo when he cut out and weighed pieces of paper of the two shapes, and later proved mathematically by his pupil Torricelli. The CYCLOID is also the curve along which a body falls from one point to another in the shortest time; a problem with which John Bernoulli challenged other mathematicians in 1697. It was solved by Newton, de l'Hospital, and the Bernoullis.

When the point which generates a CYCLOID is anywhere inside the wheel rolling on a straight line the result is still a series of arches. The width of each is again equal to the circumference of the rolling circle; but the arches are low and hang in the air above the line, they do not rest on it as in the COMMON CYCLOID. Such a curve is called a PROLATE CYCLOID. When the generating point is outside the wheel on a radius line extended beyond the circumference the curve is a series of arches with a loop below the line where each arch stops and the next begins. This is called a CURTATE CYCLOID. A portion of the COMMON CYCLOID is sometimes used in cutting the faces of gear teeth so that they roll easily.

134. *REGULAR POLYHEDRON* (*pŏl-ĭ-hē'-drŏn*). A solid bounded by regular polygons.

The word POLYHEDRON comes from the Greek πολύεδρον (polyedron), the neuter of the adjective πολύεδρος (polyedros), with many bases, a combination of πολίς (polis), many, and ἕδρα (hedra), seat. From the same Greek ἕδρα (hedra), seat,

Any solid all of whose faces are equal equilateral plane figures.

FORM C. 23.	CH	FORM CA. 17.	CH	LA	NY	NY	PH	SUM
polygons	19	polygon	4	6	18	79	16	123
REGULAR		REGULAR						
POLYHEDRA	33	POLYHEDRON	25	20	54	129	41	269
hexahedra	3	hexahedron	4	4	13	13	6	40
dodecahedra	2	dodecahedron	2	1	2	12	3	20
rectangloids	11	rectangloid	5	5	10	43	5	68
unmarked	0	unmarked	0	1	0	1	3	5
total	68	total	40	37	97	277	74	525

FORM CB. 18.	NY
polygon	24
REGULAR POLYHEDRON	46
hexahedron	6
dodecahedron	0
rectangloid	8
unmarked	2
total	86

comes the architectural term EXEDRA (*ĕks'-ĕ-drah*), an outdoor seat or bench, on a raised platform with six or eight wide steps, often by the roadside for rest and conversation. A POLYHEDRON is a solid with many bases. POLY- takes part in many words, as: POLYGAMY, by derivation many married, much married; and POLYTECHNIC, dealing with many arts.

To the question: 'Any solid all of whose faces are equal equilateral plane figures', 269 persons out of 525 answer REGULAR POLYHEDRON; and 123 answer POLYGON. A POLYHEDRON is a solid in three dimensions. A POLYGON is a plane figure, flat, in two dimensions. POLYGON comes from the Greek πολύγωνον (polygonon), a polygon, the neuter of πολύγωνος (polygonos), many angled. This is a combination of the same πολίς (polis), many, and γωνία (gonia), corner, angle, a word already met in DIAGONAL (15). A POLYGON is a closed figure with numerous angles formed by the intersection of a number of straight lines, each with two others. A REGULAR POLYGON is a POLYGON all of whose angles are equal and all of whose sides are also equal. A REGULAR POLYHEDRON is a solid all of whose faces are regular and equal POLYGONS. The percentages who mark this particular item correctly are: Chicago, 54 per cent; Los Angeles, 54 per cent; New York, 50 per cent; and Philadelphia, 55 per cent.

There are only five regular POLYHEDRONS: the regular TETRAHEDRON, bounded by four equilateral triangles, three meeting at each point; the regular OCTAHEDRON, bounded by eight equilateral triangles, four meeting at each point; and the regular ICOSAHEDRON, bounded by twenty equilateral triangles, five meeting at each point. Six equilateral triangles meeting at a point make a plane, flat figure, and so cannot bound a solid. The two remaining regular POLYHEDRONS are the regular HEXAHEDRON, the cube, bounded by six squares, three meeting at each point, four squares meeting at a point are flat and so cannot bound a solid; and the regular DODECAHEDRON, bounded by twenty five-sided figures.

135. *RADICAL INDEX* (răd'-ĭ-kăl ĭn'-dĕks). The number written over the radical sign to distinguish the particular root. Reread RADICAL (105).
The word INDEX comes from the Latin *index, indicis,* informer, spy, discoverer, also indicator, also forefinger. The noun *index* comes from the verb *indicare,* to point at, show, a combination of *in,* in, and *dicare,* to declare, say, the source of the English word DICTION, choice of words, manner of saying, expression of ideas by words. The INDEX written in the radical sign indicates the root to be taken.

To the question: 'The a in the expression $\sqrt[a]{x}$', 205 persons out of 357 answer RADICAL INDEX; while 61 answer EXPONENT, the most frequently marked mislead. An EXPONENT (42) is a symbol placed above and at the right of another symbol to show how many times the latter is to be multiplied by itself. It is an indicator of power. A root can be converted to an EXPONENT. Thus the cube root of a quantity can be written

The a in the expression $\sqrt[a]{x}$.

FORM B. 38.	NY	MISC.	SUM
exponent	8	53	61
coefficient	6	23	29
factor index	5	21	26
constant	0	2	2
RADICAL INDEX	26	179	205
unmarked	3	31	34
total	48	309	357

either with the radical sign: $\sqrt[3]{x}$, or as a fractional EXPONENT $x^{1/3}$, or the fourth root $\sqrt[4]{x}$ as a fractional EXPONENT $x^{1/4}$. The RADICAL sign with its INDEX is not an operational symbol, does not obey mathematical laws, and is gradually becoming obsolete in favor of the fractional EXPONENT; and it may be this which leads so many to mark EXPONENT for RADICAL INDEX.

136. *TYMPANUM* (*tĭm'-pă-nŭm*) *n.* Ear-drum, middle ear separated from the outer ear by a stretched membrane, cavity between the outer ear and the inner ear or labyrinth. The word comes through the Latin *tympanum*, from the Greek τύμπανον (tympanon), a drum, also a roller. This in turn comes from the verb τύπτειν (typtein), to beat, strike.

Ganot, in his Physics, says the external ear collects the sound, which is transmitted through the auditory passage to the drum or TYMPANUM. 'This is a tightly stretched membrane or skin which separates the outer ear from the middle ear or TYMPANIC CAVITY'. The word TYMPANUM is used by some for the cavity and by others for the stretched membrane which separates this cavity from the outer ear. Of these two uses Alexander J. Ellis, translator of Helmholtz, says: 'In common parlance the DRUM-

SKIN of the ear, or TYMPANIC MEMBRANE, is spoken of as the drum itself. Anatomists as well as drummers distinguish the membranous cover (drumskin) which is struck, from the hollow cavity (drum) which contains the resonant air'. Following Ellis the term TYMPANUM should be used for the cavity and its walls, and not merely for the separating membrane.

This was not done in the first form of the physics vocabulary test, which read: 'The membrane commonly known as the ear-drum'. To this 58 per cent of students answer correctly TYMPANUM, but 18 per cent answer AURICLE. The word AURICLE is used perhaps most frequently today to designate the two upper cavities of the heart; 'Called AURICLES', says William Youall, 1776 to 1847, 'from their supposed resemblance to the

Ear-drum or middle ear.

FORM BA. 18.	%	FORM D. 24.	NY	%
cochlea	9	cochlea	30	8.6
TYMPANUM	60	TYMPANUM	165	47.1
basilar membrane	24	basilar membrane	47	13.4
mucous membrane	5	mucous membrane	16	4.6
stapes	1	auricle	81	23.2
unmarked	1	unmarked	11	3.1
total	100	total	350	100.0

FORM DA. 24.	%	FORM DB. 17.	NY
cochlea	7	cochlea	25
TYMPANUM	58	TYMPANUM	37
basilar membrane	13	basilar membrane	24
fovea	3	labyrinth	9
auricle	18	auricle	11
unmarked	1	unmarked	0
total	100	total	106

ear of a dog', for AURICLE comes from the Latin *auricula*, the external ear, the diminutive of *auris*, ear. From this comes the English noun AURIST, an ear specialist. AURICLE originally in English meant external ear, the outer visible ear, more especially the lower lobe of the ear. Though the word AURICLE is seldom if ever used in this way today this early meaning sur-

vives enough somewhere to lead 18 per cent of students to mark
AURICLE for EAR-DRUM, another instance of the most frequently
marked mislead revealing some historical connection with the
right answer.

From Helmholtz as translated by Ellis comes: 'The construction of the ear may be briefly defined as follows: The fine ends
of the fibres of the auditory nerves are expanded on a delicate
membrane in a cavity filled with fluid. Owing to the involved
form this cavity is known as the LABYRINTH. To conduct the
vibrations of the air with sufficient force into the fluid of the
LABYRINTH is the office of a second portion of the ear, the
TYMPANUM or drum and its parts.'

Of Hermann von Helmholtz, who lived from 1821 to 1894,
William Kingdon Clifford says in his Seeing and Thinking: 'In
the first place he began by studying physiology, dissecting the
eye and the ear, and finding out how they acted, and what was
their precise constitution; but he found that it was impossible
to study the proper action of the eye and ear without studying
also the nature of light and sound, which led him to the study
of physics. He had already become one of the most accomplished physiologists of this century when he commenced the
study of physics, and he is now one of the greatest physicists
of this century. He then found it was impossible to study
physics without knowing mathematics; and accordingly he
took to studying mathematics and he is now one of the most
accomplished mathematicians of this century.'

137. *DRAG* (*drăg*) *n*. Resistance along the line of flight, head
       resistance, that component of the total air force on a body
which is parallel to the relative wind, resistance offered by an
object to the flow of air, fluid resistance offered to any part of
an airplane. Reread INDUCED DRAG (95).

The noun DRAG, resistance, and the verb to DRAG with the
same spelling, although associated, do not seem to have come
either one from the other as so often happens with such a pair.
Instead both noun and verb come independently from the same
source. DRAG, DRAGGLE, DRAW, to pull, DRAWL, to drag along
heavily, to speak slowly with lack of interest, DRAY, and DRAIN,

all go back through Middle English to the Anglo-Saxon word *dragan*, to draw, drag. All are closely associated with Swedish, Danish, and Icelandic nautical terms for grapnel, drag-anchor, and the iron rim on the keel of a ship.

To the question: 'The component of the total air force on a body parallel to the relative wind', 254 persons out of 515 mark DRAG, the correct answer; while 63 mark LIFT; 68, SKIN FRICTION; and 60, RESULTANT. DRAG includes SKIN FRICTION, as well as FORM DRAG, dependent upon the shape of the part moving through the air, and the INDUCED DRAG, an essential part of the LIFT. INDUCED DRAG (95), where the examinee is asked to distinguish PARASITE DRAG, PROFILE DRAG, and INDUCED DRAG, is marked correctly by 321 out of 515 persons, or by 62 per cent.

Form A. The component of the total air force on a body parallel to the relative wind.
Form AA. Resistance along the line of flight.

FORM A. 21.	FW	LA	NY	NY	NY	PH	SUM	FORM AA. 23.	NY
skin friction	3	6	7	8	24	20	68	skin friction	8
DRAG	13	33	16	30	62	100	254	DRAG	51
lift	0	5	6	13	15	24	63	lift	2
resultant	1	4	3	2	22	28	60	resultant	0
velocity	1	5	4	7	15	20	52	velocity	2
unmarked	0	1	1	6	2	8	18	unmarked	0
total	18	54	37	66	140	200	515	total	63

To do so they must have some idea of the meaning of DRAG, and yet only 254 of the same 515 persons mark this item correctly. The trouble is probably the difficult terms in the present question: COMPONENT and RELATIVE WIND, the last, word number 341 of this book. In the revised form AA the question has been changed to read: 'Resistance along the line of flight'; and the correct answer DRAG is chosen by 51 of the 63 whose scores have been tabulated, or by 81 per cent, making the term easier than INDUCED DRAG as it should be.

In stress analysis the DRAG is the resistance parallel to the relative wind, the LIFT is the force up, the component at right angles to the DRAG, and the RESULTANT is the result produced by the combination of these two forces or components.

138. *DIRECTIONAL GYRO* (*jī'-rō*). A gyroscopic instrument for indicating direction, containing a free gyroscope which holds its position in azimuth and thus indicates angular deviation from the course.

A GYROSCOPE (*jī'-rō-skōp*) consists essentially of a solid rotating wheel mounted in a ring, with its axis free to turn in any direction. It is a balanced flywheel, universally mounted with

Form A. An instrument in an aircraft for measuring the number of degrees of a turn to the right or left.

Form AA. 16. An aircraft instrument which indicates degrees of a turn during a bank.

FORM A. 40.	FW	LA	NY	NY	NY	PH	SUM	FORM AA. 16.	NY
compass	1	18	9	11	28	52	119	compass	10
altimeter	0	1	0	1	3	1	6	bank indicator	32
tachometer	1	1	5	6	15	15	43	tachometer	6
DIRECTIONAL GYRO	15	33	21	39	91	120	319	DIRECTIONAL GYRO	15
aneroid barometer	1	0	0	0	1	0	2	automatic pilot	0
unmarked	0	1	2	9	2	12	26	unmarked	0
total	18	54	37	66	140	200	515	total	63

three degrees of freedom about its center of gravity, and may be driven by an air turbine. When the wheel revolves at high speed, 10,000 revolutions per minute, its plane of rotation tends to remain always parallel to itself in space.

Jean Bernard Léon Foucault, improving on Bohnenberger's earlier apparatus, invented the GYROSCOPE to show the rotation of the earth by the tendency of the wheel to rotate in the same plane in space independent of the earth's motion. He also coined the French term *gyroscope*, in 1852, from the Greek γῦρος (gyros), ring, circle, spiral, and σκοπεῖν (scopein), to view.

To the question: 'An instrument in an aircraft for measuring the number of degrees of a turn to the right or left', 319 in a total population of 515 answer correctly DIRECTIONAL GYRO; but 119 answer COMPASS. The DIRECTIONAL GYRO is often called a GYROCOMPASS, and in this sense COMPASS is a correct answer.

But the magnetic COMPASS in a steep turn ceases to function, while the DIRECTIONAL GYRO operates as well as in straight flight. Also during a turn the COMPASS runs ahead of the plane or lags behind depending upon whether the turn is to the north or south.

With the feeling that the original question did not emphasize the bank, and that COMPASS might be a correct answer for a slow gradual turn, the wording was changed in the revised form AA: 'An aircraft instrument which indicates degrees of a turn during a bank'. Now 32 persons out of 63 mark BANK INDICATOR, and only 15 DIRECTIONAL GYRO. A BANK INDICATOR shows the tip of the wings from the horizontal, one below and the other above a level position, the rotation of the plane about a horizontal axis running from front to back. The DIRECTIONAL GYRO shows the turn of the plane from right to left or left to right, its rotation about a vertical axis.

A serious error of the DIRECTIONAL GYRO is its tendency to creep as much as 3 degrees in 15 minutes. Also, unlike the COMPASS, the DIRECTIONAL GYRO has no directive force but remains in any position in which set. It must therefore be set to correspond with the magnetic compass. But it does not overswing or oscillate like the compass and so provides a more positive reference for steering. A turn of an exact number of degrees to a desired new heading can be made without the assistance of a stop watch merely by observing the instrument.

139. *CHORD* (*kōrd*) *n.* A line which joins the ends of any arc of a circle.

The word CHORD comes from the Latin *chorda*, and this from the Greek χορδή (chorde), the string of a musical instrument. The spelling CORD, of the same word, comes through Middle English and French originally from the same Latin and Greek words. CORD today, without the H, means a string. But in music, for the sound of three or more tones together, and in geometry, the word is spelt with an H as it was in both Latin and Greek, CHORD.

To the question: 'A straight line whose extremities lie on the circumference of a single circle', 209 persons out of 357 answer CHORD; while 71 answer DIAMETER. With the present wording DIAMETER is correct. The DIAMETER is a straight line whose extremities lie on the circumference of a circle, it is a

A straight line whose extremities lie on the circumference of a single circle.

FORM B. 32.	NY	MISC.	SUM
secant	3	14	17
CHORD	27	182	209
tangent	5	24	29
section	0	1	1
diameter	11	60	71
unmarked	2	28	30
total	48	309	357

CHORD through the center of the circle. CHORD is the general term for any straight line from side to side of a circle. DIAMETER is that particular CHORD which goes through the center.

140. *IMAGINARY ROOT* (ĭm-ăj'-ĭ-nā-rē). The even root of any negative quantity; the Century Dictionary says: 'Unreal and feigned in accordance with the theory of imaginary quantities'. IMAGINARY quantities are sometimes called IMPOSSIBLE quantities.

The square root of a positive number may be either positive or negative; for two positive numbers multiplied together give a positive product, while two negative numbers likewise give a positive product. As no number squared gives a negative answer, it is impossible to obtain the square root of a negative quantity.

The same holds true for any even number of negative quantities. Four negative quantities, or eight, multiplied together give a positive product; and in consequence every even root of a negative quantity is unobtainable, imaginary. From Arithmetic and Algebra in their Principles and Application, 1859, by Barnard Smith: 'The square root or any even root of a negative quantity is called an IMAGINARY quantity'.

The word IMAGINARY comes from the Latin *imaginarius*, seeming, imaginary, from *imago*, *imaginis*, an image, a copy, likeness, the source also of the verb to IMITATE, to copy.

To the question: 'In an equation, a solution containing the square root of a negative quantity', 205 persons out of 357 answer IMAGINARY ROOT; while 64 answer IRRATIONAL ROOT; and only 28 answer the symbol i. This last is a correct answer, for i is the symbol widely used for the square root of minus 1. The word ROOT in the question no doubt steers many toward the

In an equation, a solution containing the square root of a negative quantity.

FORM B. 33.	NY	MISC.	SUM
i	4	24	28
irrational root	4	60	64
e	0	1	1
surd	3	22	25
IMAGINARY ROOT	35	170	205
unmarked	2	32	34
total	48	309	357

answers IMAGINARY ROOT and IRRATIONAL ROOT. An IRRATIONAL ROOT is one which can be approximated but never obtained with absolute accuracy. Thus the square root of 2 and the cube root of 4 can both be carried to any number of decimal places. Both can be obtained to any desired degree of accuracy, but never with absolute accuracy. An IMAGINARY ROOT is unobtainable, though often used in equations and written $\sqrt{-a}$.

141. *OVERSHOT* (ō'-ver-shŏt) *adj.* A type of water-wheel, used for high heads, which receives water at the top and turns largely by the dead weight of the water in the buckets. OVERSHOT WHEELS have been made as much as a hundred feet in diameter, but they are always a few feet less than the head of water. For greatest efficiency the water should strike the wheel as near the top as possible and the bottom stand above the tail water.

From Elements of Physics or Natural Philosophy, by Neil Arnott, M.D., first published in 1827, comes: 'In a water-wheel, whether the water is the moving power, as where a stream acts to drive machinery, or the resistance, as in the case of the PADDLE-WHEELS of a steam boat, the impulse on the flat faces of the vanes or float-boards is proportional to the area. When a wheel with float-boards has its lower part merely dipping into the stream of water, to be driven by the momentum of the water as it floats along, it is called an UNDERSHOT WHEEL. When the water reaches the wheel near the middle of its height, and turns it by falling on the float-boards of one side, as they sweep downwards in a curved trough fitting them, the weight of the water also is called into play; and this modification is called a BREAST-WHEEL. When the float-boards are shut in by

Type of water-wheel turned by the weight of water alone.

FORM AB. 18.	%	FORM D. 15.	NY	%
undershot	4	undershot	29	8.3
breast	5	breast	18	5.1
Pelton	11	Pelton	48	13.7
reaction	8	reaction	8	2.3
OVERSHOT	71	OVERSHOT	245	70.0
unmarked	1	unmarked	2	0.6
total	100	total	350	100.0

FORM DA. 4.	%	FORM DB. 14.	NY
undershot	9	undershot	13
breast	1	breast	3
Pelton	13	Pelton	11
paddle	19	paddle	22
OVERSHOT	58	OVERSHOT	55
unmarked	0	unmarked	2
total	100	total	106

flat sides, so as to form cavities or buckets round the wheel, into which the water is allowed to fall at the top of the wheel, and to act almost by its weight only, the modification is called the OVERSHOT WHEEL. To have a maximum of effect from wheels acted on by the moving force of water, they are generally made to turn with a velocity about one-third as great as that of the water; and wheels moved by the simple weight of water usually have their circumference turning with a velocity of about three feet per second. The subject of water-wheels is one of the most important in practical mechanics;

seeing that, where water power is supplied ready to hand, it would be useless waste to employ steam power'.

To the question: 'Type of water-wheel turned by the weight of water alone', 58 per cent answer correctly OVERSHOT; but 19 per cent answer PADDLE, and 13 per cent PELTON. Two PADDLE WHEELS, located about midships, one on each side, propel the type of lake or river steamer called a SIDE-WHEELER. A single PADDLE WHEEL at the stern drives a STERN-WHEELER. But the term PADDLE WHEEL is not ordinarily used for a WATER-WHEEL.

OVERSHOT and BREAST-WHEELS are driven largely by the dead weight of the water in their buckets. Despite this, BREAST-WHEEL, which is almost as correct as OVERSHOT, is marked by only 1 per cent, the least frequently marked of the five choices.

When built of steel and correctly designed it is said that OVERSHOT WHEELS may reach an efficiency of 75 per cent. In the OVERSHOT WHEEL the water flows into the buckets at the top, which moves in the direction of the flowing water. But it is largely the weight of the water which turns the wheel. In the BREAST-WHEEL the water flows into the buckets in the middle of the wheel, at about the level of the axis of the wheel, and the wheel turns in the opposite direction from the OVER-SHOT WHEEL.

Carl R. Weidner, in Theory and Test of an OVERSHOT Water Wheel, Bulletin 529 of the University of Wisconsin, says that today the circumference of an OVERSHOT WHEEL travels at 5 to 7 feet per second. The diameter should be a foot or two less than the available fall of water. TURBINES have today displaced this earlier form of hydraulic motor.

142. *SURFACE TENSION* (ser'-făs tĕn'-shŏn). The effect of cohesion at the surface of a liquid, apparent tension of the surface film.

To the question: 'The property of a liquid which makes a small drop assume a spherical form', 63 per cent of students answer SURFACE TENSION, but 24 per cent answer COHESION, a mislead added in 1934 in the revision of form D which led to form DA. It replaced RESILIENCE which attracted almost no one in the two earlier forms. COHESION is the force by which the molecules of a material are bound together so as to form continuous, homogeneous matter; hardness, softness, tenacity, elasticity, malleability, ductility, and cleavage are properties dependent upon COHESION.

SURFACE TENSION is the name which has been assigned to the phenomenon which makes the surface of a liquid act almost like a stretched elastic sheet. SURFACE TENSION is due to CO-HESION, to the steady pull on each surface particle back towards the liquid; so that COHESION is fundamentally a correct answer

The property of a liquid which makes a small drop assume a spherical form.

FORM BA. 5.	%	FORM D. 3.	NY	%
adhesion	9	adhesion	66	18.9
density	0	viscosity	39	11.1
resilience	1	resilience	3	0.8
SURFACE TENSION	88	SURFACE TENSION	230	65.7
elasticity	0	elasticity	10	2.9
unmarked	2	unmarked	2	0.6
total	100	total	350	100.0

FORM DA. 6.	%	FORM DB. 9.	NY
adhesion	7	adhesion	5
viscosity	6	viscosity	19
cohesion	24	cohesion	21
SURFACE TENSION	63	SURFACE TENSION	58
elasticity	0	tensile-strength	3
unmarked	0	unmarked	0
total	100	total	106

to the present question. The reason for leaving this choice in the test is that high-scoring examinees, those who score forty or more correct out of the total fifty items of the test as a whole, mark SURFACE TENSION and not COHESION; only those who score a little lower, between perhaps thirty and thirty-five correct out of fifty, mark COHESION more often than SURFACE TENSION.

The word LIQUID in the definition may eliminate COHESION for high-scoring examinees, for COHESION is the attraction of like molecules in both solids and gases as well as in liquids, while the specious term SURFACE TENSION applies only to liquids.

143. *DIOPTER* (dī-ŏp'-ter) *n.* A unit employed by opticians for magnifying power, the refractive power of a lens with a focal length of one meter. Reread FOCAL LENGTH.

The ability of a lens to make a beam of light converge is directly proportional to the reciprocal of the focal length. Flat glass, with an infinite focal length, has no power to concentrate light rays. But a lentil-shaped piece, thick at the center and thin at the edges, makes light rays bend. The more sharply they bend, the closer the point where the rays cross, that is the shorter the focal length, the more powerful the lens. Thus lens power is inversely proportional to the focal length.

One DIOPTER, as spectacle-makers use the term, is the relative magnifying power of a lens with a focal length of one meter; two DIOPTERS is the power of a thicker lens with a focal length of half a meter; four DIOPTERS the power of a lens with a focal length of one quarter of a meter.

The word DIOPTER comes from the Greek διά (diá), through, which becomes DI before a vowel, and the adjective ὀπτικός (optikos), pertaining to seeing. From the same Greek ὀπτικός (optikos) comes OPTICS, that branch of physics which treats of light. In his Treatise on Optics, published in Edinburgh in 1831, and in America two years later, Sir David Brewster says: 'Light through transparent bodies is transmitted according to particular laws, the consideration of which constitutes the subject of DIOPTRICS'. As early as 1644 OPTICS was divided into DIOPTRICS and CATOPTRICS, both spelt with an R after the T because, though both come from the same Greek root as OPTICS, they come through the word διόπτρα (dioptra), the name of a leveling instrument. DIOPTRICS is that branch of OPTICS which dealt with the refraction of light, with its going through glass and other materials. CATOPTRICS dealt in the same way with the reflection of light back from the surface.

E. Atkinson in 1863, in his translation of Ganot's Physics, says: 'The telescopes previously described are refracting or DIOPTRIC telescopes. It is, however, only in recent times that it has been possible to construct achromatic lenses of large size; before this, a concave metallic mirror was used instead of the object-glass. Telescopes of this kind are called reflecting or CATOPTRIC telescopes'. Though OPTICS survives as an important term, DIOPTRICS and CATOPTRICS in these senses never appear in modern texts. Because DIOPTRICS dealt with refraction, the word DIOPTRIC came to be used as a noun for the unit of refractive power. Finally in about 1890 DIOPTRIC began to be shortened to DIOPTER.

With the definition: 'The power of a lens with a focal length of one meter', 53 per cent of students who take the physics vocabulary test answer correctly DIOPTER; but 14 per cent choose the unusual word ANASTIGMAT as the correct answer. This comes from the same source as the more familiar word ASTIGMATISM, the inability of a lens to focus refracted rays at a single point. It occurs with a lens made of a single kind of

Power of a lens which has a focal length of one meter.

FORM BA. 31.	%	FORM D. 36.	NY	%
anastigmat	20	anastigmat	80	22.8
sagitta	9	sagitta	31	8.9
umbra	16	umbra	45	12.9
DIOPTER	38	DIOPTER	127	36.3
hefner	12	hefner	48	13.7
unmarked	5	unmarked	19	5.4
total	100	total	350	100.0

FORM DA. 33.	%	FORM DB. 21.	NY
anastigmat	14	anastigmat	17
sagitta	6	sagitta	10
umbra	11	umbra	18
DIOPTER	53	DIOPTER	46
hefner	11	hefner	12
unmarked	5	unmarked	3
total	100	total	106

glass when the point source of light is not on the main axis of the lens. It can be corrected by making a lens of two or more kinds of glass, originally by combining a lens of highly refractive crown glass with another lens of less refractive flint glass. Such a lens is called ANASTIGMATIC, or sometimes merely ANASTIGMAT, starting with the Greek privative ἀ (a), which becomes ἀν (an) before a vowel, that is not ASTIGMATIC.

The action of a lens depends partly on the material of which it is made, partly on its focal length, and partly on its diameter. The familiar symbol F/10 or F/20 is really a fraction, the diameter of the lens opening divided by the focal length; except that the units in which the focal length are expressed are so chosen as to make the numerator, F, always one. Thus an F/20 lens might have twice the focal length of an F/10, or its effective diameter might be cut down to one half the diameter of the F/10. The speed of a lens is proportional to the square of its effective radius and to the reciprocal of its focal length. The DIOPTER is only this last factor, the reciprocal of the focal length, starting with one DIOPTER as the power of a lens of one meter focal length.

144. *WAVE ANGLE* (*wāv ăng'-gl*). The angle between the horizontal and the transmitted wave or radiation.

The WAVE ANGLE or ANGLE OF RADIATION is the angle between a sky wave and the surface of the earth. When such a sky wave leaves the antenna it travels upward at an angle to the horizontal until it strikes a layer of ionized air called the IONOSPHERE, extending from 30 miles above the earth's surface to 200, ioniza-

The angle which a radio wave makes with a tangent to the earth.

FORM A. 43.	NY	NY	NY	SUM
skip zone	5	2	21	28
phase angle	4	4	22	30
elevation	4	6	22	32
dip	5	3	18	26
WAVE ANGLE	12	24	63	99
unmarked	7	1	1	9
total	37	40	147	224

tion being most intense at about 70 miles. Here the sky wave is refracted or bent back downward again so that it strikes the earth's surface at some distance from its origin, the degree of refraction depending upon the frequency of the sky wave and the intensity of the ionization. The signal from such a refracted sky wave may be stronger than from a ground wave much closer to the transmitting antenna.

The theory of the IONOSPHERE, sometimes called the HEAVISIDE LAYER, and of refraction from it was developed simultaneously by Arthur Kennelly in the United States and Heaviside in England. Oliver Heaviside, who suggested the presence of such a conducting layer in the upper atmosphere which prevents electromagnetic waves from spreading out into space, was employed by the Great Northern Telegraph Company in New Castle, England, but was forced by deafness to retire at the age of 24. Because of the unusual methods which he often used in solving his problems, many of his papers were not accepted for publication and finally in 1892 he published them himself in two volumes.

To the question: 'The angle which a radio wave makes with a tangent to the earth', 99 persons out of 224 answer WAVE ANGLE; while 32 answer ELEVATION. The term ELEVATION is used in gunnery for this same angle, the tilt of the gun up from the horizontal, and ought to be used in radio for the tilt of the transmitted wave up from the horizon. But scientists tend to develop their own jargons, and in radio this is called the WAVE ANGLE.

145. *ACCOMMODATION* (ăk-kŏm-mō-dā'-shŏn) *n.* In physiology, the automatic adjustment of the eye to distinct vision at different distances.

The verb to ACCOMMODATE comes directly from the Latin *accommodare*, a combination of *ad*, to, and *commodare*, to fit, the source of the English adjective COMMODIUS, fit, suitable. This in turn comes from *com-*, with, according to, and *modus*, measure, the source of MODERATE, to hold within measure, restrain, and MODE, a manner of acting.

ACCOMMODATION is accomplished by changing the convexity of the crystalline lens of the eye, altering its shape by making it either more convex on each side and so thicker, or flatter and thinner, in order to change its focal length. As the distance from the lens to the back of the eye cannot be changed, the focal length of the lens is changed in order to focus the rays from a near-by object, by making the lens thicker, with greater curvature on each side. Reread FOCAL LENGTH (7).

To the definition: 'Power of adjustment of the lens of the eye for objects at different distances', 348 persons out of 537 answer ACCOMMODATION; but 79 answer EXTENSIBILITY. Judged by the small population tabulated in the special study, the word ACCOMMODATION is an intimate part of a general English literary vocabulary, for of 40 persons high in English vocabulary 36 answer correctly, while of 40 low in English vocabulary only 14

Power of adjustment of the lens of the eye for objects at different distances.

FORM E. 25.	BO	FW	LA	NY	NY	NY	NY	PH	TU	SUM
ACCOMMODATION	14	21	25	12	17	23	142	74	20	348
transformation	2	8	1	0	0	2	17	5	3	38
amplification	4	9	2	2	2	5	21	6	2	53
balance	2	2	1	1	0	1	5	2	0	14
extensibility	4	9	4	5	1	8	32	13	3	79
unmarked	2	1	0	0	0	1	1	0	0	5
total	28	50	33	20	20	40	218	100	28	537

FORM E. 25.	ENGLISH VOCABULARY	
	HIGH	LOW
ACCOMMODATION	36	14
transformation	2	3
amplification	2	8
balance	0	3
extensibility	0	12
unmarked	0	0
total	40	40

answer correctly, 12 marking EXTENSIBILITY. EXTENSIBILITY comes from the Latin verb *extendere*, to extend, grow longer, larger in area. EXTENSIBILITY is the capacity of being extended, quality of being extensible, as: 'The EXTENSIBILITY of a fiber or of a metal plate'. EXTENSIBILITY is almost a description of what happens to the lens of the eye when it ACCOMMODATES itself to seeing a distant object, for it flattens itself out, almost extends, so that parallel rays focus on the back of the eye.

Sir David Brewster, who lived from 1781 to 1868, author of Life, Writings, and Discoveries of Sir Isaac Newton, published in Edinburgh in 1855, wrote in 1831: 'The ACCOMMODATION of the eye to the distant vision of external objects'.

146. *EUSTACHIAN TUBE* (*ū-stă'-kĭ-ăn*). The communica- tion between the middle ear and the mouth, canal from the cavity of the tympanum to the upper part of the pharynx which supplies air to the ear-drum. Reread TYMPANUM (136).

The adjective EUSTACHIAN is the distinctive epithet in the names of several anatomical structures discovered by Bar- tolomeo Eustachio, an Italian anatomist who died in 1574. The

The air-passage-equalizing channel leading from the back of the mouth to behind the ear-drum.

FORM C. 17.		FORM CA. 18.	BO	NY HIGH	NY NEXT	NY REST	NY MISC.	SUM
sinus	45	sinus	7	15	39	178	21	260
semicircular		semicircular						
canal	30	canal	8	19	35	171	40	273
middle ear	25	pharynx	6	13	31	170	11	231
EUSTACHIAN		EUSTACHIAN						
TUBE	238	TUBE	73	336	261	399	148	1217
bronchial		bronchial						
passage	56	passage	6	17	34	182	13	252
unmarked	6	unmarked	0	0	0	0	1	1
total	400	total	100	400	400	1100	234	2234

proper name came originally from the Greek εὔσταχυς (eu- stachus), rich in corn, fruitful, blooming, a combination of εὖ (eu), well, good, as in EUGENIC, well born, and στάχυς (stachus), an ear of corn.

To the question: 'The air-passage-equalizing channel leading from the back of the mouth to behind the ear-drum', 54 per cent answer EUSTACHIAN TUBE, while the remainder divide al- most evenly among the four misleads.

From Hermann L. F. Helmholtz, Sensations of Tone, 1862: 'The drum of the ear is consequently completely shut off from the external passage and from the labyrinth. But it has free access to the upper part of the pharynx or throat, through the so-called EUSTACHIAN TUBE (generally pronounced *yoo-stai'-kĭ-ăn* but sometimes *yoo-stai'-shĭ-ăn*), which in Germany is termed a TRUMPET, because of the trumpet-like expansion of its pharyngeal extremity, and the narrowness of its opening into the drum. The end which opens into the drum is formed of bone, but the expanded pharyngeal end is formed of thin flexible cartilage or gristle, split along its upper side. The edges of the split are closed by a sinewy membrane. By closing the nose and mouth and either condensing the air in the mouth by pressure, or rarefying it by suction, air can be respectively driven into or drawn out of the drum through this tube. At the entrance of air into the drum, or its departure from it, we feel a sudden jerk in the ear, and hear a dull crack. Air passes from the pharynx to the drum, or from the drum to the pharynx only at the moment of making the motion of swallowing. When the air has entered the drum it remains there, even after nose and mouth are opened again, until we make another motion of swallowing. Then the air leaves the drum as we perceive by a second cracking in the ear, and the cessation of the feeling of tension in the drumskin which had remained up till that time. These experiments show that the tube is not usually open, but is opened only during swallowing, and this is explained by the fact that the muscles which raise the *velum-palati* or soft palate, and are set in motion on swallowing, arise from part of the cartilaginous extremity of the tube. Hence the drum is generally quite closed, and filled with air, which has a pressure equal to that of the external air, because it has from time to time, that is whenever we swallow, the means of equalising itself with the same by free communication.'

From Huxley in his Physiology: 'The function of the EUSTACHIAN TUBE is probably to keep the air in the tympanum of about the same tension as that on the other side'. Thomas Henry Huxley, the English biologist, 1825 to 1895, who at age 8 had two years of a 'pandemonium of a school', and after that, he says in his Life, 'neither help nor sympathy in any intellectual direction' until manhood, published his first paper at age twenty, when the aptitude inductive reasoning is at its height.

147. *INSTRUMENT FLYING* (ĭn'-strŭ-mĕnt flī'-ĭng). Controlling an aircraft solely by instruments, flying by electrical devices with no natural horizon continuously available, determining altitude and path by flight instruments.

To the question: 'Flight in which the course is determined not by landmarks but by calculation and the use of flight instruments', 289 persons out of 515 answer INSTRUMENT FLIGHT, 104 persons answer BLIND FLYING, and 93, DEAD RECKONING. With the present wording of the question all three are probably correct. Under INSTRUMENT FLYING Baughman's Aviation

Form A. Flight in which the course is determined not by landmarks but by calculation and the use of flight instruments.
Form AA. Determining a course by electrical devices with no natural horizon visible.

FORM A. 23.	FW	LA	NY	NY	NY	PH	SUM	FORM AA. 21.	NY
dead-reckoning	4	13	3	16	15	42	93	dead-reckoning	0
blind-flying	3	9	14	14	32	32	104	navigation	2
INSTRUMENT-FLIGHT	9	26	18	33	87	116	289	INSTRUMENT-FLYING	51
piloting	1	5	0	0	5	4	15	air piloting	0
contact-flying	1	0	1	0	1	1	4	contact-flying	4
unmarked	0	1	1	3	0	5	10	unmarked	0
total	18	54	37	66	140	200	515	total	57

Dictionary says: 'Improperly called BLIND FLYING'. Under BLIND LANDING The Illustrated Aviation Encyclopedia says: 'See INSTRUMENT LANDING'. BLIND FLYING and INSTRUMENT FLYING seem today to be synonymous, though BLIND FLYING is the older term used for flying with the old crude instruments before modern devices were available.

DEAD RECKONING, the only other frequently marked mislead, is determining geographical location by keeping an account, a reckoning, of the distance traveled and the course followed from the point of departure, or from the last accurately determined location. To eliminate DEAD RECKONING as a correct answer the question has been changed in the revised form AA to read: 'Determining a course by electrical devices with no natural horizon visible'. Out of 57 persons whose scores have been tabulated no one has marked DEAD RECKONING.

148. *DIFFRACTION GRATING* (*dĭf-frăk'-shŏn grā'-tĭng*).
A number of parallel narrow bars with open slots between through which light passes; now usually a sheet of glass with

Instrument for obtaining spectra.

FORM E. 29.	BO	FW	LA	NY	NY	NY	NY	PH	TU	SUM
sonometer	3	7	1	1	1	4	15	5	4	41
DIFFRACTION-GRATING	10	20	28	9	16	20	133	76	22	334
Geissler-tube	6	13	2	6	2	13	31	14	1	88
grid	2	2	0	2	0	1	9	0	0	16
reflecting-grating	3	5	2	2	1	1	26	3	1	44
unmarked	4	3	0	0	0	1	4	2	0	14
total	28	50	33	20	20	40	218	100	28	537

FORM E. 29.	ENGLISH VOCABULARY	
	HIGH	LOW
sonometer	1	7
DIFFRACTION-GRATING	32	15
Geissler-tube	2	7
grid	4	2
reflecting-grating	1	8
unmarked	0	1
total	40	40

straight parallel scratches which stop the light, and clear glass between which allows it to go through.

DIFFRACTION is easily defined as the bending of light around a corner. It is really the phenomenon which depends upon each point of light becoming a new source from which waves radiate in all directions. Each slot or transparent line in a diffraction grating is a source from which light waves emerge in an ever expanding cylinder with the slit as the central axis. Two or more such wave fronts show the phenomenon known as INTER-FERENCE, first demonstrated by Thomas Young in 1801. As the angle at which INTERFERENCE occurs depends upon the wave length, a DIFFRACTION GRATING breaks up the original light into its component colors or wave lengths.

To the question: 'Instrument for obtaining spectra', 334 persons out of 537 answer DIFFRACTION GRATING; but 88 answer GEISSLER TUBE. Heinrich Geissler was a German glassblower, 1814 to 1879, a maker of chemical and physical apparatus at Bonn. After sealing an electrode at each end of a glass tube, he pumped out nearly all the air. Under high voltage the tube glowed with a pale light. This is today the principle of the neon sign. Though a GEISSLER TUBE radiates different colors depending on the gas inside, a brilliant red when filled with neon instead of air, an intense yellow when filled with sodium, and almost pure white with carbon dioxide, a GEISSLER TUBE makes each gas glow with its own characteristic color; it does not break a complex ray of light into its constituent wave lengths, the essence of the spectrum.

The first DIFFRACTION GRATINGS were made by Joseph von Fraunhofer, 1787 to 1826, for whom the absorption lines in the sun's spectrum are now named. His gratings were of fine wires stretched parallel to one another. Modern gratings are made by drawing delicate lines with a diamond point on transparent glass or on a metallic mirror. The scratched lines stop the light, while the intervening unscratched spaces of transparent glass allow it to pass through undisturbed. This modern type of DIFFRACTION GRATING was first successfully ruled by Henry A. Rowland of Johns Hopkins University. DIFFRACTION GRATINGS commercially available have 15,000 to 25,000 lines to the inch, or occasionally as many as 30,000.

149. *PASCAL'S LAW* (*pahs-kahlz' law*). Pressure applied anywhere to a body of confined liquid is transmitted by the liquid so as to act with undiminished force on every square centimeter of the containing vessel, any change of pressure in an enclosed fluid at rest is transmitted undiminished to all parts of the fluid, extra pressure applied to liquids from outside is felt undiminished in all parts of the liquid.

Blaise Pascal was a French religious philosopher and mathematician who lived from 1623 to 1662, and who by the age of
17 had written: Traité des Sections Coniques. Through his
work on the equilibrium of fluids he is sometimes called one
of the founders of hydrodynamics or the dynamics of liquids.

To the question: 'The law that pressure is transmitted equally
in all directions at a given level in a fluid at rest', 56 per cent of
2234 persons answer PASCAL'S LAW; while 17 per cent answer

The law that pressure is transmitted equally in all directions
at a given level in a fluid at rest.

FORM C. 10.		FORM CA. 14. BO		NY HIGH	NY NEXT	NY REST	NY MISC.	SUM
Boyle's law	81	Boyle's law	27	44	58	207	47	383
Snell's law	16	Snell's law	4	5	18	148	10	185
PASCAL'S LAW	258	PASCAL'S LAW	60	321	292	439	131	1243
Stoke's law	20	Stoke's law	4	13	16	156	20	209
Le Chatelier's law	24	Le Chatelier's law	2	17	16	150	23	208
unmarked	1	unmarked	3	0	0	0	3	6
total	400	total	100	400	400	1100	234	2234

BOYLE'S LAW, the most frequently marked mislead in every
tabulation. Robert Boyle lived from 1627 to 1691; Pascal from
1623 to 1662. Both BOYLE'S LAW and PASCAL'S LAW deal with
pressures. BOYLE'S LAW applies to gases, PASCAL'S to liquids.
BOYLE'S LAW says that with pressure the volume of a gas becomes less. A liquid does not change in volume under pressure
as does a gas; so that PASCAL'S LAW deals with the distribution
of pressure through the liquid, not with its change in volume.
The principle is applied in mechanics to exert great force as
in the hydraulic press.

For thirty-five years of their lives Boyle and Pascal were
contemporaries, and their laws are today almost equally well
known, Boyle's law known to 44 per cent of those who have
been tested, Pascal's to 39 per cent. This is a single instance of
the finding that scientific discoveries of approximately the same
date are often about equally well known today.

Of the twelve scientific laws which appear in the present forms of the physics test and for which we have statistics, the six oldest, which date back to the seventeenth century or before, are known to the largest percentage of tested persons. Five of the laws are nineteenth century discoveries and, with the one exception of Ohm's law, are known to fewer persons.

This unexpectedly close relationship between the age of a law and its present familiarity suggests that students grasp scientific principles in about the order in which they were revealed historically. It might be said that students relive the his-

% UN-KNOWN	LAW	DATES OF SCIENTIST		DATE OF LAW
43	Archimedes' principle	287BC	to 212BC	
64	Kepler's laws	1571	to 1630	1609–1618
62	Pascal's law	1623	to 1662	1653
81	Hooke's law	1635	to 1703	1660
57	Boyle's law	1627	to 1691	1662
39	Newton's laws	1642	to 1727	1687
99	Charles' law	1746	to 1823	1787
99	Dalton's law	1766	to 1844	1802
19	Ohm's law	1787	to 1854	1827
98	Joule's law	1818	to 1889	1841
94	Stokes' law	1819	to 1903	1851
99	Joule-Thomson effect	1824	to 1907	1854
91	Stefan-Boltzmann law	1844	to 1906	1879
98	Zeeman effect	1865	to 1943	1896

tory of physics as they learn. Or, as a corollary, discoveries are made in approximately their relative order of difficulty. Technical concepts which are the easiest for the human mind to grasp were formulated first; while the more recent ones are harder for the mind to apprehend. The Laboratory believes that physical laws should be presented in physics textbooks in approximately their order of difficulty as indicated by the percentage of persons who mark each correctly in a test.

150. *VECTOR* (*věk'-tŏr*) *n*. A line of measured length and direction, drawn on a diagram, to represent a quantity which has corresponding magnitude and direction, a line which

by its direction represents the direction of a force or velocity or similar quantity, and by its length represents the strength or amount of the same quantity, a directive quantity, one which is fully determined by its magnitude and direction in space. VECTORS are equal only when their directions and magnitudes are both the same.

The word VECTOR, equivalent to the French *vecteur*, comes from the Latin *vector*, one who carries. This comes in turn from the past participle *vectus* of the verb *vehere*, to carry, convey, bear, the source of VEHICLE, a carriage, and CONVECTION, the carrying of heat from one place to another usually by the motion of hot air. As early as 1704 John Harris, in his Lexicon

Forms AB. 13, and D. 10. A vector quantity.

Form DA. 22. Having size and direction.

FORM AB. 13.	%	FORM D. 10.	%
density	3	density	20.3
volume	6	volume	15.7
size	10	size	9.7
FORCE	79	FORCE	47.7
temperature	2	temperature	3.2
unmarked	0	unmarked	3.4
total	100	total	100.0

FORM DA. 22.	%
density	5
potential	14
VECTOR	63
length	5
volume	12
unmarked	1
total	100

Technicum, defined VECTOR: 'A Line supposed to be drawn from any Planet moving round a Center, or the Focus of an Ellipsis, to that Center or Focus, is by some writers of the New Astronomy, called the VECTOR; because 'tis that line by which the Planet seems to be carried round its Center'. This is today called the RADIUS VECTOR, with the plural RADII VECTORES. A

RADIUS VECTOR is the length and direction of the line joining a variable point to a fixed origin.

The Human Engineering Laboratory has used two formats for its vocabulary tests. In one, five choices follow the test word, all easier than the test word, and one, the correct answer, a synonym of the test word. In the other format each item starts with a definition stated in simple terms, followed by five choices, one of which is the test word and fits the definition. This last type is used for the technical vocabulary tests; for in science there is rarely a close synonym, and the first type, demanding a synonym, is often impossible. Therefore in nearly all items of these technical vocabulary tests the test word is one of the five choices, and the question is stated in simple terms. But in some of the early versions the mistake was occasionally made of putting the test word in the question. Thus in item 13

Having direction and magnitude.

FORM C. 33. NY		FORM CA. 14. BO	NY HIGH	NY NEXT	NY REST	NY MISC.	SUM
directed	23	directed	5	8	35	178	15	241
VECTOR	180	VECTOR	44	297	156	273	147	917
scalar	58	scalar	20	21	53	195	14	303
graphic	55	graphic	13	27	79	222	32	373
linear	56	linear	17	46	71	232	25	391
unmarked	28	unmarked	1	1	6	0	1	9
total	400	total	100	400	400	1100	234	2234

of the original form AB of the physics vocabulary test designed in 1935, and retained in the resorting of items called form D, the question read: 'A VECTOR quantity', and the five choices were: DENSITY, VOLUME, SIZE, FORCE, and TEMPERATURE, to which 79 per cent of engineering students answered FORCE, and 48 per cent of a more unselected group. FORCE, as that word is used in physics, has not only amount but also direction. FORCES, acting in the same direction, can be added; but FORCES acting in different directions must be added geometrically, with direction taken into account. The word VECTOR calls attention to the fact that direction must be considered as well as magnitude. FORCE, VELOCITY, ACCELERATION, and MOMENTUM, are VECTOR quantities, while DENSITY, VOLUME, SIZE, and TEMPERATURE are not. In form DA the question was changed to: 'Having size and direction', and the test word VECTOR made one of the five choices.

The same word VECTOR was included in form CA of the physics vocabulary tests where it reads: 'Having direction and magnitude'; and also in form A of the aviation vocabulary. In form CA, 39 per cent answer VECTOR; while 18 per cent answer LINEAR. LINEAR (*lĭn'-ē-ahr*) means involving measurement in

Form A. A line representing a force and having a given length and direction.
Form AA. Straight line from leading edge to trailing edge.

FORM A. 16.	FW	LA	NY	NY	NY	PH	SUM	FORM AA. 18.	NY
chord	0	2	6	5	7	18	38	CHORD	32
vortex	0	2	3	6	12	12	35	vortex	9
VECTOR	15	30	16	33	79	116	289	vector	3
streamline	0	2	3	1	8	7	21	streamline	5
mean-line	3	18	8	17	34	42	122	mean-line	12
unmarked	0	0	1	4	0	5	10	unmarked	2
total	18	54	37	66	140	200	515	total	63

one direction only and can almost be justified. But among 400 persons, who score highest in a study of 1900 New York cases, 297 mark VECTOR and only 46 LINEAR. Among the 1100 lowest in the same 1900, 273 mark VECTOR and 232 LINEAR. VECTOR means showing LINEAR length in a specified direction in space.

In the earlier study of form C, where 45 per cent chose VECTOR, another 14 per cent chose SCALAR, the most frequently marked mislead. The terms VECTOR and SCALAR are often together in textbooks; they are almost opposites. A SCALAR is an ordinary number, without reference to direction. DENSITY, VOLUME, SIZE, and TEMPERATURE, are SCALAR quantities.

In form A of the aviation vocabulary test, where the question read: 'A line representing a force and having length and direction', 289 persons out of 515, or 56 per cent, answer VECTOR; while 122 answer MEAN LINE. In aviation, the term MEAN LINE, sometimes called the MEDIAN LINE, is half way between the upper and lower contours of an airfoil profile.

In his Elements of Quaternions, on which he was working at the time of his death in 1865 and which was published a year later, Sir William Rowan Hamilton says: 'A line, considered as having not only length, but also direction, is said to be a VECTOR'. Hamilton worked on an algebra of VECTORS in space, which before his time had been limited to a plane; but he wrote so fastidiously that he published comparatively little of the keen and original mathematical thinking which he seems to have done. A VECTOR, added to a point in space, gives a point at a certain distance and in a certain direction from the first.

151. *INTERFEROMETER* (*ĭn-ter-fĕ-rŏm'-ē-ter*) *n.* An apparatus to produce interference between two light waves from the same source, used to measure small displacements, distances, and movements, by means of this interference.

The word INTERFERENCE is a combination of the Latin *inter*, between, and *ferire*, to strike; while INTERFEROMETER, from the same source, ends with the Greek μέτρον (metron), measure, added most often today to signify the measuring instrument, as already discussed under PHOTOMETER (60), an instrument for comparing the brightness of two lights. The term INTERFERENCE was probably first applied to light by Dr. Thomas Young, professor of natural philosophy at the Royal Institution, London, in 1801 or 1802: 'It occurred to me that their cause must be sought in the INTERFERENCE of two portions of light'. As this explanation conflicted with the accepted corpuscular theory of light, Young was viciously attacked by Lord Brougham, a fanatical contributor to the Edinburgh Review and later Lord Chancellor of England. The term INTERFEROMETER seems not to have been coined until 1880 when it was used for the instrument designed by A. A. Michelson of Chicago.

To the question: 'Instrument used to measure lengths in terms of wave lengths of light', 332 persons out of 537 answer INTERFEROMETER, but 122 answer PRISM. Of 40 persons high in English vocabulary 34 answer correctly INTERFEROMETER; while of 40 low in English vocabulary 20 answer INTERFEROMETER, 10 PRISM. As early as 1728 Ephraim Chambers used phenomena associated with the PRISM as a basis for reasoning about the nature of light much as a hundred years later Young used INTER-

FERENCE. Chambers writes: 'PRISM, PRISMA, thus called from
πρίσμα (prisma), something sawn or cut off, in geometry, an
oblong solid or body, contained under more than four planes,
and whose bases are equal, and alike situated.

'The PRISM is generated by the motion of a rectilinear figure
descending always parallel to itself.

'PRISM, in dioptrics, is a glass in form of a triangular prism,
much used in experiments about the nature of light and
colours'.

The Michelson INTERFEROMETER separates the original light
beam into two wave trains which travel off at right angles to
one another. Each is then reflected back from a mirror, and the
two are reunited in the instrument. Moving one of the two

Instrument used to measure ordinary length in terms of wave
lengths of light.

FORM E. 36.	BO	FW	LA	NY	NY	NY	NY	PH	TU	SUM
grating	1	5	2	2	2	2	24	9	3	50
prism	6	13	6	8	5	7	56	15	6	122
compass	0	2	0	0	0	0	1	1	0	4
INTERFEROMETER	17	27	25	8	13	28	126	69	19	332
candle	1	3	0	2	0	0	8	5	0	19
unmarked	3	0	0	0	0	3	3	1	0	10
total	28	50	33	20	20	40	218	100	28	537

FORM E. 36. ENGLISH VOCABULARY

	HIGH	LOW
grating	5	3
prism	1	10
compass	0	0
INTERFEROMETER	34	20
candle	0	6
unmarked	0	1
total	40	40

mirrors a quarter of a wave length farther away or nearer
causes the two beams to differ by half a wave length. This produces complete INTERFERENCE by making the peaks of one wave
train coincide with the troughs of the other. Michelson and

Morley used this INTERFEROMETER in 1881 in their crucial experiment intended to show ether drift. The negative result lead to the theory of relativity.

GRATING is the only mislead chosen more often by high-English-vocabulary examinees and is the type of mislead which should be used in order to reduce the correlation of English vocabulary and physics vocabulary.

152. *STABLE EQUILIBRIUM* (stā'-bl ē-kwĭ-lĭb'-rē-ŭm).
Conditions in which any small change raises the center of gravity, a situation such that after a slight displacement conditions return to the original. EQUILIBRIUM is STABLE when the center of gravity of a system is already at its lowest point. Reread EQUILIBRIUM (6).

The word STABLE goes far back in English literature, perhaps to the year 1300. From 1591 comes: 'He which is tottering himſelfe, had neede leane unto a ſtable thing'. This adjective STABLE, as well as the corresponding noun STABLE, a building for horses, cattle, or domestic animals, come through Middle English and Old French from the Latin verb *stare*, to stand. A STABLE is a place where horses stand. The adjective STABLE means fixed, firm, steadfast, established, not easily overthrown. STABLE EQUILIBRIUM is a situation firmly enough established so that a slight disturbance does not overthrow it. A block on a table tilted by lifting one edge a little or one corner returns to its original position.

The word EQUILIBRIUM (6) is known to practically every high-school student; but the three kinds of equilibrium: STABLE, NEUTRAL, and UNSTABLE, are less familiar. With the definition: 'State in which a body if displaced returns to its original position', 285 persons in 537 mark STABLE EQUILIBRIUM; but 96 mark BALANCE OF INERTIA; 75 NEUTRAL EQUILIBRIUM; and 46 UNSTABLE EQUILIBRIUM.

UNSTABLE means not firm, insecure, unsteady. Un- is an Anglo-Saxon prefix meaning not, equivalent to the Latin prefix *in-*, not. UNSTABLE EQUILIBRIUM is a situation in which a very slight displacement lowers the center of gravity, as a block delicately balanced on one edge or a bar balanced on a knife edge, where the slightest touch destroys the balance.

NEUTRAL EQUILIBRIUM is where conditions can be changed without changing the center of gravity up or down, the new situation is as stable as the original. A cylinder on its side on a flat surface can be rolled over without raising or lowering the center of gravity. It was and is in NEUTRAL EQUILIBRIUM.

State in which a body if displaced will return to its original position.

FORM E. 15.	BO	FW	LA	NY	NY	NY	NY	PH	TU	SUM
neutral equilibrium	4	8	4	2	1	6	36	12	2	75
STABLE EQUILIBRIUM	12	24	20	9	14	20	111	56	19	285
unstable equilibrium	2	5	3	2	0	5	17	8	4	46
rest	1	3	3	2	2	3	11	7	0	32
balance of inertia	6	10	3	5	3	6	43	17	3	96
unmarked	3	0	0	0	0	0	0	0	0	3
total	28	50	33	20	20	40	218	100	28	537

FORM E. 15.   ENGLISH VOCABULARY

	HIGH	LOW
neutral equilibrium	1	9
STABLE EQUILIBRIUM	33	15
unstable equilibrium	6	6
rest	0	3
balance of inertia	0	7
total	40	40

A body in UNSTABLE EQUILIBRIUM continues to move in the direction given to it by a slight disturbing force.

A body in NEUTRAL EQUILIBRIUM remains stationary in its new position.

A body in STABLE EQUILIBRIUM returns to its original position after being slightly disturbed.

153. DENSITY (dĕn'-sĭ-tē) n. Mass per unit volume; weight in grams or in pounds of a specified amount of matter, usually a cubic centimeter or a cubic foot.

The noun DENSITY and the corresponding adjective DENSE

come from the Latin *densus*, close, thick, dense. DENSE, in literary use, means close, compact, as: 'A DENSE forest'. The corresponding noun is usually DENSENESS, as: 'The DENSENESS of the forest'. DENSITY is reserved for the scientific concept mass per unit volume.

To the question: 'Mass per unit volume', 55 per cent of 2234 people answer correctly DENSITY; but 15 per cent answer SPECIFIC GRAVITY, the most frequently marked mislead in every

Mass per unit volume.

FORM C. 20. NY		FORM CA. 13. BO		NY HIGH	NY NEXT	NY REST	NY MISC.	SUM
specific		specific						
volume	42	volume	12	14	31	180	19	256
DENSITY	263	DENSITY	51	310	290	425	163	1239
heaviness	13	compactness	3	0	7	131	2	143
specific		specific						
gravity	50	gravity	20	45	45	198	32	340
specific		specific						
weight	26	weight	14	31	27	166	18	256
unmarked	6	unmarked	0	0	0	0	0	0
total	400	total	100	400	400	1100	234	2234

tabulation. DENSITY depends upon the units in which both MASS and VOLUME are measured. Since the English system ordinarily gives MASS in pounds and VOLUME in cubic feet, DENSITY equals pounds per cubic foot. In the metric system where MASS is in grams, VOLUME in cubic centimeters, DENSITY becomes grams per cubic centimeter. SPECIFIC GRAVITY is the DENSITY of any substance compared with the DENSITY of a standard, usually water. Thus:

$$\text{SPECIFIC GRAVITY} = \frac{\text{DENSITY OF SUBSTANCE}}{\text{DENSITY OF STANDARD (water)}}.$$

SPECIFIC GRAVITY is a ratio and independent therefore of the units. It is the same in both the English and metric systems.

In the metric system and when the standard of comparison is water SPECIFIC GRAVITY and DENSITY are numerically identical. One cubic centimeter of water weighs one gram and the DENSITY of water, the denominator of the SPECIFIC GRAVITY ratio, is therefore unity. But DENSITY and SPECIFIC GRAVITY are not synonymous, for in the English system the DENSITY of water equals 62.5 pounds per cubic foot; and the DENSITY of any substance is 62.5 times as great as its SPECIFIC GRAVITY.

154. *MOMENTUM* (*mō-mĕn'-tŭm*) *n.* That property of a moving body which makes it difficult to stop, quantity of motion, mass times velocity. Double the velocity of a moving automobile and its MOMENTUM doubles; double its mass and its MOMENTUM doubles.

The word MOMENTUM comes from the Latin *momentum*, movement, from *movere*, to move. The Latin suffix *-mentum* is frequently added to a verb to form the corresponding noun, the result of an act. Thus *frangere* is to break, and *fragmentum* is a

The product of mass and velocity.

FORM BA. 24.	%	FORM D. 29.	%
kinetic energy	43	kinetic energy	26.8
MOMENTUM	46	MOMENTUM	56.6
torque	1	moment	0.9
potential energy	6	potential energy	7.7
moment of inertia	4	moment of inertia	6.4
unmarked	0	unmarked	1.7
total	100	total	100.1

FORM DA. 15.	%	FORM DB. 12.	NY
kinetic energy	24	kinetic energy	39
MOMENTUM	61	MOMENTUM	40
shear	0	work	7
potential energy	9	potential energy	11
moment of inertia	6	moment of inertia	8
unmarked	0	unmarked	1
total	100	total	106

piece broken off. From the Latin verb *ornare*, to equip, fit out, and then to adorn, came *ornamentum*, at first equipment, and then furniture, trappings, and then adornment, embellishment. From the verb *alere*, to nourish, came *alimentum*, nourishment, more familiar today as the adjective ALIMENTARY, pertaining to food, nourishment, as: the ALIMENTARY CANAL. Usually in English this Latin suffix *-mentum* becomes -MENT, as FRAGMENT, ORNAMENT, and the unusual ALIMENT, food; but the technical term MOMENTUM has retained the full Latin ending, only MO- coming from the original verb *movere*, to move.

'The product of mass and velocity' is marked correctly by 61 per cent of students as MOMENTUM; but by another 24 per cent is thought to be KINETIC ENERGY. Both KINETIC ENERGY and MOMENTUM are directly proportional to mass. KINETIC ENERGY is proportional to the square of the velocity; the formula being:

$$\tfrac{1}{2} \times \text{mass} \times \text{velocity}^2.$$

The KINETIC ENERGY of a body, called by G. G. Coriolis its VIS VIVA, is the amount of work which has been done to give the body its present MOMENTUM. KINETIC ENERGY is a scalar quantity, work done; MOMENTUM, called by Descartes QUANTITY OF MOTION, is a vector quantity, for MOMENTUM has direction. MOMENTUM is proportional to velocity. The formula for MOMENTUM is:

$$\text{mass} \times \text{velocity}.$$

From Ephraim Chambers' Cyclopaedia published in 1728, the year after Newton's death, comes: 'This is called MOVING FORCE, *vis motrix*, and by some late writers, *vis viva*, to distinguish it from the *vis mortua* spoken of before; and by these appellations, however different, the same thing is understood by all mathematicians; namely, that power of displacing, of withstanding opposite moving forces, or of overcoming any dead resistance, which resides in a moving body, and which, in whole or in part, continues to accompany it, so long as the body moves'.

'The Newtonians and Cartesians maintain, that the moving FORCE is in proportion to the velocity with which the bodies move. But the Leibnizians assert, that the moving FORCE is in proportion to the square of the velocity; so that if the velocity of a moving body be double, triple, quadruple, &c. that of another equal body, the FORCE of the former will be four times, nine times, sixteen times as great as that of the latter'.

Of this controversy Florian Cajori says in his History of Physics, which should be owned by every young scientist: 'There arose a curious dispute between the Cartesians and the

Leibnizians on the measure of the efficiency of a moving body. Descartes took the efficacy to be proportional to the velocity; Leibniz took it to vary as the square of the velocity. The controversy lasted over half a century, until, finally, it was brought to a close by Jean-le-Rond D'Alembert's remarks in the Preface to his Dynamique, 1743. The long dispute was merely one of words. The efficiency of a body in motion varies as its velocity, if we consider the time. A body thrown vertically upward with double the velocity ascends twice as long a time. The efficiency varies as the square of the velocity, if we consider the distance. A body thrown vertically upward with double the velocity ascends four times as far'. Cajori then adds: 'Those parts of mechanics which a beginner usually finds hard to learn are the parts which, in the development of the science, were difficult to overcome'.

Today that characteristic of a moving body which varies with the square of its velocity is called ENERGY; that which varies directly with the velocity is called MOMENTUM.

155. *FUNCTION* (*fŭnk'-shŏn*) *n.* Any variable quantity dependent on the value of one or more other variables, an expression written in terms of variables on which its own value depends, a mathematical quantity which has a definite value when special values are assigned to other quantities, a variable regarded as determined by other variables.

This use of the word FUNCTION, or to be more precise of the Latin *functio*, is due to Gottfried Wilhelm Leibniz, spelt Leibnitz in most English texts though Cajori uses the German Leibniz. It appeared first in the Latin correspondence, later published in two volumes, 1745, between Leibnitz, 1646 to 1716, and Jean Bernoulli, 1667 to 1748, brother of Jacques Bernoulli and a member of the scientifically illustrious Bernoulli family.

To the question: 'A variable whose value varies with the value assigned to another variable', 58 persons out of 132 answer FUNCTION; while 25 answer INDEPENDENT VARIABLE. The INDEPENDENT VARIABLE is the quantity on which the value of the FUNCTION depends. It is the variable to which various values are assigned in order to compute the corresponding values of the FUNCTION. The FUNCTION is the DEPENDENT VARIABLE.

In the 1779 edition of Ephraim Chambers' Cyclopaedia there appeared: 'The term FUNCTION is used in algebra, for an analytical expression any way compounded of a variable quantity,

A variable whose value varies with the value assigned to another variable.

FORM A. 15	BO	NY	SUM	FORM AA. 22.	NY
independent				independent	
variable	4	9	13	variable	25
abscissa	1	4	5	abscissa	13
ordinate	3	5	8	ordinate	23
FUNCTION	12	23	35	FUNCTION	58
argument	0	0	0	expression	12
unmarked	0	0	0	unmarked	1
total	20	41	61	total	132

and of numbers, or constant quantities'. It is not any special value of FUNCTION of x, $f(x)$, which is the FUNCTION, but the quantity $f(x)$ considered as a variable and dependent on x.

156. *KEPLER'S THREE LAWS* (*kĕp'-ler*). First: Each planet moves in an ellipse with the sun at one focus; second: The line from the sun to the planet sweeps over equal areas in equal times; and third: The cube of the planet's mean distance from the sun is proportional to the square of its period of revolution.

These three laws depend upon the complementary labors of two great men: Tycho Brahe the observer, and Johann Kepler who traced integrating threads. A year before Tycho's sudden death in 1601 Johann Kepler became his assistant at Prague, and later succeeded him as principal mathematician to Rudolph the Second, the German emperor.

Starting with the assumption that the planets move in circles with the sun at the center, Kepler computed the position of the planet Mars as seen from the earth at the time of each Tycho observation. Kepler's theory and Tycho's precise facts failed to agree. After trying other diameters for the orbits of Mars and the earth, Kepler reverted to the Ptolemaic notion of the earth as the center and, using an epicycle on a deferent, a small circle moving around a large one, he reduced the discrepancies; but still his computed positions differed from Tycho's painstaking observations by as much sometimes as eight minutes of arc, a quarter of the apparent diameter of the moon. Believing that Tycho's recorded positions were not in error by so much, Kepler abandoned the circle and, after more floundering, tried

Three laws stating the paths, speeds, and periods, of the planets.

FORM BA. 23.	%	FORM D. 28.	%
Kirchhoff's laws	26	Kirchhoff's laws	21.7
Newton's laws	14	Newton's laws	14.0
Faraday's laws	5	Faraday's laws	8.6
laws of falling bodies	6	laws of falling bodies	10.3
KEPLER'S LAWS	47	KEPLER'S LAWS	40.8
unmarked	2	unmarked	4.6
total	100	total	100.0

FORM DA. 30.	%	FORM DB. 19.	NY
Kirchhoff's	9	Kirchhoff's	13
Newton's	19	Newton's	18
Faraday's	10	Faraday's	14
laws of falling bodies	4	Laplace's	15
KEPLER'S	55	KEPLER'S	45
unmarked	3	unmarked	1
total	100	total	106

an ellipse with the sun at one focus. Theory agreed with observation. Each simple assumption had required enormous labor to test against Tycho's observations; but Kepler persisted until he found one of the most far-reaching groups of laws of all science.

In answer to the question: 'Three laws stating the paths, speeds, and periods, of the planets', 55 per cent of students answer correctly Kepler's; but 19 per cent answer Newton's. Starting with Kepler's third law, Sir Isaac Newton, who was born twelve years after Kepler's death, reasoned that the attractive force between two bodies should vary inversely as the square of the distance between them. He then attempted to apply this conclusion by comparing the drop of the moon toward the earth each second with 16 feet, the distance an object drops at the earth's surface in the first second. He failed much as Kepler had failed at first, but for a different reason. Kepler had Tycho's accurate observations and it was Kepler's own early assumptions which were wrong. Newton's inverse square assumption, which he had made before he was twenty-three, was correct, but the radius of the earth which he used in his computations was wrong. Nearly twenty years elapsed before a new measurement of the earth's radius enabled Newton to repeat his computations and find as did Kepler an agreement between theory and observations. Newton needed Kepler's third law with which to start; and Kepler needed Tycho's observations.

157. *SUBLIMATION* (*sŭb-lĭ-mā'-shŏn*) *n.* The change from a solid to a gas without passing through the intermediate liquid phase.

The noun SUBLIMATION, and the corresponding verb, to SUBLIME (*sŭb-līm'*), are from the Latin *sublimare*, to lift up, raise on high. The Latin verb comes in turn from the adjective *sublimis*, high, lofty, uplifted. From this comes the English adjective SUBLIME, high in excellence, surpassing, exalted, a word in literary use, but unknown to 36 per cent of students, and to 20 per cent of adults in general.

To the question: 'Change of state from a solid to a gas without passing through the liquid phase', 52 per cent of 2234 people answer SUBLIMATION; but 15 per cent answer EFFLORESCENCE, and 14 per cent EVAPORATION. In the earlier study of form C 68 per cent answered SUBLIMATION; 12 per cent, EFFLORESCENCE; and 11 per cent, EVAPORATION. EFFLORESCENCE is a highly technical term with a sharply defined meaning. It is the process by which crystals give up their water of crystallization when exposed to the air. One molecule of sodium carbonate (Na_2CO_3) combines with ten molecules of water to form a white crystal, washing soda. The formula is $Na_2CO_3 \cdot 10H_2O$. Upon exposure to the air at ordinary temperatures part of the water of crystallization evaporates and the crystals crumble into white powder. With similar crystals of sodium sulphate

($Na_2SO_4 \cdot 10H_2O$) loss of water of crystallization occurs on exposure to air. This process is called EFFLORESCENCE. EFFLORESCENCE occurs only at ordinary temperatures and applies only to water of crystallization. SUBLIMATION has nothing to do with water of crystallization and does not usually occur at ordinary temperatures, except for a few substances such as camphor and moth balls.

The word EVAPORATION (20) describes the change from a liquid to a gas. SUBLIMATION is the change of a solid into a gas without going through the liquid stage. Solids MELT and be-

Change of state from a solid to a gas without passing through the liquid phase.

FORM C. 3.	NY	FORM CA. 12.	BO	NY HIGH	NY NEXT	NY REST	NY MISC.	SUM
evaporation	44	evaporation	15	10	47	203	31	306
SUBLI-								
MATION	272	SUBLIMATION	50	344	269	362	145	1170
efflorescence	48	efflorescence	19	25	48	205	36	333
boiling	4	distillation	1	3	3	145	3	155
ebullition	29	ebullition	14	18	33	185	18	268
unmarked	3	unmarked	1	0	0	0	1	2
total	400	total	100	400	400	1100	234	2234

come liquids. Liquids EVAPORATE and become gases. Solids SUBLIME and become gases directly without passing through the liquid stage. The corresponding nouns are: MELTING, EVAPORATION, and SUBLIMATION.

158. *EFFUSIOMETER* (*ĕf-fū-sĭ-ŏm'-ē-ter*) *n*. An instrument to measure relative rates of diffusion of gases, a glass jar with a tiny hole in the top and a large one immersed in water at the bottom.

The verb to EFFUSE, and the noun EFFUSION, both come from the Latin *effusus*, the past participle of *effundere*, to pour out, flow forth. This verb is a combination of *ex*, out, forth, and *fundere*, to pour. From *fundere*, to pour, comes FOUNDRY, a place where metals are poured. EFFUSION is outpouring, flowing forth, spilling, shedding. In literature, an EFFUSION is an outpouring of thought in writing. In physics, the word was first used by Thomas Graham (grām), the Scottish chemist, who formulated the law of DIFFUSION of gases in 1834. DIFFUSION is the gradual mixing of two substances, the spread of each

Glass jar with tiny hole in top and large one in bottom immersed in water, used to measure relative rates of diffusion of gases.

FORM BA. 8.	%	FORM D. 9.	%
chronometer	2	chronometer	2.0
EFFUSIOMETER	79	EFFUSIOMETER	64.9
hygrometer	12	hygrometer	15.1
manometer	6	manometer	2.6
analyzer	1	hypsometer	12.0
unmarked	0	unmarked	3.4
total	100	total	100.0

FORM DA. 7.	%	FORM DB. 25.	NY
hydrometer	10	hydrometer	9
EFFUSIOMETER	50	EFFUSIOMETER	60
hygrometer	15	hygrometer	16
manometer	7	manometer	8
hypsometer	16	hypsometer	12
unmarked	2	unmarked	1
total	100	total	106

into the other. EFFUSION is the gradual escape of a gas into a vacuum. A DIFFUSIOMETER measures the DIFFUSION between two gases. An EFFUSIOMETER, a term seldom used, measures the EFFUSION of a gas, its escape through tiny holes, into a vacuum.

To the question: 'A glass jar with a tiny hole in the top and a large one where it is immersed in water at the bottom, which is used to measure relative rates of diffusion of gases', 50 per cent of students answer correctly EFFUSIOMETER; but 16 per cent answer HYPSOMETER and 15 per cent HYGROMETER. In a previous study of this test 12 per cent of students chose HYPSOMETER and 15 per cent HYGROMETER. The word HYPSOMETER (*hĭp-sŏm'-ē-ter*) comes from the Greek ὕψι (hypsi), high, aloft, and μέτρον (metron), measure. The HYPSOMETER is a thermometric barometer; it measures the temperature of boiling water under different atmospheric pressures and by changes in this temperature indicates altitudes.

The word HYGROMETER (*hī-grŏm'-ē-ter*) comes from the Greek ὑγρός (hygros), wet, moist, and the same μέτρον (metron), measure. The HYGROMETER determines the amount of moisture in the atmosphere, specifically the ratio of the actual amount to complete saturation.

The EFFUSIOMETER measures EFFUSION, the escape of gas molecules through a tiny hole.

159. *SLOPE INTERCEPT* (*slōp ĭn'-ter-sĕpt*). An equation in which one term gives the slope of a straight line and a second term its y intercept.

Form of equation of the first order represented by: $y = ax + b$.

FORM C. 19.	CH	FORM CA. 22.	CH	LA	NY	NY	PH	SUM
two-point	11	two-point	3	4	9	38	5	59
intercept	9	intercept	3	4	10	28	7	52
normal	12	normal	10	7	17	49	12	95
polar	4	polar	2	2	3	12	3	22
SLOPE								
INTERCEPT	32	SLOPE INTERCEPT	21	17	56	146	43	283
unmarked	0	unmarked	1	3	2	4	4	14
total	68	total	40	37	97	277	74	525

FORM CB. 22.	NY
two-point	13
intercept	16
normal	9
polar	6
SLOPE INTERCEPT	39
unmarked	3
total	86

The equation: $y = mx + b$ is a straight line. When the second term, b, equals zero, $y = mx$; or transposing: $m = y / x$. This is the SLOPE of a straight line through the origin. A road is said to rise one foot in twenty, one foot up parallel to the y axis for every twenty feet measured horizontally, parallel to the x axis. The beaches in Normandy rise one foot in a hundred. The constant m, that is the rise y divided by the horizontal distance x, is the SLOPE.

At the point where x equals zero, the line crosses the vertical, y axis. The constant b is therefore the y INTERCEPT, the distance from the origin to the point at which the line crosses the y axis. Knowing the direction, the SLOPE, and the exact location of any point fixes a line. The SLOPE-INTERCEPT equation gives the SLOPE m and the INTERCEPT b.

Many of the terms in this book fall statistically about where one might expect; but this concept of SLOPE INTERCEPT seems far more difficult than its position as word 159. Yet several independent studies agree within the expected error. SLOPE, which is only half of SLOPE INTERCEPT, should, it would seem, be understood first; and yet SLOPE is word 176, seventeen words further along and so approximately the same difficulty as SLOPE INTERCEPT, certainly not easier.

160. *SIMILAR* (*sĭm'-ĭ-lahr*) *adj.* Of the same shape; 'Such as have their angles severally equal, and the sides about those angles proportional'.

John Harris, the high-flying clergyman, who wrote the definition given above, says of SIMILAR triangles: 'Such as have their three angles respectively equal to one another'; and of SIMILAR segments of a circle he says: 'Such as contain equal angles'. The same Charles Hutton who is credited with helping to establish the present incorrect meaning of TRAPEZOID wrote in his Course of Mathematics: 'Equiangular triangles are SIMILAR, and are proportional to the squares of their like sides'. Dionysius Lardner, in his Treatise on Geometry, 1840: 'Two geometrical figures which have the same shape or form, but are constructed on a different scale, are said to be similar figures'.

SIMILAR comes from the Latin *similis*, like, the source of numerous English words. DISSIMILAR means not alike, different. To SIMULATE is to pretend a likeness, assume a false appearance of likeness, to DISSEMBLE, a word from the same source. A SIMILITUDE is a likeness in constitution, a similarity; while a

VERISIMILITUDE is like the truth, similar to the truth, a likelihood. A SIMILE is a statement of likeness between two things. Finally through Old French come a number of words of which DISSEMBLE and RESEMBLE, to be like, are illustrations.

To the question: 'Two triangles having all their corresponding angles equal', 316 persons out of 525 answer correctly SIMILAR. But 124 answer CONGRUENT. According to Edward Phillips, 1706, CONGRUENT figures: 'Are such as being laid one upon

Form CB. 19. Triangles having all their corresponding angles equal but not their sides.

FORM C. 25.	CH	FORM CA. 9.	CH	LA	NY	NY	PH	SUM
commensurate	0	equivalent	2	1	8	3	8	22
congruent	24	congruent	16	5	20	70	13	124
SIMILAR	38	SIMILAR	16	24	59	171	46	316
comple-								
mentary	3	complementary	4	2	6	8	0	20
coangular	2	coangular	2	4	4	25	5	40
unmarked	0	unmarked	0	1	0	0	2	3
total	67	total	40	37	97	277	74	525

FORM CB. 19.	NY
equivalent	3
congruent	23
SIMILAR	52
dissimilar	0
coangular	6
unmarked	2
total	86

another, will exactly meet and cover one another'. From Charles Leudesdorf's translation of Cremona's Elements of Projective Geometry: 'Two figures are said to be CONGRUENT when the one may be superposed upon the other so as exactly to coincide with it'.

By derivation CONGRUENT comes from *congruens, congruentis*, the present participle of *congruere*, to agree, suit, fit, accord. In literature CONGRUENT means agreeing, corresponding, and so might easily be used of similar triangles; but in geometry CONGRUENT has come to mean having both sides and angles equal, while SIMILAR means having the angles equal.

Euclid, in his Elements consisting of thirteen books, says: 'SIMILAR solid figures are such as have their solid angles equal, each to each, and are contained by the same number of similar planes'.

As the word SIMILAR is applied to figures which have all their corresponding angles equal, it follows, for ordinary Euclidean space, that all their corresponding lengths are proportional, their corresponding areas are in the ratios of the squares of their lengths, and their volumes in the ratios of the cubes of their lengths.

161. *RADIAN* (*rā'-dĭ-ăn*) *n.* An angle at the center of a circle made between two radii separated by an arc of the circle whose curved length equals the radius, an angle subtended at

The angle formed by lines to the center of a circle from the ends of an arc which is equal to the radius.

FORM C. 28.	CH	FORM CA. 14.	CH	LA	NY	NY	PH	SUM
RADIAN	27	RADIAN	23	23	61	137	42	286
inclination	2	inclination	0	1	1	7	1	10
triangulation	5	triangulation	0	0	13	36	9	58
vector angle	23	vector angle	13	9	12	71	15	120
sextant	9	sextant	4	4	10	25	6	49
unmarked	2	unmarked	0	0	0	1	1	2
total	68	total	40	37	97	277	74	525

FORM CB. 17.	NY
RADIAN	57
solid angle	2
inclination	5
vector angle	16
sextant	6
unmarked	0
total	86

the center of a circle by an arc equal in length to the radius. Called UNIT ANGLE in circular measure. Reread RADIUS (17).

Since the circumference of a circle equals π times the diameter or 2π times the radius, there are 2π RADIANS in a complete circle. A RADIAN is therefore just under 60 degrees, actually $57°\ 17'\ 44''.80625$.

From a Treatise on Natural Philosophy, 1867, by Sir William Thomson and Peter G. Tait comes: 'The usual unit angle is that which subtends at the center of a circle an arc whose length is equal to the radius; for brevity we shall call this angle a RADIAN'. A majority of mathematical terms date back historically and, in line with the Laboratory's notion that the present understanding of a word is proportional to its age, are better known than this recently coined addition.

To the question: 'The angle formed by lines drawn to the center of a circle from the ends of an arc which is equal to the radius', 286 persons out of 525 answer RADIAN; while 120 answer VECTOR ANGLE, by far the most frequently marked mislead. The VECTOR ANGLE is the angle between some sort of reference line and a line to any point which it is desired to place. This line is also called the RADIUS VECTOR. The VECTOR ANGLE places the position of a point in polar coordinates. A RADIAN is a unit of angular measurement. From Mensuration by George B. Halsted, 1881: 'The number which expresses any angle in RADIANS also expresses its intercepted arc in terms of the radius'.

162. $\neq$. This symbol means NOT EQUAL. It is defined by Eliakim Hastings Moore of Chicago, in his General Analysis of 1910, as LOGICAL DIVERSITY.

To the question: 'The symbol $\neq$', 35 persons out of 61 answer UNEQUAL, while 14 answer EQUAL AND IDENTICAL. The sign for equality, $=$, now used so generally, was introduced into England by Robert Recorde, in his Arithmetic. Robert Recorde, who lived from about 1500 to 1558, entered the University of Oxford about 1525; and was elected a fellow of All Souls College in 1531. In 1540, before going to Cambridge to take a medical degree in 1545, he published the Grounde of Artes, octavo, about the size of a modern novel. Returning to Oxford, he once more taught arithmetic and mathematics publicly as he had before going to Cambridge, that is, for the university as a whole and not for any one college. Still later in London he acted as physician to Edward VI and to Queen Mary. There in 1557 he published The Whetstone of Witte, the first book on algebra in English. He died in the King's Bench prison, Southwark, where he was confined for debt.

Before Recorde, and even for many years after, the words EQUAL, AEQUALES, and the abbreviation AEQ. were used in place

The symbol $\neq$.

FORM A. 48.	BO	NY	SUM
equal and			
identical	3	11	14
greater	0	2	2
less	0	0	0
UNEQUAL	12	23	35
disproved	3	5	8
unmarked	2	0	2
total	20	41	61

of any symbol, even by such men as Kepler, Galileo, Napier, and Briggs. A line drawn through the modern equal sign, $\neq$, means just what it ought to mean, NOT EQUAL.

163. *DIHEDRAL* (*dī-hē'-drăl*) *adj.* Contained between two planes, having two sides, with two plane faces.
The adjective DIHEDRAL comes from the Greek δι- (di-), which stands for δίς (dis), twice, and ἕδρα (hedra), a seat, base, already met and discussed under POLYHEDRON (134), many seated, many based. This Greek word ἕδρα (hedra), a base, seat, enters numerous geometrical terms, as: OCTAHEDRON, ending in the -ON of the noun instead of the -AL of the adjective, an eight-based figure; and DODECAHEDRON, a twelve-based figure. The H of these words, all of which have at times in the past been spelt without the H, comes from the Greek ASPER, the mark over the Greek ε (e), which is represented in English by the letter H: ἑ (he). Thus the Greek ἕλιξ (elix) is written HELIX in English; the Greek ἡλιοτρόπιον (eliotropion), HELIOTROPE.
To the question: 'Angle formed by the intersection of two planes', 252 persons out of 525 answer DIHEDRAL; and 109 VECTOR. A VECTOR is a line which represents a force or other quantity

with both magnitude and a definite direction. A VECTOR angle
is therefore an angle between a line and some other reference
line, often the angle between a radius vector and some reference
line. A DIHEDRAL angle is the angle between two planes.

In the revised form CB the new mislead INCIDENCE, replacing
the useless SHEAF, has proved even more attractive than VECTOR,
and is marked by 21 out of the 86 whose scores have been
tabulated. The word INCIDENCE comes from the Latin *incidens*,

Angle formed by the intersection of two planes.

FORM C. 37.	CH	FORM CA. 12.	CH	LA	NY	NY	PH	SUM
sheaf	5	sheaf	1	2	3	16	2	24
vector	17	vector	12	5	19	59	14	109
directrix	6	directrix	6	4	8	37	8	63
right	9	right	4	1	17	38	8	68
DIHEDRAL	31	DIHEDRAL	17	25	50	120	40	252
unmarked	0	unmarked	0	0	0	7	2	9
total	68	total	40	37	97	277	74	525

FORM CB. 21.	
incidence	21
vector	15
directrix	7
right	10
DIHEDRAL	33
unmarked	0
total	86

incidentis, the present participle of the verb *incidere*, to fall
upon, a combination of *in*, on, and *cadere*, to fall. The ANGLE
OF INCIDENCE is the angle between a ray of light striking a surface and a perpendicular to that surface.

A DIHEDRAL ANGLE is the angle between two planes which
meet at an edge, it is the mutual inclination of two intersecting
flat faces, also sometimes the angular space between them. In
airplane construction the lift of the wing when the tip rises
above the wing root, above the point at which the wing joins
the body of the plane, the angle between the horizontal and the
long axis of the wing, is called the DIHEDRAL angle.

164. *RHUMB LINE* (*rŭmb līn*). The path followed by a ship
sailing on one compass course always in the same direction
relative to the north pole, curve which cuts all meridians at the
same angle. Called also LOXODROMIC CURVE (*lŏk-sō-drŏm'-ĭk*)
and LOXODROMIC SPIRAL, from the Greek λοξός (loxos), slanting,
and δρόμος (dromos), a running course. A ship by following it
approaches nearer and nearer the pole without ever arriving.

The word RHUMB (*rŭmb*) comes through Old French from
a Spanish *rumbo* meaning a point of the compass, also a ship's
course. This in turn comes from the Latin *rhombus*, a magician's
circle; and this from the Greek ῥόμβος (rhombos), a spinning
top, magic wheel, whirling motion. The Greek ASPER, just discussed under DIHEDRAL (163), when over a vowel, is written

Form A. A line on a chart or on the surface of the earth which
crosses all meridians at the same angle.

Form AA. A line which crosses all meridians at the same angle.

FORM A. 49.	FW	LA	NY	NY	NY	PH	SUM	FORM AA. 24.	NY
beam	0	2	4	1	16	11	34	great circle	30
projection	0	5	7	9	21	32	74	projection	5
RHUMB LINE	15	24	13	23	73	98	246	RHUMB LINE	17
millibar	2	11	4	8	14	22	61	millibar	5
fix	1	7	6	12	14	20	60	fix	6
unmarked	0	5	3	13	2	17	40	unmarked	0
total	18	54	37	66	140	200	515	total	63

in English as an H before the vowel; but the same ASPER over
the Greek rho, ῥ (r), appears in English as an H after the R.
Thus the Greek word ἱπποπόταμος (ippopotamos) starts in Eng-
lish with H; while the Greek ῥινόκερως (rinoceros) is written
RHINOCEROS. A RHUMB is a point on the compass, and a RHUMB
LINE is a compass line.

To the question: 'A line on a chart or on the surface of the
earth which crosses all meridians at the same angle', 246 persons
in a population of 515 mark RHUMB LINE, while 74 mark PRO-
JECTION. The term PROJECTION is used regularly of various
systems of charting the surface of the globe on a flat plane. The
verb to PROJECT (*prō-jĕkt'*) comes from the Latin *pro*, forth,
and *jacere*, to throw. A PROJECTION may be something thrown

on a screen. In connection with map making a PROJECTION is
the lines of the round globe thrown onto a flat surface. Place
a roll of paper, like a cylinder, around the globe so that it
touches the globe all around at the equator, and so that from
top to bottom it is the same height as the diameter of the globe
from the North to the South Pole. Now pass a plane through
the globe, parallel to the plane of the equator, and PROJECT it
out to the surrounding cylinder. When the cylinder is unrolled
this PROJECTION appears as a straight line and represents one of
the parallels on the globe, one of the circles on the globe parallel
to the equator. The meridians, the great circles around the
globe passing through the poles and perpendicular to the
equator, are straight vertical lines on MERCATOR'S PROJECTION,
as this type of map is called. A RHUMB LINE on this sort of PRO-
JECTION, on Mercator's map, is a straight line. It is a fixed
compass course which continues to make the same angle with
the north and which therefore crosses all meridians at the same
angle. A RHUMB LINE on the globe goes round and round the
pole approximating an equiangular spiral.

In the revised form AA, where GREAT CIRCLE replaces the un-
popular BEAM, the new mislead attracts 30 out of the 63 whose
scores have been tabulated, nearly twice as many as the 17 who
mark the correct answer. A GREAT CIRCLE is any circle whose
center is the same as the center of the sphere on which it is
drawn. Any plane through the center of a sphere cuts the surface in a GREAT CIRCLE. Though in geometry a GREAT CIRCLE
seems a simple concept, and though on the globe a GREAT CIRCLE
is the shortest distance between two points, it is easier to navi-
gate a straight compass course, a RHUMB LINE.

165. *MODULUS OF ELASTICITY* (*mŏd'-ū-lŭs ŏv ē-lăs-tĭs'-
ĭ-tē*). The stretching force per unit area of cross-section
divided by the stretch per length; called also STRETCH COEFFI-
CIENT and YOUNG'S MODULUS.

This STRETCH COEFFICIENT or YOUNG'S MODULUS varies from
one material to another, varies also with the heat treatment,
and with the work which the material has undergone. Expressed
in dynes per square centimeter, YOUNG'S MODULUS or the CO-
EFFICIENT OF STRETCH for steel is about 20×10^{11}. Expressed

in tons per square inch the same figure is 13,000 or more. This means that to stretch steel one inch per inch, doubling its length, would require 13,000 tons per square inch. More practically

Force required to stretch an object to double its normal length.

FORM E. 20.	BO	FW	LA	NY	NY	NY	NY	PH	TU	SUM
torsion	4	5	3	1	1	15	39	9	3	80
MODULUS OF ELASTICITY	12	22	20	14	13	17	122	63	15	298
breaking strength	3	3	2	0	1	2	9	7	2	29
range of elasticity	6	14	8	5	3	5	41	18	6	106
wrench	1	5	0	0	2	0	7	3	2	20
unmarked	2	1	0	0	0	1	0	0	0	4
total	28	50	33	20	20	40	218	100	28	537

FORM E. 20.	ENGLISH VOCABULARY	
	HIGH	LOW
torsion	5	10
MODULUS OF ELASTICITY	28	14
breaking strength	3	2
range of elasticity	4	14
wrench	0	0
total	40	40

to compress it one thousandth of an inch per inch, or one thousandth of a foot per foot, requires 13 tons per square inch.

The slightly more difficult HOOKE'S LAW (214) states that the extension of a stretched wire is proportional to the stretching force. Expressed as an equation HOOKE'S LAW is:

$$\frac{\text{stretching force}}{\text{stretch}} = \text{constant.}$$

YOUNG'S MODULUS or COEFFICIENT is this constant obtained for different materials; it is the ratio of the tensile stress or longitudinal force per unit cross-section, in a stretched elastic solid, to the change in length per unit length.

To the question: 'Force required to stretch an object to double its normal length', 298 persons out of 537, or 55 per cent, answer MODULUS OF ELASTICITY; but 106 answer RANGE OF ELASTICITY and 80 TORSION. TORSION is a twisting, a change in shape, whereas YOUNG'S MODULUS OF ELASTICITY applies only to elongation or contraction. In his article on ELASTICITY in the Ninth Edition of the Encyclopaedia Britannica, Sir William Thomson, later Lord Kelvin, wrote: 'Thomas Young called THE MODULUS OF ELASTICITY of an elastic solid the amount of the end-pull or end-thrust required to produce any infinitesimal elongation or contraction. In this definition the definite article is clearly misapplied. There are, as we have seen, two moduluses of elasticity for an isotropic solid,—one measuring elasticity of bulk, the other measuring elasticity of shape'. The tendency of a material to twist or shear, to change shape, is expressed by the MODULUS OF RIGIDITY or SHEAR COEFFICIENT. Both this MODULUS OF RIGIDITY and the MODULUS OF ELASTICITY or YOUNG'S MODULUS differ from one material to another; the higher the MODULUS or COEFFICIENT the more the material resists twist or shear in one case, stretch or compression in the other.

166. *GALVANOMETER* (găl-vă-nŏm'-ē-ter) *n*. A delicate instrument for detecting the existence and determining the strength and direction of an electric current.
From Elementary Lessons in Electricity and Magnetism by Silvanus P. Thompson comes: 'An instrument for measuring the strength of electric currents by means of their electromagnetic action'.

The word GALVANOMETER is a combination of GALVANIC and the Greek μέτρον (metron), a measure, or more often a measuring instrument, as mentioned under INTERFEROMETER (151) and PHOTOMETER (60). The word GALVANIC comes from the proper name of the Italian Luigi Galvani, also called Aloisio Galvani, 1737 to 1798, professor of anatomy at Bologna.

To the question: 'An electromagnetic instrument used for comparing minute currents or voltages', 54 per cent of 2234 persons answer correctly GALVANOMETER; while 18 per cent answer AMMETER. This was also the most frequently marked mislead in the previous study where 75 per cent of 400 persons answered GALVANOMETER, and 10 per cent AMMETER. The same S. P. Thompson says: 'An AMMETER is a GALVANOMETER graduated so that its index reads directly on the scale the number of amperes flowing through the coil'. An AMMETER is an electromagnetic instrument which measures currents; but the word is usually applied to a commercial instrument, less accurate than a GALVANOMETER and with the scale calibrated in amperes.

It is said that J. S. C. Schweigger made the first GALVANOMETER in Germany in 1819, with a stationary coil and moving magnet. Claude Servais Mathias Pouillet, a professor in Paris, reversed the design in 1837 to a moving coil and stationary

An electromagnetic instrument for comparing minute currents or voltages.

FORM C. 14. NY		FORM CA. 10. BO	NY HIGH	NY NEXT	NY REST	NY MISC.	SUM
wattmeter	20	wattmeter	6	1	4	140	14	165
GALVA-		GALVA-					
NOMETER	299	NOMETER	64	328	300	384	132	1208
electrometer	30	electrometer	3	11	6	180	13	213
ammeter	41	ammeter	13	22	60	261	54	410
solenoid	7	poten-					
		tiometer	13	38	30	135	21	237
unmarked	3	unmarked	1	0	0	0	0	1
total	400	total	100	400	400	1100	234	2234

magnet, enabling the magnet to be made strong enough so that the earth's magnetism could be ignored. This type of GALVANOMETER was reinvented by Despretz and D'Arsonval about 1862, and is usually known today as the D'Arsonval GALVANOMETER.

167. *FUNDAMENTAL* (*fŭn-dă-měn′-tăl*) *n.* The lowest frequency at which current in a wire will be resonant. Reread FREQUENCY (51).

RESONANCE (40) is the vibration of one circuit or object or system in sympathy with another. The phenomenon occurs with sound and with mechanical objects as well as with electricity. A child's swing must be pushed in rhythm with its natural vibration so that each push adds a little to the motion. In this case the swing is the resonant body reacting to the push. The swing can go back and forth twice for every push, or three times. Its frequency can be double or treble. But a push more often than its natural period tends to stop it.

In music and electricity the natural period is called the FUNDAMENTAL. A wire held at each end vibrates as a whole emitting its FUNDAMENTAL note. A vibrating tuning fork of the

The lowest frequency at which current in a wire will be resonant.

FORM DA. 13.	%	FORM DB. 20.	NY
harmonic	21	harmonic	8
node	12	node	13
FUNDAMENTAL	54	FUNDAMENTAL	65
antinode	4	antinode	9
secondary	8	secondary	10
unmarked	1	unmarked	1
total	100	total	106

same note brought near it sets it in vibration. The same wire also vibrates as two halves each emitting a note double the frequency of the FUNDAMENTAL. This is the first HARMONIC.

Faraday discovered that variations of an electric current in one circuit create corresponding variations in another circuit near by. As current increases in one circuit magnetic lines travel outward from it and, by linking with a second circuit, induce in it a current.

To the question: 'The lowest frequency at which current in a wire will be resonant', 54 per cent of students mark FUNDAMENTAL, but 21 per cent mark HARMONIC. The first HARMONIC vibrates at double the frequency of the FUNDAMENTAL; the next HARMONIC at three times the FUNDAMENTAL. The trouble may be the wording of the question. There are two frequencies involved in resonance: one, that of the body sending out the vibrations and causing the resonance, the other, that of the body receiving the vibrations and vibrating in sympathy with the first. The receiving circuit vibrates with its own FUNDAMENTAL frequency and with multiples of it.

168. *DISSONANCE* (dĭs'-sō-năns) *n.* A combination of unrelated tones, discordance; Ellis in his beautiful translation
of Helmholtz says: When the united sound of two musical
tones is disturbed by the beats of the upper partials, so that a
greater or less part of the whole mass of sound is broken up into
pulses of tone, and the joint effect is rough.

The word DISSONANCE comes from the Latin *dis-*, apart, and
sonare, to sound. By derivation DISSONANCE is sounding apart,
the opposite of CONSONANCE, sounding together.

With this item the percentage of persons who mark the correct answer has changed comparatively little over the years.

The result of mingling incommensurable frequencies.

FORM BA. 25.	%	FORM D. 31.	%
resonance	6	resonance	6.9
harmonics	10	harmonics	6.9
standing waves	4	standing waves	4.9
overtones	33	overtones	23.7
DISSONANCE	46	DISSONANCE	55.6
unmarked	1	unmarked	2.0
total	100	total	100.0

FORM DA. 16.	%	FORM DB. 16.	NY
resonance	6	resonance	5
harmonics	9	harmonics	14
overtones	26	overtones	25
DISSONANCE	58	DISSONANCE	58
reinforcement	0	upper partials	4
unmarked	1	unmarked	0
total	100	total	106

Form B, revised to form BA in 1934, was combined with form
AA to become form D in 1936. This became form DA in 1938.

To the question: 'The result of a mingling of incommensurable frequencies', 9 per cent mark HARMONICS. The first
HARMONIC has twice the frequency of the fundamental. It
sounds an octave higher than the fundamental, in harmony with
it. The frequency of the second HARMONIC is three times the
frequency of the fundamental. An HARMONIC is a vibration with

a frequency an exact multiple of the fundamental. Such HAR-
MONICS sounding together produce a mingling of commensurable frequencies; for commensurable means measurable in the
same units, evenly divisible one into the other. HARMONICS, the
second most frequently marked mislead, is therefore an exact
opposite of the correct answer.

OVERTONE, marked by 26 per cent, the most frequently
marked mislead, is a more general term for all sorts of higher
frequencies given off by a vibrating body. The OVERTONES or
upper vibrations of a clarinet are not in harmony with the
fundamental, for the vibrating reed is held at one end only. The
rods of a xylophone are supported at two points and the
vibrating frequencies are incommensurable: 1, 2.756, 5.404,
8.933, etc. In this restricted sense OVERTONES might be a correct
answer. But for strings the OVERTONES are all HARMONICS.

In 1875 Alexander J. Ellis, an editor of the Oxford New English Dictionary and a president of the Philological Society,
translated Professor Helmholtz's Sensations of Tone, one of the
great translations of a scientific work. A pencil note by a
former owner on the flyleaf of my copy says: 'The original
contributions by the remarkable translator extend to 280 pages'.
In a footnote the translator says: 'Prof. Helmholtz's term
Obertöne is merely a contraction for Oberpartialtöne, but has
led Prof. Tyndall to the translation OVERTONE, which, on many
accounts, I prefer avoiding'. Despite this comment by Ellis the
word OVERTONE has found its way into most textbooks for any
frequency of vibration above the fundamental.

An HARMONIC is an OVERTONE with a frequency which is an
exact multiple of the fundamental. DISSONANCE is the sound
produced when an OVERTONE and a fundamental sound together and the OVERTONE is not an HARMONIC; or when two
OVERTONES which are not HARMONICS sound together.

Two tones sufficiently near in pitch sounding simultaneously
produce beats. When few in number they give rise to separate
sensations and can be counted; but if numerous they blend so
as to give roughness or DISSONANCE to the interval. This roughness or DISSONANCE is most disagreeable with about 33 beats
falling on the ear per second, a sensation of DISSONANCE which
Helmholtz compares to a flickering light on the eye.

169. *MEAN* (*mēn*) *n*. In mathematics: An arithmetic average, any set of figures added together and divided by their number.

The word MEAN comes from the French *moyenne*, mean, short for, or, as grammarians say, ELLIPTICAL for *quantite moyenne*, mean quantity. The ARITHMETIC MEAN, commonly called the MEAN, is the sum of a number of quantities divided by their number.

To the question: 'Sum of all observations divided by the number', 185 persons out of 357 answer correctly MEAN; but 70 answer NORM. A MEAN and a NORM may be the same numerical figure. But the purpose of the two differs. A NORM is a

Sum of all observations divided by the number.

FORM B. 4.	NY	MISC.	SUM
mode	1	8	9
median	7	47	54
MEAN	27	158	185
deviation	3	29	32
norm	10	60	70
unmarked	0	7	7
total	48	309	357

standard, pattern, model, type. Of NORM the modern Webster's Dictionary says: 'A set standard of development or achievement, usually the average or median achievement of a large group'.

With the present question the word ALL may lead to the marking of NORM; for though one may obtain NORMS for an age, for a school grade, or for any selected group, the word suggests enough observations to represent the whole group to which the NORM applies. In obtaining a NORM one may use the MEDIAN, the middle figure in size; or the MODE, the figure of most frequent occurrence; or the MEAN, the sum of the figures divided by their number. For a number of observations of a single quantity which vary from one another by chance, or which are caused to vary by a large number of different factors, the MEAN is the most accurate mathematical technique for obtaining an average or indication of central tendency.

170. *ASPECT RATIO* (*ăs'-pĕkt rā'-shō*). The ratio of the
length of an airfoil to its mean width, in technical terms
the ratio of the span to the mean chord. The ASPECT RATIO may
be computed by dividing the square of its length by the area
of the airfoil.

The word ASPECT comes from the Latin *aspectus*, look, appearance, seeing, countenance, from *aspicere*, to look, see, be-
hold, a combination of *ad*, to, and *specere*, to look. This Latin
verb *specere*, to look, already discussed under SUBSCRIPT (67),
is the source also of the English verb to INSPECT (*ĭn-spĕkt'*), to
look into, to SUSPECT (*sŭs-spĕkt'*), by derivation to look under,
and so distrust, to RESPECT (*rē-spĕkt'*), to look back at, to look

The ratio of the span to the mean chord of an airfoil.

FORM A. 28.	FW	LA	NY	NY	NY	PH	SUM
compression ratio	1	3	8	4	9	25	50
pitch ratio	1	3	7	7	39	22	79
thickness ratio	2	11	4	8	25	42	92
lapse rate	1	3	4	2	13	13	36
ASPECT RATIO	13	32	12	39	53	90	239
unmarked	0	2	2	6	1	8	19
total	18	54	37	66	140	200	515

at again, and so finally to look at with reverence, esteem, and
the corresponding noun RESPECT (*rē-spĕkt'*), accented like the
verb on the last syllable, and not on the first like ASPECT (*ăs'-
pĕkt*). ASPECT may mean appearance, as: 'Of such vinegar
ASPECT that they'll not show their teeth in way of smile'.
ASPECT RATIO is almost the appearance which the wing presents
to the advancing air.

To the question: 'The ratio of the span to the mean chord of
an airfoil', 239 persons out of 515 answer correctly ASPECT
RATIO; while 92 answer THICKNESS RATIO. The terms SPAN,
CHORD, and AIRFOIL are all too technical for a definition of
ASPECT RATIO; for although AIRFOIL is word 36 in this book, and
so easier than ASPECT RATIO, it is nevertheless missed by 146 persons in a population of 515. Definitions should be couched in
words known to practically everyone. The definition: 'Ratio of
the length of a wing to its mean width', is accurate and simpler.

Increasing the ASPECT RATIO, that is narrowing the wing without changing its length, or lengthening it without changing its width, results in better performance but creates construction difficulties. To gain the advantage of a high ASPECT RATIO some early planes were designed with a number of long narrow wings almost like a Venetian blind.

171. *LONGERON* (*lŏng-jĕ-rŏng'*) *n.* A principal fore-and-aft member in the framing of an airplane fuselage or nacelle, a chord member in a truss, one of the major longitudinal members of the frame of a fuselage usually continuous across a num-

The long steel tubes forming the framework of the plane's body.

FORM A. 4.	FW	LA	NY	NY	NY	PH	SUM
spacers	0	1	2	1	7	1	12
flanges	0	4	1	2	10	5	22
spars	7	11	13	25	52	59	167
LONGERONS	11	38	19	38	66	128	300
gussets	0	0	1	0	4	5	10
unmarked	0	0	1	0	1	2	4
total	18	54	37	66	140	200	515

ber of points of support, formerly said to extend from the engine mount to the rudder post, but this is not always true in modern airplanes.

To the question: 'The long steel tubes forming the framework of the plane's body', 300 persons out of 515 answer correctly LONGERON, but 167 answer SPAR. Both LONGERONS and SPARS are long principal structural members. Both are continuous across numerous points of support. A SPAR runs the length of a wing, spanwise from the body of the airplane out to the wing tip. A LONGERON runs the length of the main body. The SPARS are the principal transverse members of the structure; the LONGERONS are the principal longitudinal members.

172. *RIGHT-HAND RULE* (*rīt-hănd rool*). Fleming's generator rule, a device thought of by John Ambrose Fleming to help the practical-minded beginner and even sometimes the advanced physicist to remember the relation in a generator be-

tween the direction of the magnetic flux, the direction of motion of the wire, and the direction of the current produced.

With thumb, index finger, and middle finger extended at right angles to one another, point the thumb in the direction

System for determining the direction of an induced current given the direction of the magnetic field.

FORM E. 13.	BO	FW	LA	NY	NY	NY	NY	PH	TU	SUM
left-hand rule	5	15	5	4	6	11	46	28	9	129
triangle of forces	1	4	0	2	0	2	14	3	2	28
Jacobi's equation	1	5	0	1	1	5	17	3	2	35
RIGHT-HAND RULE	19	20	25	10	13	22	123	63	15	310
Legrange's equation	0	6	2	3	0	0	18	3	0	32
unmarked	2	0	1	0	0	0	0	0	0	3
total	28	50	33	20	20	40	218	100	28	537

FORM E. 13.	ENGLISH VOCABULARY	
	HIGH	LOW
left-hand rule	12	6
triangle of forces	3	5
Jacobi's equation	0	5
RIGHT-HAND RULE	23	22
Legrange's equation	2	2
total	40	40

of the motion of the moving wire, the first or index finger in the direction of the magnetic lines, and the middle finger shows the direction of the current or induced electromotive force.

To the boy who has spent pleasant hours playing with magnets and electric coils, assembling and reassembling toy motors and tiny generators, the relative directions of magnetic fields and electric currents become instinctive, and a rule of this sort seems superficial; but to the novice, trying to learn, a catch phrase or a clever rule by rote may aid memory.

To some extent the relation of these three directions may be reached by reasoning. According to Lenz's law the opposition to a wire moving through a magnetic field comes from a repulsion of one set of magnetic lines to another. Therefore the current in the wire runs in such a direction as to produce magnetic lines in the same direction as the magnetic field. One must now turn to another memory device, the screwdriver rule, for the relation between the direction of current and the direction of the magnetic lines.

To the question: 'System for determining the direction of an induced current given the direction of the magnetic field', 310 persons out of 537 answer correctly RIGHT-HAND RULE. The common incorrect answer, given by 129 persons, is LEFT-HAND RULE. Fleming's left-hand rule applies to motors. Knowing the direction of the magnetic flux, and the direction of the current in the moving wire, this LEFT-HAND RULE gives the direction of motion. It is the only left-hand rule. There are several RIGHT-HAND RULES. Of these Fleming's RIGHT-HAND RULE gives the direction of the current produced knowing the direction of the magnetic field and the direction of motion of the moving wire.

Such rules as these are MNEMONICS ($n\bar{e}$-$m\breve{o}n'$-$\bar{i}ks$), artificial aids to memory. The phrase: 'Jack left port' helps one who has never sailed to connect the word PORT with the LEFT side. But such memory aids are not laws of nature, not like Newton's law of gravitation, which gives the relation between natural phenomena, between masses, their distance apart, and mutual attraction. A mnemonic or memory device is an association between something one knows, or can learn and remember easily, and something else one wants to remember.

173. *PRIME* (*prīm*) *adj.* Not divisible by any other whole number except unity, incapable of being separated into simpler factors, indivisible without a remainder.

The PRIME numbers are: 1, 2, 3, 5, 7, 11, 13, 17, 19, 23, 29, 31, 37, 41, 43, 47, 53, 59, 61, 67, 71, 73, 79, 83, 89, 97, 101, 103, 107, 109, 113, etc.

The word PRIME comes from the Latin *primus*, first, a superlative, from *pro*, forward, used as a prefix to many words, as: PROGRAM, written beforehand. PRIOR, from the Latin *prior*, is the comparative, earlier, former, previous. Directly from *primus* come PRIMER (*prĭm'-er*), a first book, elementary reader; PRIMARY, first, chief, principal; PRIMITIVE, earliest, first of its kind; and PRIMORDIAL, first in order.

To the question: 'A number which cannot be divided by any other number except itself or one', 71 persons out of 132 answer correctly PRIME; while 35 answer IRRATIONAL. An IRRATIONAL number is one which cannot be reduced to a fraction, an ex-

A number which cannot be divided by any other number except itself or one.

FORM A. 11.	BO	NY	SUM	AA. 24.	NY
odd	2	4	6	odd	13
irrational	5	9	14	irrational	35
surd	1	5	6	surd	8
PRIME	10	23	33	PRIME	71
duodecimal	1	0	1	aliquot	5
unmarked	1	0	1	unmarked	0
total	20	41	61	total	132

pression which cannot be completely performed, as: $\sqrt{2}$, $\sqrt[3]{5}$, or $\sqrt[3]{7}$. A PRIME number is one which cannot be divided evenly by any other whole number.

174. *IDENTITY* (*ĭ-děn'-tĭ-tē*) *n.* The state of being the same, absolute sameness, the relation of anything to itself.
IDENTITY, equivalent to the French *identite* (*ē-děn-tē-tā'*), comes from the Latin *idem*, the same. This Latin *idem* (*ĭ'-děm*) is sometimes used to mean the same as above, to avoid repetition. It is sometimes shortened to *id*. The *i* at the beginning of this word comes from the Latin pronoun *is*, he, that. IDENTITY is complete sameness, oneness. The only true IDENTITY is the relation of the thing to itself.
To the question: 'The equality of two straight lines whose ends are the same', 207 persons out of 525 answer IDENTITY; but 95 answer SIMILARITY and 131 CORRESPONDENCE. Both of these words express partial sameness, but not complete IDENTITY. The adjective SIMILAR (160) means alike in some ways but not in others. SIMILAR triangles have their angles equal but not their sides. SIMILARITY (*sĭm-ĭ-lăr'-ĭ-tē*) is the corresponding noun, likeness in some respects but not in others. IDENTICAL triangles can be superimposed. CORRESPONDENCE, the noun, and CORRESPOND, the verb, come from the Latin *com-*, together,

mutually, and *respondere*, to answer. To CORRESPOND is to be in the same relation to one set of objects that something else is to another, to be as an individual of a set, related to an indi-

The equality of two straight lines whose ends are the same.

FORM C. 4.	CH	FORM CA. 29.	CH	LA	NY	NY	PH	SUM
congruence	28	correspondence	5	3	17	93	13	131
similarity	12	similarity	4	10	15	54	12	95
homogeneity	4	homogeneity	6	1	7	13	3	30
IDENTITY	18	IDENTITY	17	18	41	93	38	207
simultaneity	4	simultaneity	8	5	16	22	6	57
unmarked	2	unmarked	0	0	1	2	2	5
total	68	total	40	37	97	277	74	525

FORM CB. 24.	NY
correspondence	22
similarity	14
homogeneity	11
IDENTITY	30
simultaneity	7
unmarked	2
total	86

vidual of another set, in a way in which every individual of the first set is related to a definite number of individuals of the second set. To be IDENTICAL is to be absolutely the same.

175. *COUNTERCLOCKWISE* (*kown'-ter-klŏk-wīz*) *adv.*
Turning contrary to the direction of the hands of a clock. The word CLOCK goes far back in many languages and is sometimes said to be an imitation of the clicking sound of the early clocks. WISE goes back to Anglo-Saxon and was originally a noun which meant way, manner, guise, mode, as: 'In no WISE', in no way, in no manner; or 'In any WISE'. The next step was to combine the noun with the preposition, as: NOWISE, LIKEWISE, OTHERWISE. Then the same WISE was added to other words, as: SIDEWISE, LENGTHWISE, and finally CLOCKWISE. CLOCKWISE means in the direction of rotation of the hands of the clock, and is frequently used in physics. The prefix

COUNTER- comes from the Latin *contra-*, which appears in CON-TRADICT, from *contra*, against, and the Latin verb *dicere*, to speak; and in CONTRAVENE, from *venire*, to come against, go counter to. COUNTER- was first used in Middle-English words. To COUNTERBALANCE is to act against with equal power.

To the question: 'Rotation around the origin such that the signs of a point become successively: —x, y; —x, —y; x, —y; x, y'; 284 persons out of 525 answer correctly COUNTERCLOCK-WISE; but the word ORIGIN, which appears in the same form of the test as COUNTERCLOCKWISE, is unknown to 90 per cent, and should not be used in the definition of an easier word such as

Rotation around the origin such that the signs of a point become successively: —x, +y; —x, —y; +x, —y; +x, +y.

FORM C. 36.	CH	FORM CA. 19.	CH	LA	NY	NY	PH	SUM
COUNTER-		COUNTER-						
CLOCKWISE	33	CLOCKWISE	17	23	48	154	42	284
clockwise	12	clockwise	6	6	13	54	7	86
positive	5	consequent	3	3	12	9	6	33
inverse	10	inverse	11	2	17	32	7	69
spiral	7	spiral	3	2	6	26	8	45
unmarked	1	unmarked	0	1	1	2	4	8
total	68	total	40	37	97	277	74	525

FORM CB. 20.	NY
COUNTERCLOCKWISE	45
clockwise	18
consequent	6
inverse	11
spiral	6
unmarked	0
total	86

this. Also the concept of Cartesian coordinates seems more difficult than the word COUNTERCLOCKWISE. But the item has been left unchanged in the next revision of the test largely for want of knowing how to change it. The four misleads are marked about equally often, CLOCKWISE, the exact opposite, by 86 persons out of 525; INVERSE, by 69; and SPIRAL, by 45.

176. *SLOPE* (*slōp*) *n.* The angle with the plane of the horizon,
inclination from the horizontal, mathematically the angle
which a line makes with the x axis; one dictionary says: The
rate of change of a scalar function of a vector, relatively to
that of the variable, in the direction in which this change is a
maximum. Reread SLOPE INTERCEPT (159).

The noun SLOPE, from the same ultimate source as the verb
to SLIP, already met in the word SLIPSTREAM (25), is one of the
few technical terms which comes from Anglo-Saxon and not
from Latin or Greek.

To plot a point in rectangular or Cartesian coordinates
move to the right horizontally along the x axis a distance x.

y/x.

FORM B. 41.	NY	MISC.	SUM
operator	1	18	19
intercept	3	42	45
SLOPE	29	138	167
sine	8	38	46
axis	3	30	33
unmarked	4	43	47
total	48	309	357

Then move up, parallel to the y axis, a distance y. This is the
position of the point x, y. The SLOPE of a line from this point
to the origin is the ordinate y divided by the abscissa x.

To the question: 'y/x', 167 persons out of 357 mark the correct answer SLOPE; but 46 choose SINE, and 45 INTERCEPT. Starting with a right-angled triangle, the SINE (103) is the height or
ALTITUDE (28) divided by the HYPOTENUSE (29), the long side,
expressed as: y/hypotenuse. In the same right-angled triangle,
the height or altitude divided by the base is called the TANGENT,
and gives the SLOPE of the hypotenuse.

177. *TRIGONOMETRIC FUNCTION* (*trĭ-gō-nō-mĕt'-rĭk*
fŭnk'-shŏn). A ratio dependent upon an angle, any one of
six ratios between the sides of a right-angled triangle. The six
TRIGONOMETRIC FUNCTIONS are: SINE (103), COSINE (120), SE-
CANT, COSECANT, TANGENT, and COTANGENT. Reread SLOPE (176).

Trigonometry goes back to the Greeks, to the 2nd century B.C., to Hipparchus, the founder of TRIGONOMETRY, and to Ptolemy, the Egyptian who followed immediately and who gathered together and recorded previous progress. The word TRIGONOMETRY starts with the Greek τρίγωνον (trigonon), a triangle, a combination of the Greek τρεῖς (treis), τρι- (tri-),

Any constant ratio dependent upon an angle.

FORM A. 31.	BO	NY	SUM	FORM AA. 27.	NY
radian	3	13	16	radian	20
parsec	0	2	2	parsec	2
theta	0	2	2	theta	9
TRIGONOMETRIC				TRIGONOMETRIC	
FUNCTION	14	21	35	FUNCTION	77
vector value	2	3	5	vector value	21
unmarked	1	0	1	unmarked	3
total	20	41	61	total	132

three, and γωνία (gonia), angle, already met near the beginning of this book in DIAGONAL (15), across from angle to angle. The adjective TRIGONOMETRIC ends with the Greek -μετρία (metria), the art of measuring, from μέτρον (metron), measure, as discussed under CALORIMETRY (26). TRIGONOMETRY is the mathematical calculation of the angles, sides, and areas of triangles.

To the question: 'Any constant ratio dependent upon an angle', 77 persons out of 132 answer TRIGONOMETRIC FUNCTION; while 21 answer VECTOR VALUE, and 20 RADIAN. A VECTOR (150) VALUE is a combination of direction and distance. It depends first upon the angle, usually made at the origin with the x axis; and upon the distance measured along this line. A TRIGONOMETRIC FUNCTION depends upon the same angle; but is a ratio of height to length.

A RADIAN (161), the second most frequently marked mislead, is the angle at the center of a circle measured by the arc of the circle which is equal in its curved length to the radius of the circle. A RADIAN is an angle; while each TRIGONOMETRIC FUNCTION is a ratio. A RADIAN depends upon the length of the arc while the TRIGONOMETRIC FUNCTIONS depend on the angle. As used today they should be called TRIGONOMETRIC RATIOS, but have come to be called FUNCTIONS (155) because they are FUNCTIONS of the angle, dependent variables, dependent upon the size of the angle. A relation which is probably not well enough known to lead to the confusion is that when the angle is small both the SINE and the TANGENT approach the value of the angle measured in RADIANS. For a small angle the vertical height is almost the same as the rounded arc for the same angle.

178. *KELVIN ZERO* (*kĕl'-vĭn*). Absolute zero, temperature at which the molecules of a gas cease to move, lowest possible temperature. Reread ABSOLUTE ZERO (39).
At the temperature of melting ice, at zero degrees centigrade, a gas decreases 1/273d of its volume with each one degree centigrade drop in temperature. Assuming the volume to be directly proportional to the temperature, that is assuming Charles' law to continue to low temperatures, a drop of 273 degrees centigrade should reduce the volume to zero. Or expressing this relationship in a different way, plot the volume up and down, as the vertical scale, and temperature across as the horizontal scale, and continue the straight line thus formed from the upper right to the lower left. It reaches zero volume at a point which corresponds to −273 degrees centigrade, or to −459.69 degrees fahrenheit. This is Charles' law, or as it is sometimes called Gay Lussac's law, carried back to zero volume.

But ABSOLUTE ZERO determined in this way depends upon measuring the volumes and temperatures of actual gases, and no gas obeys perfectly the gas laws. Lord Kelvin, starting with the Carnot cycle, where the theoretical efficiency increases with drop in temperature, assumed perfect efficiency and computed the temperature. This differs only a part of a degree from the figure obtained from gases; for the gas scale and the Kelvin scale are practically identical except at the extremes. For this reason the Kelvin scale is used with very high and very low temperatures, and with computations involving the gas laws and laws of radiation.

Given the definition: 'The zero temperature at which the volume of a gas would vanish on the perfect gas assumption', 58 per cent of students answer KELVIN, 27 per cent CENTIGRADE, and only 5 per cent CELSIUS; though in the earlier version, where 60.3 per cent answered KELVIN, 15.7 per cent had answered CELSIUS, and only 7.4 per cent CENTIGRADE.

The zero temperature at which the volume of a perfect gas would vanish.

FORM AB. 9. (Original Form)	%	FORM D. 6. (First Revision)	%
centigrade zero	5	centigrade zero	7.4
fahrenheit zero	2	fahrenheit zero	2.6
Celsius zero	3	Celsius zero	15.7
KELVIN ZERO	86	KELVIN ZERO	60.3
Réaumur zero	3	Réaumur zero	11.7
unmarked	1	unmarked	2.3
total	100	total	100.0

FORM DA. 11. (Second Revision)	%	FORM DB. 15. (Third Revision)	NY
centigrade	27	centigrade	15
Kekule	4	Kekule	3
Celsius	5	Celsius	5
KELVIN	58	KELVIN	76
Réaumur	5	Réaumur	7
unmarked	1	unmarked	0
total	100	total	106

Thermometric scale with boiling point of water at 373.

FORM D. 8.	%
Celsius	16.3
fahrenheit	3.7
KELVIN	58.3
Réaumur	14.9
centigrade	3.4
unmarked	3.4
total	100.0

Much the same item appeared in an early form of the physics vocabulary test, designed in 1936 and based on the study of a still earlier test. It read: Thermometric scale with boiling point of water at 373. Here 58.3 per cent mark KELVIN, the correct answer; 16.3 per cent CELSIUS, the most frequently marked mislead; 14.9 per cent mark RÉAUMUR, the most popular mislead earlier for the test item ABSOLUTE ZERO (39); and in this instance only 3.4 per cent mark CENTIGRADE. The percentage of persons marking the correct answer varies with the population tested; but the most popular mislead usually remains constant, and rarely shifts as in this item.

The KELVIN thermometer scale differs from the CENTIGRADE or CELSIUS scale only in the position of the zero point. Each degree on the two scales is the same; but the KELVIN zero is 273.18 degrees below the CENTIGRADE zero.

179. *HEAT OF FUSION* (hĕt ŏv fū'-shŏn). Quantity of heat absorbed by a substance per unit mass on passing from solid to liquid state, or released upon solidification, without change of temperature, quantity of heat required to change a substance from the solid to the liquid state without changing its temperature.

HEAT OF FUSION is sometimes called LATENT HEAT OF FUSION and sometimes HEAT EQUIVALENT OF FUSION.

To the question: 'The quantity of heat required to change one gram of a substance from the solid to the liquid state without change of temperature', 45 per cent of 2234 persons answer HEAT OF FUSION; but 16 per cent answer GRAM-CALORIE. In the earlier study of form C, 63 per cent answered HEAT OF FUSION; 12 per cent CALORIE; and 11 per cent GRAM-CALORIE. The CALORIE and the GRAM-CALORIE are two terms for the same unit of measurement, the amount of heat required to raise one gram of water one degree centigrade. Among the 400 New York cases who score highest in the physics vocabulary test as a whole, out of a total 1900, 79 per cent answer correctly HEAT OF FUSION.

The word CALORIE comes from the Latin *calor*, heat, a noun from the verb *calere*, to be hot. No common literary words come from *calor*, but there are other technical terms, as: CALORIMETRY (26), the quantitative study of heat, measurement of heat, and CALORIMETER (kăl-ō-rĭm'-ē-ter), an instrument for the measurement of heat produced or absorbed.

The noun FUSION comes from the Latin *fusus*, the past participle of the verb *fundere*, to melt, pour, already met in the term EFFUSIOMETER (158). To FUSE a metal is to melt it, liquefy it by heat. The word may also be used figuratively to mean melt together, unite by melting. From the past participle *fusus* comes a large family of English words, many of which differ only in their prefix. A CONFUSION is by derivation a melting together, pouring together. An INFUSION is the liquid extract obtained by pouring boiling water over a vegetable substance;

The quantity of heat required to change one gram of a substance from the solid to the liquid state without change of temperature.

FORM C. 19. NY		FORM CA. 15. BO		NY HIGH	NY NEXT	NY REST	NY MISC.	SUM
heat of va-		heat of va-						
porization	35	porization	13	32	36	206	31	318
Joule's								
equivalent	18	mean calorie	3	7	24	159	8	201
HEAT OF		HEAT OF						
FUSION	252	FUSION	53	316	210	326	109	1014
calorie	47	calorie	11	15	61	199	48	334
gram-calorie	42	gram-calorie	19	30	69	210	38	366
unmarked	6	unmarked	1	0	0	0	0	1
total	400	total	100	400	400	1100	234	2234

tea is often called an INFUSION. In DIFFUSION and EFFUSION the termination *fusus* has lost its original meaning of melt and means pour. The DIFFUSION of a gas is its pouring apart in all directions, gradual spread. The noun FUSION is the operation of melting, and figuratively in literature the uniting of diverse elements by melting them together, union of individuals. In politics, FUSION may mean the uniting of two parties, the coalition of two factions. In science, the word retains its original meaning, the act of melting.

HEAT OF FUSION is therefore the heat absorbed in the process of melting, more specifically, the number of CALORIES required to melt one gram of a solid without changing its temperature. Similarly, HEAT OF VAPORIZATION, the most popular mislead among the 400 who score highest, is the number of calories required to change one gram of liquid to a gas without change of temperature. To raise one gram of water from the freezing point to the boiling point, from 0° centigrade to 100° centigrade, requires one hundred calories. To change one gram of

<table>
<tr><td></td><td>Heat of Fusion
in calories</td></tr>
<tr><td>aluminum</td><td>92</td></tr>
<tr><td>ice</td><td>80</td></tr>
<tr><td>copper</td><td>42</td></tr>
<tr><td>zinc</td><td>28</td></tr>
<tr><td>silver</td><td>21</td></tr>
<tr><td>tin</td><td>14.6</td></tr>
<tr><td>bismuth</td><td>13.0</td></tr>
<tr><td>sulphur</td><td>9.4</td></tr>
<tr><td>lead</td><td>5.6</td></tr>
<tr><td>mercury</td><td>2.8</td></tr>
</table>

ice at 0° centigrade to one gram of water at 0° centigrade requires eighty calories. This is the HEAT OF FUSION of ice. It is probably the heat required to separate the molecules from the compact state in which they exist in the solid.

180. *MECHANICAL ADVANTAGE* (*mĕ-kăn'-ĭ-kăl ăd-văn'-tāj*). Force-multiplying capacity, ratio of weight lifted to the force applied, force produced by the machine divided by the force put into it.

Both ADVANTAGE and the corresponding verb to ADVANCE go back to the Old French *avantage* and *avancer*, both given by Randle Cotgrave in his French English Dictionary of 1611 and both spelt without the D, as strictly both should be spelt in English. But in the 15th and 16th centuries the mistake was occasionally made in French of adding D after the initial A as if the word had come from the Latin *ad*. This did not affect the French pronunciation, but has survived in English.

To the question: 'Ratio of force exerted to force applied in a force-multiplying machine', 52 per cent of the students whose scores have been tabulated for form DA, and 59.5 per cent for form D, answer correctly MECHANICAL ADVANTAGE, but 24 per cent, form DA, answer EFFICIENCY. EFFICIENCY (52) is a work ratio; MECHANICAL ADVANTAGE, a force ratio. EFFICIENCY is the work (49) put out by a machine divided by the work put into it. MECHANICAL ADVANTAGE is the force put out by a machine divided by the force put into it. The EFFICIENCY of every actual machine is less than one (1.00); the work which comes out is always less than the work which goes in because of the work wasted in overcoming friction. In a perfect machine, were such possible, the EFFICIENCY would be 1.00, but never greater.

The MECHANICAL ADVANTAGE on the other hand might be far greater than 1.00, for in lifting a heavy weight by hand with a

The ratio of force exerted to force applied in a force-multiplying machine.

FORM BA. 22.	%	FORM D. 26.	%
efficiency	26	efficiency	11.7
work ratio	14	work ratio	15.1
lever arm	4	lever arm	6.0
MECHANICAL ADVANTAGE	51	MECHANICAL ADVANTAGE	59.5
mechanical equivalent	4	mechanical equivalent	4.0
unmarked	1	unmarked	3.7
total	100	total	100.0

FORM DA. 12.	%	FORM DB. 22.	NY
efficiency	24	MECHANICAL ADVANTAGE	62
work ratio	14	work ratio	14
lever arm	6	lever arm	6
MECHANICAL ADVANTAGE	52	efficiency	16
mechanical equivalent	4	rating	7
unmarked	0	unmarked	1
total	100	total	106

jack or pulley or lever, the force exerted may be only a fraction of the weight lifted.

WORK is FORCE multiplied by DISTANCE. In lifting a heavy car with a jack the work done is just as great as if the car were lifted directly with no jack; but to lift it by hand the force needed must be reduced, and the distance which the hand moves increased in proportion. This is the function of the force-multiplying machine. Its MECHANICAL ADVANTAGE is the proportion in which it reduces the force needed. It is the force exerted by the machine divided by the force exerted by the hand or other agent which operates the machine.

181. The symbol i (i). The imaginary quantity $\sqrt{-1}$, the square root of minus one. Reread IMAGINARY ROOT (140). To the question: 'The meaning of the symbol i', 182 persons out of 357 answer correctly SQUARE ROOT OF MINUS ONE; but 84 answer ANY IMAGINARY NUMBER. ANY IMAGINARY NUMBER may be written using the symbol i. Thus, $\sqrt{-4}$ may be written as: i $\sqrt{4}$ or as 2 i. Or the square root of minus three, $\sqrt{-3}$, may be written as i $\sqrt{3}$. The square root of minus four, $\sqrt{-4}$, and the square root of minus three, $\sqrt{-3}$, are both IMAGINARY numbers; but i means specifically the SQUARE ROOT OF MINUS ONE, $\sqrt{-1}$.

According to Florian Cajori, in his History of Mathematical Notations, small i, signifying the SQUARE ROOT OF MINUS ONE, was first used by Leonhard Euler (*oi'-ler*) in 1777 in a paper before the Academy in St. Petersburg. Euler, who was born

The symbol i.

FORM B. 14.	NY	MISC.	SUM
any imaginary number	7	77	84
log base	4	16	20
first derivative	2	19	21
index	2	34	36
SQUARE ROOT OF MINUS			
ONE	33	149	182
unmarked	0	14	14
total	48	309	357

in Basel, Switzerland, in 1707, and who had been a pupil of Jean Bernoulli in Basel, was invited to St. Petersburg in 1727 by the Empress Catherine. There he became professor of physics at the age of twenty-three and remained until 1741, but returned in 1766. Twenty-five years later Gauss used i systematically for $\sqrt{-1}$. For uniformity this symbol should be written as the English i, with a dot, not as occasionally happens as the Greek ι, iota (*ē-ō'-tah*), without the dot above.

182. *MENISCUS* (mĕ-nĭs'-kŭs) *n.* A crescent like the moon
in its first quarter, concave on one side and convex on the
other.

The word MENISCUS comes from the Greek μηνίσκος (men-
iskos), a crescent, the diminutive of μήνη (mene), moon. Other
English words starting with MEN-, such as MENSTRUAL, monthly,
recurring once a month, seem more closely associated with the
Greek μήν (men), month, but must have come originally in
some way from μήνη (mene), the moon, though the etymology
is not clear.

MENISCUS as applied to a lens means convex on one side,
concave on the other, and thick at the center, like the moon

The upper curved surface of a column of liquid confined in a
narrow tube.

FORM BA. 30.	%	FORM D. 35.	%
capillary	47	capillary	38.3
viscosity	2	caustic	3.4
tympanic membrane	3	tympanic membrane	2.6
MENISCUS	40	MENISCUS	41.7
panchromatic film	7	panchromatic film	11.1
unmarked	1	unmarked	2.9
total	100	total	100.0

FORM DA. 29.	%	FORM DB. 24.	NY
capillary	23	capillary	27
caustic	3	mentum	7
convex	18	convex	14
MENISCUS	51	MENISCUS	55
panchromatic film	3	nimbus	3
unmarked	2	unmarked	0
total	100	total	106

in its first quarter, crescent-shaped. The same word MENISCUS
is used for the convex or concave surface of a liquid in a
capillary tube.

Given the definition: 'The upper curved surface of a column
of liquid confined in a narrow tube', 51 per cent of students
mark MENISCUS, but 23 per cent choose CAPILLARY. This word

is used both as an adjective and as a noun. It comes from the Latin adjective *capillaris*, pertaining to the hair, from *capillus*, hair. This in turn comes from *caput*, *capitis*, the head. A CAP-ILLARY tube is a hairlike tube, slender, with a small bore. Or CAPILLARY can be used alone as a noun to mean a small tube. When the top of mercury in a CAPILLARY tube bulges up it is called a CONVEX MENISCUS. When the top of a column of water is concave, the top is called a CONCAVE MENISCUS.

183. *PISTON* (*pĭs'-tŏn*) *n.* A flat disk designed to move back and forth in a cylinder or pump barrel, a movable piece usually round at the end of a PISTON ROD, a sliding short cylinder moved by or moving against fluid pressure.

The word PISTON comes from the Latin *pistare*, to pound. This is the frequentative of *pistere*, also spelt *pisere*, to pound,

A pump depending on reciprocating action.

FORM AB. 22.	%	FORM D. 17.	%
centrifugal	12	centrifugal	16.9
molecular	0	mercury	1.1
displacement	6	displacement	13.7
rotary	13	rotary	10.8
PISTON	68	PISTON	55.2
unmarked	1	unmarked	2.3
total	100	total	100.0

FORM DA. 17.	%	FORM DB. 29.	NY
centrifugal	16	centrifugal	11
oscillator	13	oscillating	10
displacement	14	displacement	20
rotary	12	rotary	8
PISTON	44	PISTON	56
unmarked	1	unmarked	1
total	100	total	106

beat; it means to pound again and again. The past participle is *pistus*. From the same source comes PESTLE, a small club-shaped instrument for grinding, pounding and breaking up a substance in a mortar, a heavy bowl. A PISTON PUMP may be a suction pump which pulls water up to its level, or it may be a force pump which pushes water up above the level of the pump.

To the question: 'A pump depending on reciprocating action', 44 per cent answer PISTON. The remaining 56 per cent divide almost equally among the four other choices: CENTRIFUGAL, 16 per cent; OSCILLATOR, 13 per cent; DISPLACEMENT, 14 per cent; and ROTARY, 12 per cent. Under such conditions the assumption seems justified that a similar number, about 14 per cent, a quarter of 56 per cent, mark the correct answer, PISTON, unaware of its correctness, selecting it as one of five equally possible choices. Although 44 per cent mark PISTON, only 30 per cent, on this assumption, know the word.

One trouble may be the word RECIPROCATING in the question, though RECIPROCAL, mutual, interchangeable, complementary, from the same source, is known to 83 per cent of adult readers. RECIPROCATING means back and forth. It seems to come from *re-*, back, and *pro-*, forward, with the adjective ending *-cus* after each, *recus procus*, backward and forward. In a RECIPROCATING steam engine steam pressure pushes the PISTON back and forth, and this motion is then communicated to the engine. In a pump some sort of motive force moves the PISTON back and forth.

A CENTRIFUGAL PUMP, the most frequently marked mislead, whirls continuously. Also it needs no valves, and for this reason is better for pumping liquid which contains dirt. A RECIPROCATING PISTON PUMP depends upon valves for its action.

184. *AQUEOUS HUMOR* (*ā'-kwē-ŭs hū'-mŏr*). Thin watery limpid fluid at the front of the eye, back of the cornea and in front of the lens.

The word AQUEOUS comes from the Latin *aqua*, water, from the same source as AQUEDUCT, a channel or conduit for conducting water, often for supplying water to a large city. From the same source come also AQUATIC, pertaining to water, and AQUARIUM, a bowl of water for fish.

The word HUMOR comes from the Latin *humor*, *humoris*, moisture, from the verb *humere*, to be moist, the source of the English HUMID, moist. Today the word HUMOR is used for a thin animal fluid. AQUEOUS HUMOR is watery liquid.

'The fluid in the human eye between the cornea and the crystalline lens' is thought correctly by 47 per cent of students to be the AQUEOUS HUMOR, but is thought by 20 per cent to be the VITREOUS HUMOR; and by another 17 per cent to be CYTOPLASM.

VITREOUS (*vĭt'-rē-ŭs*) comes from the Latin adjective *vitreus*, pertaining to glass, from *vitrum*, glass. From the same source comes VITRIOL (*vĭt'-rē-ŏl*), a word first used for the sulphate of iron and for the sulphates of other metals, because of their resemblance to glass. The word was used in this way as early as 1386 by Chaucer. Some two hundred years later the same word came to be used for concentrated sulphuric acid; and from this

The fluid in the human eye between the cornea and the crystalline lens.

FORM BA. 26.	%	FORM D. 33.	%
vitreous humor	29	vitreous humor	33.6
endolymph	9	endolymph	10.3
AQUEOUS HUMOR	45	AQUEOUS HUMOR	36.3
mucoid	14	mucoid	10.0
serum	1	plasma	6.9
unmarked	2	unmarked	2.9
total	100	total	100.0

FORM DA. 34.	%	FORM DB. 27.	NY
vitreous humor	20	vitreous humor	35
endolymph	6	endolymph	11
AQUEOUS HUMOR	47	AQUEOUS HUMOR	36
mucoid	7	mucoid	17
cytoplasm	17	cytoplasm	7
unmarked	3	unmarked	0
total	100	total	106

comes the modern VITRIOLIC (*vĭt-rē-ŏl'-ĭk*), biting like acid, sharp, caustic, malignant, used in this way largely by the lesser writers of the nineteenth century. The Latin *vitreus*, glass, comes in turn from *videre*, to see, and by derivation means a transparent substance. VITREOUS today may mean like glass in its material structure, hard and brittle; or it may mean transparent, hyaline. In the phrase VITREOUS HUMOR the word is used in this last sense. VITREOUS HUMOR is a pellucid gelatinous substance, back of the crystalline lens, between it and the retina at the back, filling four fifths of the eye ball. The AQUEOUS HUMOR of the eye is much smaller in amount, and at the front of the eye, just back of the cornea, between it and the crystalline lens which separates the AQUEOUS HUMOR at the front from the VITREOUS HUMOR at the back. The AQUEOUS HUMOR is a thin limpid watery fluid.

185. *DIVISOR* (*dĭ-vī'-zŏr*) *n.* The number by which another is to be divided, the denominator in a fraction, below the line in a fraction.

A number, the DIVIDEND, for example 8, divided by another number, the DIVISOR, for example 4, gives the QUOTIENT, 2; or, expressed as in the test question, 4 is the DIVISOR by which 8, the DIVIDEND, is to be divided. In the expression a/b, b is the DIVISOR by which a is to be divided.

The word DIVISOR comes from the Latin *divisor, divisorem*, from *dividere*, to divide, the source also of the words DIVIDEND and DIVISION. DIVISION is the inverse of MULTIPLICATION. DIVISION is the process of finding how many times one number is contained in another; or from Robert Recorde, 1540: 'The

The quantity by which another quantity is to be divided.

FORM B. 31.	NY	MISC.	SUM
dividend	15	89	104
remainder	0	0	0
DIVISOR	26	176	202
quotient	4	12	16
ratio	0	3	3
unmarked	3	29	32
total	48	309	357

partition of a greater summe by a lesser', of finding a QUOTIENT (45) which multiplied by the DIVISOR produces the DIVIDEND. Writing in 1706 in his Synopsis Palmariorum Matheseos or A New Introduction to the Mathematics, William Jones states in his nice manner: 'DIVISION is a manifold subduction; or the taking of one number out of another number as often as possible'.

To the question: 'The quantity by which another quantity is to be divided', 202 persons out of 357 answer DIVISOR; while 104 answer DIVIDEND. The large number attracted to this mislead may be due in part to the wording of the question. The DIVIDEND is the number which is to be divided by another. The number divided by another is the DIVIDEND. The number by which another is divided is the DIVISOR. Again from Robert Recorde, in his Graphic Arts of 1542: 'Then begyne I at the hyest lyne of the divident and seke how often I may have the DIVISOR therein'.

186. *DOUBLE CONVEX* (*dŭb'-l kŏn-věks'*) *adj.* Bulging out on both faces, type of lens which is thicker at the center than at the edges, thin at the circumference. Reread MENISCUS (182).

There are three types of CONVERGING lenses, all thicker at the center than at the circumference: PLANO CONVEX, bulging out on one side and flat on the other; CONCAVO CONVEX, bending in on one side but out more on the other to remain thicker at the center than at the edge, called also MENISCUS (182); and DOUBLE CONVEX, bulging on both sides. All such lenses, thicker at the center than at the edge, bend light rays together to meet at a point; but only the DOUBLE CONVEX bends rays at both surfaces, as they enter the lens and again as they leave.

To the question: 'A lens both of whose faces tend to converge light', 51 per cent of students answer correctly DOUBLE CONVEX; but 26 choose DOUBLE CONCAVE. The difficulty may be the adjective CONVEX; for the noun CONVEXITY is unknown to 31 per cent of adult readers. To 23 per cent CONVEXITY means HOLLOWNESS. CONVEXITY is roundness, bulging. The noun CONVEXITY and the adjective CONVEX both come from the Latin *convexus*, vaulted, arched, rounded, convex. The words *convexus* and *convectus* are collateral, that is come from the same source; both are past participles of *convehere*, to bring together. This in turn is a combination of *com-*, together, and *vehere*, to carry. The derivation may suggest bringing together the two ends to form an arch, as the ends of a bow are drawn together when it is bent.

The meaning of CONCAVE is easier to follow from its derivation, for it comes from the Latin *concavus*, hollow, a combination of *com* and *cavus*, hollow, the source of the English CAVE. DOUBLE CONCAVE means dug out on both sides. A DOUBLE-

A lens both of whose surfaces tend to converge light.

FORM AB. 47.	%	FORM D. 48.	NY	%
concave	2	concave	24	6.9
convex	8	convex	20	5.7
double concave	17	double concave	78	22.3
DOUBLE CONVEX	64	DOUBLE CONVEX	173	49.4
convex-concave	9	convex-concave	43	12.3
unmarked	0	unmarked	12	3.4
total	100	total	350	100.0

FORM DA. 20.	%	FORM DB. 23.	NY
concave	9	concave	6
collector	1	telephoto	2
double concave	26	double concave	31
DOUBLE CONVEX	51	DOUBLE CONVEX	53
convex-concave	13	convex-concave	12
unmarked	0	unmarked	2
total	100	total	106

CONCAVE lens spreads rays of light apart as they enter, and still further apart as they leave. A DOUBLE-CONVEX lens bends the rays together as they enter, and still closer together as they leave. A DOUBLE-CONCAVE lens is a DIVERGING lens; a DOUBLE-CONVEX lens a CONVERGING lens.

187. *COORDINATE* (*kō-or′-dĭ-năt*) *n*. The general term for either of two or more magnitudes used to define the position of a point with reference to a fixed system of lines. Read also QUADRANT (188), and reread SLOPE (176).

George Crabb, born in Suffolk, England, in 1778, who died at Hammersmith near London in 1851, author of Dictionary of

English Synonymes, says in his Technological Dictionary of 1823: 'Co-ORDINATES (geometry), a term applied to the absciss and ordinates when taken in connexion'.

The word COORDINATE, which comes from the Latin *coordinatus*, ordered, arranged, the past participle of *ordinare*, to order, may have been formed originally to parallel SUBORDINATE, one arranged under another, by derivation under in order.

To the question: 'In plane analytic geometry, an expression showing the position of a point with reference to either axis', 146 persons out of 357 answer COORDINATE; while 52 answer VECTOR, probably correct with the present wording of the question. In POLAR COORDINATES, the COORDINATES of any point are the length of a straight line from the pole or origin to the

In plane analytic geometry, an expression showing the position of a point with reference to either axis.

FORM B. 42.	NY	MISC.	SUM
abscissa value	3	25	28
COORDINATE	23	123	146
ordinate	5	43	48
vector	7	45	52
discriminant	6	35	41
unmarked	4	38	42
total	48	309	357

point, called the RADIUS VECTOR, and the angle which this line makes with the axis. This defines the position of a place by its distance and bearing from a reference point. In a rectangular system, the COORDINATES are the ORDINATE of the point, its distance up or down from the horizontal line, and the ABSCISSA of the point, its distance right or left of a vertical axis.

188. *QUADRANT* (*kwŏd'-rănt*) *n.* One of the four regions into which a plane is divided by a vertical and a horizontal line. Reread COORDINATE (187).

The word QUADRANT is also used for the quarter of a circle, for the arc of a circle containing 90 degrees, and for the figure included between this arc and the two radii drawn from the center to the ends of this arc.

The word QUADRANT comes from the Latin *quadrant, quadrantis*, a quarter, fourth part, applied to a coin, to weights, and to measures. The word comes from *quattuor*, four, already met in QUADRILATERAL (70).

To the question: 'Division of area determining whether values of coordinates are positive or negative in plane analytic geometry', 70 persons out of 132 answer QUADRANT; while 29 answer ORDINATE and 15 others ORIGIN. In rectangular or Cartesian coordinates the two axes, one horizontal and the other vertical, divide a plane into quarters. The ORIGIN is the point at which these two lines or axes cross. The ORDINATE of any point to be plotted is its distance up or down from the horizontal line. An ORDINATE above the line is called positive; one

Division of area determining whether values of coordinates are positive or negative in plane analytic geometry.

FORM A. 26.	BO	NY	SUM	FORM AA. 35.	NY
QUADRANT	12	17	29	QUADRANT	70
parameter	1	5	6	parameter	11
ordinate	2	9	11	ordinate	29
octant	0	1	1	octant	6
origin	4	9	13	origin	15
unmarked	1	0	1	unmarked	1
total	20	41	61	total	132

below the line negative. It is also customary to call anything to the right of the vertical line positive; and anything to its left, negative. Thus in the QUADRANT to the upper right all values are positive. This QUADRANT is by custom labeled I. All values in the lower left-hand QUADRANT, called III, are negative. In the upper left-hand QUADRANT, called II, for the QUADRANTS are numbered COUNTERCLOCKWISE (175), the values of x are negative, but those of y positive; while in the lower right-hand QUADRANT, IV, the values of x are positive, and y negative.

189. *COMBINATION* (kŏm-bĭ-nā′-shŏn) *n*. A number of individuals regarded together, a group of objects independent of their order, in mathematics the union of individuals in different groups each containing a certain number.

The suffix -ATION is of Latin origin, the result usually of adding -*tion* to a verb ending in -*are*, as *combinare*, to combine. The suffix comes through the French -*ation*, from the Latin -*atio*, -*ationis*, with the accusative -*ationem*. It occurs most frequently in abstract nouns of action, and is equivalent to the English -ING. The verb to COMBINE comes from the Latin *com-*, together, plus *bini*, two by two, the source also of BINARY, two fold, composed of two things, as: 'A BINARY star', two stars revolving about one another and moving together as one.

To the question: 'Groupings taken without regard to the order in which things are arranged', the frequently marked mislead is PERMUTATIONS, chosen by 105 persons out of 525, as compared with 245 who mark COMBINATIONS. A PERMUTATION is a linear arrangement of objects resulting from a change in their

Groupings taken without regard to the order in which things are arranged.

FORM C. 10.	CH	FORM CA. 20.	CH	LA	NY	NY	PH	SUM
series	11	series	5	3	14	50	6	78
permutations	14	permutations	6	9	23	50	17	105
COMBINATIONS	30	COMBINATIONS	21	18	46	128	32	245
progressions	6	progressions	1	1	4	19	4	29
integrations	7	integrations	7	5	8	29	13	62
unmarked	0	unmarked	0	1	2	1	2	6
total	68	total	40	37	97	277	74	525

FORM CB. 26.	NY
series	8
permutations	15
COMBINATIONS	36
correlations	12
integrations	12
unmarked	3
total	86

order. The word comes from the Latin *per-*, through, which intensifies the meaning as in PERACUTE, very acute, and MUTATION. A MUTATION is a change; in genetics, the sudden appearance of a changed gene. A PERMUTATION is by derivation a change throughout, really a change in the order often of the same objects, of the same COMBINATION. There are several PERMUTATIONS of each COMBINATION. A new COMBINATION can be made only by replacing some or all of the things combined.

190. *GEOMETRIC PROGRESSION* (*gē-ō-mĕt'-rĭk prō-grĕsh'-shŏn*). A succession of terms in which each after the first is formed by multiplying the preceding by the same number. Reread ARITHMETIC PROGRESSION (33).

An INCREASING GEOMETRIC PROGRESSION is: 1, 3, 9, 27, 81, where each term is multipled by the COMMON RATIO, plus 3, to obtain the next. The adjective GEOMETRIC comes from the Greek γεωμετρικός (geometrikos), from γεωμέτρης (geometres), a land-measurer, a combination of γῆ (ge), land, the earth, and μέτρον (metron), measure. The meaning of GEOMETRIC, in the phrase GEOMETRIC PROGRESSION, goes back to a time long before

A series constructed by multiplying the first term by a constant to obtain the second, the second term by the same constant to obtain the third, et cetera.

FORM B. 17.	NY	MISC.	SUM	%
Taylor's series	4	15	19	5.3
Fourier's	5	17	22	6.2
arithmetic	8	57	65	18.2
GEOMETRIC	25	136	161	45.1
exponential	6	61	67	18.8
unmarked	0	23	23	6.4
total	48	309	357	100.0

Robert Recorde and Blundevil, when problems involving multiplication were dealt with by geometry. From Robert Recorde, The Grounde of Artes, teachinge the perfect Worke and Practise of Arithmeticke, both in whole numbers and fractions, 8vo., 1540, comes: 'Arithmeticall progression is a rehearsing of many numbers in suche sorte, that betweene every two next numbers the difference be equall. Progression Geometricall is when the numbers increase by a like proportion'.

To the question: 'A series constructed by multiplying the first term by a constant to obtain the second, the second term by the same constant to obtain the third, et cetera', 161 persons out of 357 answer GEOMETRIC PROGRESSION; while 67 answer EXPONENTIAL SERIES; and 65 ARITHMETIC PROGRESSION. Letting a be any first term, and r the constant ratio, a GEOMETRIC PROGRESSION may be written as:

$$a, \ ar, \ ar^2, \ ar^3, \ ar^4,$$

and this may lead to the marking of EXPONENTIAL. An ARITHMETIC PROGRESSION is a succession of terms in which each after the first is found by adding the same number, a COMMON DIFFERENCE, to the one before. An ARITHMETIC PROGRESSION is 1, 4, 7, 10, 13, where each term is obtained by adding the common difference 3 to the preceding term. From Blundevil's Exercises of 1594: 'What is PROGRESSION GEOMETRICALL? It is that wherein every number exceedeth his fellow by like Proportion, for as six contayneth three twice, so doth twelve contayn six twice.'

191. *T.D.C.* This abbreviation stands for TOP DEAD CENTER, called also: TOP CENTER POSITION. This is the position of the piston when it has reached its farthest distance from the

Form A. The position of the piston when farthest removed from the crankshaft.
Form AA. Position of piston when farthest from center line of crankshaft.

FORM A. 33.	FW	LA	NY	NY	NY	PH	SUM
A.B.D.C.	3	5	3	8	10	19	48
A.T.C.	3	10	5	9	28	35	90
B.C.D.	2	6	6	7	24	32	77
B.T.U.	0	1	7	4	17	18	47
T.D.C.	9	29	12	26	56	82	214
unmarked	1	3	4	12	5	14	39
total	18	54	37	66	140	200	515

center line of the crankshaft. It is also called TOP OF THE STROKE. Reread PISTON DISPLACEMENT (94).

TOP CENTER, when the crank is vertical and the piston at the top of the cylinder, is the point at which compression stops and the power stroke begins.

Numerous abbreviations designate various events and piston positions in the timing diagram. In order of occurrence, starting with TOP DEAD CENTER, they are:

	T.D.C.	TOP DEAD CENTER
	or D.C.	DEAD CENTER
	E.C.	EXHAUST CLOSES
at perhaps 20°	A.T.C.	AFTER TOP CENTER
	E.O.	EXHAUST OPENS
at perhaps 80°	B.B.C.	BEFORE BOTTOM CENTER
	B.D.C.	BOTTOM DEAD CENTER
	or B.C.	BOTTOM CENTER
	I.C.	INTAKE CLOSES
at perhaps 80°	A.B.C.	AFTER BOTTOM CENTER
	I.O.	INTAKE OPENS
at perhaps 20°	B.T.C.	BEFORE TOP CENTER

The most frequently marked mislead in the four largest populations, A.T.C., is the point at which the exhaust closes.

192. *DAMP OUT* (*dămp owt*). To reduce sound or deaden vibration.

The verb to DAMP goes back to the Middle English *dampen*, where it meant extinguish. It is closely related to Dutch, Danish, and Swedish words which mean extinguish, smother,

Form A. Suppress any vibrations which occur as the result of the disturbance of the plane's stability.
Form AA. To suppress vibrations in a plane.

FORM A. 29.	FW	LA	NY	NY	NY	PH	SUM	FORM AA. 22.	NY
DAMP OUT	11	42	9	26	64	105	257	DAMP OUT	29
pull out	0	0	6	3	13	9	31	pull out	7
dive	0	0	2	3	10	4	19	strengthen	3
oscillate	2	2	5	4	14	26	53	oscillate	3
modulate	5	10	13	24	37	50	139	modulate	21
unmarked	0	0	2	6	2	6	16	unmarked	0
total	18	54	37	66	140	200	515	total	63

and deaden; and to DAMP in English may have any of these meanings, smother, suffocate, extinguish. In the literary sense of wet, moisten, DAMPEN is now more frequent than DAMP. The same verb to DAMP is used specifically to mean diminish the oscillation of a metallic body. In 1824 Dominique François Jean Arage observed the DAMPING of the vibrations of a magnetic needle suspended over a copper plate.

To the question: 'Suppress any vibrations which occur as the result of the disturbance of the plane's stability', 257 persons out of 515 answer correctly DAMP OUT; but 139 answer MODULATE, and 53 OSCILLATE. To MODULATE is to change, vary, modify. To MODULATE may be to change the frequency of an oscillation, often in some characteristic manner as in sending radio signals or in broadcasting; or it may be to vary the amplitude of a wave train. To DAMP OUT is to reduce, deaden, wipe out.

To OSCILLATE, the second mislead, is to vibrate, shake back and forth. To DAMP OUT is to stop such an OSCILLATION.

193. *SOLAR CONSTANT* (*sō'-lahr kŏn'-stănt*). A number which expresses the quantity of radiant heat received from the sun by the outer layer of the earth's atmosphere in a unit of time, the intensity of solar radiation falling in unit area of a

Amount of heat per unit area of wave front received from the sun.

FORM C. 25. NY SOLAR	FORM CA. 16. BO SOLAR	NY HIGH	NY NEXT	NY REST	NY MISC.	SUM
CONSTANT 243	CONSTANT 70	316	235	350	130	1101
small calorie 3	specific heat 2	6	17	165	16	206
large calorie 12	large calorie 0	8	12	140	5	165
cosmic	cosmic					
radiation 89	radiation 18	41	99	288	57	503
lumen 40	lumen 10	29	37	157	24	257
unmarked 13	unmarked 0	0	0	0	2	2
total 400	total 100	400	400	1100	234	2234

surface placed perpendicular to the incoming beam and at a height sufficiently great to be free from the scattering and absorption of the atmosphere. Reread CONSTANT (104).

The Astrophysical Observatory of the Smithsonian Institution of Washington, when under the direction of C. G. Abbot, estimated the intensity of the sun's radiation at the limit of the earth's atmosphere as 1.95 gram-calories per square centimeter per minute, with a variation of 5 per cent on either side. A long series of measurements at the Carnegie Institution's Observatory on Mount Wilson shows the intensity to range from 1.90 to 1.98. This variation is due to real changes in solar radiation and not to conditions on the earth. Abbot found a period of 15⅔ months in this variation of the solar constant and a connection with sun-spot periodicity.

To the question: 'The amount of heat per unit area of wave front received from the sun', 49 per cent of 2234 persons answer SOLAR CONSTANT; but 23 per cent answer COSMIC RADIATION. In the earlier study of form C, 61 per cent answered SOLAR CONSTANT; and 22 per cent COSMIC RADIATION, the most frequently marked mislead in both studies. COSMIC is the adjective corresponding to the noun COSMOS, universe, from the Greek κόσμος (kosmos), universe. From its name, COSMIC RADIATION should come from the COSMOS, the universe. It is a penetrating radiation of unknown origin apparently traversing interstellar space. It is detected by the ionization which it produces.

The English adjective SOLAR comes from the Latin *solaris*, of the sun, solar. This comes from the Latin noun *sol*, the sun. SOLAR RADIATION is sun radiation, from the sun. The SOLAR CONSTANT applies to the sun, not to the stars and the universe.

194. *NODE* (*nōd*) *n.* Place at rest in a vibrating body; a quiet point, line, or plane, at which there is comparatively little or no oscillation or fluctuation.

The corresponding adjective NODAL was used by Faraday in 1831. A NODAL point is a quiescent point in a vibrating string held at each end. The NODES in vibrating plates are usually lines at rest called NODAL LINES.

NODE comes from the Latin *nodus*, a word used in English as early as 1400 for a knot in a string or rope. In 1572 the same word NODE was used for a knot in the sense of a complication; and a few years later for a knot meaning a small swelling. By 1665 NODE appeared in astronomy for the point of intersection of the orbit of a planet with the ecliptic, or for the point of intersection of any two great circles. Although most physics textbooks define NODE as a point of rest, it is by derivation the intersection of a wave with the central horizontal reference line, the point at which the wavy line crosses the axis.

With the textbook definition of a NODE: 'Place at rest in a vibrating body', 308 persons in 537 answer correctly; but 135 answer ANTINODE. The prefix ANTI-, ending with I, is of Greek origin and was originally used only with words themselves of Greek origin. It means against, opposed to, antagonistic to, in contrast to. When the prefix ANTI- is used with a noun, as in

Places in a vibrating body which are at rest.

FORM E. 23.	BO	FW	LA	NY	NY	NY	NY	PH	TU	SUM
antinodes	6	14	8	4	5	14	51	26	7	135
segments	3	7	2	3	1	1	21	3	0	41
NODES	13	22	22	11	13	17	127	64	19	308
loops	0	1	0	2	1	3	7	1	0	15
phase	4	5	1	0	0	4	12	6	2	34
unmarked	2	1	0	0	0	1	0	0	0	4
total	28	50	33	20	20	40	218	100	28	537

FORM E. 23.	ENGLISH VOCABULARY	
	HIGH	LOW
antinodes	12	11
segments	2	7
NODES	24	18
loops	1	0
phase	1	4
total	40	40

ANTINODE, the accent is customarily on the prefix (ăn'-tĭ-nōd). When the same prefix ANTI- is used with an adjective, as ANTI-CHRISTIAN, the accent is on the radical element (ăn-tĭ-krĭs'-chăn). In ANTINODE the prefix does not mean antagonistic to the NODE, but rather in contrast to the NODE. The ANTINODE is the point, line, or surface, between two nodes, where the amplitude of the vibration is greatest.

An elaborate definition of NODE is: 'A point, line, or surface, in a vibrating medium at which the amplitude of the vibration is zero because of the interference of opposing wave trains'.

195. *CHANDELLE* (shăn-dĕl') *n.* A flight maneuver combining climb and turn, approach to a stall and recovery to normal flight. The simple CHANDELLE is an exaggerated 180 degree climbing turn in which the bank and climb are both increased to the 90 degree point. Here climb is reduced and the bank shallowed until flight is straight and level at the 180 degree point and speed just above stalling.

The word *chandelle* is the modern French for candle. It comes from the Latin *candela*, a candle, from the verb *candere*, to be white, bright, shining, the source of the English CANDID, open and sincere, outspoken, frank and honest, and also of

Form A. An abrupt climbing turn to approximately a stall in which the momentum of the airplane is used to obtain a higher rate of climb than would be possible in unaccelerated flight.
Form AA. A combination of banking and climbing almost to a stall.

FORM A. 50.	FW	LA	NY	NY	NY	PH	SUM	FORM AA. 30.	NY
CHANDELLE	12	22	9	27	54	87	211	CHANDELLE	24
wing over	3	4	2	4	16	17	46	wing over	14
zoom	0	5	8	6	6	15	40	zoom	2
Immelmann	3	13	9	10	19	30	84	Immelmann	11
pull-up	0	8	6	9	43	37	103	pull-up	12
unmarked	0	2	3	10	2	14	31	unmarked	0
total	18	54	37	66	140	200	515	total	63

CANDIDATE, because in Rome those who sought office wore a glittering white toga. Through the French *chandelle* come CHANDELIER (shăn-dĕ-lēr'), originally an ornamental branched candle holder, now one which hangs from above, and CHANDLER (chand'-ler), one who makes and sells candles, extended to other dealers, as a SHIP-CHANDLER, CORN-CHANDLER.

To the question: 'An abrupt climbing turn to approximately a stall in which the momentum of the airplane is used to obtain a higher rate of climb than would be possible in unaccelerated flight', 211 persons out of 515 answer CHANDELLE; but 103 answer PULL-UP, and 84 IMMELMANN. A CHANDELLE and a PULL-UP are both climbs. A PULL-UP is a short climb, usually from level flight; a CHANDELLE is a longer, higher climb made possible by the greater speed of a plane which has been descending.

Both the CHANDELLE and the IMMELMANN are abrupt climbing turns in which the momentum of the airplane is used to obtain a higher rate of climb than would be possible in unaccelerated flight. Both leave the plane going in the opposite direction and at a higher level than before the turn. The IMMELMANN is the first half of a vertical loop flown straight up vertically with a half roll at the top to bring the plane which is upside down back to normal flight. The CHANDELLE is not a loop but a steep climb and bank almost to stalling.

196. *ISOTOPE* ($\bar{i}'$-$s\bar{o}$-$t\bar{o}p$) *n.* One of two or more varieties of the same chemical element which have the same atomic number but different atomic masses, each of two or more closely allied elements or atoms of an element possessing identical chemical properties and occupying the same position in the periodic table but having different atomic weights.

The term ISOTOPE was coined by Frederick Soddy in 1913. It starts with the Greek ἴσος (isos), equal, the same, already met in ISOTHERMAL (125), applied to a reaction which takes place at the same temperature, with no change in temperature, and ISOSCELES (34), having two legs alike. The second part of ISOTOPE comes from the Greek τόπος (topos), place, the source of TOPOGRAPHY, by derivation the description of a place. The Oxford New English Dictionary says that a more appropriate word than ISOTOPE would have been HOMOTOPE.

To the question: 'The different forms of the atoms of a simple element which can be distinguished by their different atomic weights', 46 per cent of 2234 persons answer ISOTOPES; but 18 per cent answer PROTONS. In the earlier study of form c, based on 400 persons, 53 per cent answer ISOTOPES; and 22 per cent PROTONS. The word PROTON comes from the Greek πρῶτον (proton), the neuter singular of πρῶτος (protos), first.

Frederick W. Aston, author of Isotopes, 2nd edition 1924, and to whom is due much more of the credit for our modern understanding of ISOTOPES than he gives himself in his article in the Encyclopaedia, says: 'The primordial atoms are of two kinds: PROTONS and ELECTRONS, the atoms of positive and negative electricity. All of the PROTONS and about half of the ELECTRONS are packed together in a positively charged nucleus, around which the remaining ELECTRONS circulate like the planets about the sun'. Watch for and own: Aston, Frederick W., Mass-Spectra and Isotopes, published Edward Arnold, 1933. Black calls it a classic written by a master in this field.

The nucleus of the lithium atom may have six positive PROTONS and three negative ELECTRONS, or seven PROTONS and four ELECTRONS, but always has three planetary ELECTRONS circling about. These planetary ELECTRONS determine the chemical properties of the atom, and its place in the periodic table; but the PROTONS determine its weight, for the mass of a PROTON

The different forms of the atoms of a single element which can be distinguished by their different atomic weights.

FORM C. 15. NY		FORM CA. 21. BO	NY	NY	NY	NY	SUM
nuclei	51	nuclei	4	19	35	182	20	260
protons	86	protons	20	28	74	244	37	403
isomers	35	isomers	16	29	42	170	7	264
positrons	11	diatoms	14	22	47	183	6	272
ISOTOPES	211	ISOTOPES	44	302	202	321	164	1033
unmarked	6	unmarked	2	0	0	0	0	2
total	400	total	100	400	400	1100	234	2234

is 1840 times that of an ELECTRON. The two lithium atoms have different atomic weights, one of six and the other of seven PROTONS; but both with three planetary ELECTRONS, and therefore identical chemical properties. Soddy says: 'The same algebraic sum of the positive and negative charges in the nucleus, when the arithmetic sum is different, gives what I call ISOTOPES or ISOTOPIC ELEMENTS'.

Ordinary lead has an atomic weight of 207.2; but Soddy predicted two leads with atomic weights of 206 and 208. Chlorine has ISOTOPES with atomic weights of 35 and 37. From J. Mills, 1922, Within the Atom, comes: 'Two atomic systems may exist which are ISOTOPIC at the periodic table, but differ in total number of PROTONS in their nuclei. In all chemical combinations or reactions these ISOTOPES are indistinguishable.'

The understanding of a scientific law seems roughly related to its age, as discussed under PASCAL'S LAW (149), the older the law the greater the percentage of persons who know it. Is today's familiarity with newly coined technical terms related in the same way to their age? Those which appeared between 1800 and 1850, and which have been studied statistically, are known to a larger number of persons than words of more recent origin; but earlier words, 1600 to 1700, though more familiar than recent ones, do not obey this rule for they are

% UN-KNOWN	COINED WORD	DATE COINED	% UN-KNOWN	COINED WORD	DATE COINED
64	SUBLIMATION	1390	18	THERMO-	
56	LOGARITHM	1614		DYNAMICS	1854
51	INERTIA	1687	99	REGELATION	1857
86	CENTRIPETAL	1687	99	AGONIC	1863
93	ABSCISSA	1698	33	HELICOPTER	1872
63	MOMENTUM	1699	89	DYNE	1873
81	ANEMOMETER	1727	99	ADIABATIC	1877
66	DIHEDRAL	1799	66	RADIAN	1879
42	POLARIZE	1811	99	POUNDAL	1879
32	SOLENOID	1832	99	EUTECTIC	1884
32	ELECTROLYSIS	1834	44	REACTANCE	1896
41	ION	1834	97	QUANTA	1900
80	CATHODE	1834	98	PHONODEIK	1908
36	RHEOSTAT	1843	75	ISOTOPE	1913
43	ANEROID	1848	99	BETA PARTICLES	1913
34	FLUORESCENCE	1852	99	CAPACITANCE	1916
55	ISOTHERMAL	1854	42	DECIBEL	1937

known to fewer persons than words a hundred years later. This is partly, though certainly not entirely, because words with exact opposites are frequently more difficult than others of the same age, and there are two in this group. Thus among the words coined by Faraday in 1834 CATHODE (211), where nearly a quarter mark ANODE, is significantly harder than the other two which have been studied. In the 17th-century words CENTRIPETAL with its opposite CENTRIFUGAL, and ABSCISSA with its opposite COORDINATE, are the two most difficult.

The coined words of the 19th century are more familiar than the newly discovered laws of the same date, making words seem easier to learn than laws, but the same relation does not hold between the words and laws of the 17th century. Again the coined words of this period seem exceptionally hard. Though age is a factor in determining difficulty, each word and each law must be included in a vocabulary test and the percentage of persons who mark it correctly determined empirically before its true difficulty in relation to other words and laws can be known with certainty.

197. *FOUCAULT PENDULUM* (*foo-kō'*). A long pendulum to demonstrate the rotation of the earth, a heavy ball of metal hung at the end of a long wire two or three stories high. To the question: 'A pendulum arranged to show the rotation of the earth', 43 per cent of 2234 persons answer FOUCAULT; but 18 per cent answer BALLISTIC. In the earlier study of form C 39 per cent answered FOUCAULT; and 36 per cent BALLISTIC. The word BALLISTIC comes from the Latin *ballista*, an ancient military engine like a bow used to hurl stones. This in turn comes from the Greek βάλλειν (ballein), to throw. A BALLISTIC PENDULUM is an apparatus invented by Benjamin Robins for ascertaining the velocity of military projectiles and so the explosive force of the gunpowder used. The bullet is fired against an iron case, filled with sand bags, which forms the ball of a pendulum. From Thomson and Tait, A Treatise on Natural Philosophy, comes: 'Robins' BALLISTIC PENDULUM, a massive cylindrical block of wood cased in a cylindrical sheet of iron closed at one end and movable about a horizontal axis'. From 1778, a hundred years earlier, from Charles Hutton, Professor of Mathematics at the Royal Academy, Woolwich, and author of Mathematical and Philosophical Dictionary, comes: 'This large BALLISTIC PENDULUM, after being struck by the ball'.

Jean Bernard FOUCAULT, who lived from 1819 to 1868, was the son of a publisher. He first studied medicine, but soon became interested in experimental physics. He invented the gyroscope, measured the velocity of light in different media, and discovered eddy currents due to induction, now called FOUCAULT CURRENTS. In 1851 he presented a memoir giving his famous demonstration of the rotation of the earth by means of a pendulum. From a footnote in A History of Physics by Florian Cajori comes the following: 'The experiment was made in four places. The first one was a cellar two metres deep at his pavilion in the Rue d'Assas. A brass ball weighing five kilogrammes was suspended by a steel wire. The ball was drawn aside, held in that position by a thread until it was at complete rest, then set free by burning the thread. The pendulum began oscillating in a fixed vertical plane, making thereby the fact of the earth's rotation experimentally evident. To the eye the plane of oscillation seemed to rotate and the earth to be at rest. Theory indicated that the angle of this apparent motion in a given time was equal to the angle through which the earth rotated in the same time, multiplied by the sine of the angle of

A pendulum arranged to show the rotation of the earth.

FORM C. 30.	NY	FORM CA. 28.	BO	NY	NY	NY	NY	SUM
compound	16	compound	9	34	26	177	26	272
simple	26	simple	10	19	34	181	18	262
ballistic	145	ballistic	16	47	78	227	37	405
Foucault	157	Foucault	51	266	216	323	107	963
Kater	31	Kater	8	34	46	192	41	321
unmarked	25	unmarked	6	0	0	0	5	11
total	400	total	100	400	400	1100	234	2234

latitude of the place where the experiment was made. An accurate verification of this law required more favorable conditions. Arago offered Foucault the use of the observatory building, where a pendulum eleven metres long enabled him to demonstrate the law with exactitude. Through the favour of Napoleon III., the Panthéon was chosen for the third test. A ball of twenty-eight kilogrammes was suspended there by a wire sixty-seven metres long and 1.4 millimetres thick. The Panthéon was thronged with visitors. The fourth exhibition was made at the Universal Exposition of 1855.' In an hour in Paris the pendulum changes its plane of motion by 11 degrees. At the north pole the rate of rotation would be 15 degrees per hour or 360 degrees in twenty-four hours. At the equator there is no such turning of the earth beneath.

198. *LAUE PATTERN* (lō păt'-tern). On a photographic
    plate a pattern of bright spots caused by X rays after pass-
ing through a crystal. Reread DIFFRACTION GRATING (148).
Max von Laue was born near Coblenz in Germany in 1879.
In 1914 he received the Nobel prize for physics. He believed
that a crystal might act as a diffraction grating for high frequency X rays, where the wave lengths were too short for the

Pattern caused by the passing of X rays through a crystal.

FORM E. 44.	BO	FW	LA	NY	NY	NY	NY	PH	TU	SUM
LAUE PATTERN	13	19	20	12	12	17	99	47	17	256
spectra	2	14	7	6	4	9	56	21	4	123
cycloid	2	5	2	0	1	4	16	5	2	37
Balmer series	2	6	3	1	1	5	26	10	2	56
Lissajous's curves	5	4	1	1	2	3	15	16	3	50
unmarked	4	2	0	0	0	2	6	1	0	15
total	28	50	33	20	20	40	218	100	28	537

FORM E. 44.	ENGLISH VOCABULARY	
	HIGH	LOW
LAUE PATTERN	31	11
spectra	4	21
cycloid	2	2
Balmer series	2	3
Lissajous's curves	1	3
unmarked	0	0
total	40	40

ordinary diffraction grating of lines scratched on glass. Two
other experimental scientists, Friedrich and Knipping, then
verified Laue's theoretical reasoning by passing a pencil of
X rays through a crystal and recording the result on a photographic plate. The plate was covered with a regular pattern of
spots, as von Laue had predicted.

The experiment gave the key to the nature of X rays and
stimulated Sir William Bragg and his son W. L. Bragg to study
the crystal structures which were causing the diffraction pat-
terns; for, though the geometric framework of crystal structure
had been worked out, the size of the cell and the positions of

the atoms were unknown. There was also at that time a controversy as to the nature of X rays. Were they corpuscular or transverse waves like light but with shorter wave lengths?

To the question: 'Pattern caused by the passing of X rays through a crystal', 256 persons out of 537 answer correctly LAUE PATTERN; but 123 answer SPECTRA. Of 40 persons who score high in the general English literary vocabulary 31 answer LAUE PATTERN and only 4 SPECTRA; but of 40 who score low in English vocabulary only 11 answer LAUE PATTERN, and 21 SPECTRA. The answer SPECTRA can probably be justified, for the LAUE PATTERN is an X-ray spectrum, except for evidence that those who know the term LAUE PATTERN, especially the high English-vocabulary group, choose it in place of SPECTRA.

199. *LATENT HEAT* (*lă'-tĕnt hēt*). The amount of heat released by a substance in freezing, in changing from a liquid to a solid, or in changing from a gas to a liquid, including HEAT OF FUSION and of VAPORIZATION. Reread HEAT OF FUSION (179).

Using the words of the German chemist Robert Wilhelm Bunsen, who lived from 1811 to 1899: 'A gram of ice at zero degrees centigrade absorbs 80.025 calories of heat in becoming a gram of water of the same temperature. As this absorbed heat is not sensible to the thermometer but nevertheless possessed by the water it is said to be hidden or LATENT HEAT.'

The word LATENT comes from the Latin *latens, latentis*, the present participle of *latere*, to lurk, lie hidden, be concealed. From William Lecky, the historian, born near Dublin, in his History of England in the Eighteenth Century, published 1878 to 1880, comes: 'Evoke the LATENT genius of the nation'. The opposite of LATENT is PATENT (*pă'-tĕnt*), open, obvious, evident, as in the legal definition of a LATENT ambiguity, a doubt as to meaning, not PATENT from a document itself, but raised by the evidence of extrinsic and collateral matter.

To the question: 'Number of calories required to change the state of one gram of a substance without changing the temperature', 258 persons out of 537 answer correctly LATENT HEAT; but 99 answer CRITICAL TEMPERATURE. Both CRITICAL TEMPERATURE (132) and LATENT HEAT apply to the change from one state to another, from gas to liquid. The CRITICAL TEMPERATURE of a gas is the temperature above which the gas cannot be liquefied no matter how great the pressure, and below which it can be. The LATENT HEAT is the amount of heat given off by the substance in changing from gas to liquid with no change in temperature. More precisely this is called HEAT OF VAPORIZATION. The amount of heat released by a liquid when it freezes, during solidification, due to its change of state, is called HEAT OF

Number of calories required to change the state of one gram of a substance without changing the temperature.

FORM E. 24.	BO	FW	LA	NY	NY	NY	NY	PH	TU	SUM
100	1	5	4	3	1	8	25	7	1	55
heat of combustion	1	3	8	5	0	4	31	10	1	63
LATENT HEAT	15	24	13	6	14	9	106	55	16	258
specific resistance	4	4	3	3	1	4	17	12	5	53
critical temperature	5	11	5	3	4	14	37	15	5	99
unmarked	2	3	0	0	0	1	2	1	0	9
total	28	50	33	20	20	40	218	100	28	537

FORM E. 24.	ENGLISH VOCABULARY	
	HIGH	LOW
100	3	8
heat of combustion	4	3
LATENT HEAT	31	15
specific resistance	1	4
critical temperature	1	10
unmarked	0	0
total	40	40

FUSION. It differs from one solid to another. It is the amount of heat per unit mass needed to melt a solid, to change it to a liquid without increase in temperature. Daniell says: 'We now know that this is not HEAT at all, but LATENT or potential energy. Work is done against molecular forces in order to convert ice to water.' The term LATENT HEAT was introduced about 1760 by Joseph Black, a Scottish chemist, son of a wine merchant. Black receives little credit for lack of detailed publications.

200. *CONVERSE* (kŏn'-vers) *n.* One of a pair of propositions having the same subject but in the reverse order, a proposition in which the datum and conclusion are the conclusion and datum of another.

The proposition that every isosceles triangle, one with two equal sides, has two of its angles equal, is the CONVERSE of the proposition that every triangle with two equal angles is isosceles, has two equal sides.

CONVERSE comes from the Latin *conversus*, turned around, the past participle of *convertere*, a combination of *com-*, together; and *vertere*, to turn, a verb already discussed under INVERSE PROPORTION (46). To REVERT, a combination of *re-*, back, and *vertere*, to turn, is to turn back; one can REVERT to a subject discussed before, turn back to it. To AVERT is to turn away; one can AVERT trouble, turn it away. To INVERT is to turn end for end, or upside down. To SUBVERT is to turn under, ruin, destroy. To CONVERT is to turn into another form, transform, as

The opposite of a proposition.

FORM A. 46.	BO	NY	SUM	FORM AA. 32.	NY
corollary	1	10	11	corollary	38
refutation	5	8	13	refutation	30
CONVERSE	10	18	28	CONVERSE	51
invalidation	2	2	4	invalidation	9
negative	0	3	3	negative	3
unmarked	2	0	2	unmarked	1
total	20	41	61	total	132

to CONVERT raw materials into a finished product. Of the corresponding adjectives, REVERSE means opposite, the REVERSE direction is the other direction, turning back. AVERSE is turned away from, turned against, AVERSE to buying, against buying. The adjective *subverse* is not used but replaced by SUBVERSIVE, destructive, overturning. CONVERSE is used constructively. Having proved a proposition, one says CONVERSELY, implying that one is about to show that the CONVERSE is also true.

To the question: 'The opposite of a proposition', 51 persons out of 132 answer CONVERSE; while 38 answer COROLLARY, and 30 REFUTATION. A REFUTATION is the disproving of an argument.

The corresponding verb to REFUTE is to disprove, overthrow by argument, prove false. From the Century Dictionary comes: 'CONVERSE is often used incorrectly in the sense of REVERSE— that is, the opposite, the contrary'; and quotes George Alfred Lawrence, the English novelist, who used CONVERSE for REVERSE. The REVERSE is the opposite truth, the contrary, almost a REFUTATION. The CONVERSE may or may not be true; it is a proposition stated in the REVERSE order.

A COROLLARY is a proposition proved incidentally in proving another, an easily drawn consequence. The Latin *corollary* was a gift, money paid for a garland, little crown, the diminutive of *corona*, a crown. A COROLLARY is a truth which follows from another with little or no proof, a theorem easily proved by means of some other theorem. A CONVERSE is a proposition so related to another that what is given in the first is to be proven in the second. Each CONVERSE must be proved, for a CONVERSE is not necessarily true. Two right angles are always equal; but the CONVERSE, two equal angles are not always two right angles.

201. *VALUE* (văl'-ū) *n*. In mathematics the special determination of a quantity, the precise amount represented by a figure.

The word VALUE comes from the Latin *valere*, to be strong, to be worth. From the same source come VALOR, strength of

Quantity assigned to a variable.

FORM B. 19.	NY	MISC.	SUM
root	7	39	46
argument	2	14	16
hypothesis	7	35	42
approximation	7	65	72
VALUE	25	133	158
unmarked	0	23	23
total	48	309	357

mind, bravery, courage, and VALIANT, strong, brave, courageous.

To the question: 'Quantity assigned to a variable', 158 persons out of 357 mark VALUE; but 72 mark APPROXIMATION, a justified answer with the present wording of the question. An APPROXI-

MATION is a VALUE nearly but not quite correct. The word comes from the Latin *ad*, to, and *proximare*, to come near, from *proximus*, the superlative of *prope*, near. In some complicated mathematical problems a VALUE is assigned to a variable, an APPROXIMATION to the truth, and a correction to this guess is then obtained mathematically as a step toward the true value.

202. *DIHEDRAL ANGLE* (*dī-hē'-drăl*) *adj.* Angle through which the wing tip is raised above the wing root, angle between a horizontal line and the long axis of the wing. Reread DIHEDRAL (163).

The DIHEDRAL ANGLE is between the horizontal and the length of a wing when the wing tip is raised, between a horizontal plane and the plane of the wing measured lengthwise, more technically the small acute angle between a line perpendicular to the plane of symmetry of the aircraft and a projection of the wing axis on a plane perpendicular to the longitudinal axis of the aircraft, angle between a horizontal line and the under surface of the wing.

To the question: 'Angle between the wing tilted upward and a horizontal line', 209 persons out of 515 answer correctly DIHEDRAL; but 118 answer ANGLE OF ATTACK, and 95 ANGLE OF INCIDENCE. Obscurity in the present wording may lead to these markings; for the question may be interpreted as meaning tipped up in width rather than in length. This ambiguity may also lead to DIHEDRAL as applied to an airplane being more difficult than DIHEDRAL (163) used mathematically for the angle between two planes, which is marked correctly by 48 per cent, while this item, as the question is worded in form A, is marked correctly by only 41 per cent. In the revised form AA, the new wording: 'Angle between a horizontal line and the long axis of the wing tilted upward', is answered correctly by 56 per cent of the 63 persons whose scores have been tabulated, making it easier than DIHEDRAL in the mathematics vocabulary test, as might be expected, instead of harder.

The ANGLE OF ATTACK is called by the British ANGLE OF INCIDENCE, which suggests that the two are much alike. Both are angles made by the wing chord or width of the wing. The ANGLE OF ATTACK is the angle of the chord with the relative wind; the ANGLE OF INCIDENCE is the angle of the chord with the longitudinal line of the plane. Both are angles made by raising the front edge of the wing. The DIHEDRAL ANGLE is made by raising the tip of the wing.

Both the ANGLE OF INCIDENCE and the DIHEDRAL ANGLE are fixed in the design of the plane. The ANGLE OF INCIDENCE is the angle between the width of the wing and the horizontal, the angle by which the leading edge of the wing is raised above the

Form A. Angle between the wing tilted upward and a horizontal line.

Form AA. Angle between a horizontal line and the long axis of the wing tilted upward.

FORM A. 19.	FW	LA	NY	NY	NY	PH	SUM	FORM AA. 27.	NY
zero-lift angle	1	6	3	1	21	17	49	zero lift	8
DIHEDRAL	5	27	20	25	40	92	209	DIHEDRAL	35
angle of incidence	5	8	5	15	31	31	95	incidence	5
angle of attack	6	10	7	16	36	43	118	attack	14
attitude of flight	1	2	1	6	12	12	34	rake	0
unmarked	0	1	1	3	0	5	10	unmarked	1
total	18	54	37	66	140	200	515	total	63

trailing edge. The ANGLE OF INCIDENCE is the fixed angle between the wing chord and the line of thrust. It may be called ANGLE OF WING SETTING. The DIHEDRAL ANGLE is the angle between the length of the wing and the horizontal, the angle by which the tip of the wing is raised above the root.

203. *DERIVATIVE* (*dē-rĭv′-ă-tĭv*) *n.* The limit of one incre-
    ment divided by another increment, a value approached by a quotient, the slope of the tangent to a curve.
The word DERIVATIVE comes from the Latin *derivare*, to lead, turn, also to draw off, used in drawing off a liquid, also to de-rive, used of deriving one word from another. This Latin verb is a combination of *de-*, from, away, and *rivus*, a stream.

To the question: 'A differential coefficient', 40 persons out of 132 answer correctly DERIVATIVE; while 40 others answer ABSOLUTE CONSTANT. It may be the word COEFFICIENT in the question which leads so many to mark CONSTANT; for a COEFFICIENT is often a constant multiplying a variable or unknown quantity. An ABSOLUTE CONSTANT (104) is one which is always the same in all problems. The Greek letter π (pi) stands for an ABSOLUTE CONSTANT, always the same.

As the term DIFFERENTIAL COEFFICIENT seems at least as difficult as DERIVATIVE, the question has been changed to: 'The limiting value of the ratio of two small quantities', which is not a complete definition of DERIVATIVE but which should be marked correctly by those who know the word.

Although the notation for DERIVATIVE,

$$\frac{dy}{dx},$$

universally accepted by modern textbooks, is due to Leibnitz as early as 1675, not until nearly 1820 was it finally accepted in England. As undergraduates at Cambridge, John Herschel, George Peacock, and Charles Babbage entered into a compact to do their best to leave the world wiser than they found it. In 1813 they established the Analytical Society to promote the principles of 'd-ism', the Leibnitz notation, dx, against those of dot-age, for the fluxional Newtonian notation was $\dot{y}$, with a dot above. In his autobiography Babbage says: 'The progress of the notation of Leibniz at Cambridge was slow. It is always difficult to think and reason in a new language, and this difficulty discouraged all but men of energetic minds. I saw however that by making it the tutor's interest to do so, the change might be accomplished. I therefore proposed to make a large collection of examples of the differential and integral calculus. I foresaw that if such a publication existed, all those tutors who did not approve of the change of the Newtonian notation would yet, in order to save their own time and trouble, go to the collection to find problems. I communicated to Peacock and Herschel my view, and proposed that they should each contribute a portion.' Later in life Charles Babbage became one of the founders of the Astronomical Society, and invented a calculating engine.

George Peacock wrote a treatise on Algebra in 1830 and became Dean of Ely in 1839. Sir John Herschel became a celebrated astronomer and physicist.

There is still much to say for Newton's notation. The double line is troublesome to print; and

$$\frac{dy}{dx}$$

is not a ratio, but a single number. The DERIVATIVE of a function or dependent variable is the limit approached by a ratio or

A differential coefficient.

FORM A. 22.	BO	NY	SUM	FORM AA. 37.	NY
parameter	4	5	9	parameter	11
antilog	2	5	7	antilog	14
sigma	0	2	2	sigma	23
				absolute	
absolute constant	3	11	14	constant	40
DERIVATIVE	10	17	27	DERIVATIVE	40
unmarked	1	1	2	unmarked	4
total	20	41	61	total	132

fraction, the ratio of a small addition to the function divided by a small addition to the independent variable on which the value of the function depends.

The increment or addition to the independent variable is called delta x, Δx. The increment or addition to the dependent variable, depending upon x for its value, is called delta y, Δy. Delta y divided by delta x is a real ratio, a fraction. The DERIVATIVE, called dy over dx is not itself a fraction, but is the limiting value of a fraction.

204. *GREAT CIRCLE* (*grāt ser'-kl*). A circle on the surface of a ball, whose plane passes through the center, the largest circle which can be drawn on the surface of a sphere, one whose radius is the same as that of the sphere. Reread RHUMB LINE (164).

'GREAT CIRCLES of the Globe, or Sphere, are those whose Plane passing thro' the Centre of the Sphere, divides it into two

equal Parts or Hemispheres; of which there are Six drawn on
the Globe, viz. The Meridian, Horizon, Equator, Eclipticke, and
the two Colures'. This definition comes from the Lexicon
Technicum, 1704, by John Harris, who in his preface is critical
of nearly every previous dictionary. He says: 'The Grand
Dictionaire Des Arts & Sciences, par M. de l'Académie Fran-
çoise, hath no Cuts nor Figures at all, and is only a bare Ex-
plication of Terms of Art; and it seems rather to have been

A circle all of whose points lie upon the surface of a sphere,
and whose center is the same as that of the sphere.

FORM B. 34.	NY	MISC.	SUM
meridian	7	50	57
GREAT CIRCLE	22	123	145
lune	5	24	29
equator	7	61	68
bisector	5	22	27
unmarked	2	29	31
total	48	309	357

design'd to improve and propagate the French Language, than
to inform and instruct the Humane Mind in general. And,
which I have often wonder'd at, 'tis filled every where with
Simple Terms, so that you are told what a Dog, a Cat, a Horse
and a Sheep is; which, tho' it may be useful to some Persons
who did not know that before, and may shew very well, that
such Descriptions can be given in French; yet how the bare
Names of Animals and Vegetables, of Metals and Minerals, can
be reckoned as Terms of Art, and consequently make the greatest part of a Dictionary of Arts and Sciences, I confess I cannot
see'.

To the question: 'A circle all of whose points lie upon the
surface of a sphere, and whose center is the same as that of the
sphere', 145 persons out of 357 answer GREAT CIRCLE; but 68
answer EQUATOR, and 57 MERIDIAN. Both the EQUATOR and the
MERIDIAN, as John Harris says, are GREAT CIRCLES, and so are
correct answers to the question as worded. EQUATOR and
MERIDIAN are specific GREAT CIRCLES; the MERIDIAN, the GREAT
CIRCLE through the poles of the earth and through the point

directly overhead. The EQUATOR is the GREAT CIRCLE whose plane is at right angles to the axis. The term GREAT CIRCLE is general to include these and all circles on the surface of a sphere whose centers coincide with the center of the sphere. The term is especially important in navigation for the GREAT CIRCLE is the shortest distance between any two points on the surface of a sphere.

205. *ELLIPSE* (*ĕl-lĭps'*) *n.* A plane closed curve, oval-shaped figure, a conic section, the appearance of a circular disk tipped about an axis at right angles to the line of sight.
From Robert Boyle, 1627 to 1691, comes: 'When a right cone is cut quite through by an inclining plane, the figure pro-

The curve whose equation is: $\dfrac{x^2}{a^2} + \dfrac{y^2}{b^2} = 1$.

FORM C. 22.	CH	FORM CA. 15.	CH	LA	NY	NY	PH	SUM
ELLIPSE	43	ELLIPSE	19	20	52	153	41	285
hyperbola	8	hyperbola	15	10	26	53	23	127
helix	6	helix	1	2	7	30	2	42
cycloid	6	cycloid	4	3	11	33	5	56
asymptote	5	asymptote	1	2	1	6	1	11
unmarked	0	unmarked	0	0	0	2	2	4
total	68	total	40	37	97	277	74	525

FORM CB. 23.	NY
ELLIPSE	43
hyperbola	22
helix	8
cycloid	8
strophoid	2
unmarked	3
total	86

duced by the section agrees well with the received notion of an ELLIPSIS, in which the diameters are of an unequal length'. From an Encyclopaedia published by Thomas Dobson in Philadelphia in 1798 comes: 'ELLIPSIS, in geometry, a curve line returning into itself, and produced from the section of a cone by

a plane cutting both its sides, but not parallel to the base'. An
ELLIPSE can be drawn by starting with two fixed points called
FOCI and making the distance from one of the fixed points to
any point on the ELLIPSE and back to the other fixed point always the same.

To the question: 'The curve whose equation is:

$$\frac{x^2}{a^2} + \frac{y^2}{b^2} = 1$$

285 persons out of 525 answer correctly ELLIPSE; while 127 answer HYPERBOLA, the popular mislead in each city which has
been tabulated. The corresponding equation for the HYPER-
BOLA is the same except for the minus sign:

$$\frac{x^2}{a^2} - \frac{y^2}{b^2} = 1$$

The word ELLIPSE comes through the Latin *ellipsis*, a want,
defect, also in geometry an ellipse. In rhetoric today an
ELLIPSIS is a figure of speech by which a word or a part of a sentence is left out. The Latin *ellipsis* came from the Greek ἔλλειψις
(elleipsis), a leaving out, ellipsis is grammar, falling short, from
λείπειν (leipein), to leave; for the Greeks constructed an ELLIPSE
by starting with a vertical line and developing on it a rectangle
which always turned out to be shorter in length than the line
with which they started. The rectangle fell short of the line;
and so the term ἔλλειψις (elleipsis), falling short. In constructing
the HYPERBOLA the same rectangle when developed is longer
than the straight line; and so the word ἱπερβολῆ (hyperbola),
given by Apollonius, from the verb ἱπερβάλλειν (hiperballein),
to throw over, from ἱπέρ (hiper), over, and βάλλειν (ballein), to
throw.

The HYPERBOLA is a curve formed by the intersection of a
plane with a double cone, two similar cones, vertex to vertex.
If the plane is at right angles to the axis of the cones it cuts of
course only one of the cones and the section is a CIRCLE. If the
plane is tipped a little, but not enough to cut both cones, the
section is an ELLIPSE. If the plane is tipped enough to be parallel
to the side of the cone, the section is a PARABOLA. If the plane is
tipped enough to cut both cones the sections are HYPERBOLAS.

206. *INTEGRAL* (*ĭn'-tē-grăl*) *n*. The expression or function of which one knows the differential, sum of infinitesimals. Knowing the DIFFERENTIAL of a function, the function itself when found is called the INTEGRAL of the given differential.

The English word INTEGRAL and the French *intégral*, spelt like the English except for the accent, come from the Latin *integer*, a combination of the privative *in*, meaning not, and

Area under a curve.

FORM A. 24.	BO	NY	SUM	FORM AA. 36.	NY
differential	3	10	13	differential	21
INTERGAL	9	17	26	INTEGRAL	28
binomial	2	3	5	amplitude	64
factorial sum	3	4	7	factorial sum	5
geometric				geometric	
progression	2	5	7	progression	13
unmarked	1	2	3	unmarked	1
total	20	41	61	total	132

tangere, to touch. An INTEGER in English is untouched, intact, a whole number. An INTEGRAL is the whole obtained by adding together its parts. The INTEGRAL sign ∫ stands for the letter s, the SUM.

In the original form A of the mathematics vocabulary test, 26 persons out of 61 answer correctly INTEGRAL to the question: 'Area under a curve'; while 13 answer DIFFERENTIAL. INTEGRATION is the inverse of DIFFERENTIATION. It is finding the function knowing the derivative of that function. There is no direct way of INTEGRATING. One must start with a large number of functions and differentiate each until one stumbles on a DIFFERENTIAL which looks like the one to be integrated. For this reason tables have been made showing just such differentials.

But in the new revised form AA 64 persons out of 132 flock to the new mislead AMPLITUDE, while only 28 mark INTEGRAL, and 21 DIFFERENTIAL. The word AMPLITUDE is used in literature for fullness, largeness. AMPLE means wide, spacious, roomy. But technically the AMPLITUDE of a swing is the distance from side to side, the breadth. The AMPLITUDE of a radio wave is its breadth from a center line to one of its peaks or troughs.

207. *COINCIDENT* (kō-ĭn'-sĭ-dĕnt) *adj*. Occupying the same place in space, the same position on a scale, coinciding.

The word COINCIDENT comes from the Latin *co-*, together, and *incidere*, to fall on, a combination of *in*, on, and *cadere*, to fall. From the same source come ACCIDENT, something which befalls, happens, occurs, and OCCIDENT, the place where the sun

A line which is a side of two geometric figures.

FORM A. 43.	BO	NY	SUM	FORM AA. 26.	NY
adjacent	7	10	17	adjacent	39
similar	1	1	2	conjugate	17
COINCIDENT	8	21	29	COINCIDENT	42
simultaneous	1	4	5	simultaneous	17
tangent	2	5	7	tangent	17
unmarked	1	0	1	unmarked	0
total	20	41	61	total	132

falls, the region of the setting sun, the west. More directly from *cadere*, to fall, comes CADENCE, the fall of the voice in reading or speaking, often at the end of a sentence, and in music a succession of chords indicating a conclusion.

ADJACENT angles, as that word is used in geometry, have a line in common, and this no doubt leads to the marking of ADJACENT in answer to the question: 'A line which is a side of two geometric figures', where 42 persons out of 132 answer COINCIDENT, and 39 ADJACENT. But ADJACENT (82) ought to mean lying near, neighboring, close, adjoining but not necessarily in contact. ADJACENT figures, in geometry, may have a line which is COINCIDENT; two lines are COINCIDENT which are everywhere infinitely near to each other.

208. *CHARACTERISTIC* (kă-răk-tē-rĭs'-tĭk) *n*. The integral part of a common logarithm, the whole number to the left of the decimal point in a Briggsian logarithm. Reread LOGARITHM (128).

Charles Hutton, the English mathematician who lived from 1737 to 1823, author of a Mathematical and Philosophical Dictionary, wrote in his Course of Mathematics, 1798: 'The integral part of a logarithm, usually called the INDEX, or CHAR-

ACTERISTIC'. The CHARACTERISTIC of the common logarithm of a number is independent of the digits which make up the number, but depends entirely on the position of the decimal point in the number. The CHARACTERISTIC of the logarithm of a positive number greater than 1 is one less than the number

Whole number in a logarithm.

FORM A. 25.	BO	NY	SUM	FORM AA. 39.	NY
prime	2	10	12	prime	25
mantissa	3	12	15	mantissa	36
CHARACTERISTIC	13	14	27	CHARACTERISTIC	59
antilog	1	3	4	antilog	5
log-log	0	2	2	log-log	5
unmarked	1	0	1	unmarked	2
total	20	41	61	total	132

of digits to the left of the decimal point in the number. Thus the CHARACTERISTIC of the common logarithm of 6.00 is 0.; the CHARACTERISTIC of 60 is 1.; and the CHARACTERISTIC of 600 is 2. The CHARACTERISTIC of a number less than 1 is negative and is one more than the number of ciphers between the decimal point and the first digit to its right. This can be written as a negative CHARACTERISTIC, -1.; but as the negative sign applies only to the CHARACTERISTIC it is more often written over the CHARACTERISTIC, and still more often written as 9.0000 $-$ 10.

The word CHARACTERISTIC comes from the Greek χαρακτηριστικός (characteristikos), from χαρακτηρίξειν (characterizein), to designate, characterize, from χαρακτήρ (character), originally an instrument for marking or engraving, and then the distinctive mark made, personal feature, character, peculiar nature. All of these come from the verb χαρίσσειν (charissein), to furrow, scratch, engrave. The noun CHARACTERISTIC was first applied to a logarithm in 1628 by Henry Briggs, a friend of Napier and the originator of common logarithms or logarithms to the base 10.

To the question: 'Whole number in a logarithm', 59 persons out of 132 answer correctly CHARACTERISTIC; while 36 answer MANTISSA, and 25 PRIME. A common logarithm consists of two parts, an integral part called the CHARACTERISTIC, and a non-

integral part, less than 1, expressed as a decimal, called the
MANTISSA. The MANTISSA of the common logarithm of a number is independent of the position of the decimal point in the
number, and depends only on the succession of digits which
make up the number. For logarithms to the base 10 the CHAR-
ACTERISTIC depends only on the position of the decimal point.

209. BINOMIAL (bī-nō'-mĭ-ăl) adj. Consisting of two terms
        only, an algebraic expression of two terms joined by either
a plus or a minus sign, as: x + y.
From the Dictionary of Edward Phillips, a nephew of Milton,
1706, comes: 'A BINOMIAL quantity or root, a quantity or root

The general equation giving the exponents and coefficients of
any term of the result of raising the sum or difference of two
variables to the power n.

FORM A. 33.	BO	NY	SUM	FORM AA. 29.	NY
theory of class	1	0	1	transcendental	11
exponential equation	4	16	20	exponential	38
BINOMIAL THEOREM	13	19	32	BINOMIAL	71
probability equation	1	5	6	De Moivre's	8
Pythagorean proposition	0	1	1	bimodal	4
unmarked	1	0	1	unmarked	0
total	20	41	61	total	132

that consists of two names or parts joined together by the sign
plus as A + B or 3 + 2'.
    The full word is BINOMINAL. The first two letters come from
the Latin bi-, two, familiar in the noun BICYCLE, a two-wheeled
vehicle, and in the adjective BIENNIAL, every two years, and
already met early in this book in the verb BISECT (5), to cut in
two. The second part comes from nominalis, pertaining to a
name. NOMINAL means in English, as in Latin, pertaining to a
name or, as a derived sense, existing in name only, ostensible,
not real. Both the Latin nominalis and the English NOMINAL
(nŏm'-ĭ-năl) come from the Latin nomen, name, term, the
source of the English NOMENCLATURE. In Latin binomius, a
shortened form of binominis, meant having two personal names.
BINOMIAL means two termed.

To the question: 'The general equation giving the exponents and coefficients of any term of the result of raising the sum or difference of two variables to the power n', 71 persons out of 132 answer correctly BINOMIAL THEOREM; while 38 answer EXPONENTIAL EQUATION. An EXPONENTIAL EQUATION is one in which the unknown is involved as an EXPONENT (42), one which has the variable as an EXPONENT, as:

$$10^x = 2$$

where x is the unknown and the exponent of 10. This sort of equation is solved by writing:

$$\log 10^x = \log 2$$

which becomes:

$$x \log 10 = \log 2.$$

The BINOMIAL THEOREM is a rule, worked out by Isaac Newton, by which any power of a BINOMIAL quantity may be found without performing the progressive multiplications, a rule for raising any BINOMIAL to any power. The BINOMIAL x + y when squared is:

$$(x + y)^2 = x^2 + 2xy + y^2;$$

or when raised to higher powers:

$$(x + y)^3 = x^3 + 3x^2y + 3xy^2 + y^3$$
$$(x + y)^4 = x^4 + 4x^3y + 6x^2y^2 + 4xy^3 + y^4$$

The exponents are obvious. Predicting the coefficients without doing the actual multiplications was Newton's real contribution. Multiplying the coefficient of any term by the exponent of x in that term and dividing by the number of the term in the series gives the coefficient of the next term. In the fourth power, multiplying the coefficient of the first term, 1, by 4, the exponent of the first term, and dividing by 1, the number of the first term, gives 4 as the coefficient of the second term. Here 4 times 3 divided by 2 gives 6 as the coefficient of the next term.

210. *TENSION* (těn'-shŏn) n. The condition of a body when forces are pulling its ends in opposite directions, a constrained condition of the particles of bodies; also the force applied to a body in such a way as to produce elongation in the direction of the force.

The word TENSION comes through the French *tension*, from the Latin *tensio, tensionis*, a stretching, from *tendere*, to stretch, extend.

To the question: 'A force which acts to pull materials apart', 242 persons out of 515 answer TENSION; while 150 answer STRAIN. J. Nicholson says: 'The STRAIN occasioned by pulling timber in the direction of its length is called TENSION'. Of TENSION, Cassell's Encyclopaedic Dictionary, which came out between 1879 and 1888, says: 'The STRAIN or the force by which a bar is pulled when forming part of a system'. Almost the next year the Century Dictionary, which came out between 1889 and 1891, changes this to read: 'The STRESS or force by which

Form A. A force which acts to pull materials apart.
Form AA. A force which acts to stretch or elongate in the direction of the force.

FORM A. 3.	FW	LA	NY	NY	NY	PH	SUM	FORM AA. 26.	NY
compression	0	0	2	0	4	6	12	deformation	0
TENSION	12	30	12	29	68	91	242	TENSION	32
strain	2	13	12	22	45	56	150	strain	14
shear	3	3	2	6	6	12	32	shear	4
torsion	1	8	8	8	17	33	75	torsion	13
unmarked	0	0	1	1	0	2	4	unmarked	0
total	18	54	37	66	140	200	515	total	63

a bar is pulled when forming part of a system'. In its modern technical sense STRAIN is not the force but the change in shape produced by the force, and so strictly is not a correct answer. But from 1600 until 1850, STRAIN was used much as TENSION today, both for the stretching force tending to pull asunder and for the condition produced. It is therefore, except for its modern restriction started in 1850 by William John M. Rankine, the Scottish physicist, professor of engineering and mechanics at Glasgow, a correct answer.

When a cord supports a weight, the TENSION at every part of the cord is equal to the weight; but, except in the phrase SURFACE TENSION, the word TENSION is not strictly technical, perhaps because it is not exact and can be used either for the condition produced or the force producing it.

211. *CATHODE* (kăth'-ōd) *n.* That electrode from which electrons or negative ions are dispersed, toward which positive ions are collected. Reread ELECTROLYSIS (50).

To the question: 'The thing to be coated in electroplating', 44 per cent of 2234 persons answer CATHODE; and as one might expect 22 per cent ANODE, and 15 per cent POSITIVE ELECTRODE.

In a paper of 1834, paragraph 663, Michael Faraday writes: 'If the magnetism of the earth be due to electric currents passing around it, the latter must be in a constant direction, which, according to present usage of speech, would be from east to west, or, which will strengthen this help to the memory that in which the sun appears to move. Upon this notion we purpose calling that towards the east the ANODE, and that towards the west the CATHODE. The ANODE is therefore that surface at which

The thing to be coated in electroplating.

FORM C. 18. NY		FORM CA. 22. BO		NY HIGH	NY NEXT	NY REST	NY MISC.	SUM
CATHODE	196	CATHODE	61	252	223	331	110	977
ion	1	cation	1	11	12	142	11	177
electrolyte	39	electrolyte	10	12	21	181	24	248
anode	84	anode	14	88	92	252	56	502
positive electrode	75	positive electrode	14	37	52	194	33	330
unmarked	5	unmarked	0	0	0	0	0	0
total	400	total	100	400	400	1100	234	2234

the electric current according to our present expression, enters: it is the NEGATIVE extremity of the decomposing body; is where oxygen, chlorine, acids, &c., are evolved; and is against or opposite the positive electrode. The CATHODE is that surface at which the current leaves the decomposing body and is its positive extremity; the combustible bodies, metals, alkalies, and bases, are evolved there, and it is in contact with the negative electrode'.

In a footnote to the word ANODE Faraday gives: ἄνω (ano), upwards, and ὁδός (hodos), a way; the way which the sun rises. In another note to CATHODE: κατά (kata), downwards, and ὁδός (hodos), a way; the way which the sun sets.

212. *POWER* (*pow'-er*) *n*. The result of multiplying a quantity by itself a specified number of times.

To the question: 'The number of times a value is used as a factor', 23 persons out of 61, or 38 per cent, answer correctly POWER; while 25 answer COEFFICIENT. A COEFFICIENT (131) indicates the number of times a quantity is to be added to itself. A POWER is the number of times it is multiplied by itself. The expression 3a, where 3 is the COEFFICIENT, means $a + a + a$; while a^3 is the third POWER of a and means $a \times a \times a$.

A difficulty may be the word FACTOR in the question, although FACTOR is word 47 of this book and so should be relatively easy. FACTOR is used in mathematics for one of two or more quantities which when multiplied together produce a

Form A. The number of times a value is used as a factor.
Form AA. The number of times a quantity is multiplied by itself.

FORM A. 42.	BO	NY	SUM	FORM AA. 42.	NY
weight	0	3	3	weight	1
beta value	1	2	3	multiple	8
POWER	10	13	23	POWER	112
coefficient	7	18	25	coefficient	6
factorial	1	5	6	factorial	5
unmarked	1	0	1	unmarked	0
total	20	41	61	total	132

product. The word FACTOR implies multiplication, not addition. A FACTORIAL (278) is a continued product. In the revised form AA, the question reads: 'The number of times a quantity is multiplied by itself'. Here 112 persons out of 132, or 85 per cent, answer POWER, instead of 38 per cent as with the previous definition, and only 6 persons answer COEFFICIENT. Though a word such as FACTOR may be statistically relatively easy when used by itself in a vocabulary test, it becomes more difficult when the mind is on something else, in this case the mathematical term POWER. To avoid this, definitions should be given in the easiest possible terms.

The first POWER of a quantity is the quantity itself; the second POWER is the quantity squared, multiplied by itself; the third POWER is the quantity cubed, multiplied by itself thrice.

213. *ANEMOMETER* (*ăn-ē-mŏm′-ē-ter*) *n.* An instrument
for measuring the speed of the wind or the speed of any
air stream.

The second half of ANEMOMETER is the familiar μέτρον (metron), measure, or more often measuring instrument, as already
discussed under PHOTOMETER (60). The first half is the Greek
ἄνεμος (anemos), wind. The equivalent word in Latin is spelt
with I, *animus*, which also means wind, or more figuratively
breath, spirit, courage, passion. From this, *animus* comes to
suggest temper, and so leads to the English ANIMOSITY, origi-

Form A. An instrument for measuring the force or speed of the
wind.
Form AA. 19. Ground instrument to measure wind speed relative
to earth.

FORM A. 39.	FW	LA	NY	NY	NY	PH	SUM	FORM AA. 19.	NY
								aneroid	
nephoscope	1	1	0	2	2	0	6	barometer	2
ANEMOMETER	11	27	16	31	79	117	281	ANEMOMETER	38
								psychrom-	
psychrometer	0	0	1	2	1	3	7	eter	0
air-speed								air-speed	
indicator	6	25	18	20	47	67	183	indicator	16
computer	0	0	0	0	9	2	11	wind vane	7
unmarked	0	1	2	11	2	11	27	unmarked	0
total	18	54	37	66	140	200	515	total	63

nally courage, but now active ill will, enmity. From the feminine form *anima* come a host of English words such as ANIMAL,
ANIMATION, spirit, life, and the verb to ANIMATE. Directly from
the original Greek ἄνεμος (anemos), spelt with an E, and not
through Latin, come ANEMONE (*ă-nĕm′-ō-nē*), by derivation
wind-flower, as well as ANEMOMETER, a wind gage, instrument
for indicating the pressure of the wind.

To the question: 'An instrument for measuring the force or
speed of the wind', 281 persons out of 515 answer ANEMOMETER,
and 183 AIR-SPEED INDICATOR. An AIR-SPEED INDICATOR is really
an ANEMOMETER; but as ordinarily applied the term AIR-SPEED
INDICATOR refers to an aircraft instrument and the term ANE-

MOMETER to a ground instrument. The usual ANEMOMETER consists of three or four cups, each at the end of a horizontal arm, and each cup tipped to catch the wind one at a time. The arms turn like the spokes of a horizontal wheel about an upright, vertical axis.

214. *HOOKE'S LAW* (*hooks law*). Within the limits of perfect elasticity the effect produced is proportional to the cause producing it. Hooke's original law was stated in Latin: *Ut tensio sic vis*, as the stretch so the force.

Robert Hooke, an English experimental physicist who lived from 1635 to 1703, engaged in a controversy with Newton over priority for the law of gravitation and argued with other scientists of his time, for he had many original ideas, which he often failed to carry far enough to get or perhaps deserve credit for their establishment. For this reason he lived the latter part of his life as a destitute embittered recluse.

Hooke stated his law in 1660, when he was twenty-five, just following the period, twenty-one to twenty-three, when the measurements of the Human Engineering Laboratory now show that the aptitude called inductive reasoning is at its height, the age at which many great scientists have recognized for the first time some fundamental law.

HOOKE'S LAW states that strain is proportional to stress. This applies to all strains if the stresses are not too great. Within the elastic limit, the extension of a stretched wire is proportional to the stretching force. One authority calls it: 'An empirical law'.

To the question: 'Within the limits of perfect elasticity, any deformation is directly proportional to the force producing the deformation', 244 persons out of 537 answer HOOKE'S LAW; but 132 answer YOUNG'S MODULUS, another name for the MODULUS OF ELASTICITY (165) already discussed. HOOKE'S LAW and YOUNG'S MODULUS are closely bound. HOOKE'S LAW applies to all materials. It says stretch is proportional to the force producing it. But different materials stretch different amounts with the same force. YOUNG'S MODULUS gives for each different material the amount of this stretch. YOUNG'S MODULUS is the stretching force divided by the stretch produced. HOOKE'S LAW says that within the elastic limit of a substance this is a constant. YOUNG'S MODULUS, a hundred and fifty years later, is the constant, gives a numerical value for each material.

The first American edition of an Encyclopaedia published in Philadelphia in 1798 says: 'Hooke (Robert), a very eminent English mathematician and philosopher. He early discovered a genius for mechanics, by making curious toys with great

Within the limits of perfect elasticity, any deformation is directly proportional to the force producing the deformation.

FORM E. 9.	BO	FW	LA	NY	NY	NY	NY	PH	TU	SUM
Brownian movement	1	2	1	3	1	3	17	4	1	33
Newton's second law	2	11	5	3	2	6	35	13	1	78
Young's modulus	7	14	5	5	6	5	56	27	7	132
HOOKE'S LAW	15	17	20	9	11	19	87	49	17	244
Fleming's rule	3	5	1	0	0	7	22	7	2	47
unmarked	0	1	1	0	0	0	1	0	0	3
total	28	50	33	20	20	40	218	100	28	537

FORM E. 9.	ENGLISH VOCABULARY	
	HIGH	LOW
Brownian movement	0	7
Newton's second law	2	6
Young's modulus	12	11
HOOKE'S LAW	25	10
Fleming's rule	1	5
unmarked	0	1
total	40	40

art and dexterity. In Westminster school he not only acquired a competent share of Greek and Latin, together with an insight into Hebrew and some other Oriental languages, but also made himself master of a good part of Euclid's elements.

'As to Mr. Hooke's character, it is not in all respects one of the most amiable. He made but a despicable figure as to his person, being short of stature, very crooked, pale, lean, and of a meagre aspect, with dark brown hair, very long and hanging over his face uncut and lank. Suitable to his person, his temper was penurious, melancholy, mistrustful: and, though possessed of great philosophical knowledge, he had so much ambition, that he would be thought the only man who could invent or discover; and thus frequently laid claim to the inventions and discoveries of others, while he boasted of many of his own which he never communicated'.

215. *INTERFERENCE* (*ĭn-ter-fēr'-ĕns*) *n*. The mutual action of two waves or systems of waves in reinforcing or neutralizing each other when their paths meet or cross, phenomenon arising from the joint effects of two or more wave trains arriving at the same point simultaneously. Reread INTERFEROMETER (151).

The term INTERFERENCE, corresponding to the French *interference*, is the verb to INTERFERE, plus the ending -ENCE. This ending -ENCE came originally through the French *-ence*, from the Latin *-entia*, and was added to participial stems ending in *-ent* to form nouns of quality, as SAPIENT, wise, and SAPIENCE, rarely nouns of action. But recently the ending has been added more indiscriminately. The word of action INTERFERENCE dates back to just before 1800 and may have been first used by Edmund Burke who needed a stronger word than any he could find for government INTERFERENCE. The verb to INTERFERE is a combination of the Latin *inter*, between, and *ferire*, to strike. In literature, to INTERFERE is to take part in the affairs of others, intermeddle.

The word was first applied to light by Dr. Thomas Young in 1801 or 1802: 'The mutual action of waves of any kind upon one another, by which the vibrations and their effects are increased, diminished, or neutralized'. Thirty years later the word in this sense had been accepted, for Sir John F. W. Herschel wrote in 1830, On the Study of Natural Philosophy: 'This principle, which is known in optics by the name of INTERFERENCE of the rays of light'; and in 1835 Mrs. Mary Fairfax Somerville, whose husband Dr. William Somerville helped her to study the physical sciences so that in 1831 she translated the *Mecanique Celeste* of Laplace, wrote in her book On the Con-

nexion of the Physical Sciences: 'Darkness results from the
INTERFERENCE of two undulations of light'.

To the question: 'The interaction of two trains of waves
whereby one is weakened or reinforced by the other', 40 per
cent of 2234 persons answer INTERFERENCE; and 20 per cent
ABERRATION. Both ABERRATION and INTERFERENCE are the combined effect of different rays of light. CHROMATIC ABERRATION
is when rays of different colors do not meet at the same point
after going through a lens. SPHERICAL ABERRATION is when rays

The interaction of two trains of waves whereby one is weakened or reinforced by the other.

FORM C. 23. NY		FORM CA. 19. BO		NY	NY	NY	NY	SUM
diffraction	53	diffraction	12	16	70	232	55	385
polarization	27	polarization	14	16	60	197	26	313
INTER-FERENCE	224	INTERFERENCE	48	289	161	296	93	887
aberration	63	aberration	23	71	86	223	46	449
dispersion	23	dispersion	2	8	23	152	13	198
unmarked	10	unmarked	1	0	0	0	1	2
total	400	total	100	400	400	1100	234	2234

do not meet at the same point because they have gone through
different parts of an uncorrected lens. ABERRATION is a deviation from the ideal, in optics a deviation of the rays of light
from a single focus when they are unequally refracted or reflected by a lens, a wandering away from the point. INTER-
FERENCE is the interaction of two waves which meet at the
same point.

Of INTERFERENCE P. G. Tait says, in the 14th edition of the
Encyclopaedia Britannica: 'When two similar and equal series
of waves arrive at a common point they interfere as it is called
with one another so that the actual disturbance of the medium
at any instant is the resultant of the disturbances which it would
have suffered at that instant from the two series separately'.
David Brewster, author of the delightful but little known
Martyrs of Science, and editor of the Edinburgh Encyclopaedia, says in his Optics of 1831: 'The doctrine of INTERFER-
ENCE is in complete accordance with the theory of undulation'.

216. *DIAMAGNETIC* (*dī-ă-măg-nĕt'-ĭk*) *adj.* Having a mag-
    netic permeability less than unity, less than a vacuum,
turning across a magnetic field.

With the definition: 'Substances which, when placed in a
magnetic field, tend to move away from the strongest part',
43 per cent choose correctly DIAMAGNETIC; but 24 per cent
choose NEGATIVE, and 21 per cent PARAMAGNETIC.

The PARAMAGNETIC substances are: iron, nickel, cobalt, palla-
dium, titanium, manganese, chromium, and oxygen. These are
also called FERROMAGNETIC. Iron, cobalt, and nickel, the most
strongly PARAMAGNETIC, occur consecutively in the periodic

Substances which, in a magnetic field, tend to move away from
the strongest part.

FORM BA. 29.	NY	FORM D. 34.	NY	%
DIAMAGNETIC	39	DIAMAGNETIC	130	37.1
electrified	12	electrified	33	9.4
negative	18	negative	57	16.3
paramagnetic	26	paramagnetic	87	24.9
ferromagnetic	4	ferromagnetic	28	8.0
unmarked	1	unmarked	15	4.3
total	100	total	350	100.0

FORM DA. 32.	NY	FORM DB. 31.	NY
DIAMAGNETIC	43	DIAMAGNETIC	56
electrified	5	positive	7
negative	24	negative	19
paramagnetic	21	paramagnetic	18
ferromagnetic	5	ferromagnetic	4
unmarked	2	unmarked	2
total	100	total	106

table, with atomic numbers of 26, 27, and 28. The DIAMAGNETIC
substances are: bismuth, antimony, silver, copper, cadmium,
gold, lead, mercury, tin, zinc, phosphorus, quartz, hydrogen,
nitrogen, and rock salt.

The words PARAMAGNETIC and DIAMAGNETIC were suggested
by William Whewell, who lived from 1794 to 1866, a famous
Cambridge figure of his time, master of Trinity College, and

best known today for his History of the Inductive Sciences. The terms were first used by Faraday in 1846. The word PARAMAGNETIC is a combination of the Greek παρά (para), be- side, and MAGNETIC, from the Greek μάγνης (magnes), μαγνητίς (magnetis), a magnet. DIAMAGNETIC is the Greek διά (dia), across, as in DIAGONAL (15), across from angle to angle, and the same MAGNETIC.

PARAMAGNETIC means turning parallel to the magnetic lines of force. A PARAMAGNETIC bar, as of iron, suspended between the poles of a strong horseshoe magnet points along the line from one pole to the other. A similar bar of DIAMAGNETIC material held in the same position turns across the line between the poles, at right angles to it. PARAMAGNETIC substances have permeabilities greater than that of a vacuum; DIAMAGNETIC ones, less than a vacuum. A few permeabilities are:

soft wrought iron	3750
machine steel	460
nickel	296
cobalt	177
vacuum	1
bismuth	0.9998.

Because the permeability of bismuth is less than that of air, the magnetic lines of a magnetic field turn away as if avoiding it, preferring the air. With a PARAMAGNETIC material the mag- netic lines crowd through the material rather than through the air.

217. *AMORPHOUS* (ă-mor'-fŭs) *adj*. Not composed of crys- tals, without determinate form, having no regular struc- ture, not crystallized even in the minutest particles, uncrys- tallized, massive.

The word AMORPHOUS starts with the Greek privative ά (a), meaning not, already met in ANEROID (93), not wet, not liquid. The rest of the word AMORPHOUS comes from the Greek μορφή (morphe), form, shape. From the same μορφή (morphe) pre- ceded by the Greek μετά (meta), over, comes METAMORPHOSIS (mĕt-ă-mor'-phō-sĭs), change of form. The study of outward forms and internal structures, both of plants and animals, without regard to function, is MORPHOLOGY, a term which often embraces the entire science of organic form. Without form, not crystallized, is AMORPHOUS.

To the definition: 'Non-crystalline', 28 per cent of students answer HYDROUS, a mislead used in the 1938 form DA in place of GRANULATED, which attracted only 4 per cent in each of the two earlier forms where AMORPHOUS was used as the question.

Forms AB and D. Amorphous.
Forms DA and DB. Non-crystalline.

FORM AB. 29.	NY	FORM D. 23.	NY	%
irregular	14	non-isotropic	36	10.3
crystalline	10	crystalline	45	12.9
granulated	4	granulated	14	4.0
powdered	11	powdered	42	12.0
NON-CRYSTALLINE	61	NON-CRYSTALLINE	202	57.7
unmarked	0	unmarked	11	3.1
total	100	total	350	100.0

FORM DA. 14.	NY	FORM DB. 26.	NY
isomorphous	16	isomorphous	12
refractory	7	refractory	5
hydrous	28	hydrous	14
AMORPHOUS	47	AMORPHOUS	68
rhombic	2	cleavable	5
unmarked	0	unmarked	2
total	100	total	106

HYDROUS, from the Greek ὕδωρ (hydor), ὑδρός (hydros), water, means containing water, watery. When water freezes it forms six-sided or hexagonal crystals. CRYSTALLINE substances form crystals when they solidify.

In his dictionary of 1731 Nathan Bailey defined AMORPHOUS: 'Without form or shape, ill-shapen'; and the word has continued to be used from time to time in this sense. But in the sciences, in chemistry and mineralogy, the term means specifically not crystalline. Glass, opal, sealing wax, and pitch are AMORPHOUS. AMORPHOUS substances behave like liquids of great viscosity.

218. *POWER* (*pow'-er*) *n.* Time rate of performing work,
foot-pounds per minute, number of horsepower, watts, or
kilowatts, work per unit time. Reread HORSEPOWER (77).
HORSEPOWER is the unit of mechanical POWER, 550 foot-pounds
per second, 33,000 foot-pounds per minute. WATT is the unit of
electrical POWER, one KILOWATT, a thousand WATTS, equaling
1.34 HORSEPOWER.

It takes POWER to lift a weight, more POWER to lift fifty
pounds than to lift twenty-five in the same time, and still more
to lift a hundred. But anyone can lift a hundred pounds a few at
a time. This however takes longer and so not so much POWER;
for speed is the essence of POWER. A POWERFUL locomotive not
only pulls a heavy train, but pulls it fast. A POWERFUL steamship
is both big and fast. In the form of an equation:

$$\text{POWER} = \text{FORCE} \times \text{SPEED}.$$

It is no doubt this speed element which leads 26 per cent of
students to answer SPEED to the question: 'Rate of doing work',
where the correct answer is POWER, given by 45 per cent. SPEED
is rate of moving, distance traveled divided by time consumed,
feet per second, miles per hour, distance per unit time. In the
form of an equation:

$$\text{SPEED} = \frac{\text{DISTANCE}}{\text{TIME}}.$$

POWER is rate of doing work, work done divided by time
consumed, ergs per second, joules per hour, work per unit time.
In the form of an equation:

$$\text{POWER} = \frac{\text{WORK}}{\text{TIME}}.$$

As:

$$\text{WORK} = \text{FORCE} \times \text{DISTANCE}$$

$$\text{POWER} = \frac{\text{FORCE} \times \text{DISTANCE}}{\text{TIME}} = \text{FORCE} \times \text{SPEED}.$$

The word POWER goes back through Middle English and Old
French to the Latin verb *posse*, to be able, the direct source of

POSSIBLE, that may be, not known not to be true. From *potens, potentis*, powerful, strong, the present participle of the verb *posse*, comes the English POTENT, strong, effective, powerful, possessed of inherent strength. Cowper says: 'The spot he loved has lost the power to please'. Milton says in Comus: 'POWER to stir up joy'; and Bacon says: 'Knowledge itself is a POWER'.

Time rate of doing work.

FORM AB. 8.	NY	FORM D. 5.	NY	%
POWER	87	POWER	168	48.0
force	1	speed	95	27.1
entropy	1	entropy	5	1.4
potential energy	3	potential energy	29	8.3
efficiency	8	efficiency	51	14.6
unmarked	0	unmarked	2	0.6
total	100	total	350	100.0

FORM DA. 23.	NY	FORM DB. 28.	NY
POWER	45	POWER	45
speed	26	speed	30
capacity	16	capacity	20
potential energy	4	inertia	2
efficiency	7	uniform motion	9
unmarked	2	unmarked	0
total	100	total	106

Perhaps the fact that time or its reciprocal SPEED is an essential element of POWER underlies the finding of the Human Engineering Laboratory that most aptitudes are measurable in time. Each aptitude is rate of doing a particular kind of work; each is a specialized POWER.

219. *PROBABILITY* (*prŏ-bă-bĭl'-ĭ-tē*) *n*. The ratio of the number of ways an event can happen favorably to the total number of ways it can happen providing the ways it can happen are all equally likely, the number of favorable cases divided by the total number. In a vocabulary test with five choices the PROBABILITY of marking the right answer by pure chance is one in five, or 0.20.

If an event can either happen or fail, the PROBABILITY of its happening is the number of times it can happen divided by the number of times it can happen added to the number of times it can fail:

$$p = \frac{h}{h+f}.$$

Where an event cannot be analyzed into the number of equally likely ways it can happen or fail, which is the usual situation in life, the PROBABILITY is the observed occurrence divided by the total number of observations. If 962 men age 50 die during the year, out of a total 69,804, the PROBABILITY of a 50-year-old man dying during the year is 962/69,804. The PROBABILITY that the sort of person tested will mark this item correctly is 25 in 61, or 0.41; or 54 in 132, or 0.41.

The word PROBABILITY comes from the Latin *probabilitas*, *probabilitatis*, probability, credibility, from *probabilitas*, probable, credible, something which may be proved. This comes in

The number of favorable occurrences of an event divided by the number of possible occurrences.

FORM A. 38.	BO	NY	SUM	FORM AA. 30.	NY
PROBABILITY	7	18	25	PROBABILITY	54
odds	5	10	15	odds	29
normal	0	2	2	normal	6
standard error	0	4	4	standard error	6
probability equation	7	6	13	probability equation	37
unmarked	1	1	2	unmarked	0
total	20	41	61	total	132

turn from *probare*, to prove, test, examine, the source of the English words PROBE and PROVE. The verb *probare* comes in turn from *probus*, good, the source of PROBITY.

To the question: 'The number of favorable occurrences of an event divided by the number of possible occurrences', 54 persons out of 132 answer PROBABILITY; and 29 answer ODDS. ODDS are stated as favorable occurrences to unfavorable; PROBABILITY as favorable occurrences to the total number. The ODDS of a certainty are infinite; the PROBABILITY of a certainty is 1.

220. *DIFFERENTIATION* (dĭf-fĕ-rĕn-shē-ā'-shŏn) *n.* The process of finding a DERIVATIVE. Reread DERIVATIVE (203). The TANGENT of an angle is the height of a right-angle triangle divided by the base. This is also the slope of a curve if the hypotenuse of the triangle is tangent to the curve. It was working with this problem that led Gottfried Wilhelm Leibnitz,

The process of finding a derivative.

FORM A. 40.	BO	NY	SUM	FORM AA. 38.	NY
DIFFERENTIATION	11	14	25	DIFFERENTIATION	44
integration	1	8	9	integration	20
triangulation	2	6	8	triangulation	11
projection	3	11	14	projection	24
analysis	1	2	3	analysis	32
unmarked	2	0	2	unmarked	1
total	20	41	61	total	132

1646 to 1716, to his discovery of the differential calculus. Today we call the height delta y and the base delta x. Then the tangent is delty y/delta x. This is a fraction. DIFFERENTIATION is the process of finding the value of this tangent or fraction as delta x approaches zero.

The four steps of DIFFERENTIATION are:

1. In any function replace x by x + delta x, and calculate the value of the new function, y + delta y.
2. Subtract the original value of the function from the new value thereby obtaining the value of delta y.
3. Divide the remainder, delta y and its value, by delta x.
4. Find the value of this quotient as delta x approaches zero.

To the question: 'Determination of the slope of a curve', 44 persons out of 132 answer DIFFERENTIATION; while 32 answer ANALYSIS, and 24 PROJECTION, the popular mislead in the earlier study. PROJECTION, in geometry, is the process of representing a solid on a flat surface. It is used in map making where the round globe is projected onto a plane. ANALYSIS, from the Greek ἀνά (ana), back, and λύειν (lyein), to loosen, already met earlier at the end of ELECTROLYSIS (50), is the general term for the loosening or shaking apart of any problem, its separating into elements, its resolution into constituent parts.

The problem of finding the slope of a curve at any point is that of finding the limit of delta y/delta x at that point. The DERIVATIVE of y with respect to x is the limiting value of delta y/delta x. The value of the derivative at any point of a curve is equal to the slope of the tangent line to the curve at that point. Finding the DERIVATIVE is called DIFFERENTIATION.

221. *COMMENSURABLE* (kŏm-mĕn'-sū-rā-bl) *adj.* Measurable in the same units, divisible by the same number, having a common measure.

The figures 12 and 18 are both divisible by 3 with no remainder. They are COMMENSURABLE. Distances of 12 feet and 18 feet are both measurable in yards, or in feet; and so are COMMENSURABLE. All whole numbers, integers, and fractions, and all rational numbers, are COMMENSURABLE. All are measurable

Capable of being measured in the same units.

FORM A. 6.	BO	NY	SUM	FORM AA. 34.	NY
similar	4	9	13	similar	27
congruent	4	6	10	congruent	25
identical	2	4	6	identical	11
COMMEN-SURABLE	7	17	24	COMMENSURABLE	45
homogeneous	3	5	8	homogeneous	24
unmarked	0	0	0	unmarked	0
total	20	41	61	total	132

in the same units, unity. But the diameter of a circle and the circumference are not COMMENSURABLE; these two distances cannot be measured in the same unit no matter how tiny the unit which is chosen. The ratio of these two distances cannot be expressed as a fraction.

The word COMMENSURABLE comes from the Latin *com-*, together, and *mensurare*, to measure. From this same Latin verb comes MENSURATION (mĕn-sū-rā'-shŏn), the art of measuring or the actual taking of measurements.

To the question: 'Capable of being measured in the same units', 45 persons out of 132 answer correctly COMMENSURABLE; while 27 answer SIMILAR. SIMILAR (160) means alike in some ways but different in others, having characteristics in common, alike in form, appearance, or sometimes in size. In geometry the word SIMILAR is used to mean of the same shape, usually with equal angles and with sides which are proportional. Triangles with equal angles are SIMILAR; but were their sides in the proportion of the diameter and circumference of a circle they would be INCOMMENSURABLE, not measurable in the same units.

222. ∫. The INTEGRAL sign in front of a differential expression. Differentiation and integration are inverse operations.

To the question: '∫', 128 persons out of 357 answer correctly LIMIT SUM; while 69 answer DERIVATIVE, practically an opposite, for integration is finding the function knowing the derivative; and 66 answer GAMMA. The Greek GAMMA is written thus: γ.

∫.

FORM B. 25.	NY	MISC.	SUM
rank	0	7	7
derivative	14	55	69
LIMIT SUM	26	102	128
factorial	3	43	46
gamma	5	61	66
unmarked	0	41	41
total	48	309	357

Leibnitz and Johann Bernoulli discussed both the name and the principal symbol of the integral calculus. Leibnitz favored *calculus summatorius* and the long letter s, ∫, as the symbol of integration. Bernoulli favored *calculus integralis* and the capital letter I. As a compromise Bernoulli's name INTEGRAL CALCULUS was adopted, and Leibnitz's symbol of summation, ∫.

223. *RADICAND* (răd-ĭ-kănd') *n.* An expression of which a root is to be extracted.

RADICAND comes from the Latin *radicandus*, the gerund of the verb *radicari*, to take root. Directly from this Latin verb comes the English verb to RADICATE, to take root, more familiar in the negative form IRRADICATE, to pull up by the roots, uproot. From the same source comes the word RADICAL, the name of the sign which indicates that a root is to be taken. The RADICAND is the quantity of which the root is to be taken. The word RADICAND appears in the six-volumed Century Dictionary of

The quantity from which a root is to be extracted.

FORM C. 12.	CH	FORM CA. 21.	CH	LA	NY	NY	PH	SUM
power	18	power	14	13	20	82	21	150
RADICAND	36	RADICAND	19	18	52	128	35	252
radix	4	radix	1	1	7	14	0	23
equation	7	equation	4	3	13	29	9	58
radical index	3	radical index	2	1	4	23	7	37
unmarked	0	unmarked	0	1	1	1	2	5
total	68	total	40	37	97	277	74	525

FORM CB. 25.	NY
power	18
RADICAND	50
binary	2
equation	4
radical index	9
unmarked	3
total	86

1891, but not in the Encyclopaedic Dictionary of 1886, nor in the great Oxford, the first volume of which appeared in 1888.

To the question: 'A quantity from which a root is to be extracted', 252 persons out of 525 whose scores have been tabulated for form CA, finished in 1947, answer RADICAND, or 48 per cent; while 150 persons answer POWER. In the original form C, designed eight years earlier, 1939, where fewer scores were tabulated, 36 out of 68 answer RADICAND, or 53 per cent; and 18 persons POWER, again the most popular mislead. In the newer form CB of 1953, where few cases are as yet available, 50 out of 86, or 58 per cent, answer RADICAND, and 18 persons POWER. In mathematics the POWER of a quantity is the result of multiplying that quantity by itself a specified number of times. POWER in suggestion is almost an opposite of RADICAND. The figure 3 to the second POWER is 9; 9 in turn may be a RADICAND of which the square root is 3.

224. *VERTICAL ANGLES* (*ver'-tĭ-kăl ăng'-glz*). Opposite angles, the angles formed by two straight lines crossing each other and which are not adjacent.

To the question: 'A ⤬ B, angles A and B', 210 persons out of 525 answer correctly VERTICAL; but 118 answer COMPLEMENTARY, and 114 INTERIOR. The word INTERIOR comes directly from the Latin *interior*, inner, the comparative form, from *inter*, within, between. INTERIOR ANGLES are rightly inside a figure, as the three angles inside a triangle. They may be acute

A ⤬ B, angles A and B.

FORM C. 38.	CH	FORM CA. 24.	CH	LA	NY	NY	PH	SUM
interior	16	interior	5	9	21	67	12	114
exterior	1	supplementary	5	4	16	16	4	45
VERTICAL	28	VERTICAL	19	11	33	116	31	210
horizontal	4	horizontal	0	3	4	11	9	27
comple-								
mentary	19	complementary	11	9	21	62	15	118
unmarked	0	unmarked	0	1	2	5	3	11
total	68	total	40	37	97	277	74	525

FORM CB. 29.	NY
interior	12
supplementary	10
VERTICAL	35
horizontal	7
complementary	20
unmarked	2
total	86

or obtuse. Of the eight angles formed when a straight line crosses two parallel lines, the four angles between the parallel lines are called INTERIOR, and are often defined as a special case. These are still inside the figure for parallel lines meet at infinity.

COMPLEMENTARY, from the Latin *complere*, to fill up, finish, fulfill, a combination of the intensive *com-* and *pliere*, to fill, means completing, making up a fixed whole. COMPLEMENTARY ANGLES are angles whose algebraic sum is 90 degrees, angles which together make up a right angle. VERTICAL ANGLES are angles whose VERTICES touch.

The adjective VERTICAL comes from the noun VERTEX, the pointed tip of an angle, and this from the Latin *vertex, verticis*. This Latin noun has numerous meanings. It comes from the verb *vertere*, to turn, and seems first to have meant a whirlpool, whirl, vortex; then apparently at one time the pole about which the heavens turn; but this soon shifted to the highest point of the heavens, the zenith, directly overhead. From this VERTEX came to mean the top of a triangle, and so the tip of any angle where two lines meet. The term VERTEX is used regularly now for the tip of any angle. VERTICAL ANGLES are not up and down, as one might think, but angles whose VERTICES touch, that is, opposite angles made by two lines which intersect.

225. *REAL* (rē'-ăl) *adj*. Applied to a number which can be obtained exactly or approximately, actual, not imaginary, pertaining to things, not merely to words and thoughts.

Root of a quadratic equation which does not contain the square root of a negative quantity.

FORM C. 42.	CH	FORM CA. 26.	CH	LA	NY	NY	PH	SUM
rational	17	rational	5	12	11	58	23	109
irrational	11	irrational	3	3	15	44	6	71
REAL	24	REAL	15	17	46	130	32	240
imaginary	13	imaginary	11	2	14	22	7	56
radical	3	radical	6	2	10	20	3	41
unmarked	0	unmarked	0	1	1	3	3	8
total	68	total	40	37	97	277	74	525

In his Cyclopaedia of 1728 Ephraim Chambers says: 'Root, If the value of x be positive, i.e. if x be a positive quantity, the root is called a REAL or true root'. W. K. Clifford in his Lectures says: 'A REAL quantity is that kind of quantity which exists from zero to infinity, and from infinity through the whole series of negative values to zero again'. REAL numbers may be either positive or negative, as: $+3$ or -5. They may be exact, as 27, or only approximately obtainable, as the value of π which may be carried to any number of decimal places but never obtained.

To the question: 'Root of a quadratic equation which does not contain the square root of a negative quantity', 240 persons out of 525 answer REAL; and 109 RATIONAL. RATIONAL numbers are expressed in finite terms, as ordinary fractions in contradistinction to continued fractions. RATIONAL applies to expres-

FORM CB. 28.	NY
rational	15
irrational	12
REAL	41
imaginary	10
radical	5
unmarked	3
total	86

sions in which no extraction of a root is left, and none such indicated which cannot be actually performed. The $\sqrt{2}$ can be obtained only approximately and is not RATIONAL. The sine of 20 degrees, 0.3420, is an IRRATIONAL NUMBER because it can be carried on indefinitely and never obtained exactly. The sine of 30 degrees, 0.5000, is RATIONAL. But both are REAL numbers.

The even roots of negative numbers are unreal, feigned, unobtainable, and so IMAGINARY, the opposite of REAL.

226. Σx (*sĭg'-mah*). Sum of x values, the sign of summation.

The symbol Σ is the Greek capital letter sigma, which corresponds to the English capital S. The Greek small s is written σ in the middle of a word, but ς, almost like an English s, at the end of a word, as: ἴσος (isos), alike, the same.

Florian Cajori, in his scholarly History of Mathematical Notations, says that Σ was first used for summation by Leonhard Euler (*oi'-ler*) in 1755, the year of Dr. Johnson's Dictionary. Euler writes: 'Summam indicabimus signo Σ'. Cajori adds that the symbol was used by Lagrange and again in 1829 in Fourier's Theory of Heat, and rarely between these periods. The elongated s, $\int$, was used instead by Leibniz, not only as a sign of integration but also to designate a sum.

To the question: 'Σx', 28 persons out of 61 answer correctly SUM OF X VALUES; but 18 answer DERIVATIVE OF X. The DERIVA-

TIVE OF X is written dx. DELTA X, written Δx, is a small real quantity. As this grows smaller it approaches dx as its limiting value. This seems a far more difficult concept than Σx, which

$$\Sigma x.$$

FORM A. 10.	BO	NY	SUM
SUM OF X VALUES	10	18	28
x-factorial	0	2	2
root-of-x	0	2	2
derivative-of-x	6	12	18
moment-of-x	4	7	11
unmarked	0	0	0
total	20	41	61

means merely the sum of all the x's. For a housewife who buys apples, oranges, and coffee, the sum of her purchases, the Σ of her purchases, is the money she owes.

227. *ORTHOGONAL* (*or-thŏg′-ō-năl*) *adj*. At right angles to something else, rectangular.

From Leonard Digges, 1571: 'Of straight lined angles there are three kindes, the Orthogonall, the Obtuse, and the Acute Angle'. Also from Digges: 'An ORTHOGONALL or right Angle'. A RIGHT ANGLE is today one of 90 degrees, a quarter of a circle; and one forgets that the original meaning of RIGHT was straight, direct, by the shortest course, keeping one's direction throughout. A RIGHT ANGLE is made by a line drawn from a point to another line by the shortest course.

ORTHOGONAL comes from the Greek ὀρθογώνιος (orthogonios), right angled, a combination of ὀρθός (orthos) and γωνία (gonia), an angle. The Greek ὀρθός (orthos) appears in ORTHOGRAPHY, correct spelling, and in ORTHOEPY (*or′-thō-ĕ-pē*) as early as 1668, correct pronunciation. The Greek γωνία (gonia), the source of -GONAL, the second half of ORTHOGONAL, occurs in POLYGONAL, many angled, and has already been met in the middle of the word TRIGONOMETRIC (177), from TRIGONOMETRY, the measurement of the triangle, a three-angled figure; and near the beginning of this book in DIAGONAL (15), across from corner to corner, from angle to angle.

To the question: 'At right angles', 148 persons out of 357 answer ORTHOGONAL; and 90 CARTESIAN. CARTESIAN COORDINATES are so often RECTANGULAR that one is apt to think of them as always at right angles. But careful writers specify RECTANGULAR CARTESIAN COORDINATES, for they may be OBLIQUE.

ORTHOGONAL is an adjective which means right angled, at right angles, and can be applied to a triangle, to coordinates, or

At right angles.

FORM B. 39.	NY	MISC.	SUM
obtuse	1	15	16
rhomboid	9	40	49
acute	1	11	12
ORTHOGONAL	18	130	148
Cartesian	16	74	90
unmarked	3	39	42
total	48	309	357

to a method of projection in which the rays are all at right angles to the plane of projection. Reread COORDINATE (187).

228. *POWER FACTOR* (*pow'-er făk'-tor*). The power available in an alternating current electrical circuit divided by the product of the electromotive force and current. Reread FACTOR (47).

With direct current the electrical power is volts multiplied by amperes, or the potential difference multiplied by the current flowing. With alternating current the power computed in this way is often theoretical and called the APPARENT POWER. Direct current flows steadily in one direction at a maximum. Alternating current rises from zero to a maximum, sinks to zero, and then runs in the opposite direction. Its average value, its ROOT-MEAN-SQUARE value as it is called, is 0.707 times its maximum. But this difference is not the POWER FACTOR.

When current and voltage start together at zero, rise to a maximum, and sink together, when they are in phase, the POWER FACTOR is unity, 1.00. But when current and voltage are not in phase, when they are not rising and falling together, there are parts of each cycle when the two flow in opposite directions, when one is positive and the other negative, and the product of the two is negative, producing negative power which reduces the total power available throughout each cycle. The POWER FACTOR is the factor, a fraction, decimal, or co-efficient by which the apparent power is multiplied to obtain the true power. With a difference in phase of 90 degrees be-

Watts divided by volt-amperes.

FORM A. 32.	NY	NY	NY	SUM
impedance	3	3	12	18
power	9	12	34	55
potential	5	5	7	17
amplification	2	2	7	11
POWER FACTOR	13	16	86	115
unmarked	5	2	1	8
total	37	40	147	224

tween current and voltage, when one lags a quarter of a cycle behind the other, the product of current and voltage is negative for one half of each cycle, and the true power throughout the cycle zero. When the lag of the current behind the voltage is expressed as an angle, the cosine of this angle is the POWER FACTOR. When current and voltage are in phase the angle is zero and the cosine of this angle 1.00.

To the question: 'Watts divided by volt-amperes', 115 persons out of 224 answer correctly POWER FACTOR; while 55 answer POWER. The WATT (126) is a unit of power. With direct current POWER, measured in WATTS, is volts times amperes. With alternating current the equation is:

WATTS = POWER FACTOR × VOLT-AMPERES,   or
TRUE POWER = POWER FACTOR × VOLT-AMPERES.

$$\frac{\text{WATTS}}{\text{VOLT-AMPERES}} = \text{POWER FACTOR}$$

$$\frac{\text{TRUE POWER}}{\text{VOLT-AMPERES (APPARENT POWER)}} = \text{POWER FACTOR.}$$

WATTS AVAILABLE is the TRUE POWER; WATTS divided by VOLT-AMPERES is the POWER FACTOR.

229. *CENTRIPETAL* (*sĕn-trĭp'-ē-tăl*) *adj.* Tending toward the
center, drawing toward some point as a center, acting as a
counterpoise to the centrifugal tendency in circular motion.
The word CENTRIPETAL starts with the Latin *centrum*, center,
already met in CONCENTRIC (31), having the same center. The
second part of CENTRIPETAL comes from *petere*, to seek, move
toward. This Latin verb *petere* may mean fall upon, rush at,

Force acting toward the center on any body constrained to
move in a circular path.

FORM C. 26. NY		FORM CA. 17. BO	NY	NY	NY	NY	SUM
centrifugal	123	centrifugal	29	76	138	338	90	671
axial	19	axial	4	2	17	156	16	195
inertial	6	radial	1	2	6	130	7	146
spheroidal	6	spheroidal	0	2	0	131	7	140
CENTRIPETAL	240	CENTRIPETAL	66	318	239	345	114	1082
unmarked	6	unmarked	0	0	0	0	0	0
total	400	total	100	400	400	1100	234	2234

attack, assault; or in a gentler, less violent way, it may mean
strive for, seek, make for, direct one's course toward; or ask
for, solicit, require, demand. From this last meaning, through
the past participle *petitus* and the noun *petitio, petitionis*, comes
the English PETITION, an entreaty, supplication, request. CEN-
TRIPETAL is by derivation seeking the center, moving toward
the center.

   To the question: 'The force acting toward the center on any
body constrained to move in a circular path', 48 per cent of
2234 people answer CENTRIPETAL, and 30 per cent CENTRIFUGAL.
Thus in this study 78 per cent, and in the earlier study 91 per
cent, know the pair of words CENTRIPETAL and CENTRIFUGAL.
But of this surprisingly large number less than a third know
which is which; for if 30 per cent guess CENTRIFUGAL, another
30 per cent, an equal number, should guess CENTRIPETAL without knowing its correctness, leaving only 18 per cent who
know the answer.

   Of the two, the derivation of CENTRIFUGAL seems the easier
to remember, though the physical significance is the more difficult. CENTRIFUGAL (*sĕn-trĭf'-ū-găl*) comes from the Latin

centrum, the center, and *fugere*, to flee, the source also of the adjective FUGITIVE, wandering, fleeing, and the noun FUGITIVE, one who flees, a runaway, deserter. CENTRIFUGAL is fleeing from the center, flying away from the center. Actually a body revolving about another would not move directly away from the center but would continue straight ahead, on a tangent to the curve, if not held to the center. For this reason Sir George Biddell Airy, 1801 to 1892, an English mathematician and astronomer, complains of the term CENTRIFUGAL FORCE, saying there is no force in operation. He would substitute CENTRIFUGAL TENDENCY. Joseph Norman Lockyer, another oft quoted astronomer, 1868: 'Were the CENTRIFUGAL TENDENCY to cease, the CENTRIPETAL FORCE would be uncontrolled, and the body fall upon the attracting mass'.

Both words, CENTRIFUGAL and CENTRIPETAL, come from Sir Isaac Newton, from the Principia, 1687: '*Haec est vis centrifuga, qua corpus urget circulum; et huic aequalis est vis contraria*. And later in the Principia, definition v: '*Vim conatui illi contrariam centripetam appello*'.

230. *MYOPIA* (*mĭ-ō'-pĭ-ah*) *n*. Short-sightedness, near-sightedness, brachymetropia, inability of the eye to accommodate to distant objects. Reread ACCOMMODATION (145).

The MYOPIC eye has a greater refractive power. In the ordinary eye, parallel rays focus on the retina. Such an eye is called EMMETROPIC (*ĕm-mĕ-trŏp'-ĭk*), with normal power of accommodation. In the far-sighted or HYPERMETROPIC eye parallel rays come to a focus behind the retina. In the MYOPIC (*mĭ-ŏp'-ĭk*), short-sighted, eye parallel rays come to a focus in front of the retina. This abnormal condition is called MYOPIA.

As the rays from a near-by object are not parallel but diverging, they must be bent more sharply than parallel rays in order to come to a focus at the retina. For this reason an ordinary eye does not form a distinct picture of an object at less than 6 to 10 inches. The MYOPIC or short-sighted eye may form an equally distinct picture at 3 to 5 inches distance. As the apparent dimensions of the near-by object are double those of one at twice the distance, the object is magnified in proportion and its details more clearly seen.

The word MYOPIA comes from the Greek μυωπία (myopia), from μύωψ (myops), short-sighted, literally closing the eye, blinking, a combination of μίειν (miein), to close, and ὤψ (ops), ὠπίς (opis), eye, which appears also in OPTICS, a study of sight, vision, seeing, and so today the study of light. The word MYOPIA appears in Blancard's Physical Dictionary of 1693; and in the Ephraim Chambers' Cyclopaedia of 1727: 'The MYOPIA is owing to the too great convexity of the eye'.

To the question: 'Near-sightedness', 38 per cent of 2234 people answer MYOPIA; while 20 per cent answer ASTIGMATISM. In the earlier study based on 400 persons 42 per cent answer MYOPIA and 27 per cent ASTIGMATISM. The term ASTIGMATISM comes from the Greek privative ἀ (a), not, and στίγμα (stigma), στίγματα (stigmata), the mark of a pointed instrument, a spot.

Near-sightedness.

FORM C. 39.	NY	FORM CA. 27.	BO	NY	NY	NY	NY	SUM
astigmatism	108	astigmatism	18	48	96	250	38	450
MYOPIA	167	MYOPIA	64	237	148	270	131	850
hyperme-		chromatic						
tropia	19	aberration	7	18	46	191	21	283
spherical		spherical						
aberration	60	aberration	6	55	69	212	28	370
presbyopia	26	presbyopia	5	42	41	177	13	278
unmarked	20	unmarked	0	0	0	0	3	3
total	400	total	100	400	400	1100	234	2234

The ASTIGMATIC eye does not focus parallel rays at a point because the lens of the eye curves differently in different sections. The lens of the MYOPIC eye curves too much as a whole and on both sides, is too convex, and cannot be flattened enough for the almost parallel rays of distant objects. For ordinary distances HYPERMETROPIA or far-sightedness is corrected with convex, converging glasses; MYOPIA, with concave glasses.

231. *TRUNCATION* (*trŭng-kā'-shŏn*) *n.* Noah Webster, in the first edition of his Dictionary, 1828, says: 'The act of lopping or cutting off'.
TRUNCATION comes from the Latin *truncatus*, the past par-

ticiple of *truncare*, to cut off, reduce to a trunk, the source of the English noun TRUNK, stump.

To the question: 'Dividing a solid by intersection with a plane', 172 persons out of 525 answer TRUNCATION; and 140 BISECTION. Neither is strictly a correct answer to the present definition, either fitting about equally well. The word to BISECT (5) is a combination of the Latin *bi-*, two, plus *sectus*,

Forms c and ca. Dividing a solid by intersection with a plane. Form cb. Cutting off the top of a solid.

FORM C. 16.	CH	FORM CA. 30.	CH	LA	NY	NY	PH	SUM
extraction	1	collineation	2	0	1	6	4	13
segmentation	11	segmentation	9	13	16	69	10	117
TRUNCATION	22	TRUNCATION	13	16	41	77	25	172
bisection	22	bisection	8	3	27	79	23	140
interception	12	interception	8	5	11	44	9	77
unmarked	0	unmarked	0	0	1	2	3	6
total	68	total	40	37	97	277	74	525

FORM CB. 34.	NY
collineation	6
segmentation	25
TRUNCATION	34
bisection	9
interception	8
unmarked	4
total	86

the past participle of *secare*, to cut. To BISECT is to cut into two parts, as to BISECT a line, an angle, or a figure. The word originally meant to cut into two equal parts; and for exactness of expression BISECT should probably be limited to this meaning. The noun, a BISECTION, may be either the act of cutting, or one of the parts.

Returning to the definition, BISECTION is dividing a solid, or more correctly dividing it into two equal parts. TRUNCATION is cutting off part of a solid, not really dividing it.

From John Harris, the high-flying clergyman, who compiled a Collection of Voyages and Travels in addition to his Lexicon

Technicum, or Dictionary of the Arts and Sciences, 1704, comes: 'TRUNCATED pyramid or cone, is one whose top is cut off by a plane parallel to its Base; and therefore the figure of the TRUNCATED top must always be similar to the Base'. Though TRUNCATION still has the general meaning of lopping or cutting off, a TRUNCATED cone or pyramid is almost always understood as one whose top or vertex is cut off parallel to the base, and a TRUNCATED crystal is one whose edges are cut off symmetrically.

The Imperial Dictionary, first published in two volumes of text and a third of illustrations, and later, 1882, in a new edition of four volumes, says of TRUNCATION: 'A term used to signify that change in the geometrical form of a crystal, which is produced by the cutting off of an angle or edge, so as to leave a face more or less large in place of the edge or angle. When the face thus produced does not make equal angles with all the contiguous faces, the TRUNCATION is said to be OBLIQUE. The secondary forms of crystals may be supposed to be produced by TRUNCATION of the solid angles or edges of any of the primary forms'.

In the revised form CB, item 34, a change in the question to: 'Cutting off the top of a solid', reduces the number who mark BISECTION from 27 per cent to 10 per cent, confirming the misunderstanding of the earlier wording. But the percentage who mark TRUNCATION has changed less, increasing only from 33 per cent to no more than 40 per cent. The popular mislead is now SEGMENTATION. In geometry, a SEGMENT, from the same *secare*, to cut, is any part cut off by a straight line or, from a solid, by a plane. SEGMENTATION ordinarily means cutting into a number of SEGMENTS; but there is no reason why the word should not be used for the cutting off of a single SEGMENT. TRUNCATION should be reserved for cutting off the top with a line or plane parallel to the base.

232. *SKIN EFFECT* (*skĭn ĕf-fĕkt'*). An opposition to the flow of an alternating current at the center of a wire, tendency of a high-frequency current to travel near the surface of a conductor and less in the interior.

Even a straight wire has one value of resistance to direct current and another to high frequency, for a direct current travels through the body of the conducting material, while an alternating current of high frequency is not uniformly distributed over the cross section but tends to concentrate near the surface, travels in a thin layer on the outside. As the frequency of the current increases, the depth of this layer grows less, the resistance increasing. The current squeezes into a smaller amount of the material. The resistance of a copper wire may be four times greater for a frequency of 200,000 cycles per second than

The tendency when a magnetic current in a wire forces the current into the outer part of the wire.

FORM A. 27.	NY	NY	NY	SUM
radiation	7	8	18	33
SKIN EFFECT	11	15	85	111
eddy current	9	10	23	42
baffle	1	1	5	7
ion effect	4	6	16	26
unmarked	5	0	0	5
total	37	40	147	224

for direct current. This effect is due to inductance, the changing current in the outer layer inducing an opposing electromotive force at the center. Because magnetic lines originate at the center and expand outward, they are more concentrated at the center and the consequent induced voltage causes an opposition to the flow. This increases as the frequency increases until at very high frequencies the current may run in the opposite direction at the center.

To the question: 'The tendency when a magnetic current in a wire forces the current into the outer part of the wire', 111 persons out of 224 answer correctly SKIN EFFECT; while 42 answer EDDY CURRENT, the most frequently marked mislead in each of the studies, and 33 mark RADIATION. Although EDDY CURRENTS and SKIN EFFECT are usually treated separately in textbooks, the answer EDDY CURRENT to this question is probably correct. The term is more general than SKIN EFFECT. EDDY CURRENTS may be set up in the iron core inside a coil, or by the magnetic field around a wire. The term SKIN EFFECT is more specific and therefore more nearly correct for those who know the phenomenon.

With a round wire the current is pushed toward the surface and avoids the center. With a square bar the greatest concentration is at the corners and the least at the center. With a flat strip the current density is greatest at the edges, least at the center.

233. *INVERSION* (*in-ver'-shŏn*) *n*. The rise of temperature with height in thin layers of the air near the earth.

To the question: 'The rapid rise in temperature with height which refracts waves back to earth', 114 persons out of 224 answer correctly INVERSION; but 63 answer VIRTUAL HEIGHT. When the temperature rises with altitude, the air growing warmer, normal conditions are INVERTED, and the condition is said to be

The rapid rise in temperature with height which refracts waves back to earth.

FORM A. II.	NY	NY	NY	SUM
INVERSION	15	18	81	114
heat wave	7	8	22	37
direct ray	0	0	7	7
normal	0	0	1	1
virtual height	15	14	34	63
unmarked	0	0	2	2
total	37	40	147	224

an INVERSION. This occurs late at night, with a clear sky and light wind, and in shallow layers of air below some 5000 feet from the earth's surface.

The noun INVERSION comes from the Latin *invertere*, to turn about, a combination of *in*, in, to, toward, and *vertere*, to turn, a verb already met in the phrase INVERSE PROPORTION (46), and the source of such English verbs as CONVERT, to effect a turnabout in position, to ADVERT, to turn the mind to, and to EVERT, to turn outward or inside out.

Temperature INVERSIONS, both near the surface and at higher altitudes, are more pronounced in the winter than in summer. In the winter, with a high barometer, accompanied by low surface temperature, there is a slow decrease of temperature to perhaps three kilometers, and then relatively warm air to 9 or 10 kilometers, and then sometimes a high upper INVERSION.

234. *MAGNETIC MOMENT* (măg-nět'-ĭk mō'-měnt). The
    turning force acting on a magnet placed at right angles to
a unit magnetic field.

MOMENT in this sense is the same as MOMENT, an indefinitely
small space of time. It comes from the Latin *momentum,* originally a balance, then a particle large enough to turn a balance;
and this may suggest its use in mechanics for a turning force.

To the question: 'In a magnet the pole strength multiplied by
the distance between the poles', 247 persons out of 537 answer
MAGNETIC MOMENT; but 124 answer E.M.F. In the small separate

In a magnet the pole strength multiplied by the distance between the poles.

FORM E. 38.	BO	FW	LA	NY	NY	NY	NY	PH	TU	SUM
e.m.f.	8	18	6	5	2	9	49	23	4	124
field	2	7	5	4	3	8	48	19	3	99
MAGNETIC										
MOMENT	11	16	20	8	14	14	96	52	16	247
impulse	2	2	1	2	0	2	11	2	1	23
lines of flow	2	5	1	1	1	5	10	3	4	32
unmarked	3	2	0	0	0	2	4	1	0	12
total	28	50	33	20	20	40	218	100	28	537

FORM E. 38.	ENGLISH VOCABULARY	
	HIGH	LOW
e.m.f.	2	12
field	9	9
MAGNETIC MOMENT	27	12
impulse	0	2
lines of flow	2	5
unmarked	0	0
total	40	40

study of 40 persons who score high in English vocabulary only
2 answer E.M.F.; while of 40 low in English vocabulary, 12
answer E.M.F., as many as mark MAGNETIC MOMENT. The common abbreviation E.M.F. stands for electromotive force, potential difference, which determines the flow of electricity from
one place to another. It is measured in volts.

A MOMENT in physics is a turning force. Its value is the distance from the axis of rotation at which a force is acting multiplied by the force. The MOMENT of one pole of a magnet is the strength of the magnetic pole multiplied by its distance from the turning point, in other words multiplied by half the distance to the other pole of the magnet.

The turning force of the magnet as a whole depends upon two poles. It is therefore twice the MOMENT of one pole. Since the MOMENT of one pole is the strength of one pole multiplied by half the distance between, the MOMENT of two poles, or the magnet as a whole, is the strength of one pole multiplied by the whole distance between. In symbols the MOMENT of one magnetic pole about the mid point between two poles is:

$$\tfrac{1}{2} \; L \; m$$

where L is the distance between the two poles, ½ L the distance to the mid point, and m the magnetic force. The turning force of two poles, or the MAGNETIC MOMENT, is twice this or:

$$L \; m.$$

The MAGNETIC MOMENT is the strength of either magnetic pole multiplied by the distance between the poles. In a unit magnetic field the magnetic moment acting on a magnet at right angles to the field is the force on either pole in dynes multiplied by the distance in centimeters between the poles.

235. *CANARD* (kă-nahrd′) *adj.* A type of airplane with the horizontal stabilizer in front of the main supporting wing, but with the rudder in the normal position at the rear.

In the CANARD airplane the horizontal stabilizer is mounted at a greater angle of attack than the main wing, and so stalls earlier. As a result major stalls of the entire airplane are rare.

The German word for DUCK is *ente*, which seems to have been the name of this plane in Germany where it had its greatest vogue. The French word for duck is *canard*, and from this comes the English term CANARD applied to this type of plane because of its resemblance to a duck in flight. The word CANARD was also used in English from 1850 to perhaps 1880 for an absurd, extravagant story, hoax; and surprisingly often a meaning of this kind survives and appears later. This type of plane differs so from others that it could easily be thought of as an extravagant, absurd hoax.

To the question: 'Type of airplane having the horizontal stabilizing and control surfaces in front of the main supporting surfaces', 185 persons in a population of 515 answer CANARD, but 130 answer PUSHER. The term PUSHER in this sense is used for a plane in which the propeller is behind the engine and so

Form A. Type of airplane having the horizontal stabilizing and control surfaces in front of the main supporting surfaces.

Form AA. Airplane with horizontal stabilizing and control surfaces in front of main supporting surfaces.

FORM A. 34.	FW	LA	NY	NY	NY	PH	SUM	FORM AA. 32.	NY
pusher airplane	4	9	9	17	41	50	130	pusher	21
tractor airplane	1	3	5	4	19	21	53	tractor	3
tailless airplane	4	12	7	7	24	29	83	tailless	14
CANARD AIRPLANE	7	26	13	24	41	74	185	CANARD	17
equivalent monoplane	1	3	1	2	12	9	28	rocket	8
unmarked	1	1	2	12	3	17	36	unmarked	0
total	18	54	37	66	140	200	515	total	63

behind the main wind or supporting surface. In the PUSHER airplane the horizontal stabilizer is the fixed horizontal surface in the tail. In the CANARD airplane this horizontal stabilizer is at the front, ahead of the wing.

236. *COULOMB* (*koo-lŏng′*) *n*. Practical unit of quantity of electricity, in the practical system of units the amount carried by one ampere in one second.

In electrolysis (50) the same amount of a given metal is always deposited by the same current of electricity in the same time; or by a smaller current in a longer time. When a given amount of metal is deposited, a definite quantity of electricity is associated with the operation. The COULOMB is the quantity of electricity required to deposit 0.001118 grams of silver from a silver solution.

To the question: 'The unit corresponding to the deposition of 0.001118 grams of silver from a silver salt solution', 35 per cent of 2234 persons answer COULOMB, but 22 per cent answer AMPERE. The AMPERE is the current which will deposit 0.001118 grams of silver per second. It is the current strength required to deposit 0.001118 grams of silver per second. The COULOMB is the amount of electricity which deposits that amount of silver no matter what the time. The distinction is a bit like the distinction between power and work. A POWERFUL man or a

The unit corresponding to the deposition of 0.001118 grams of silver from a silver salt solution.

FORM C. 28. NY		FORM CA. 20. BO	NY	NY	NY	NY	SUM
volt	43	volt	5	11	23	151	17	207
COULOMB	209	COULOMB	40	210	153	277	91	771
erg	40	erg	18	35	71	228	47	399
farad	58	farad	16	39	56	219	34	364
watt	32	ampere	19	105	97	225	43	489
unmarked	18	unmarked	2	0	0	0	2	4
total	400	total	100	400	400	1100	234	2234

POWERFUL machine does work in a short time. POWER is a function of time. AMPERES express the power of the current. But a weak man or machine can do the same quantity of work in a longer time. The COULOMB is similarly a quantity of electricity which may be used rapidly or more slowly.

Charles Augustin Coulomb, who lived from 1736 to 1806, started as a military engineer, spending nine years in the West Indies. After his return to France, and at the outbreak of the French revolution, he retired in 1789 to Blois and devoted himself to scientific research. His papers on electrical repulsions and attractions were published between 1785 and 1789. It was not until 1881 that the Paris Electric Congress adopted Coulomb's name for the quantity of electricity conveyed in one second by a current of one ampere. The COULOMB is the charge past any given point carried by one ampere in one second. It is equal to the charge borne by 6.3×10^{18} electrons.

237. *BRIGHT-LINE SPECTRUM* (*brīt-līn spĕk′-trŭm*). Un-
evenly spaced colored lines against a dark background,
given off by the atoms of chemical elements in a gaseous state
at low pressures and high temperatures and viewed with a
SPECTROSCOPE (61).

To the question: 'Spectra given by incandescent or luminescent vapors', 212 persons out of 537 answer correctly BRIGHT
LINE; but 105 answer CONTINUOUS, and 72 DARK LINE. In the
small group of 40 persons high in the English literary vocabu-

Spectra given by incandescent or luminescent vapors.

FORM E. 28.	BO	FW	LA	NY	NY	NY	NY	PH	TU	SUM
absorption	2	3	4	3	0	0	25	11	4	52
continuous	3	9	6	7	7	9	47	15	2	105
dark line	3	7	4	3	1	12	18	20	4	72
BRIGHT LINE	13	18	18	5	10	12	82	42	12	212
dark band	3	12	1	2	2	6	39	10	6	81
unmarked	4	1	0	0	0	1	7	2	0	15
total	28	50	33	20	20	40	218	100	28	537

FORM E. 28.   ENGLISH VOCABULARY

	HIGH	LOW
absorption	1	8
continuous	7	8
dark line	4	2
BRIGHT LINE	26	14
dark band	2	2
unmarked	0	6
total	40	40

lary 26 mark BRIGHT LINE compared with only 14 of the 40 low
in English vocabulary. That a glowing vapor under low pressure produces a BRIGHT-LINE SPECTRUM and not a CONTINUOUS
one seems like knowledge of physics, and yet goes with a large
English vocabulary.

CONTINUOUS SPECTRA are given off by incandescent solids,
by liquids, and by gases under high pressure. Thus the incandescent tungsten or incandescent carbon in an electric light
bulb produces a continuous spectrum. BRIGHT-LINE SPECTRA are

emitted by the atoms of chemical elements in a gaseous state at low pressures. Thus lithium chloride held in a Bunsen flame vaporizes and gives a bright red and a bright orange line.

BRIGHT-LINE SPECTRA are given off directly by the atoms of a glowing gas under low pressure and high temperature. DARK-LINE SPECTRA are produced by the same gas when a brighter CONTINUOUS SPECTRUM shines through the gas from behind. A DARK-LINE SPECTRUM is an absorption spectrum. For each chemical element the positions of the lines are exactly the same in a BRIGHT-LINE and DARK-LINE SPECTRUM; but in one the lines are bright colors against a dark background, in the other the lines are dark against a rainbow background. One is the reverse of the other. A BRIGHT-LINE SPECTRUM is an EMISSION SPECTRUM produced by a self-luminous source which gives off, emits light, with no intervening absorber.

238. *ASYMPTOTE* (*ăs'-ĭm-tōt*) *n.* A straight line which a curve gradually approaches but never meets.

The word ASYMPTOTE comes from the Greek ἀσύμπτωτος (asymptotos), not close, not falling together. The Greek privative ἀ (a), not, at the beginning of this word has already been

Lines whose distance from the locus of a hyperbola become infinitesimal as the hyperbola is extended toward infinity.

FORM C. 39.	CH	FORM CA. 25.	CH	LA	NY	NY	PH	SUM
major axes	6	major axes	8	2	11	31	8	60
minor axes	7	minor axes	3	6	13	27	10	59
ASYMPTOTES	27	ASYMPTOTES	11	15	40	109	33	208
directrices	9	directrices	8	3	10	33	6	60
hyperbolic		hyperbolic						
functions	19	functions	9	9	22	72	13	125
unmarked	0	unmarked	1	2	1	5	4	13
total	68	total	40	37	97	277	74	525

met in AMORPHOUS (217), without form, and earlier in ANEROID (93), not liquid, not wet. The second syllable comes from the Greek σύν (syn), together; and the end from πτωτίς (ptotis),

falling, apt to fall, from πίπτειν (piptein), to fall. An ASYMPTOTE
is a line which never falls together with a curve but approaches
it ever closer.

To the question: 'Lines whose distance from the locus of an
hyperbola become infinitesimal as the hyperbola is extended
toward infinity', 208 persons out of 525 answer correctly
ASYMPTOTE; while 125 answer HYPERBOLIC FUNCTIONS. The HY-

FORM CB. 32.	NY
major axes	10
minor axes	18
ASYMPTOTES	34
latus rectum	7
hyperbolic functions	14
unmarked	3
total	86

PERBOLIC FUNCTIONS are the sine, cosine, tangent, etc. referred
to the rectangular hyperbola much as the ordinary sine, cosine,
and tangent are referred to the circle.

When two straight lines cross at right angles, RECTANGULAR
HYPERBOLAS can be drawn in two opposite angles thus formed,
with the closed curved ends pointing toward one another and
each side of the hyperbola approaching one of the straight lines
but never meeting it. The straight lines are ASYMPTOTES.

239. *ELLIPTIC FOCI* (ĕl-lĭp'-tĭk fō'-sī). Two points on the
        principal axis of the ellipse so located that the distance
from one of them to any point on the ellipse and back to the
other is always the same. Reread ELLIPSE (205).

This was Euclid's description of the ellipse as it appeared in
The Elements, written in Greek about 300 B.C.

To the question: 'Two points the sum of whose distances
from a moving point is fixed in a conic', 114 persons out of 357
answer ELLIPTIC FOCI, and 65 answer MAJOR AXES. The MAJOR
AXIS of an ellipse, also called the TRANSVERSE AXIS or sometimes
the PRINCIPAL AXIS, is a straight line through the center of the

ellipse, and through the two foci. It extends the long way of the ellipse, from one rounded end, through a FOCUS, through

Two points the sum of whose distances from a moving point is fixed in a conic.

FORM B. 21.	NY	MISC.	SUM
directrices	5	48	53
latus rectum	4	14	18
ELLIPTIC FOCI	17	97	114
parabolic foci	8	62	70
major axes	14	51	65
unmarked	0	37	37
total	48	309	357

the center of the ellipse, through the other FOCUS, to the other rounded end of the ellipse.

240. *ELECTRON* (ē-lĕk'-trŏn) *n.* A negatively charged particle with a mass about 1/1840th of the hydrogen atom. Reread ELECTRON (98).
All ELECTRONS are the same. The charge carried by each is 4.767×10^{-10} electrostatic units, or 1.589×10^{-20} electromagnetic units, or 15.89×10^{-20} coulombs. The mass of each ELECTRON is 9.00×10^{-28} grams, or 1/1840th the mass of the hydrogen atom.

ELECTRONS shot from radium are called BETA RAYS or BETA PARTICLES. ELECTRONS shot from the cathode in a vacuum tube are now called CATHODE RAYS, but were formerly called CORPUSCLES.

To the question: 'Particles free to move through a metallic conductor', 69 per cent of those tested answer ELECTRON; but to the present question: 'The particle with the smallest known mass' only 44 per cent answer ELECTRON, another 32 per cent answering ATOM. There is much justification for this confusion. The ATOM is commonly regarded as the smallest or ultimate particle of matter. The word comes from the Greek ἄτομος (atomos), indivisible, that cannot be cut, a combination of the Greek privative ἀ (a), not, and τομός (tomos), an adjective from the verb τέμνειν (temnein), to cut. In literature the word ATOM is often used for the smallest conceivable portion of anything. But since 1777, when Priestley wrote: 'By ATOM I mean an ultimate component part of any gross body', the word has come to be used with far greater precision.

Today an ATOM is the smallest particle of a chemical element, which retains the characteristics of the element and takes part in chemical reactions, the smallest particle in which the chemi-

Particle with the smallest known mass.

FORM AB. 33.	%	FORM D. 30.	NY	%
ELECTRON	47	ELECTRON	134	38.3
atom	12	atom	124	35.4
ion	11	ion	27	7.7
proton	12	proton	26	7.4
alpha particle	18	alpha particle	37	10.6
unmarked	0	unmarked	2	0.6
total	100	total	350	100.0

FORM DA. 31.	%	FORM DB. 30.	NY
ELECTRON	44	ELECTRON	37
atom	32	atom	40
ion	5	molecule	8
proton	11	proton	5
alpha particle	6	alpha particle	16
unmarked	2	unmarked	0
total	100	total	106

cal elements combine either with themselves or with each other. ATOMS differ with each chemical element; some are heavy like radium, others light, depending on the mass of the nucleus at the center. The hydrogen atom is the lightest of all.

In the hydrogen ATOM only one single ELECTRON revolves around the nucleus. In other ATOMS the number of free ELECTRONS equals the atomic number of the chemical element, the number of its position in the periodic table. The number of such ELECTRONS in each ATOM, and their arrangement around the nucleus, differ from one chemical element to another, and determine the chemical properties, but add substantially nothing to its mass which is concentrated in the nucleus and even in the lightest ATOM is some 2000 times greater than the mass of the ELECTRON. Reread ISOTOPE (196).

241. *TORQUE* (*tork*) *n.* A turning force, the moment of a twisting force, the integrated resultant of moments, that arising from a system of forces equivalent to a couple. Reread MAGNETIC MOMENT (234).

Hawkins' Mechanical Dictionary of 1909 defines TORQUE as the turning effect applied to a shaft, as by the various cranks; and adds that the term originated in electrical engineering.

The word TORQUE comes directly from the Latin *torques, torquis,* a twisted metal neck-ring, collar, necklace, worn by the ancient Gauls. The noun comes from the verb *torquere,* to twist, turn, and so wring, distort, and torture. From this verb

Force times perpendicular distance from axis.

FORM C. 12. NY moment of		FORM CA. 30. BO moment of		NY HIGH	NY NEXT	NY REST	NY MISC.	SUM
inertia	91	inertia	14	96	87	223	56	476
lever	84	lever	10	40	105	219	40	414
TORQUE	146	TORQUE	51	212	111	248	103	725
stress	34	stress	20	18	44	209	15	306
work	42	work	4	34	53	201	18	310
unmarked	3	unmarked	1	0	0	0	2	3
total	400	total	100	400	400	1100	234	2234

come TORTUOUS, twisting, winding, zigzag, crooked; and TORTURE, pain by twisting. The word TORQUE seems to have been first used by James Thomson in 1884, older brother of William Thomson who became Lord Kelvin.

From Silvanus P. Thompson, 1894: 'When two equal and opposite forces act on the ends of a rigid bar they simply tend to turn it round. Such a pair of forces form what is called a COUPLE, and the TORQUE, or tendency to turn (formerly called the MOMENT of the couple), is obtained by multiplying one of the two forces by the perpendicular distance between the directions of the forces. Such a couple tends to produce a motion of rotation, but not a motion of translation'. 'A magnetic needle placed in a magnetic field across the lines of force experiences a TORQUE, tending to rotate it round into the magnetic meridian'.

The effectiveness of a force in producing rotation depends upon two factors, one the magnitude of the force, the other its lever arm. A force of one pound with a lever arm of two feet is as effective as a force of two pounds with a lever arm of one foot. Force times lever arm is called TORQUE, or the MOMENT OF THE FORCE.

To the question: 'Force times perpendicular distance from axis', 32 per cent of 2234 persons answer TORQUE; 21 per cent MOMENT OF INERTIA; and 19 per cent LEVER. In the earlier study of form c, based on 400 cases, 36 per cent answer TORQUE; 23 per cent MOMENT OF INERTIA; and 21 per cent LEVER. INERTIA (116) is the unwillingness of a body to start moving, or to change its velocity if moving. INERTIA is measured by the force needed to give a unit mass unit acceleration. MOMENT OF INERTIA is the unwillingness of a body to start moving around in a circle, or to change its rotational speed. It is measured by the MOMENT OF FORCE, that is, by the TORQUE needed to give unit mass unit angular acceleration. The MOMENT OF INERTIA of a body about an axis is equal to the TORQUE required to produce unit angular acceleration. When the TORQUE is just enough to give unit mass unit acceleration, then TORQUE equals MOMENT OF INERTIA; but TORQUE is the general term for any rotational force.

'If you hold one end of a rod and I hold the other, and I twist it round in your hands, that is because I am giving it a TORQUE greater than you can resist', says the Daily Chronicle. TORQUE, or turning-moment, is a measurable quantity, the twisting or rotary force in a piece of mechanism, the moment of a system of forces producing rotation.

242. *PIEZO-* (*pī'-ĕ-zō*). Pertaining to pressure, caused by pressure, resulting in pressure.

From **Crystallography**, 1895, by Story-Maskelyne: 'Compression of a crystal of tourmaline along its morphological axis produces electrification'.

The combining form PIEZO- comes from the Greek πιέξειν (piezein), to press, squeeze. The use of this combining form is

not new with radio, but dates back at least to 1820 in the word
PIEZOMETER (*pī-ē-zŏm'-ē-ter*), an instrument for measuring
pressures. From J. Perkins, in the Philosophical Transactions
of 1820: 'Having believed for many years, that water was an
elastic fluid, I was induced to ascertain the fact by constructing
an instrument which I call a PIEZOMETER'. From William
Brande, Dictionary of Literature, Science, and Art, 1842:

Showing potential difference when subjected to mechanical
stress.

FORM A. 17.	NY	NY	NY	SUM
PIEZO	15	13	70	98
lever	3	5	9	17
filter	3	4	12	19
potentiometric	11	15	38	64
radiation	4	3	16	23
unmarked	1	0	2	3
total	37	40	147	224

'PIEZOMETER, an instrument for ascertaining the compressibility
of liquids'. From the second edition of the Imperial Dictionary
of 1882 edited by Ogilvie, and usually bound in four volumes,
comes: 'PIEZOMETER, an instrument consisting essentially of a
vertical tube inserted into a water main to show the pressure
of the fluid at that point, by the height to which it ascends in
the tube of the PIEZOMETER'.

   The terms PIEZO-ELECTRICITY and PIEZOELECTRIC, for electricity produced by pressure in certain crystals, are comparatively recent. The PIEZOELECTRIC EFFECT is the relationship
between mechanical force and electrical stress, the property
exhibited by certain crystals of becoming electrically polarized
and of developing charges of PIEZO-ELECTRICITY when subjected
to mechanical strain. The PIEZOELECTRIC EFFECT is the property
of certain asymmetric crystals of producing charges of positive
and negative electricity on opposing faces when under pressure. The signs of these charges are reversed when the pressure
is replaced by tension. The inverse PIEZOELECTRIC EFFECT occurs if the crystals are subjected to an electric potential, an
alteration in size of the crystal taking place.

To the question: 'Showing potential difference when subjected to mechanical stress', 98 persons out of 224 answer correctly PIEZO; but 64 answer POTENTIOMETRIC, the most popular mislead in three separate studies. POTENTIOMETRIC is an adjective made from the noun POTENTIOMETER.

The PIEZOELECTRIC quartz crystal in its natural state is six sided in cross section with pointed ends. A slab of such a crystal, properly cut with reference to the optical and electrical axes, develops an electrical voltage across the faces when compressed. This happens in a crystal microphone where the sound waves exert a pressure on the face of a crystal of Rochelle salt which produces a voltage across the faces.

243. *CAP-STRIP* (*kăp'-strĭp*) *n.* The stiffening around the edge of a wing rib used in attaching the covering to the rib.

To the definition: 'A continuous member on the outer edge of a wing rib', 198 persons out of 515 answer correctly CAP-STRIP; while 153 others answer FAIRING. The word FAIRING is defined both by the Century Dictionary and by the Oxford, 1901, as a gift bought at a fair. Not until the Oxford supplement of 1933 does the word FAIRING appear as applied to ship

A continuous member on the outer edge of a wing rib.

FORM A. 14.	FW	LA	NY	NY	NY	PH	SUM	FORM AA. 31.	NY
heading	1	6	7	5	23	20	62	heading	8
CAP-STRIP	7	31	18	27	45	70	198	CAP-STRIP	26
bulkhead	1	0	1	1	16	5	24	boundary layer	4
fairing	4	10	7	22	40	70	153	fairing	17
former	5	6	3	7	16	30	67	former	8
unmarked	0	1	1	4	0	5	11	unmarked	0
total	18	54	37	66	140	200	515	total	63

and aircraft construction. It is a thin sheet of metal used to give a fair surface. H. Barker in his Aeroplane Speaks of 1916 describes a FAIRING as a thin sheet of aluminum or wood bent round a detrimental surface in order to give it a fair or streamlike shape and so reduce the drag of that part.

A RIB is a cross section of a wing, running fore and aft. Each RIB gives shape to the wing section and carries air loads from the covering to the internal spars or beams. The CAP-STRIP is a strip around the outer edge of a rib. With wooden ribs the CAP-STRIPS are also of wood. The CAP-STRIP has two functions. It provides a surface to which the covering is attached, and it helps stiffen the rib.

244. *DYNE* (*dīn*) *n*. A unit of force, that force which acting for one second on a mass of one gram gives it a velocity of one centimeter per second.

The following quotation from the Reports of the British Association for the Advancement of Science, 1873, shows how technical terms are devised for newly discovered scientific concepts: 'As regards the name to be given to the C.G.S. unit of force, we recommend that it be a derivative of the Greek δύναμις (dynamis). The form DYNAMY appears to be most satisfactory to etymologists. DYNAM is equally intelligible, but awkward in sound to English ears. The short form, DYNE, will probably be generally preferred in this country'.

Lewis Campbell and William Garnett, in their delightful life of James Clerk Maxwell published in 1882 and which should be read by every young scientist, say Maxwell was fond of writing quaint verses which he brought round to his friends, 'with a sly chuckle at the humour, which, though his own, no one enjoyed more than himself'. Of the newly coined term:

> And when in tuning my guitar
> The interval would *not* come right,
> 'This string', you said, 'is strained too far,
> 'Tis forty dynes, at least too tight!'.

The Greek noun δύναμις (dynamis), force, already met early in this book in THERMODYNAMICS (27), comes from the verb δύνασθαι (dynasthai), to be powerful. From the same Greek source come DYNAMO and the English adjective DYNAMIC (*dī-năm'-ĭk*), pertaining to force which produces motion.

To the question: 'The force to accelerate one gram one centimeter per second', 32 per cent of 2234 persons answer DYNE; but 21 per cent answer GRAM-CENTIMETER; and 18 per cent ERG.

From the same 1873 Report of the British Association comes: 'We propose to denote it by some derivative of the Greek ἔργον. The forms ERGON, ERGAL, and ERG have been suggested. We propose, for the present, to leave the termination unsettled; and we request that the word ERGON or ERG be strictly limited to the c.g.s. unit of work, or what is for purposes of measurement, equivalent to the c.g.s. unit of energy'.

Again from the Life of Maxwell:

'Your sum of Vital energy
Is not the millionth of an ERG'.

An ERG is the quantity of work done by a force which, acting for one second upon a mass of one gram produces a velocity of one centimeter per second. The DYNE is the force. If a DYNE

The force to accelerate one gram one centimeter per second per second.

FORM C. 22. NY		FORM CA. 26. BO		NY	NY	NY	NY	SUM
erg	79	erg	19	70	60	211	44	404
dyne-		dyne-						
centimeter	108	centimeter	14	60	50	204	30	358
joule	26	joule	5	17	45	208	13	288
gram	8	gram-centimeter	18	43	124	231	54	470
DYNE	169	DYNE	40	210	121	246	91	708
unmarked	10	unmarked	4	0	0	0	2	6
total	400	total	100	400	400	1100	234	2234

of force acts through a centimeter, one DYNE-CENTIMETER of work, called an ERG, is accomplished. The ERG is the energy communicated by a DYNE, acting through a centimeter.

245. *MECHANICS* (*mĕ-kăn'-ĭks*) *n.* Originally the theory of machines, the science of machinery; now the mathematical study of motion, that branch of science which considers the laws of equilibrium and the motion of solid bodies.

The ending -ICS, formerly -ICKS, from -ικος (-ikos), was used even by the Greeks as an ending of nouns belonging to the arts and sciences. In words which entered the English language before 1500 the ending is merely -IC, as in MUSIC, ARITHMETIC,

LOGIC, MAGIC, and RHETORIC. Since the year 1500 the ending -IC is more often the adjective and -ICS the noun, the name of an art or science, as AESTHETICS, MATHEMATICS, ECONOMICS, ETHICS, METAPHYSICS, OPTICS, ATHLETICS, POLITICS, and GYMNASTICS. As so often happens in life the least learned of these strive for

That branch of science which deals with the motion of bodies in space.

FORM E. I.	BO	FW	LA	NY	NY	NY	NY	PH	TU	SUM
quantum	12	10	7	3	5	11	59	22	7	136
statistics	6	10	1	0	2	8	10	12	3	52
wave motion	0	10	4	2	2	7	28	11	5	69
sound	1	3	1	2	0	0	12	2	0	21
MECHANICS	9	13	20	13	11	14	106	53	13	252
unmarked	0	4	0	0	0	0	3	0	0	7
total	28	50	33	20	20	40	218	100	28	537

FORM E. I.	ENGLISH VOCABULARY	
	HIGH	LOW
quantum	4	9
statistics	1	9
wave motion	1	6
sound	0	6
MECHANICS	34	10
unmarked	0	0
total	40	40

conventional correctness and follow the plural form, as: GYM-NASTICS are; POLITICS are; TACTICS are; but the more exact sciences, despite the plural form of the noun, take the singular verb, as: MATHEMATICS is; PHYSICS is; METAPHYSICS is; and MECHANICS is.

To the question: 'That branch of science which deals with the motion of bodies in space', surprisingly few students mark MECHANICS, the correct answer. The most popular mislead is QUANTUM. A QUANTUM is a tiny bit of energy, a small definite amount, almost like an atom of energy. It may be the expression QUANTUM MECHANICS, the study of ATOMIC structure, which leads 136 students out of 537 to mark QUANTUM.

The third most popular mislead, chosen by 52 persons, is STATISTICS. This is probably a confusion of STATISTICS with STATICS; for STATICS and DYNAMICS were at one time the two branches of KINETICS; while KINETICS and KINEMATICS were the two great branches of MECHANICS. Alfred Daniell, in the 1904 edition of his Principles of Physics, which originally appeared in 1884, devotes nearly a hundred pages to KINEMATICS, the study of motion without reference to the force producing it.

In his essay Nineteenth Century, Thomas H. Huxley wrote: 'Newton defined the laws, rules, or observed order of the phenomena of motion which come under our daily observation with greater precision than had been before obtained; and, by following out with marvellous power and subtlety the mathematical consequences of these rules, he almost created the modern science of pure MECHANICS'.

In 1671, In Confiderations on the ufefulnefs of experimental and natural philofophy, Robert Boyle wrote: 'I do not here take the term, MECHANICKS, in that ftricter and more proper fenfe, wherein it is wont to be taken, when tis uf'd onely to fignifie the Doctrine about the Moving Powers, (as the Beam, the Leaver, the Screws, and the Wedg) and of Framing Engines to multiply Force; but I here underftand the word MECHANICKS in a larger fenfe for thofe Difciplines that confift of the Applications of pure Mathematicks to produce or modifie Motion in inferior Bodies'.

246. *CONJUGATE FOCI* (*kŏn'-jŭ-gāt fō'-sī*). Two points at opposite sides of a lens so situated that an object at one forms an image at the other.

FOCI is the plural of FOCUS. Though most English words form the plural by the addition of -s or -ES to the singular, and though H. W. Fowler, in Modern English Usage, says that the plural of FOCUS is FOCUSES or FOCI, practically all physics textbooks use the second, the Latin plural FOCI (pronounced *fō'-sī*). Other words which still retain their Latin plurals are TERMINI (*ter'-mĭ-nī*), the plural of TERMINUS, a boundary, end, directly from the Latin *terminus;* FUNGI (*fŭng'-gī*), the plural of FUNGUS, a mushroom; ALUMNI, the plural of ALUMNUS, and LOCI, the plural of LOCUS.

To the question: 'The object and image of a group of lenses', 286 persons out of 537, or 53 per cent, answer CONJUGATE FOCI; while 173 answer RESULTANT IMAGE. Among the 40 persons who score high in English vocabulary, 26 answer CONJUGATE FOCI, and only 11 RESULTANT IMAGE.

From the Minor Encyclopaedia comes: 'Focus, in geometry and conic sections, a point where the rays reflected from all parts of a curve concur and meet'. Airy in his Optics says: 'A

The object and image of a group of lenses.

FORM E. 37.	BO	FW	LA	NY	NY	NY	NY	PH	TU	SUM
lamina	0	2	1	0	0	2	13	4	3	25
objective	1	4	0	1	0	2	17	3	2	30
moving axes	0	1	1	0	0	2	2	4	0	10
resultant image	8	20	11	6	6	14	66	33	9	173
CONJUGATE FOCI	15	21	20	13	14	17	117	55	14	286
unmarked	4	2	0	0	0	3	3	1	0	13
total	28	50	33	20	20	40	218	100	28	537

FORM E. 37.   ENGLISH VOCABULARY

	HIGH	LOW
lamina	0	1
objective	3	5
moving axes	0	1
resultant image	11	15
CONJUGATE FOCI	26	17
unmarked	0	1
total	40	40

FOCUS is the point to which a spherical wave converges, or from which it diverges, the point at which little waves from all parts of a great wave arrive at the same time'.

CONJUGATE comes from the Latin *conjugatus*, the past participle of *conjugare*, to join together, yoke, a combination of *con-*, together, and *jugare*, to join, yoke. CONJUGATE means united in pairs, coupled. The word is used generally in physics of any two objects or points so reciprocally related that any property of the first with respect to the second is true of the second with respect to the first. CONJUGATE FOCI are two points such that rays emitted from a luminous body at either point are refracted to the other, or with a mirror are reflected to the other. Of CONJUGATE FOCI, David Brewster in his Optics of 1831 says: 'If either of them be the radiant point the other will be the focal point'.

247. *ORDINATE* (ŏr'-dĭ-nāt) *n.* The distance of a point up or down from a horizontal axis, the vertical distance up or down from a horizontal line. Reread COORDINATE (187).

To the question: 'Measurements parallel to the Y axis in a graph', 22 persons out of 61 choose ORDINATE VALUE, as the answer appeared in the earlier form A; while 15 choose ABSCISSA VALUE; and 14 X INTERCEPT. In the revised form AA, where the word VALUE is omitted after both ORDINATE and ABSCISSA, 42 persons out of 132 answer X INTERCEPT, the popular choice; 30 answer ORDINATE; 29, ABSCISSA; and 27, Y INTERCEPT. The X INTER-

Measurements parallel to the Y axis in a graph.

FORM A. 18.	BO	NY	SUM	FORM AA. 41.	NY
ORDINATE VALUE	9	13	22	ORDINATE	30
abscissa value	5	10	15	abscissa	29
x intercept	3	11	14	x intercept	42
Y intercept	2	6	8	Y intercept	27
root	0	1	1	radius vector	3
unmarked	1	0	1	unmarked	1
total	20	41	61	total	132

CEPT, choice of the majority, and so correct if one follows popular opinion as sometimes suggested in determining the modern meanings of words, is the horizontal distance along the x axis from the origin to the point at which a line or curve crosses the x axis. The X INTERCEPT is found by making Y, in the equation of a line or curve, equal to zero and solving for x. ABSCISSA is a more general term for any horizontal distance measured parallel to the x axis, from the upright, vertical, Y axis, to any point or line. By custom the Y axis is the vertical, up-and-down axis; and the ORDINATE of a point is measured up and down, parallel to the Y axis, perpendicular to the x axis in rectangular coordinates. The ORDINATE is the Y coordinate.

In rectangular coordinates the ORDINATE and the ABSCISSA of a point are at right angles, one measured up and down, the other right and left. The problem is to remember which is which, as shown by the fact that for the up-and-down distance 30 persons choose ORDINATE and 29 ABSCISSA. There is little even in the derivation of the word ORDINATE to help. It comes from the Latin *ordinatus*, well-ordered, ordained, appointed, the past participle of *ordinare*, to order, ordain. The Latin *ordinare* may have come from an original root which meant to rise, which suggests the up-and-down dimension; and to ordain may be to rule from above. However one remembers, the ORDINATE is the distance up from the horizontal.

248. *MINUEND* (*mĭn'-ū-ĕnd*) *n.* The number from which another number is to be deducted in the process of subtraction.

The word MINUEND comes from the Latin *minuendus*, to be diminished, the gerundive of *minuere*, to lessen, make smaller,

The quantity from which another quantity is to be subtracted.

FORM A. 49.	BO	NY	SUM	FORM AA. 28.	NY
prime number	2	0	2	inflection	0
MINUEND	10	21	31	MINUEND	58
ordinal	0	1	1	ordinal	6
subtrahend	6	18	24	subtrahend	64
first member	0	1	1	first member	4
unmarked	2	0	2	unmarked	0
total	20	41	61	total	132

diminish. From the same source come MINOR, smaller, and MINUTE (*mī-nūt'*), very small.

To the question: 'The quantity from which another quantity is subtracted', 58 persons out of 132 answer correctly MINUEND; but 64 answer SUBTRAHEND. The SUBTRAHEND is the number to be taken away from another in the same operation of subtraction. It comes from the Latin *sub*, under, and *trahere*, to draw, drag, the source also of the unusual ATTRAHENT and CONTRAHENT. The SUBTRAHEND is drawn away from another. The MINUEND is the number from which the SUBTRAHEND is taken.

249. *ORIGIN* (ŏr'-ĭ-jĭn) *n.* In mathematics, a fixed point from
which measurements are made, more specifically the point
of intersection of the axes in Cartesian coordinates. Reread
ORDINATE (247).

The word ORIGIN comes through the French *origine*, from
the Latin *origin*, *originem*, beginning, source, rise, from the
verb *oriri*, to arise.

To the question: 'x_1, y_1, $z_1 = 0$ in solid analytic geometry',
218 persons out of 525 answer ORIGIN; while 125 answer
EQUATION OF PLANE. In three-dimensional Cartesian coordinates,
there are three axes. The x axis runs horizontally from left to

x_1, y_1, z_1, $= 0$ in solid analytic geometry.

FORM C. 17.	CH	FORM CA. 27.	CH	LA	NY	NY	PH	SUM
equation of plane	20	equation of plane	6	10	18	67	24	125
ORIGIN	26	ORIGIN	19	15	41	123	20	218
paraboloid	7	paraboloid	5	3	14	23	5	50
hyperboloid	6	hyperboloid	1	4	8	24	6	43
sphere	7	sphere	9	3	15	33	16	76
unmarked	2	unmarked	0	2	1	7	3	13
total	68	total	40	37	97	277	74	525

FORM CB. 33.	NY
equation of plane	19
ORIGIN	31
paraboloid	6
hyperboloid	10
sphere	14
unmarked	6
total	86

right. The Y axis is still horizontal but at right angles to the
x axis, running toward the observer. The z axis extends up and
down, vertically, at right angles to the first two. The point
where these three cross is called the ORIGIN.

Any equation of the first degree in x, y, z, which may be
written: $ax + by + cz + k = 0$ is a plane. The point in space
at which $x = 0$, $y = 0$, and $z = 0$, is the ORIGIN.

250. *COTANGENT* (*kō-tăn'-jĕnt*) *n.* The base of a right-angle triangle divided by its height. Reread COSINE (120). The word COTANGENT was coined by the English mathematician Edmund Gunter about 1620; and perhaps because of this comparatively recent origin is marked correctly by only about half as many persons as know the word SINE which dates back to the Greeks. The prefix CO- at the beginning of a trigonometric function always means the function of the complement of the angle. The COSINE is the SINE of the complement of the angle, that is the SINE of 90 degrees minus the angle. The COSECANT is the SECANT of the complement of the angle, of 90 degrees minus the angle. The COTANGENT is the TANGENT of the complement of the angle, the TANGENT of 90 degrees minus the angle. The COTANGENT is also the reciprocal of the TANGENT, but this relationship is not inherent in the word COTANGENT, and is not true of the other pairs.

To the question: ' A | a Function of the angle A obtained by dividing the length of side b by the length of side a', 52 persons out of 132 answer correctly COTANGENT; while 34 answer the reciprocal TANGENT, a/b; and 32 answer COSINE.

The relation of the COTANGENT to the COSINE, the second most frequently marked mislead, is given by the equation:

$$\cot a = \frac{\cos a}{\sin a}.$$

The word TANGENT comes from the Latin *tangens, tangentis,* the present participle of *tangere,* to touch. From this Latin verb and its various parts and modifications come numerous English words. From the past participle *tactus* come TACTILE, capable of being touched, and CONTACT, touch. From the Latin *contingere,* a combination of *con* and the same *tangere,* come CONTINGENT, originally touching but often used today to mean dependent upon some other happening for its occurrence, and CONTIGUOUS, spelt without the N, but from the same original source, which means touching, in actual contact. Also without the N comes CONTAGION, communication of disease by touch. A TANGENT, in geometry, is a line which just touches a curve. The slope of this line is sometimes said to be the slope of the curve at the point of contact. TANGENT, in trigonometry, is the func-

a Function of the angle A obtained by dividing the length of side b by the length of side a.

FORM A. 21.	BO	NY	SUM	FORM AA. 40.	NY
COTANGENT	10	14	24	COTANGENT	52
tangent	5	13	18	tangent	34
cosecant	3	2	5	cosecant	12
versine	0	0	0	argument	2
cosine	1	11	12	cosine	32
unmarked	1	1	2	unmarked	0
total	20	41	61	total	132

tion which gives the slope of the line if the line is the hypotenuse of a right-angle triangle. The height of the triangle divided by the base is the TANGENT. The base divided by the height is the COTANGENT.

251. *CONIC* (*kŏn'-ĭk*) *n.* Any plane section of a right circular cone, a conic section.

The word CONIC comes from the Greek κωνικός (konikos), cone-shaped, conical, having the form of a cone; and the study of the CONICS as sections of cones goes back to the Greeks. But an Italian mathematician, Ruggieno Giuseppe Boscovich, who was born at Ragusa in Dalmatia, and lived from about 1711 to 1787, the date of his birth is uncertain, redefined the CONICS as curves traced by a moving point whose distance from a fixed point and a fixed straight line are always in the same proportion. When the distance to the fixed point and to the straight line are always equal to one another, the CONIC is a PARABOLA. When the distance to the fixed point is less than the distance to the fixed line, but always in the same proportion, the CONIC is an ELLIPSE. When the distance to the point is greater than the distance to the line, but again always in the same proportion, the CONIC is an HYPERBOLA.

To the question: 'The curve made by a moving point whose distance from a fixed point and a fixed straight line are in constant proportion', that is to Boscovich's definition, only 41 persons out of 132 answer CONIC; while 42 answer CYCLOID. By coincidence one of Boscovich's many dissertations while he was professor of mathematics at Collegium Romanum, in 1740, was on the CYCLOID. The CYCLOID is the curve traced by a point on the edge of a circle while it rolls along a fixed straight line. It is a series of arches which rest on the straight line as a base.

The CYCLOID and two of the CONIC SECTIONS, the PARABOLA and the HYPERBOLA, are more or less U-shaped. The U of the CYCLOID is upside down, resting on a horizontal line, with the line across the open end of the inverted U. If the two U-shaped

The curve made by a moving point whose distance from a fixed point and a fixed straight line are in constant proportion.

FORM A. 13.	BO	NY	SUM	FORM AA. 43.	NY
cycloid	4	13	17	cycloid	42
CONIC	12	11	23	CONIC	41
rosette	1	4	5	rosette	13
hypocycloid	2	8	10	hypocycloid	19
epicycloid	1	4	5	epicycloid	15
unmarked	0	1	1	unmarked	2
total	20	41	61	total	132

CONIC SECTIONS be placed in the same position, with their open ends down, the line on which they depend is still horizontal but above the rounded end of the inverted U, separated from it; and the bottom ends of the U do not stop at a specific point, as do the bottom ends of the CYCLOID, but continue indefinitely.

252. *BEARING* (băr'-ĭng) *n.* Originally the point of the compass at which an object is seen giving its direction from a ship, now more often the angular distance clockwise of an object from a reference point such as true north, magnetic north, or the direction an aircraft is traveling.

With a word of so many meanings as the verb to BEAR it is difficult to see how each develops. To BEAR upon one heavily means to press upon one, weigh down upon one. To BEAR down upon the enemy means to press him. To BEAR upon the point means to have weight in the discussion. BEARING on the subject then comes to mean relation to the subject. And so on shipboard BEARING means relation to the ship, position on the compass.

The word BEARING is used for the direction of one geographical point from another expressed as an angle measured

The direction of one object from another expressed as an angle measured clockwise from true north.

FORM A. 46.	FW	LA	NY	NY	NY	PH	SUM	FORM AA. 29.	NY
constant								constant	
bearing	2	7	5	6	16	20	56	bearing	5
track	0	2	3	6	10	8	29	inclination	5
BEARING	11	23	11	22	57	84	208	BEARING	33
collision									
course	1	4	2	1	9	8	25	declination	5
true heading	4	16	13	20	46	63	162	true heading	14
unmarked	0	2	3	11	2	17	35	unmarked	1
total	18	54	37	66	140	200	515	total	63

clockwise from the north. TRUE BEARING is from true north, from the true meridian, from the earth's geographic pole as distinct from the magnetic pole or magnetic north.

To the question: 'The direction of one object from another expressed as an angle measured clockwise from true north', 208 persons out of 515 answer BEARING, but 162 answer TRUE HEADING. HEADING is the direction in which the nose of an airplane is pointed as differentiated from its course or path over the ground. TRUE HEADING is the angle the plane is pointing measured clockwise from true north. HEADING refers to the direction a plane is pointing, actually to the direction in which it is heading. BEARING refers to the direction of some other object as seen from the plane.

253. *MERIDIAN* (mĕ-rĭd'-ĭ-ăn) *n.* Any circle through both poles of a revolving globe, a great circle of a sphere passing through the poles.
The word MERIDIAN comes from the Latin *meridies*, midday, the south, from *medius*, middle, plus *dies*, day. From the same

Latin *medius*, middle, and *aevum*, age, period, comes MEDIEVAL, pertaining to the middle ages. From the same *medius*, middle, come the two adjectives MEDIAL and MEDIAN, both meaning pertaining to the middle. MEDIAN is also used as a noun by statisticians to mean the middle case in a distribution. MERIDIAN seems to have been at first spelt *medidian*, with D in place of the present R. It was changed probably because of the awkwardness of the original sound.

From John Harris, 1704, Lexicon Technicum, the first and, despite its Latin title, one of the great technical dictionaries in English: 'MERIDIAN, is a great Circle paſſing through the Poles of the World, and both Zenith and Nadir, croſſeth the Equi-

Forms C and CA. A great circle in the plane of the axis of a revolving sphere.

Form CB. A great circle through the poles of a revolving sphere.

FORM C. 11.	CH	FORM CA. 36.	CH	LA	NY	NY	PH	SUM
equator	22	equator	8	11	21	97	22	159
involute	3	involute	0	3	3	21	4	31
directrix	5	spheroid	8	2	11	17	7	45
MERIDIAN	19	MERIDIAN	15	17	42	76	22	172
longitude	18	longitude	9	4	18	65	16	112
unmarked	1	unmarked	0	0	2	1	3	6
total	68	total	40	37	97	277	74	525

FORM CB. 35.	NY
equator	10
rhumb line	6
spheroid	10
MERIDIAN	38
longitude	19
unmarked	3
total	86

noctial at Right Angles, and divideth the Sphere into two equal Parts, one Eaſt, the other Weſt; and has its Poles in the Eaſt and Weſt Points of the Horizon. 'Tis called MERIDIAN, becauſe when the Sun cometh to the South Part of this Circle, 'tis then *Meridies*, Mid-day, or High-noon; and then the Sun hath his greateſt Altitude for that Day, which therefore is called the MERIDIAN ALTITUDE.

'Theſe MERIDIANS are various, and change according to the Longitudes of Places; ſo that they may be ſaid to be infinite in Number, for that all Places from Eaſt to Weſt have their ſeveral MERIDIANS: But there is (or ſhould be) one Fix'd, which is called the FIRST MERIDIAN'.

To the question: 'A great circle in the plane of the axis of a revolving sphere', 172 persons out of 525 answer correctly MERIDIAN; but 159 others answer EQUATOR. This may be a real confusion of opposites, a confusion of MERIDIAN, a circle through the poles, with the great circle at right angles to the MERIDIAN; or it may be the wording of the definition. To test this last, the definition has been changed to read: 'A great circle through the poles of a revolving sphere'. Here 38 persons out of the 86 whose scores have been tabulated, or 44 per cent, answer correctly MERIDIAN, compared with the earlier 33 per cent, and only 10 persons now mark EQUATOR; but 19 answer LONGITUDE. LONGITUDE is the angle at the pole which the MERIDIAN through a particular place makes with some standard MERIDIAN.

254. *CIRRO-CUMULUS* (*sĭr'-rō-kū'-mū-lŭs*). According to Luke Howard: 'Small, well defined, roundish masses, in close horizontal arrangement or contact'. CIRRO-CUMULUS clouds may be transparent or cast a slight shadow.

Luke Howard was an eminent meteorologist who, in an essay of 1802 On the Modifications of Clouds, proposed a system of nomenclature and classification which has since been commonly adopted.

To the question: 'Small white rounded masses of cloud at a high altitude usually in groupings known as mackerel sky', 134 persons out of a population of 515 answer correctly CIRRO-CUMULUS; but almost as many, 104, answer ALTO-CUMULUS, and 100 CIRRUS. ALTO-CUMULUS, the most frequently marked mislead, fits the definition perhaps too closely; for the ALTO-CUMULUS sky is much like the CIRRO-CUMULUS, except that the cloudlets are larger. Also ALTO-CUMULUS clouds are of medium height, 7,000 to 20,000 feet, while CIRRO-CUMULUS are high clouds. Also a CIRRO-CUMULUS sky is known popularly as

MACKEREL SKY, because it is said to resemble a mackerel's back.

Both CIRRUS, the second most frequently marked mislead, and CIRRO-CUMULUS clouds are high, 20,000 feet or more. A CIRRO-CUMULUS sky is a combination of CIRRUS and CUMULUS clouds. CIRRUS clouds are delicate white, fibrous or silky, usually without shading. The word CIRRUS, which comes from the Latin *cirrus*, a curl, tuft of hair, crest of feathers, is used in many sciences. In botany it means a tendril by which a plant may climb. In zoology the same word designates a long threadlike

Small white rounded masses of cloud at high altitude usually in groups known as mackerel sky.

FORM A. 38.	FW	LA	NY	NY	NY	PH	SUM	FORM AA. 38.	NY
cirrus	4	12	8	13	23	40	100	cirrus	18
cumulus	4	7	6	8	32	29	86	cumulus	5
CIRRO-								CIRRO-	
CUMULUS	6	15	7	13	36	57	134	CUMULUS	17
alto-cumulus	4	12	8	13	25	42	104	alto-cumulus	13
nimbo-stratus	0	6	6	10	22	20	64	nimbo-stratus	10
unmarked	0	2	2	9	2	12	27	unmarked	0
total	18	54	37	66	140	200	515	total	63

organ which projects from the shell of a sea animal and sweeps gently back and forth. Of the same word the supplement to Chambers' Cyclopaedia, 1753, says: 'CIRRUS, certain oblong and soft appendiculae hanging from the under jaw of fishes'. In meteorology CIRRUS is a form of cloud, generally at a high elevation, presenting the appearance of diverging filaments or wisps, often resembling a curl or lock of hair or wool. Of CIRRUS Luke Howard says: 'Parallel, flexuous, or diverging fibers, extensible by increase in any or in all directions'.

In his book Physiography, an Introduction to the Study of Nature, published in 1892, T. H. Huxley says: 'Delicate white fleecy clouds may often be seen floating in the upper regions of the atmosphere, where they are arranged in groups running in more or less parallel directions. Frequently a cloud of this class will present the appearance of a hair, or feather, with its fibers curled, and hence it has received the name of CIRRUS (a curl).

The CIRRUS clouds are always lofty, sometimes as much as ten miles above the surface of the earth; and, being wafted along by currents in the upper regions of the atmosphere, they may often be seen to move in a direction opposite to that of the wind which happens to be blowing over the surface. It is these clouds that are supposed to be made up of minute ice particles, since they produce, when they come between us and the sun or moon, those colored circles which are known as HALOS'.

The CIRRO-CUMULUS sky, called MACKEREL SKY, is a beautiful CIRRUS sky but with numerous detached flakes, globular masses, and rolls.

255. *STEFAN-BOLTZMANN LAW* (*stĕf′-ăn-bŏltz′-măn*).

The total emissive power of a black body is proportional to the fourth power of its absolute temperature.

To the question: 'The law that the rate at which heat is radiated from one black body to another is proportional to the difference of the fourth powers of the absolute temperatures of the bodies', 659 persons out of 2134 answer STEFAN-BOLTZMANN LAW; while 440 answer DULONG AND PETIT LAW. Pierre Louis Dulong, 1785

Law that the rate at which heat is radiated from one black body to another is proportional to the difference of the fourth powers of the absolute temperatures of the bodies.

FORM CA. 29.	NY	NY	SUM
Dulong & Petit's law	49	391	440
STEFAN-BOLTZMANN'S LAW	78	581	659
Steinmetz's law	50	383	433
Newton's law	20	233	253
Brewster's law	33	312	345
unmarked	4	0	4
total	234	1900	2134

to 1838, a French chemist and physicist, worked with Alexis Thérèse Petit, 1791 to 1820, on the measurement of temperatures and the transference of heat. They discovered the empirical relation that the product of the specific heats of the elements and their atomic weights is approximately constant, 6.4. The law of Dulong and Petit usually states that the specific heats of metals are inversely proportional to their atomic weights, for the law did not hold for the lighter elements.

Stefan's law was originally an empirical expression of doubtful significance. Tyndall had found that the radiation from white hot platinum at what he estimated as 1200 degrees centigrade was 11.7 times its radiation when dull red at 525 degrees. In 1879 the Austrian physicist Josef Stefan noticed that this ratio is nearly the ratio of the fourth powers of the absolute temperatures. The assumption that radiation varies as the fourth power also fitted the experiments of Dulong and Petit, of many years earlier.

Five years later, 1884, Ludwig Boltzmann of Vienna, who lived from 1844 to 1906, using radiation as the working substance in a Carnot cycle, showed that the energy of radiation from a black body should be proportional to the fourth power of the absolute temperature.

256. *DIFFRACTION* (dĭf-frăk'-shŏn) *n.* The bending of a light wave or sound wave in passing near an obstacle or through a slit or opening.

To the question: 'The bending of waves around an obstacle', 623 out of 2134 answer correctly DIFFRACTION; while 603 answer REFRACTION. In the earlier study of form c, based on 400 persons, DIFFRACTION was marked by 114, and REFRACTION by 132. In still another study DIFFRACTION was marked by 30 per cent, and REFRACTION by 48 per cent. Both DIFFRACTION and REFRACTION come from the Latin verb *frangere*, to break, or more accurately from the past participle *fractus*, broken. The word REFRACTION starts with the Latin *re-*, back; DIFFRACTION, with *dis-*, apart; but these derivations help little in separating the technical meanings of these two words.

REFRACTION is the opposite of REFLECTION, perhaps the easiest contrast to remember among these three confusing words. There are REFLECTING and REFRACTING telescopes; REFLECTING and REFRACTING lenses. REFLECT means turn back. A REFLECTING lens stops light and turns it back as from a mirror, while it goes on through a REFRACTING lens. REFRACTION occurs when light goes from one medium into another, and depends upon a different velocity of light in the new medium. A wave front, entering glass at an angle, slows down at the edge which first enters. This causes the ray to turn. This turning is called RE-FRACTION.

DIFFRACTION is also a turning, but due to a different cause. A tiny hole, through which a ray of light has passed, acts as a source of light and on leaving such a hole light travels not straight ahead but spreads in all directions. If the hole is large this spreading is noticeable only at the edges.

From A Treatise on Optics by Sir David Brewster, first published in America in 1833 after having appeared a year earlier in England, comes: 'Having thus described the changes which light experiences when refracted by the surfaces of transparent

The bending of waves around an obstacle.

FORM CA. 38.	NY	NY	SUM
refraction	521	82	603
attenuation	307	26	333
reflection	263	21	284
DIFFRACTION	540	83	623
dissonance	269	17	286
unmarked	0	5	5
total	1900	234	2134

bodies, and the properties which it exhibits when thus decomposed into its elements, we shall now proceed to consider the phenomena which it presents when passing near the edges of bodies. This branch of optics is called the INFLEXION or the DIFFRACTION of light.

'This curious property of light was first described by Grimaldi in 1665, and afterwards by Newton; but it is to the late M. Fresnel that we are indebted for a most successful and able investigation of the phenomena'.

From the Encyclopaedic Dictionary comes: 'DIFFRACTION, that particular modification which light undergoes when it passes by the edge of an opaque body by being deflected from its direct course'. Dr. Thomas Young writing in 1807 says: 'Of the light which passes by a dense substance of any kind, the greatest part pursues its course undisturbed, but there is always a certain divergence, which has been called by Grimaldi DIF-

FRACTION, and by Newton INFLECTION'. The word DIFFRACTION should be limited today to Grimaldi's original intention; but a number of writers including no less an authority than the great Oxford New English Dictionary use or define DIFFRACTION as the breaking up of a beam of light into a series of colored spectra due to interference of the rays when deflected from their straight course at the edge of an opaque body or through a narrow aperture or slit. DIFFRACTION alone does not break up white light into its colors. This necessitates a combination of DIFFRACTION and INTERFERENCE. A single slot in a DIFFRACTION GRATING (148) diffracts light but does not break up white light into its spectrum. Only when two or more slots each become a source of illumination does INTERFERENCE (215) cause the spectrum. DIFFRACTION should be restricted to the bending of a ray from its straight course at the edge of an opaque body.

257. *COUPLE* (*cŭp'-l*) *n.* A system of two parallel forces act-
ing at different points and oppositely directed which tend to make a body rotate; a pair of two equal antiparallel forces; from Alfred Daniell comes: 'The Standard Definition of a COUPLE is—two equal and parallel forces opposed in direction, but not in the same straight line'. Reread TORQUE (241).

The word COUPLE, identical in spelling with the French *couple*, goes back to the Latin *copula*, a bond, link, a contrac-tion of *co-*, together, and *apere*, to join. A COUPLE are two per-sons joined together. The word was first used technically, to mean two opposite forces not in the same straight line, by the French mathematician Louis Poinsot (*pwang-sō'*) in 1804.

To the question: 'A pair of equal, parallel, and opposite, but not collinear forces', 200 persons out of 537 answer COUPLE; 124, CONCURRENT; and 104, EQUILIBRANT, in suggestion an op-posite of the correct meaning. An EQUILIBRANT is a single force which acting against others produces equilibrium. No single force of any kind acting in any direction balances a couple. Of this the French physicist Adolphe Ganot says: 'Two equal parallel forces acting towards contrary parts possess the re-markable property that they are incapable of being balanced by any single force whatsoever'. In explanation Daniell says: 'Two forces always have a resultant and may be balanced by a third except in one case, viz. that in which the two forces are equal and opposed in their direction, but not opposed in the same straight line'.

There are two schools of thought in dictionary building. One believes in trying to hold the meanings of words. The other follows usage. In the small group of 40 persons high in English vocabulary 31 mark COUPLE in answer to the definition.

A pair of equal, parallel, and opposite, but not collinear forces.

FORM E. 31.	BO	FW	LA	NY	NY	NY	NY	PH	TU	SUM
COUPLE	7	19	14	8	13	6	73	44	16	200
resultant	0	2	1	2	0	8	19	6	3	41
concurrent	5	11	7	5	3	15	56	20	2	124
equilibrant	6	7	8	2	1	9	42	24	5	104
parallelogram	7	11	3	3	3	1	25	6	2	61
unmarked	3	0	0	0	0	1	3	0	0	7
total	28	50	33	20	20	40	218	100	28	537

FORM E. 31.   ENGLISH VOCABULARY

	HIGH	LOW
COUPLE	31	6
resultant	0	4
concurrent	4	14
equilibrant	5	7
parallelogram	0	9
unmarked	0	0
total	40	40

In the group of 40 low in English vocabulary 14 mark CON-CURRENT; 9, PARALLELOGRAM; 7, EQUILIBRANT; and only 6 COUPLE. Were the usage of this group to be followed, or even were it to color general usage, the nice, clear-cut, technical meaning of COUPLE would soon be lost.

258. *GRAVITATION* (gră-vĭ-tā'-shŏn) *n*. The attraction of every particle of matter for every other particle.

The word GRAVITATION, and the corresponding verb to GRAVI-TATE, go back to the Latin *gravitas, gravitatis*, heaviness, weight, pressure, gravity. This comes in turn from the adjective *gravis,* heavy, weighty, also important, serious, the source of the English adjective GRAVE, serious. This Latin *gravis* parallels etymologically the Greek βαρύς (barus), heavy, the source of the technical noun BAROMETER.

By his law of universal GRAVITATION Sir Isaac Newton, in a brilliant generalization, unified the work of Copernicus, Galileo, and Kepler: Every particle of matter in the universe attracts

The attraction of one stone for another, not in contact.

FORM C. 13. NY		FORM CA. 23. BO		NY	NY	NY	NY	SUM
magnetism	133	magnetism	22	79	139	287	97	624
adhesion	28	adhesion	3	9	21	171	8	212
		mutual						
weight	1	inductance	17	35	68	216	22	358
cohesion	42	cohesion	5	14	32	180	20	251
GRAVITATION	193	GRAVITATION	53	263	140	246	87	789
unmarked	3	unmarked	0	0	0	0	0	0
total	400	total	100	400	400	1100	234	2234

every other particle with a force which varies directly as the product of their masses and inversely as the square of the distance between.

To the question: 'The attraction of one stone for another, not in contact', 35 per cent of 2234 persons answer GRAVITATION; and 28 per cent answer MAGNETISM. In the earlier analysis of form C, based on 400 persons, 193 answered GRAVITATION, and 133 MAGNETISM. The two ideas have not always been differentiated. From 1645 comes the quotation: 'If the opinion be true, that GRAVITATION is from the MAGNETISM of the earth, then, the more remote from the earth the less is the gravity'.

The word MAGNETISM, by its derivation, calls attention to a particular material, for it goes back to the Greek μάγνης (magnes), an adjective from the proper name Μαγνησία (Magnesia), a district in Thessaly where magnetic iron ore was first discovered. On the other hand, a MAGNET in Latin was often called *magnes lapis*, magnetic stone, and in Greek μάγνης λίθος (magnes lithos), stone of Magnesia. It may be this association of STONE with magnet, and the word STONE in the question, which leads to marking MAGNETISM, rather than GRAVITATION.

From the ninth edition of the Encyclopaedia Britannica, an article on GRAVITATION by Robert Staywell Ball, Royal Astronomer of Ireland: 'The familiar instance of the action of a magnet upon a piece of iron will suffice to illustrate what is meant by the word ATTRACTION. In virtue of certain properties possessed by the iron and the magnet, they are drawn together. The magnet draws the iron, and the iron draws the magnet. This particular kind of attraction is of a very special character. Thus the magnet appears to have no appreciable influence on a piece of wood or a sheet of paper, and has indeed no considerable influence on any known substance except iron.

'By the attraction of gravitation every body attracts every other body whatever be the materials of which each is composed. In this we see a wide difference between the attraction of GRAVITATION and that form of attraction which is known as MAGNETIC ATTRACTION. Nor is the contrast between the intensities of these two different attractions less striking. MAGNETIC attraction is enormously greater than GRAVITATIVE attraction; in fact, under ordinary circumstances as to intensity and dimensions, the intensity of the attraction of GRAVITATION will not be nearly so much as a millionth part of the magnetic attraction'.

259. *DELTA X* (*dĕl'-tah ĕks*). An addition to x, an increment, a small amount added to x.

Knowing the relation between two quantities, such as x and y, it is possible to obtain the relation between an addition to x and an addition to Y. If: $y = x^2$, then:

$$y + \text{delta } y = (x + \text{delta } x)^2 \qquad \text{or:}$$
$$y + \text{delta } y = x^2 + 2x \text{ delta } x + \text{delta } x^2.$$

Subtracting from this the original equation gives:

$$\text{delta } y = 2x \text{ delta } x + \text{delta } x^2.$$

Dividing by delta x gives:

$$\frac{\text{delta } y}{\text{delta } x} = 2x + \text{delta } x.$$

This ratio of two increments, an addition to a dependent variable divided by an addition to the independent variable, is the fundamental concept of calculus.

To the question: 'Delta x', 162 persons out of 525 answer correctly ABSCISSA DIFFERENCE; but 126 answer DERIVATIVE, and 100 DIFFERENTIATION. DELTA X is an increment added to x, a small but real addition to x. Both DELTA X and DELTA Y are finite quantities, and DELTA Y/DELTA X is a real fraction. As DELTA X approaches zero as a limit this fraction becomes the DERIVATIVE (203), the most frequently marked mislead for DELTA X; and the

Forms c and ca. Delta x.
Form cb. A small finite amount added to a quantity.

FORM C. 7.	CH	FORM CA. 40.	CH	LA	NY	NY	PH	SUM
derivative	16	derivative	6	13	17	74	16	126
slope	5	slope	5	3	8	38	6	60
integral	9	integral	5	5	16	24	5	55
differentiation	17	differentiation	10	6	20	47	17	100
ABSCISSA		ABSCISSA						
DIFFERENCE	19	DIFFERENCE	13	9	33	80	27	162
unmarked	2	unmarked	1	1	3	14	3	22
total	68	total	40	37	97	277	74	525

FORM CB. 39.	NY
derivative	10
slope	8
integral	26
differentiation	16
DELTA X	24
unmarked	2
total	86

process of finding the DERIVATIVE is called DIFFERENTIATION (220), the second most frequently marked mislead. Both of these words ought, it would seem, to be more difficult than DELTA X, which is nothing but a small finite addition, an increment. But in form CA of the mathematics vocabulary test, DELTA X is defined as ABSCISSA DIFFERENCE; and ABSCISSA is word 260, the next word in this book. Some examinees may know DELTA X, but not know ABSCISSA. To examine this the question is changed in the revised form CB: 'A small finite amount added to a quantity'; and of the 86 cases tabulated thus far only 27 per cent mark DELTA X instead of the 31 per cent in the previous form. INTEGRAL has become the popular mislead, marked more often than the correct answer. Although as a concept a small addition should be easy, the notation Δx is comparatively recent for it did not appear clearly until about 1800.

260. *ABSCISSA* (*ăbs-sĭs'-sah*) *n*. In mathematics, the distance measured horizontally from the origin to any point to be placed in rectangular coordinates. The plural is ABSCISSAE (*ăbs-sĭs'-sē*). Reread ORDINATE (247).

Literally an ABSCISSA is a distance cut off, or a line cut off; and the word has often been used in this way in the past. It comes from the Latin *abscissa*, cut off, the past participle of *abscindere*, to cut off, the source of ABSCIND, a word which appeared in Bailey's Dictionary, 1731: 'ABSCIND, to cut off'. The Latin *abscindere* is a combination of *ab*, off, away, and *scindere*, to tear, rend.

There are two Latin words *scindere* and *cindere*, so much alike that it seems hardly worth the struggle to keep them separate. On the other hand a CAT and a BAT are not the same despite the fact that the two words differ in only a single letter. The Latin *scindere* meant to tear, rip, rend, divide, cut, perhaps correctly with the idea of tearing, ripping, rather than cutting. The Latin *cindere* meant to cut. From *cindere*, to cut, comes INCISION, a cutting into. In the 16th and 17th centuries INCISION was sometimes spelt with an s, *inscision*, as if it had come from *scindere;* and SCISSORS still starts with an s because of a 16th-century mistake which has survived. But ABSCISSA really comes from *scindere*, and means part of a line cut off in almost any way.

To the question: 'Distance measured parallel to the x axis', 100 persons out of 357 answer ABSCISSA VALUE; 76 answer ORDINATE VALUE; 69, X INTERCEPT; and 63, Y INTERCEPT. The confusion of ABSCISSA and ORDINATE has already been found with ORDINATE (247). The verb to INTERCEPT, as: 'To INTERCEPT a person', is to interrupt his passage, bring to a stop. In geometry, the word INTERCEPT is used as a noun to mean that part of a line between any two points where it is intersected by other lines. The Century Dictionary says specifically: 'INTERCEPTED axis,

in geometry, the ABSCISSA'. X INTERCEPT can probably be justified as a correct answer if one accepts this dictionary definition;
but to differentiate the two terms, X INTERCEPT should be used
for the distance measured along the x axis to the point at which
a line or a curve crosses the axis. ABSCISSA should be the distance measured horizontally, parallel to the x axis, to any point
which it is desired to place in space.

The Y INTERCEPT is the vertical distance, and the term AB-
SCISSA is used most frequently today for the horizontal distance,

Distance measured parallel to the x axis.

FORM B. 45.	NY	MISC.	SUM
ABSCISSA VALUE	16	84	100
x intercept	10	59	69
y intercept	9	54	63
ordinate value	8	68	76
root	1	6	7
unmarked	4	38	42
total	48	309	357

though it has often been used in the past for any part of a line
cut off.

Two distances are required to place a point in rectangular
coordinates, a horizontal and a vertical distance, or a distance
parallel to the x axis, and another distance parallel to the y axis.
The vertical or up-and-down distance is ordinarily called the
ORDINATE, and the horizontal, right and left, the ABSCISSA.

261. *ANOXEMIA* (ăn-ŏks-ē'-mĭ-ah) *n*. Lack of oxygen in the
blood.

The term ANOXEMIA starts with the Greek privative ἀ (a),
not, which is written ἀν (an-), before a vowel. This Greek
privative ἀ (a) appears clearly in ASYMPTOTE (238), not falling
together, and in AMORPHOUS (217), without form. Ox-, the
second syllable of ANOXEMIA, stands for OXYGEN; and the end of
the word comes from the Greek αἷμα (haima), blood. The more
familiar ANEMIA is a combination of the same Greek privative
ἀν (an-), not, and the same αἷμα (haima), blood. ANEMIA is a
deficiency of blood in the body. ANOXEMIA by translating the

Greek literally is not enough oxygen in the blood. The Greek letters αι (ai) usually became *ae* in Latin and may still be written AE in English; so that two spellings ANOXEMIA and ANOXAEMIA are both found.

To the question: 'Lack of oxygen in the blood', 164 persons out of 515 answer correctly ANOXEMIA, but 171 answer BLACK-ING-OUT. A BLACKOUT is a temporary dulling or complete loss of the senses experienced by pilots in tight turns or quick pull-

Lack of oxygen in the blood.

FORM A. 10.	FW	LA	NY	NY	NY	PH	SUM	FORM AA. 36.	NY
bends	4	4	6	12	17	30	73	bends	7
blacking-out	2	15	21	18	58	57	171	blacking-out	22
nausea	0	0	1	1	6	3	11	anemia	3
aeroembolism	4	13	6	16	19	34	92	aeroembolism	9
ANOXEMIA	8	22	3	18	40	73	164	ANOXEMIA	22
unmarked	0	0	0	1	0	3	4	unmarked	0
total	18	54	37	66	140	200	515	total	63

ups. Sight is sometimes lost momentarily in making a fast short turn in an air race. Centrifugal force due to the sudden change of direction checks the flow of blood to the head. ANOXEMIA is lack of oxygen in the blood.

262. *ACHROMATIC* (ăk-rō-măt'-ĭk) *adj.* Having the same focal length for all wave lengths of light, free from color, not showing color in the decomposition of light, destitute of color, free from coloration, transmitting light without decomposing it, sensibly free from chromatic aberration.

ACHROMATIC comes from the Greek ἀχρώματος (achromatos), colorless, without color, a combination of the Greek privative ἀ (a), not, just met in ANOXEMIA (261), and χρῶμα (chroma), χρῶματις (chromatis), color, complexion. From this come numerous technical terms, as: CHROMIUM, the metal, a chemical element, so named because of the beautiful colors of its compounds; CHROMATIN, the winding thread in the germ cell which can be easily stained and so studied under the microscope, and which breaks up into the CHROMOSOMES; and CHROMOSPHERE, the rose-colored layer around the sun.

To the question: 'Refracting light without decomposing it', 30 per cent of 2234 persons answer ACHROMATIC; but 24 per cent answer PRISMATIC. In the earlier study, based on 400 persons, 117 answered ACHROMATIC, and 122 PRISMATIC. PRISMATIC

Refracting light without decomposing it.

FORM C. 34. NY		FORM CA. 35. BO		NY HIGH	NY NEXT	NY REST	NY MISC.	SUM
prismatic	122	prismatic	23	61	108	272	73	537
ACHROMATIC	117	ACHROMATIC	38	224	111	231	71	675
plano-convex	71	plano-convex	12	31	49	181	27	300
astigmatic	33	astigmatic	7	39	38	184	16	284
aplanatic	37	concave-convex	18	45	94	232	46	435
unmarked	20	unmarked	2	0	0	0	1	3
total	400	total	100	400	400	1100	234	2234

may mean having the shape of a prism; but it also means varied in color, separated into its colors as if by a prism. In this sense it is an exact opposite of ACHROMATIC which means not separated into its colors.

As far back as 1756 Matthew Maty, an English-Dutch medical writer, spoke of: 'A very good ACHROMATIC telescope'. Brewster in his Optics of 1831 says: 'They will refract white light to a single focus free of color. Such a lens is called ACHROMATIC'. Parkinson in his Optics of 1859 says: 'A combination of prisms or lenses is said to be ACHROMATIC when the dispersion of the pencils of light refracted through them is reduced within the narrowest possible limits'.

263. BURBLE (ber'-bl) n. The breakdown of the streamline flow about an airfoil, specifically a breakdown over the upper surface of an airfoil which results in a loss of lift and increase of drag.

This use of the noun BURBLE as applied to an air stream is the resurrection of a word which in 1889 the Century Dictionary called obsolete. A BURBLE is a bubble, and the verb to BURBLE meant to bubble. Both BURBLE and BUBBLE are imitative; and BURBLE is called a variation of BUBBLE.

To the question: 'Breakdown of the streamline flow about a body', 169 persons answer BURBLE, while 169 others answer EDDY. An EDDY is a more or less well developed whirling, a circulatory fluid flow. EDDY and BURBLE may be too close in meaning to be fair in the same item. They are often defined in much the same terms, and the same number of examinees mark the two.

Form A. Breakdown of the streamline flow about a body.
Form AA. Irregular breakdown of the streamline flow about a moving body.

FORM A. 17.	FW	LA	NY	NY	NY	PH	SUM	FORM AA. 35.	NY
flutter	3	6	7	8	25	32	81	flutter	10
eddy	4	19	15	25	46	60	169	eddy	5
stall	2	6	4	8	19	23	62	stall	3
feather	0	2	2	1	9	14	28	turbulence	37
BURBLE	9	21	8	22	41	68	169	BURBLE	7
unmarked	0	0	1	2	0	3	6	unmarked	1
total	18	54	37	66	140	200	515	total	63

But when differentiated an EDDY is any whirl or vortex, and may be caused by air moving past a stationary obstacle. A BURBLE is specifically the breakdown of the streamline flow above a moving body. The confusion occurs when the term EDDY is correctly used for a well-developed vortex caused by such a moving body.

Before removing EDDY as a mislead a study should be made of examinees who score high in the test as a whole to see if they differentiate BURBLE and EDDY. But the accuracy of such a study depends upon the accuracy of selecting those who do well. The more accurate the test the more accurate is this selection. Such a study is therefore one of the last steps in the improvement of a test and is misleading if made too early. In the revised form AA both EDDY and BURBLE are retained, the definition changed with the hope of making BURBLE more clearly the correct choice for those who know the distinction, and a third word, TURBULENCE, of much the same sort, added to force those who know the distinction to consider before marking. Instead of having this effect, TURBULENCE has attracted 37 of the 63 persons whose scores have been tabulated and left only 7 marking BURBLE. TURBULENCE comes from the Latin *turbulentus*, restless, stormy, from the verb *turbare*, to trouble, agitate. This in turn comes from the noun *turba*, mass, throng, crowd, disturbance. The ending -ULENT of the corresponding adjective, from the Latin *-ulentus*, suggests full of, abounding in, as FRAUDULENT, OPULENT, and TURBULENT. TURBULENCE is the irregular motion caused when air moves over an uneven surface, usually over stationary obstacles on the earth's surface. BURBLE is caused by a body moving through the air.

264. *CARNOT ENGINE* (*kahr-nō' ĕn'-jĭn*). The ideal engine, the most efficient theoretical machine.

N. L. Sadi Carnot, who lived from 1796 to 1832, was the second son of Napoleon's celebrated minister of war. Carnot pub-

Theoretically most efficient machine.

FORM E. 49.	BO	FW	LA	NY	NY	NY	NY	PH	TU	SUM
Diesel	10	14	5	6	3	16	64	21	7	146
CARNOT	6	10	19	6	12	6	65	47	13	184
steam	1	14	6	2	3	2	27	8	3	66
Compton	1	1	0	0	1	2	9	6	2	22
reciprocating	7	11	3	6	1	12	49	17	3	109
unmarked	3	0	0	0	0	2	4	1	0	10
total	28	50	33	20	20	40	218	100	28	537

FORM E. 49.	ENGLISH VOCABULARY	
	HIGH	LOW
Diesel	8	18
CARNOT	25	4
steam	4	5
Compton	1	0
reciprocating	2	13
unmarked	0	0
total	40	40

lished his *Réflexions sur la Puissance Motrice du Feu* in Paris in 1824 when he was twenty-eight years of age, having done much of the underlying thinking at the height of his inductive reasoning, between the ages of twenty-one and twenty-three.

Peter Guthrie Tait, the Scottish mathematician, who was professor of natural philosophy in Edinburgh University from 1860 to 1901, says: 'The conservation of energy, alone, gives us an altogether inadequate basis for reasoning on the work of a heat-engine. It enables us to calculate how much work is equivalent to an assigned amount of heat, and *vice versa*, provided the transformation can be effected; but it tells us nothing with respect to the percentage of either which can, under given circumstances, be converted into the other. For this purpose we require a special case of the law of transformation of energy. This was first given in Carnot's extraordinary work.

'The chief novelties of Carnot's work are the introduction of the idea of a cycle of operations, and the invaluable discovery of the special property of a reversible cycle. It is not too much to say that, without these wonderful novelties, thermodynamics as a theoretical science could not have been developed'.

To the question: 'Theoretically most efficient machine', 184 persons out of 537 answer CARNOT; 146, DIESEL; and 109, RE-CIPROCATING. But in the small group low in English vocabulary DIESEL is the popular answer, chosen by 18 out of 40 persons, RECIPROCATING second in popularity, chosen by 13 of the 40; while CARNOT, the correct answer, is fourth in popularity. The relative efficiencies of five practical types were once:

locomotive engines	about 10%
triple-expansion marine engines	about 20%
steam turbines	about 25%
automobile engines	about 25%
Diesel engines	about 35%.

This efficiency is the total heat given off by the fuel consumed divided into the amount of heat turned into mechanical work. Among practical engines the Diesel is one of the most efficient. The Diesel is an internal combustion engine in which air is drawn into the cylinder and compressed to very high pressure, almost adiabatically, for it is done quickly. A fine spray of oil is then spurted into the hot air and ignites from the heat, burning relatively slowly without exploding.

The CARNOT is a theoretical engine. No other can be more efficient, for according to CARNOT its reversibility makes this type of heat-engine the most efficient conceivable. Carnot imagined a one-cylinder engine with perfectly non-conducting walls and piston, and a base which could be altered at will from a perfect conductor to a perfect non-conductor. He further imagined two large reservoirs of heat, one at a higher temperature than the other, large enough so that their temperatures would remain constant. The cylinder was filled with a perfect gas. Starting with this gas under compression it pushes the piston, thereby doing external work. The temperature does not fall because the cylinder is equipped with a perfectly conducting base and heat is supplied by the high temperature reservoir. This quarter of the operation is isothermal, at constant temperature.

At this point the connection with the reservoir which has supplied heat is cut off; as the gas continues to expand it cools since no heat is supplied from the outside. This quarter of the operation is adiabatic, that is, without gain or loss of heat from the outside.

The cylinder is now connected with the low temperature reservoir; and the piston on its return stroke compresses the gas which causes heat which escapes to the low temperature reservoir.

In the fourth and final step the piston continues to compress the gas but the connection with the low temperature reservoir is cut off. This means that the compression of the gas raises its temperature. This continues adiabatically, without loss or gain of heat to or from the outside, until the temperature of the gas in the cylinder is the same as that of the high temperature reservoir.

265. *STOKES' LAW* (*stōks law*). The force which resists the motion of a small sphere through a viscous fluid is proportional to the radius of the sphere, to its speed, and to the coefficient of viscosity of the liquid.

A falling ball in a viscous fluid accelerates at first and then reaches a steady velocity. This limiting velocity is inversely proportional to the coefficient of viscosity of the liquid. Letting

F represent the force which resists the motion of the descending sphere:

$$F = 6\pi\eta\,rv$$

v = velocity of a small sphere,
r = radius of the sphere, and
η = coefficient of viscosity of the liquid.

STOKES' LAW is named for Sir George Gabriel Stokes, a British physicist who lived from 1819 to 1903, a contemporary of Clerk Maxwell and Lord Kelvin, all of whom worked at Cambridge, England, in the middle of the 19th century.

To the question: 'Law connecting the size of a spherical particle and its rate of fall', 181 persons out of 537 answer correctly STOKES' LAW, while 143 others answer MOSELEY'S LAW.

Law connecting the size of a spherical particle and its rate of fall.

FORM E. 46.	BO	FW	LA	NY	NY	NY	NY	PH	TU	SUM
Moseley's law	8	18	5	4	3	5	62	26	12	143
Huygens' principle	1	10	8	4	1	6	31	18	3	82
STOKES' LAW	8	14	11	7	11	12	74	36	8	181
Nicol's principle	1	4	6	2	2	4	19	12	3	53
Koenig's principle	7	3	2	3	3	8	26	7	1	60
unmarked	3	1	1	0	0	5	6	1	1	18
total	28	50	33	20	20	40	218	100	28	537

FORM E. 46.	ENGLISH VOCABULARY	
	HIGH	LOW
Moseley's law	8	12
Huygens' principle	5	6
STOKES' LAW	23	8
Nicol's principle	2	8
Koenig's principle	1	5
unmarked	1	1
total	40	40

In 1913 H. G. J. Moseley found a relationship between the X-ray spectra of the chemical elements and their positions in the Mendeléjeff periodic table. The square roots of the frequencies of the X-ray spectrum lines have a straight line relation to the atomic numbers. Plotting the atomic number of a chemical element horizontally across the bottom of a graph and the square root of the frequency of one of its X-ray spectrum lines up and down as ordinate gives practically a straight line relationship.

In nearly every item of these vocabulary tests the most frequently marked mislead is in some way closely associated with the correct answer. But in this instance there seems little connection between MOSELEY'S LAW, which applies to X-ray spectra, and STOKES' LAW, which applies to the viscosity of a fluid, until one realizes that there are two Stokes' laws, one relating to the fall of a sphere in a viscous fluid and the other dealing with X rays. In 1897 Stokes worked on the ether pulse theory of X rays. According to his law in this field, the exciting primary radiation must be of shorter wave length than the wave length of the fluorescent radiation which it excites.

Stokes' other law is used in drawing conclusions from the rate of settling of the famous Wilson cloud caused by the condensation of water vapor on individual ions, where each drop of water condensed on an ion is a falling sphere.

266. *SYNCHRONOUS MOTOR* (sĭn'-krō-nŭs). A constant-speed motor with which the power factor can be varied over a wide range by changing the field excitation.

A SYNCHRONOUS MOTOR turns at one speed only, directly proportional to the frequency of the alternating current, a pole on the rotor passing a conductor on the stator every half cycle of the alternating current which operates the motor. With increased load the motor holds its speed or stops completely; it cannot operate at any other speed. A SYNCHRONOUS MOTOR must start under direct current until it reaches synchronous speed.

SYNCHRONOUS comes through the Latin *synchronus*, from the Greek σύνχρονος (synchronos), occurring at the same time. This starts with the Greek σύν (syn), with, together, already met as the second syllable of ASYMPTOTE (238). The second part of SYNCHRONOUS comes from χρόνος (chronos), time. From χρόνος (chronos), time, come such literary words as CHRONICLE, an account of events in order of time, and CHRONIC, lasting a long time, as well as more technical terms such as CHRONOM-ETER, an instrument for measuring time, CHRONOGRAPH, a recorder of time. A SYNCHRONOUS MOTOR is one in which a pole approaches a conductor at the same time as a wave of the current.

To the question: 'A constant-speed, adjustable power-factor motor', 32 per cent of students answer correctly SYNCHRONOUS; but 25 per cent answer POLYPHASE, and 24 per cent answer INDUCTION. An INDUCTION MOTOR is one in which the rotor cur-

A constant-speed, adjustable power-factor motor.

FORM AB. 17.	%	FORM D. 14.	NY	%
multipolar	13	multipolar	52	14.9
squirrel-cage	6	squirrel-cage	28	8.0
induction	6	induction	40	11.4
SYNCHRONOUS	70	SYNCHRONOUS	153	43.7
polyphase	4	polyphase	63	18.0
unmarked	1	unmarked	14	4.0
total	100	total	350	100.0

FORM DA. 26.	%	FORM DB. 34.	NY
multipolar	13	multipolar	9
squirrel-cage	4	universal	24
induction	24	induction	15
SYNCHRONOUS	32	SYNCHRONOUS	39
polyphase	25	polyphase	18
unmarked	2	unmarked	1
total	100	total	106

rent is introduced into the rotor windings by electromagnetic induction instead of by brushes. The POLYPHASE INDUCTION MOTOR, the commonest type of motor used, is fundamentally a constant-speed motor but slows slightly under heavy load, and as it slows gains power.

A POLYPHASE INDUCTION MOTOR operates with a current which always lags behind the voltage; the power-factor is not adjustable. With a weak field a SYNCHRONOUS MOTOR takes a lagging current. With a stronger field, called NORMAL EXCITA-TION, current and voltage are in phase and the power-factor unity. With still stronger field excitation the current leads the voltage and the power-factor is again less than one.

267. *REAL IMAGE* (rēl ĭm′-āj). Image formed where light rays actually cross after passing through a converging lens, or where they cross when reflected back from a concave mirror.

With a single lens the REAL IMAGE is always upside down. It is formed at the point where rays meet in fact and can be caught on a screen, at the point where sufficiently powerful rays, as from the sun, burn paper. It is the point of convergence of light rays, the point where a photographic plate would receive an impression. This may lead 64 persons out of 537 to mark PHOTOGRAPHIC image in answer to the definition: 'Image formed where a bundle of rays of light converge and cross', instead of REAL IMAGE, the correct answer given by 206 out of 537.

The popular mislead is VIRTUAL, answered by 159 out of 537; and chosen more often than REAL by the small group of 40 persons low in English vocabulary. The confusion of opposites is the final step in the learning process.

The word VIRTUAL comes from the Latin *virtus*, strength, courage, bravery, worth, physical and intellectual excellence, the qualities of a man, from the Latin *vir*, man. The adjective VIRTUAL originally meant effective, capable, with none of the current implication of the word that a thing need not be real to be effective. This first appeared in 1664, in Jeremy Taylor's Dissuasive from Popery: 'But even this attention is not necessary that it should be actual, but it suffices to be VIRTUAL'. Much more recently Worcester says of the adjective VIRTUAL in its literary sense: 'Being in effect though not in fact'.

Ephraim Chambers, in his Cyclopaedia of 1728, writes: 'Lens, in dioptrics, properly fignifies any fmall, roundifh glafs, of the figure of a lentil; but is extended to any optic glafs, not very thick, which either collects the rays of light into a point, in their paffage through it, or difperfes them further apart'. The REAL IMAGE is formed at the point where converging rays actually collect. The VIRTUAL image is the point from which diverging rays seem to come. As far back as 1704 John Harris, in his Lexicon Technicum, said: 'VIRTUAL focus, or point of divergence in a concave glass'. A quarter of a century later Ephraim Chambers said: 'Lenses, concave, the rays will diverge from the axis; and the point of divergence, or dispersion, called the VIRTUAL focus'. A century later, George Crabb wrote in his Technological Dictionary: 'VIRTUAL focus, a point in the axis of a glass where the continuation of a refracted ray meets it'.

At the same time, 1831, Sir David Brewster in his Treatise on Optics said: 'In convex mirrors the image is always a VIRTUAL one formed behind the mirror'; also: 'The point behind

Image formed where a bundle of rays of light converge and cross.

FORM E. 21.	BO	FW	LA	NY	NY	NY	NY	PH	TU	SUM
chromatic	6	9	5	2	0	7	20	11	1	61
virtual	7	11	13	7	5	11	61	38	6	159
mirror	5	3	1	2	2	2	20	6	2	43
REAL	6	18	10	8	13	14	88	33	16	206
photographic	2	9	4	1	0	5	29	11	3	64
unmarked	2	0	0	0	0	1	0	1	0	4
total	28	50	33	20	20	40	218	100	28	537

FORM E. 21. ENGLISH VOCABULARY

	HIGH	LOW
chromatic	3	6
virtual	12	15
mirror	1	2
REAL	19	13
photographic	5	4
unmarked	0	0
total	40	40

the mirror is called their VIRTUAL focus because they only tend to meet in that focus'. Still more recently, in 1859, Stephen Parkinson, in A Treatise on Optics, said: 'A familiar instance of a VIRTUAL image is that formed by a common looking-glass of an object in front of it'. In general English words which date back tend today to be among the more familiar; but this distinction between the VIRTUAL image from which diverging rays seem to come, where diverging rays would cross if extended back, and the REAL IMAGE where converging rays actually cross, seems to be a particularly troublesome concept.

268. *RÉAUMUR* (*rä-ō-mūr'*). A thermometer scale on which the freezing point of water is zero and the boiling point 80. Reread KELVIN ZERO (178).

Although René Antoine Ferchault de Réaumur is best known for his thermometric scale, he worked on the chemical difference between iron and steel, improved industrial processes, and wrote six volumes on insects, which came out between 1734 and 1742, a few years before the first three volumes of Buffon's Natural History, 1749.

To the question: 'Thermometric scale with boiling point of water at 80 and freezing point at zero', 29 per cent of 2234 people answer RÉAUMUR; and 22 per cent KELVIN. In the earlier

Thermometer scale with boiling point of water at 80 and freezing point at o.

FORM C. 16.		FORM CA. 32.	BO	NY HIGH	NY NEXT	NY REST	NY MISC.	SUM
centigrade	70	centigrade	27	25	58	223	52	385
absolute	25	absolute	5	9	28	195	24	261
		thermo-						
Celsius	81	dynamic	6	63	116	231	34	450
Kelvin	79	Kelvin	24	98	103	225	44	494
RÉAUMUR	136	RÉAUMUR	37	205	95	226	78	641
unmarked	9	unmarked	1	0	0	0	2	3
total	400	total	100	400	400	1100	234	2234

study of form c, based on 400 persons, 34 per cent answered RÉAUMUR; 20 per cent CELSIUS, the most frequently marked mislead in that study; another 20 per cent KELVIN; and 18 per cent CENTIGRADE.

Anders Celsius (*sĕl'-sē-ŭs*), who lived from 1701 to 1744, was professor of astronomy at Upsala in Sweden. In a paper which he read in 1742, he introduced the CENTIGRADE thermometer, sometimes called the CELSIUS thermometer. This has two fixed points, the freezing point of water at o, and the boiling point of water at 100. The space between is divided into a hundred degrees. The CENTIGRADE thermometer is today the most frequently used by scientists in ordinary laboratory work, possibly because, with its hundred degrees, it seems to conform with the metric system. The two misleads in the earlier form c, CELSIUS and CENTIGRADE, are exactly synonymous.

Réaumur suggested his scale a dozen years before Celsius, about 1730. His zero is the same as that of Celsius, the freezing point of water, but he used no other fixed point. Instead he took the expansion of the liquid which he used as his standard, each degree equaling an expansion of one thousandth of the volume, at zero degrees, of the total amount of liquid with which he started. It was chance that the boiling point of water fell at 80 degrees.

The KELVIN scale, the most frequently marked mislead in 2234 cases tabulated for form CA, is based on thermodynamic laws but corresponds exactly with the scale which would be given by the expansion of a perfect gas. Thus both the KELVIN scale and the RÉAUMUR depend upon the expansion of a substance, the KELVIN scale on the expansion of a perfect gas, the RÉAUMUR scale on the expansion of the alcohol he used.

269. *FRONTOLYSIS* (*frŏn-tŏl'-ĭ-sĭs*) *n*. The process which tends to destroy a pre-existing front.

A FRONT, in meteorology, is a definite boundary or mixing zone, a few miles wide, which occurs between two dissimilar air masses; or a surface of discontinuity between two juxtaposed currents of air possessing different densities; or more simply the boundary between two different air masses which have been brought together. FRONTOGENESIS (*frŏn-tō-gĕn'-ĭ-sĭs*) is the formation of such a front; FRONTOLYSIS, its breaking up.

To the question: 'Area in which pre-existing fronts tend to be destroyed', 121 persons out of 515 mark REGION OF FRONTOLYSIS; but still more, 163, mark CENTER OF PRESSURE. According to the POLAR-FRONT theory, developed by two Norwegian meteorologists, V. Bjerknes and his son J. Bjerknes, the mass of cold air which covers the polar regions, and the warm air over the tropics, circulate in opposite directions leaving a boundary discontinuity. This causes eddies, each of which may develop into a CENTER OF LOW PRESSURE. There is therefore a remote connection between FRONT and CENTER OF PRESSURE. But FRONTOLYSIS is definitely the breaking up of a front.

The end of the word FRONTOLYSIS, from the Greek λύσις (lysis), a loosening, setting free, releasing, from the verb λύειν (lyein), to loosen, has already been met at the end of ELECTROL-

Form A. Area in which pre-existing fronts tend to be destroyed.
Form AA. The breaking up of a weather front.

FORM A. 43.	FW	LA	NY	NY	NY	PH	SUM	FORM AA. 41.	NY
center of								center of	
pressure	7	19	9	17	48	63	163	pressure	19
gradient	0	7	7	2	9	10	35	gradient	7
REGION OF									
FRON-									
TOLYSIS	5	10	5	18	29	54	121	FRONTOLYSIS	18
frontogenetic									
region	4	8	7	10	24	37	90	frontogenesis	6
elastic center	1	4	7	4	26	20	62	elastic center	11
unmarked	1	6	2	15	4	16	44	unmarked	2
total	18	54	37	66	140	200	515	total	63

YSIS (50), a loosening, releasing by means of electricity. The medical term LYSIS (lī'-sĭs), from the same source, is the breaking up, the gradual recession of a disease. FRONTOLYSIS is by derivation the setting free, breaking up, of a weather front.

270. *CONVECTION* (kŏn-vĕk'-shŏn) *n.* Transfer of heat by transfer of actual matter, circulation in a fluid of non-uniform temperature due to differences of density.

The term CONVECTION comes from the Latin *convehere*, to carry together, convey, with its past participle *convectus*, a combination of *com*, together, and *vehere*, to carry, the source of VEHICLE. CONVECTION is heat carried by a moving VEHICLE.

To the question: 'The transfer of heat by moving heated particles', 33 per cent of 2234 persons answer CONVECTION, but 28 per cent answer CONDUCTION, and 23 per cent RADIATION. In the earlier study of form C, based on 400 persons, 43 per cent marked CONVECTION; 28 per cent CONDUCTION; and 24 per cent

RADIATION. CONDUCTION, the most frequently marked mislead, is the transference of heat without the actual motion of matter, as when heat travels from one end of an iron rod to the other. In this instance atoms of iron at the hot end oscillate violently and, colliding with their neighbors, transfer kinetic energy. This passes gradually as heat toward the cooler end. CONVECTION is the transfer of heat by the motion of the hot body as a whole. The Gulf Stream and the Trade Winds are natural CONVECTION currents.

From Clerk Maxwell, Theory of Heat, comes: 'The term CONVECTION is applied to those processes by which the diffusion

The transfer of heat by moving heated particles.

FORM C. 24. NY		FORM CA.	BO	NY HIGH	NY NEXT	NY REST	NY MISC.	SUM
radiation	97	radiation	31	48	105	259	68	511
evaporation	3	infiltration	7	8	8	168	6	197
conduction	114	conduction	20	113	145	262	76	616
spheroidal-state	8	spheroidal-state	2	2	1	160	1	166
CONVECTION	172	CONVECTION	40	229	141	251	83	744
unmarked	6	unmarked	0	0	0	0	0	0
total	400	total	100	400	400	1100	234	2234

of heat is rendered more rapid by the motion of the substance from one place to another, though the ultimate transfer of heat may still take place by CONDUCTION'.

RADIATION, the second most frequently marked mislead, is the transmission of energy by electromagnetic waves. Such waves are not heat. They transmit energy which becomes heat when the waves fall upon matter and set its molecules in vibration. The empty space between the earth and the sun is not heated, but transmits waves. These are called RADIANT ENERGY or RADIATION. Such RADIATION has all the properties of light but is not visible; its wave lengths are too great.

CONVECTION, according to the Encyclopaedic Dictionary of Cassell, which quotes Ganot: Is the mode by which heat is propagated through liquids. This is by the portion heated becoming lighter than the rest, and ascending to the surface, a colder one descending to take its place. Because heated air is less dense than colder air it rises in the pipes of a hot-air furnace. Because water expands when heated it rises in a hot-water heating system. Smoke rises in a chimney because of CONVECTION.

271. *ORDER* (*or'-der*) *n.* As applied to a determinant, the square root of the number of its constituents, called also DEGREE.

The word ORDER goes back through Middle English and Old French to the Latin *ordo, ordinis,* a row, series, regular ar-

Forms C and CA. Third as describing a matrix containing nine entries arranged in a square.

Form CB. General word for the number of rows or columns when coefficients of equations are arranged in a square.

FORM C. 44.	CH	FORM CA. 37.	CH	LA	NY	NY	PH	SUM
ORDER	28	ORDER	18	12	33	106	30	199
class	7	class	3	5	15	40	10	73
determinant	25	determinant	15	12	31	81	26	165
minor	2	minor	4	1	7	16	5	33
major	3	major	0	5	7	24	0	36
unmarked	3	unmarked	0	2	4	10	3	19
total	68	total	40	37	97	277	74	525

FORM CB. 31.	NY
ORDER	34
class	11
determinant	21
minor	3
degree	14
unmarked	3
total	86

rangement. The word is used today in numerous ways. In zoology, an ORDER is smaller than a CLASS, and larger than a FAMILY. In classical architecture there are five ORDERS, as: DORIC, IONIC, and CORINTHIAN.

To the question: 'THIRD as describing a matrix containing nine entries arranged in a square', 199 persons out of 525 answer

ORDER, the expected answer; but 165 answer DETERMINANT. A matrix containing nine entries arranged in a square is a DE-TERMINANT. The word was first used in mathematics by Gauss in 1801, and was given its present sense by Cauchy. A DETER-MINANT of four numbers arranged in two columns of two each, or two rows of two each, is called a DETERMINANT OF ORDER TWO. It is used in solving two simultaneous equations in two vari-ables.

A DETERMINANT of nine numbers arranged in three columns of three numbers each, or three rows of three numbers each, is called a DETERMINANT OF ORDER THREE. A DETERMINANT with 16 numbers in four columns and four rows is called a DETERMI-NANT OF ORDER FOUR.

272. *DUODECIMAL* (*dū-ō-dĕs'-ĭ-măl*) *adj.* Counting by twelves, relating to the number twelve, reckoning by powers of twelve, pertaining to twelve parts.
DUODECIMAL comes from the Latin *duodecim, duodecimus,* twelve. This is a combination of *duo,* two, and *decem,* ten, the

A scale or system of counting based on the number 12.

FORM	B. 10.	NY MISC.	SUM
abacus	6	45	51
dodecagonal	21	95	116
decimal	2	11	13
metric	6	29	35
DUODECIMAL	13	121	134
unmarked	0	8	8
total	48	309	357

source of the English word DECIMAL, pertaining to tens, count-ing by tens. These Latin words *duo* and *decem,* while not ap-parently directly from the Greek, are equivalent to the cor-responding Greek words δύο (duo), two, and δέκα (deca), ten, which combine to form δυώδεκα (duodeca), twelve.

To the question: 'A scale or system of counting based on the number 12', 134 persons out of 357 answer DUODECIMAL; but 116 answer DODECAGONAL. The noun DODECAGON (*dō-dĕk'-ă-gŏn*) comes from the Greek δωδεκάγωνον (dodecagonon), a combination of δώδεκα (dodeca), twelve, and γωνία (gonia), angle. The Greek twelve is usually δώδεκα (dodeca), as in DODECAGONAL and DODECAHEDRON; but sometimes more poetically δυώδεκα (duodeca), as in DUODECIMAL. A DODECAGON is a flat figure with twelve angles. DODECAGONAL (*dō-dĕ-kăg'-ō-năl*) is the corresponding adjective and means having twelve angles, pertaining to the DODECAGON, a twelve-angled figure, often called twelve sided.

The adjective DUODECIMAL characterizes a method of multiplying lengths in feet, inches, and twelfths of an inch, without reducing them to tenths.

273. *COSECANT* (*kō-sē'-kănt*) *n.* The hypotenuse of a right-angled triangle divided by the height, the hypotenuse over the side opposite the angle, in a circle the radius forming the

The reciprocal of sine A.

FORM C. 24.	CH	FORM CA. 28.	CH	LA	NY	NY	PH	SUM
COSECANT	19	COSECANT	14	16	34	87	31	182
secant	13	secant	7	4	10	42	9	72
cosine	28	cosine	15	14	41	114	26	210
tangent	3	tangent	2	0	8	15	3	28
coversine	5	coversine	2	3	3	19	2	29
unmarked	0	unmarked	0	0	1	0	3	4
total	68	total	40	37	97	277	74	525

FORM CB. 30.	NY
COSECANT	28
secant	11
cosine	35
tangent	8
coversine	2
unmarked	2
total	86

upper side of an angle divided by a perpendicular to the other side of the angle. Reread COTANGENT (250).

When the trigonometric functions were defined as lengths of lines, instead of ratios as today, the COSECANT was the length of a line from the center of a circle, drawn past the end of an arc and continued until it met a tangent to the circle parallel to the radius drawn to the other end of the arc. Because of this involved definition Ephraim Chambers says merely: 'Co- SECANT, in geometry, the SECANT of an arch, which arch is the COMPLEMENT, of another arch to 90 degrees'. But in the present study COSECANT is marked correctly slightly more often than SECANT, and can hardly be defined in terms of the latter.

To the question: 'The reciprocal of sine A', 182 persons out of 525 answer correctly COSECANT; but still more, 210, answer COSINE. The COSINE is the complement of the SINE. The COSINE of an angle is the same as the SINE of the complement of the angle; for co-, introduced by Edmund Gunter in 1620, stands for COMPLEMENT. The COMPLEMENT of an angle is the angle subtracted from 90 degrees, the difference between the angle and a right angle. The COSINE OF A is the SINE of $(90° - A)$. The COSECANT is the reciprocal of the SINE, one over the SINE. In a right-angled triangle the SINE is the height over the hypotenuse; the COSECANT is the hypotenuse over the height, and is always 1.00 or greater.

274. *TOTAL POSSIBILITY* (tō'-tăl pŏs-sĭ-bĭl'-ĭ-tē). The total number of times an event happens either favorably or unfavorably, the number of times an event can happen. Reread PROBABILITY (219).

$$p + q = 1.$$

FORM B. 30.	NY	MISC.	SUM
curve of error	5	28	33
probability	11	59	70
improbability	2	20	22
TOTAL POSSIBILITY	16	83	99
normal curve ordinate	11	74	85
unmarked	3	45	48
total	48	309	357

To the question: 'p + q = 1', 99 persons out of 357 answer correctly TOTAL POSSIBILITY; but 85 answer NORMAL CURVE ORDINATE. In statistics and the study of probability the letter p is often used for the probability of success, that is for the probability of a certain event happening in a certain way. The letter q is used in the same way for the probability of failure. The probability that an event will happen or fail to happen is 1.

In the NORMAL CURVE drawn on a horizontal base, the abscissa or horizontal coordinate may be the departure of a measurement from the mean, the error of the measurement. The ordinate or vertical is then the number of times this error occurs in the total number of measurements made. The ordinate is the frequency of occurrence of the event which is plotted horizontally. The total area under the curve is the total possibility.

275. *QUANTUM* (*kwŏn'-tŭm*) *n.* A discrete portion of energy, a definite amount first associated with intra-atomic and intra-molecular processes involving changes among the electrons and corresponding radiation, a unit quantity of energy emitted from an atom and proportional to the frequency of radiation.

The word QUANTUM is the neuter of the Latin *quantus*, how much, how great, the source of the English word QUANTITY.

The fundamental discrete elements in Planck's theory of radiation.

FORM C. 42. NY		FORM CA. 36. BO		NY HIGH	NY NEXT	NY REST	NY MISC.	SUM
gausses	45	gausses	12	33	44	201	26	316
neutrons	126	neutrons	32	71	129	244	72	548
ergs	22	ergs	5	21	52	200	17	295
QUANTA	113	QUANTA	32	208	76	230	86	632
oersteds	62	oersteds	9	67	99	225	29	429
unmarked	32	unmarked	10	0	0	0	4	14
total	400	total	100	400	400	1100	234	2234

The plural is QUANTA, which follows the plural of the Latin neuter noun.

The QUANTUM theory was proposed in 1900 by Max Planck, a German physicist born in 1858. It arose from the failure of the classical or Newtonian physics to account for the experimentally observed distribution of energy in the spectrum of a black body, which drops with very short wave lengths instead of continuing to rise.

To the question: 'The fundamental discrete elements in Planck's theory of radiation', 28 per cent answer QUANTA, while 25 per cent answer NEUTRONS. In the previous study of form c, based on 400 persons, 28 per cent answer QUANTA, compared with 32 per cent who answer NEUTRONS. NEUTRONS is the mislead most frequently marked by the 400 persons who score highest in a New York population of 1900 which has been tabulated, and is marked nearly twice as often as the correct answer by the 400 who score next highest on the physics vocabulary test as a whole. This usually means that it is marked because of some knowledge but not quite enough to lead to the right answer.

A NEUTRON, a word first used by Professor Rutherford, is an electrically neutral combination of a positive PROTON and a negative ELECTRON. The existence of the NEUTRON was first demonstrated by Chadwick in 1932. It is an apparently stable particle having a mass approximately equal to that of the PROTON. The confusion with QUANTUM may perhaps be through PHOTON, a word proposed by G. N. Lewis in 1926. A PHOTON is a QUANTUM of light, a corpuscle or unit particle of light.

In 1913 Niels Bohr wrote: 'Planck's constant, or as it is often called the elementary QUANTUM of action'. In accordance with the QUANTUM theory exchange of energy can take place only by finite jumps, no quantity less than a QUANTUM being ever transferred.

276. *CARTESIAN* (*kahr-tē'-zhŏn*) *adj.* The Latinized form of the proper name Descartes. CARTESIAN COORDINATES are the distances of a point from each of two axes measured parallel to the other axis. Reread COORDINATE (187).

René Descartes was born in France, in Touraine, in the château country, in 1596. Until the age of thirty-three he spent much of his life in the army, and then moved to Holland where he lived for twenty years in some twenty-four different abodes in thirteen different towns, moving each time to gain peace and solitude and moving again as soon as his whereabouts became known. Despite isolated solutions of algebraic problems by using geometrical constructions, geometry and algebra had grown up independently, and it was not until 1637 that Descartes, in his Geometria, founded analytic geometry, the union of algebra and geometry. This demanded the plotting of quantities, referring geometric figures to fixed axes now called CARTESIAN COORDINATES. Drawing two lines at right angles Descartes measured horizontal distances on one, and vertical distances on the other. With these two figures he located a definite point in the plane of the two lines.

To the question: 'A system of geometry taking account of the position of figures by employing coordinates', 91 persons out of 357 answer CARTESIAN; 81 EUCLIDEAN; and another 81 PROJECTIVE. PROJECTIVE can probably be justified as an answer

A system of geometry taking account of the position of figures by employing coordinates.

FORM B. 22.	NY	MISC.	SUM
CARTESIAN	18	73	91
Euclidean	11	70	81
non-Euclidean	2	20	22
projective	9	72	81
spherical	8	35	43
unmarked	0	39	39
total	48	309	357

to the present wording of the question. PROJECTIVE GEOMETRY starts often with three planes and PROJECTS a solid onto any one of them by extending lines, all perpendicular to the plane, to each point of the solid. COORDINATES locate a position with two distances on a plane or with three distances in space.

EUCLID's thirteen books are pure geometry and theory of numbers; they are not algebra. After the definitions and postulates of the first book, the second deals with the parallelogram; the third with the circle; and the fourth with inscribing and circumscribing. The last three, the eleventh, twelfth, and thirteenth, are solid geometry. DESCARTES' COORDINATES are designed for plotting plus and minus values, for plotting algebraic equations graphically, and for expressing geometric figures in symbols. DESCARTES' COORDINATES unite geometry and algebra.

277. *LONGITUDE* (lŏn'-jĭ-tūd) *n*. The angle at the pole of the earth contained between two great circles, one of the two passing through an established reference point, the distance along the equator measured in degrees, minutes, and seconds. Reread MERIDIAN (253).

The GREAT CIRCLE or meridian passing through the Royal Observatory of Greenwich is the reference point for English-

Distance measured, from the meridian, along an arc of a great circle whose plane is at right angles to the plane of the meridian.

FORM C. 29.	CH	FORM CA. 43.	CH	LA	NY	NY	PH	SUM
latitude	24	latitude	16	16	32	99	27	190
LONGITUDE	22	LONGITUDE	19	17	45	106	28	215
parsec	1	parsec	2	1	7	19	3	32
orientation	3	orientation	0	1	1	7	0	9
curvature	13	curvature	2	1	8	42	11	64
unmarked	5	unmarked	1	1	4	4	5	15
total	68	total	40	37	97	277	74	525

FORM CB. 27.	NY
latitude	32
LONGITUDE	43
parsec	3
azimuth	4
curvature	3
unmarked	1
total	86

speaking countries. The Royal Observatory was built in 1675, in the same year as St. Paul's cathedral and only five miles from it, on the southeast edge of London.

To the needlessly complicated question: 'Distance measured, from the meridian, along an arc of a great circle whose plane is at right angles to the plane of the meridian', 215 persons out of 525 answer LONGITUDE; and 190 LATITUDE. Nearly the same happened in the earlier study of form C where 22 out of 68 persons answered LONGITUDE, and 24 LATITUDE. LONGITUDE is the distance measured along the equator; LATITUDE is the distance up and down, north and south, above and below the equator. In this complicated question a MERIDIAN is any circle from one pole of the earth to the other pole and so crossing the equator at right angles. The GREAT CIRCLE whose plane is at right angles to the plane of the meridian is the equator.

From Lectures on the English Language by George Perkins Marsh, member of Congress from Vermont, 1842 to 1849, comes: 'The ancients supposed the torrid and the frigid zones to be uninhabitable and even impenetrable by man; but while the earth, as known to them, was bounded westwardly by the Atlantic Ocean, it extended indefinitely towards the east. The dimensions of the habitable world, then (and ancient geography embraced only the home of man), were much greater measured from west to east than from south to north. Accordingly, early geographers called the greater dimension, or the east and west line, the length, *longitudo*, of the earth; the shorter dimension, or the north and south line, they denominated its breadth, *latitudo*'.

278. *FACTORIAL* (*făk-tōr'-ĭ-ăl*) *n.* A continued product in which every factor after the first is derived from the preceding by increasing it by unity.

The term FACTORIAL is recent both as an adjective and as a noun. It does not appear in the first edition of Noah Webster's Dictionary of 1828; nor in Chambers, 1728; nor in John Harris, 1704. The word comes from the Latin noun *factor*, a doer, performer, maker, agent; and the word FACTOR is occasionally used in English for an estate agent. The Latin *factor* comes from the verb *facere*, to do, make, perform, which appears so frequently as the -FY at the end of English verbs, as in RECTIFY (78), to make straight. Of the noun FACTOR in mathematics John Harris says: 'Often called FACTORS, because they do *Facere Productum*, make or constitute the Product'.

In the two early forms of the mathematics vocabulary test the question reads:

$$n \, (n-1) \, (n-2) \, (n-3) \, \ldots \, 1.$$

To this, 183 persons out of 525 answer FACTORIAL, the correct answer; while 173 answer GEOMETRIC PROGRESSION. In the revised form CB the question is rewritten in what seems the simpler and more usual form:

$$1 \times 2 \times 3 \times \ldots \times n.$$

To this 46 persons out of 86 whose scores have been tabulated answer GEOMETRIC PROGRESSION, and only 10 FACTORIAL n. The

Forms C and CA. n (n—1) (n—2) (n—3) . . 1.
Form CB. 1 × 2 × 3 × . . . × n.

FORM C. 34.	CH	FORM CA. 31.	CH	LA	NY	NY	PH	SUM
binomial sum	12	binomial sum	9	4	7	43	8	71
geometric progression	16	geometric progression	6	17	39	88	23	173
FACTORIAL n	23	FACTORIAL n	14	8	36	97	28	183
integral permutations	5	sequence	8	5	10	18	8	49
integral combinations	11	integral combinations	3	1	4	27	5	40
unmarked	1	unmarked	0	2	1	4	2	9
total	68	total	40	37	97	277	74	525

FORM CB. 38.	NY
binomial sum	4
geometric progression	46
FACTORIAL n	10
sequence	14
integral combination	11
unmarked	1
total	86

numbers: 1, 2, 3, 4, etc. are an ARITHMETIC PROGRESSION, for each is obtained from the preceding by adding 1. A GEOMETRIC PROGRESSION (190) is a succession of numbers each derived from the preceding by multiplying by a constant factor. Ephraim Chambers gives the progression:

$$2, 6, 18, 54, 162, \text{ etc.},$$

in which each number comes from the preceding by multiplying by three.

From John Harris, 1704: 'PROGRESSION GEOMETRICAL, or GEOMETRICAL PROPORTION CONTINUED, is when Numbers, or other Quantities, proceed by equal Proportion or Ratio's, (properly so called) that is, according to one Common Multiplier, or Exponent of the Common Ratio, whether Increasing or Decreasing. As,

$$2. \ 4. \ 8. \ 16. \ 32. \ 64. \ \&$$

Or, in Species, supposing a the First Term, and r the Ratio, here equal to 2.

$$a. \ ra. \ rra. \ rrra. \ rrrra. \ rrrrra. \ \&$$

For every Term, but the first, arises from the multiplication of the Ratio, or some Power of it, into it'.

A PROGRESSION is an orderly sequence of numbers which are neither multiplied together nor added. A PROGRESSION goes on indefinitely. A FACTORIAL is a product, usually a definite number of figures multiplied together. In a GEOMETRIC PROGRESSION each number is multiplied to get the next; but the terms are not multiplied together. In a FACTORIAL each number is increased by unity to get the next.

Today the most frequent meaning of FACTORIAL is the product of an integer multiplied by all the lower integers. Thus FACTORIAL 4 is: $1 \times 2 \times 3 \times 4 = 24$. The word is used in this sense in working with permutations and probabilities. An earlier more general meaning was the product of a series of factors in ARITHMETIC PROGRESSION.

279. *PHONODEIK* (*fō'-nō-dīk*) *n.* An instrument which records graphically on a moving film the wave form of any sound.

The word PHONODEIK, according to Dayton Clarence Miller who devised the instrument in 1908, was suggested by Professor Edward W. Morley. It comes from the Greek φωνή (phone), a sound, tone, voice; and the Greek δεικτικός (deiktikos), serving to show, from the verb δείκνυμι (deiknumi), to show. This appears in the unusual English adjective DEICTIC (*dīk'-tĭk*), direct, used in logic for reasoning which proves directly. A PHONODEIK shows sounds.

Professor Miller describes the PHONODEIK in his early book: Science of Musical Sounds, 1916, and again in his later: Sound Waves: Their Shape and Speed. The receiver is a collecting horn, with a sensitive diaphragm closing the small end. A tiny mirror is mounted on a vertical axis set in jeweled bearings. Fibers of silk, attached to the center of the diaphragm, turn

Instrument which records curves showing the actual vibrations of air particles.

FORM E. 35.	BO	FW	LA	NY	NY	NY	NY	PH	TU	SUM
seismograph	6	16	3	9	5	8	73	25	10	155
isobar	5	9	3	3	2	5	31	8	1	67
lactometer	2	5	6	1	2	7	21	12	2	58
coulometer	4	12	11	5	3	8	44	23	3	113
PHONODEIK	8	8	10	2	8	8	43	31	12	130
unmarked	3	0	0	0	0	4	6	1	0	14
total	28	50	33	20	20	40	218	100	28	537

FORM E. 35.	ENGLISH VOCABULARY	
	HIGH	LOW
seismograph	5	19
isobar	3	8
lactometer	2	4
coulometer	6	5
PHONODEIK	24	4
unmarked	0	0
total	40	40

once around a minute pulley on the axis of the mirror, and are then held taut by a delicate spring. Any back-and-forth motion of the diaphragm, under the action of a sound wave, turns the mirror by means of the silk thread. Light from a pinhole, focused on the mirror, reflects back to a moving photographic film, and traces the magnified shape of the sound wave.

To the question: 'Instrument which records curves showing the actual vibrations of air particles', 130 persons out of 537 answer correctly PHONODEIK; while 155 others answer SEISMOGRAPH. The word SEISMOGRAPH (sīz'-mō-grăf) is an English version of the Italian sismografo, a word first used in about

1850 by Luigi Palmieri, director of the meteorological observatory on Mount Vesuvius. The SEISMOGRAPH records earth waves started by an earthquake much as the PHONODEIK records air waves started by a sound. Frederick A. Saunders says of the SEISMOGRAPH: 'The whole record is very like one showing the sound vibrations from a bell'. An earth tremor starts two sets of waves. One set travels through the body of the earth and reaches the SEISMOGRAPH first; the other travels along the earth crust more slowly. By observing the difference in time at which these two waves reach the SEISMOGRAPH the distance of the disturbance can be computed. By doing the same from three stations the disturbance can be placed.

The PHONODEIK plots complicated sound waves as from an oboe, clarinet, piano, or violin, as well as the human voice. The book Sound Waves shows these analyzed into their partials, into simple sine waves.

280. *LUNE* (*lūn*) *n.* A crescent, the shape of the new moon before it has reached the half, a figure formed by two arcs of circles.

The term LUNE comes through the French *lune*, from the Latin *luna*, the moon, a noun which seems to have come orig-

FORM A.	BO	NY	SUM	FORM AA. 45.	NY
chord	1	6	7	chord	10
spherical segment	7	8	15	spherical segment	43
LUNE	5	10	15	LUNE	25
spherical triangle	2	5	7	spherical triangle	10
ellipse	4	11	15	ellipse	43
unmarked	1	1	2	unmarked	1
total	20	41	61	total	132

inally from *lucere*, to shine. From the Latin *luna* come the adjectives LUNAR, of the moon, pertaining to the moon, and LUNATIC, moonstruck. A LUNE is crescent-shaped like the moon.

To the question: 'A figure bounded by two arcs of circles intersecting at their extremities', 25 persons out of 132 answer correctly LUNE; but 43 others answer ELLIPSE, and still another 43 SPHERICAL SEGMENT. A LUNE and an ELLIPSE are both closed curves, more or less oval in shape. But the ends of an ELLIPSE are rounded; the ends of a LUNE are pointed. The LUNE of Hippocrates of Chios is famous as being the first curvilinear space whose area was exactly determined.

In a crescent and in the new moon before it has reached the half the two arcs belong to circles with the same radii, one seen at an angle. A true LUNE is formed by the arcs of circles of different radii.

281. *SECANT* (*sē'-kănt*) *n.* The hypotenuse of a right-angled triangle divided by the base.

Ephraim Chambers, in his beautifully worded five-volumed

 Function of the angle A represented by dividing

the length of side h by the length of side b.

FORM C. 48.	CH	FORM CA. 33.	CH	LA	NY	NY	PH	SUM
SECANT	16	SECANT	11	11	28	67	24	141
cosecant	11	cosecant	3	5	14	36	10	68
cosine	22	cosine	13	13	22	78	18	144
sine	11	sine	6	6	19	49	10	90
cotangent	8	cotangent	7	2	12	43	9	73
unmarked	0	unmarked	0	0	2	4	3	9
total	68	total	40	37	97	277	74	525

FORM CB. 40.	NY
SECANT	22
cosecant	15
cosine	16
sine	12
cotangent	19
unmarked	2
total	86

folio Cyclopaedia of 1728, says: 'Secant, denotes a right line, drawn from the center of a circle, which, cutting the circumference, proceeds, till it meets with a tangent, to the same circle'. These old definitions, when all trigonometric terms were defined as line lengths, rather than as ratios, still hold if the radius of the circle is unity, and are often easier to remember than the modern ratios, with both numerator and denominator.

The word SECANT comes from the Latin *secans*, *secantis*, the present participle of *secare*, a verb already met through its past participle in BISECT (5). The SECANT is a line which cuts the circle, a line longer than the radius.

To the question: ' [diagram of right triangle with hypotenuse h, base b, angle A] Function of the angle A represented by dividing the length of side h by the length of side b', 141 persons out of 525 answer correctly SECANT; but 144 answer COSINE. The COSINE is the reciprocal of the SECANT,

$$\text{COSINE} = \frac{1}{\text{SECANT}}.$$

The COSINE is the base divided by the hypotenuse. The COSINE is less than 1.00, or 1.00 exactly; the SECANT is greater than 1.00, or again 1.00 exactly. If the radius of the circle is one, the SECANT is a line from the center of the circle, extended through one end of the arc of the circle until it meets the tangent to the circle drawn at the other end of the arc.

282. *PYRHELIOMETER* (*per-hē-lĭ-ŏmʹ-ē-ter*) *n*. An instrument for measuring the intensity of the sun's heat; also called PYROHELIOMETER.

The PYRHELIOMETER was designed by Claude Servais Mathias Pouillet (*poo-yăʹ*) who lived from 1791 to 1868, a French physicist interested in meteorology. The instrument consists fundamentally of a shallow dish made of silver or copper, containing water or mercury. A thermometer immersed in the liquid measures the rise in temperature.

To the question: 'Instrument for measuring the heat received at the earth's surface from the sun', PYRHELIOMETER is marked by 153 persons out of 537; and THERMOMETER by 190. Of the group who score low in English vocabulary, 28 out of 40 mark THERMOMETER compared with only 4 who mark the more precise answer PYRHELIOMETER. The low-vocabulary group almost by definition have trouble with words. But it is also conceivable that they have trouble with ideas. For lack of words with which to think they may be unable to separate clearly two such ideas as HEAT and TEMPERATURE. A THERMOMETER measures rise in TEMPERATURE. This is greater when the sun shines on some substances than when it shines on others. The PYRHELIOMETER measures the heat received which causes the rise in temperature.

Instrument for measuring the heat received at the earth's surface from the sun.

FORM E. 22.	BO	FW	LA	NY	NY	NY	NY	PH	TU	SUM
pyrometer	3	2	1	1	3	6	23	8	3	50
heliograph	3	6	3	4	0	3	59	14	3	95
PYRHELIOMETER	7	10	15	4	10	10	40	42	15	153
thermometer	12	24	12	10	6	15	81	27	3	190
thermo-couple	1	7	2	1	1	5	14	9	4	44
unmarked	2	1	0	0	0	1	1	0	0	5
total	28	50	33	20	20	40	218	100	28	537

FORM E. 22.   ENGLISH VOCABULARY

	HIGH	LOW
pyrometer	1	1
heliograph	6	3
PYRHELIOMETER	28	4
thermometer	4	28
thermo-couple	1	4
unmarked	0	0
total	40	40

Perhaps the choice of the right answer depends as much upon Greek as upon physics; for of 40 high in English vocabulary 28 mark the correct answer and only 4 THERMOMETER. PYR- comes from the Greek πῦρ (pyr), fire, the source of the English PYRE, a funeral pile for burning, the source also of PYROTECHNICS, the art of making fireworks. HELIO- comes from the Greek ἥλιος (helios), sun, the source of HELIOCENTRIC, with the sun at the center; the source also of HELIUM, the chemical element first discovered in the spectrum of the sun; and of HELIOTROPE, the flower turning toward the sun. The end of the word, -METER, comes of course from the Greek μέτρον (metron), measure, that by which anything is measured.

Although in the original PYRHELIOMETER a THERMOMETER measured the rise in temperature of some substance which absorbed the sun's heat, more recent and more accurate PYRHELI-OMETERS use no thermometer but instead a thermo-couple balancing the heat of an electrically heated block against that of another heated by the sun or by the source to be measured, keeping the two the same.

283. *ZEEMAN EFFECT* (*zā'-măn ĕf-fĕkt'*). Change in spectrum lines when the source of light is in a strong magnetic field.

With this definition, 138 persons out of 537 answer ZEEMAN EFFECT; while 132 answer FARADAY EFFECT and 109 STROBOSCOPIC EFFECT. The STROBOSCOPIC (*strō-bō-skŏp'-ĭk*) EFFECT, the second most frequently marked mislead, is catching regularly spaced glimpses of something moving periodically, so that when the time between glimpses coincides with the period of the moving object the latter seems to stand still. The effect may be gained by illuminating the moving object with flashes of light, or by viewing it through holes in a rotating disk, or in a revolving mirror. A motion picture may show the spokes of a moving wheel standing still because the camera makes an exposure every twenty-fourth of a second and in that time the wheel may turn just the angle between two spokes and so be seen in the same position as a twenty-fourth of a second earlier. The word STROBOSCOPIC comes from the Greek στρόβος (strobos), a twisting, whirling, from the verb στρέφειν (strephein), to turn, twist; and σκοπεῖν (skopein), to view. A STROBO-SCOPE is an instrument for viewing a whirling object, or more generally any body in periodic motion.

The FARADAY EFFECT, the most frequently marked mislead, like the ZEEMAN EFFECT, is the effect of a strong magnetic field on light. The FARADAY EFFECT is the turning of the plane of vibration of polarized light as it goes through a block of glass in a magnetic field. The ZEEMAN EFFECT is a change in wave length and also polarization when the source of light is in a

magnetic field. One of the differences between the two, perhaps
the fundamental difference, is that the FARADAY EFFECT is the
effect on a beam of light on going through a magnetic field;
the ZEEMAN EFFECT is the effect on a beam of light when the
source is in a magnetic field.

This effect was sought by Faraday in 1862 when he examined
sodium lines from a flame placed between the poles of a magnet,
but was not found until 1896 by Professor P. Zeeman, professor
of physics at the University of Amsterdam. A single spectrum
line from a short spark in a strong magnetic field is broken up

Change in the lines observed in the spectrum of a source of
light when the source is placed in a strong magnetic field.

FORM E. 50.	BO	FW	LA	NY	NY	NY	NY	PH	TU	SUM
ZEEMAN EFFECT	5	8	11	5	8	6	54	35	6	138
Faraday effect	9	14	9	7	1	9	51	24	8	132
D'Arsonval principle	4	4	1	1	2	5	19	8	1	45
Bohr's effect	3	10	5	1	5	4	43	20	9	100
stroboscopic effect	4	12	7	6	4	13	47	12	4	109
unmarked	3	2	0	0	0	3	4	1	0	13
total	28	50	33	20	20	40	218	100	28	537

FORM E. 50.	ENGLISH VOCABULARY	
	HIGH	LOW
ZEEMAN EFFECT	24	1
Faraday effect	6	14
D'Arsonval principle	0	8
Bohr's effect	5	5
stroboscopic effect	4	12
unmarked	1	0
total	40	40

into a close group when looked at in a direction at right angles
to the magnetic lines. Sometimes a single line becomes three,
sometimes more. The lines of the group are polarized, the outer
lines vibrating perpendicular to the magnetic lines, the inner
lines parallel.

The ZEEMAN EFFECT appears in the sun's spectrum, revealing the presence of a general magnetic field, as well as localized stronger ones in the vicinity of sun spots.

284. *CHROMATIC ABERRATION* (*krō-măt'-ĭk ă-ber-rā'-shŏn*). The rainbow fringe around an optical image when the foci for different colors do not coincide, the prismatic effect of dispersion upon the distinctness of the edge of an image.

The term ABERRATION comes from the Latin *aberratio, aberrationis,* from the verb *aberrare,* to stray from, a combination of *ab,* from, and *errare,* to stray, the source of the English verb to ERR. ABERRATION is a wandering away, an error or deviation

The inability of a lens to focus all wave lengths of light at the same point.

FORM C. 35. NY		FORM CA. 44. BO		NY HIGH	NY NEXT	NY REST	NY MISC.	SUM
spherical		spherical						
aberration	135	aberration	26	130	104	238	57	555
diffraction	52	diffraction	7	11	49	196	23	286
CHROMATIC		CHROMATIC						
ABERRATION	82	ABERRATION	31	167	81	229	69	577
astigmatism	60	astigmatism	20	58	84	220	43	425
distortion	57	distortion	15	34	82	217	38	386
unmarked	14	unmarked	1	0	0	0	4	5
total	400	total	100	400	400	1100	234	2234

from the ideal. In optics it is a deviation of the rays of light when they are bent unequally on passing through a lens or reflected by a mirror, so that in converging they do not meet in a point or focus, but form an indistinct image; it is lack of point to point correspondence between an object and its image.

The adjective CHROMATIC comes from the Greek χρῶμα (chroma), χρῶματις (chromatis), color, already met in ACHROMATIC (262), not colored, and the source of CHROMO, an abbreviation of CHROMOLITHOGRAPH, from λίθος (lithos), stone, and γραφή (graphe), drawing, writing, a colored print made by printing successively, from several stones, in different hues. CHROMATIC ABERRATION is the fringing of an image with prismatic colors arising from the unequal bending of different colors.

To the question: 'The inability of a lens to focus all wave lengths of light at the same point', 26 per cent of 2234 persons answer CHROMATIC ABERRATION; and another 25 per cent SPHERICAL ABERRATION. In the earlier study of form c, based on 400 persons, 20 per cent answer CHROMATIC ABERRATION, and 34 per cent SPHERICAL ABERRATION.

ABERRATION is called SPHERICAL when the blurring arises from the curvature of the lens or mirror. It takes place when light passes through a lens or reflects back from a mirror curved like a portion of a sphere, instead of being parabolic in shape. ABERRATION is called CHROMATIC when the foci for different colors do not coincide. CHROMATIC ABERRATION is due to the material of which the lens is made and can be corrected by a proper combination of lenses of different materials.

285. *WATTHOUR METER* (*wŏt'-our mē'-ter*). An energy meter, an accumulating instrument which records total electrical energy used, the product of power and time.

Robeson in his Physics hyphenates the word WATT-HOUR; Black spells it as one word, WATTHOUR. Such a compound tends to lose its hyphen with time; and though it is easy to over-burden the language until it becomes heavy and cumbrous, the WATTHOUR METER is one of the most extensively used of all electric measuring devices, is standard equipment in every building where electrical energy is purchased, and in consequence WATTHOUR is spelt here as a single word.

A WATTHOUR METER, said to have been invented in 1894 by O. B. Shallenberger, of the Westinghouse Electric Company, is fundamentally a WATTMETER in which the movable part turns continuously. In a WATTMETER the fixed coils take the full current of the line. The movable coil is connected across the line, so that its current is proportional to the voltage. As a result the deflection of the movable coil is proportional to the product of the current in the fixed coils multiplied by the voltage in the movable coil. Current times volts equals watts. The movable coil in a WATTMETER turns against a spring indicating number of watts at each instant. Remove the spring, allowing the coil to rotate continuously, and the number of rotations during any given time is proportional to the watts which have been used.

A WATTHOUR METER consists essentially of a small electric motor, a brake, and a register. The motor may be of the commutator, the induction, or the mercury and disk type. Its torque is proportional to the electric power, that is to the watts in the load. During any interval of time the number of revolutions is proportional to the energy which has gone through the meter.

As inertia would carry the rotating part on after the current stopped, it is electrically damped. This brake is often an aluminum disk, conducting but non-magnetic, which rotates between the poles of a permanent magnet. The opposing torque

An integrating measuring instrument.

FORM C. 21. NY		FORM CA. 31. BO Wheatstone		NY HIGH	NY NEXT	NY REST	NY MISC.	SUM
wattmeter	31	bridge	29	138	155	254	43	619
potenti-ometer	132	potenti-ometer	7	50	79	219	50	405
WATTHOUR METER	136	WATTHOUR METER	47	182	102	243	79	653
voltmeter	46	voltmeter	7	13	27	178	21	246
galvan-ometer	40	galvan-ometer	6	17	37	206	34	300
unmarked	15	unmarked	4	0	0	0	7	11
total	400	total	100	400	400	1100	234	2234

of the brake is proportional to the speed of the disk. The register, or clock as it is called, records on dials the number of disk revolutions, and so the number of kilowatthours of electricity consumed. On the reading depends the monthly bill.

To the question: 'An integrating measuring instrument', 29 per cent of 2234 persons tabulated in the study of form CA, answer WATTHOUR METER; and 28 per cent are recorded as answering WHEATSTONE BRIDGE, with 18 per cent answering POTENTIOMETER. In the previous study of form C, where the mislead WHEATSTONE BRIDGE was not used, 34 per cent answered WATTHOUR METER, and another 33 per cent POTENTIOMETER. A WHEATSTONE BRIDGE is a laboratory instrument, primarily for measuring resistances by comparing an unknown resistance with one accurately known, an ohmmeter.

POTENTIOMETER, the most frequently marked mislead in form c, is an instrument for measuring an unknown electromotive force or potential difference by balancing it against a known potential. A POTENTIOMETER shows the conditions in the circuit from moment to moment. A WATTHOUR METER is not designed to show the momentary conditions, but to accumulate a record of the total amount of power used over a period of time.

286. *JOULE'S LAW* (*joolz law*). The quantity of heat generated by an electric current is proportional to the resistance of the conductor through which it flows, to the square of the current strength, and to the time during which it flows.

From a paper published in the Philosophical Magazine in 1841: On the Heat Evolved by Metal Conductors of Electricity, James Prescott Joule, Esq. says in paragraph 13: 'Other trials

The law for computing the heating of a conductor.

FORM C. 27. NY		FORM CA. 40. BO		NY HIGH	NY NEXT	NY REST	NY MISC.	SUM
Joule	97	Joule	26	150	107	232	64	579
Faraday	59	Faraday	18	50	80	221	46	415
Ohm	150	Ohm	32	115	119	257	74	597
Kirchhoff	37	Kirchhoff	14	71	65	200	26	376
Coulomb	41	Charles	5	14	29	190	21	259
unmarked	16	unmarked	5	0	0	0	3	8
total	400	total	100	400	400	1100	234	2234

were made with results of precisely the same character; they all conspire to confirm the fact, that *when a given quantity of voltaic electricity is passed through a metallic conductor for a given length of time, the quantity of heat evolved by it is always proportional to the resistance which it presents, whatever may be the length, thickness, shape, or kind of that metallic conductor*'.

In paragraph 17 Joule continues: 'We see, therefore, that *when a current of voltaic electricity is propagated along a metallic conductor, the heat evolved in a given time is proportional to the resistance of the conductor multiplied by the square of the electric intensity*'.

To the question: 'The law for computing the heating of a conductor', 26 per cent answer JOULE; while another 27 per cent answer OHM. In the earlier study of form c, based on 400 persons, only 24 per cent answered JOULE, while 38 per cent answered OHM. Both OHM'S LAW and JOULE'S LAW involve current flowing against resistance. OHM'S LAW states that the current multiplied by the resistance equals the electromotive force required. OHM'S LAW gives the voltage needed to push a desired current through a known resistance. JOULE'S LAW states that the square of the current multiplied by the resistance equals the heat generated in unit time.

The rate of heat generation, the number of heat units developed in a conductor, is proportional:

to its resistance,

to the square of the strength of the current, and

to the time.

A current of one ampere flowing through a resistance of one ohm develops 0.24 calories per second.

287. *IRRATIONAL* (*ĭr-ră'-shō-năl*) *adj.* Pertaining to a number which cannot be expressed in finite terms, a real number which is not a quotient of two whole numbers, incommensurable, a surd. Reread COMMENSURABLE (221).

The Latin *in-* means not, as: INCORRECT, not correct, INACCURATE, not accurate. Before a word beginning with R, such as RATIONAL, this *in-* becomes *ir-*. Thus IRRATIONAL means not RATIONAL. The word RATIONAL comes from the Latin *rationalis*, reasonable, belonging to reason. This Latin word seems to have been used to translate the Greek word ῥητός (ratos), expressible. A RATIONAL number can be expressed in finite terms; a RATIONAL number is a real number which can be stated as the quotient of two whole numbers, as one divided by the other. IRRATIONAL means not expressible.

To the question: 'A number which is not a whole number or a fraction', 53 persons out of 132 answer IRRATIONAL, while 32 answer ROOT, and 25 IMAGINARY. Neither an IMAGINARY nor an IRRATIONAL number can be expressed, but for different reasons. An IMAGINARY number is the square root of a negative quantity, or any even root of a negative quantity, as: $\sqrt{-4}$. An IRRA-

TIONAL number can be obtained to any number of decimal places but never quite accurately.

The confusion of IRRATIONAL with ROOT is perhaps because many IRRATIONAL numbers are ROOTS. Thus $\sqrt{2}$ is an IRRATIONAL number because no matter how far it is carried out it can never be obtained quite exactly. Another IRRATIONAL number is the

A number which is not a whole number or a fraction.

FORM A. 30.	BO	NY	SUM	FORM AA. 33.	NY
imaginary	7	18	25	imaginary	25
cardinal	2	0	2	eccentricity	5
ordinal	1	2	3	ordinal	16
root	2	4	6	root	32
IRRATIONAL	7	17	24	IRRATIONAL	53
unmarked	1	0	1	unmarked	1
total	20	41	61	total	132

cube root of 5. But not all IRRATIONAL numbers are ROOTS, for π is an IRRATIONAL number which can be obtained to any number of decimal places but never with final precision. It is the quotient of two incommensurable distances, the circumference of a circle divided by the diameter.

288. *VERSINE* (*vers'-sĭn*) *n*. The segment of the diameter between the foot of the sine and the foot of the arc; or more often today the ratio of this distance to the radius.

VERSINE is an abbreviation of VERSED SINE. The Oxford New English Dictionary gives a quotation using VERSED SIGNE in connection with the variation of the compass as early as 1596. VERSED in this sense of turned, turned over, INVERTED, comes from the Latin *vertere*, to turn, overturn, change, transform, already met in the meteorological term INVERSION (233), and still earlier in INVERSE PROPORTION (46).

To the question: 'One minus the cosine of angle A', 102 persons out of 525, whose scores have been tabulated for form CA, answer correctly VERSINE A; while 150 others answer COVERSINE A, the most popular answer also in the newly revised form CB. As discussed under COTANGENT (250), the prefix CO-, in trigonometric functions, stands for complement. The COVERSINE of

A is the VERSINE of the complement of A, the VERSINE of 90 degrees minus A, or the VERCOSINE of A. The VERCOSINE of A is in turn: 1 — sine A. The COVERSINE A, the most frequently marked mislead, is therefore:

$$1 - \sin A;$$

while the VERSINE A, the correct answer, is:

$$1 - \cos A.$$

When the COSINE was defined as a distance, it was the horizontal distance from the center of a circle to the foot of the perpendicular dropped from the top of the arc to the diameter.

Forms C and CA. One minus the cosine of angle A.
Form CB. One minus the cosine of an angle.

FORM C. 8.	CH	FORM CA. 42.	CH	LA	NY	NY	PH	SUM
VERSINE A	9	VERSINE A	6	11	18	46	21	102
coversine A	16	coversine A	11	8	28	82	21	150
secant A	23	secant A	7	4	21	60	15	107
cosecant A	10	cosecant A	11	8	16	49	8	92
cotangent A	10	cotangent A	4	4	10	38	5	61
unmarked	0	unmarked	1	2	4	2	4	13
total	68	total	40	37	97	277	74	525

FORM CB. 43.	NY
VERSINE	12
coversine	28
secant	23
cosecant	15
cotangent	6
unmarked	2
total	86

When the radius of the circle is unity the COSINE, expressed as a ratio, is this distance divided by unity. The radius of the circle minus the cosine, when the cosine was a length, equals the VERSED SINE, when that was also a length.

In modern usage, where the trigonometric functions are regarded as ratios, the COSINE is the distance from the center of a circle to the foot of the perpendicular divided by the radius; or the base of a right-angle triangle divided by the hypotenuse, where the base and the hypotenuse are the two sides of the angle in question. The VERSINE is the radius minus the length of the cosine divided by the same radius. Whether the trigonometric functions be lengths or ratios, the VERSINE is:

$$1 - cosine.$$

The SECANT, the second most frequently marked mislead, and still more popular than the correct answer, is one over the COSINE, the reciprocal of the COSINE:

$$\text{SECANT} = \frac{1}{\text{COSINE}}.$$

The VERSINE is one minus the COSINE.

289. *SERIES MOTOR* (sē'-rĭ-ēz). A direct current motor with the coils of the field magnets and of the armature connected in series so that the whole current flows through one and then the other.

Direct current electric motors are of at least three fundamental types: SERIES, SHUNT, and COMPOUND, depending on the electrical connections of the magnetizing coils on the field mag-

A direct-current motor whose speed is dangerously high at no load.

FORM C. 41. NY		FORM CA. 34. BO		NY HIGH	NY NEXT	NY REST	NY MISC.	SUM
under-		under-						
compound	23	compound	6	38	41	183	10	278
shunt	88	shunt	16	62	68	232	48	426
cumulative-		cumulative-						
compound	55	compound	22	90	103	232	62	509
SERIES	121	SERIES	32	133	68	206	58	497
over-		over-						
compound	90	compound	21	77	120	247	53	518
unmarked	23	unmarked	3	0	0	0	3	6
total	400	total	100	400	400	1100	234	2234

nets. In the SERIES MOTOR the field coils are relatively few turns of heavy wire connected in SERIES with the armature winding, so that the same current flows through the field coils and the armature winding. In the SHUNT motor the current divides, part flowing through the field coils, which are many turns of fine wire, and part flowing through the armature. The field coils and the armature are in parallel or, expressed differently, the field coils are SHUNTED across the armature. In the COMPOUND motor there are two windings on the field magnets, one in series with the armature and the other in parallel.

As the load on the motor varies the speed of the SHUNT motor remains practically constant. The choice SHUNT motor is therefore perhaps furthest from a correct answer. The speed of the COMPOUND motor increases as the load lightens, and this is therefore more nearly a correct answer; but the speed does not become dangerously great. With the SERIES motor the speed increases rapidly as the load lightens, and with little or no load becomes dangerously great.

290. *SIDEREAL* (*sĭ-dē′-rē-ăl*) *adj.* Pertaining to the fixed stars, stellar, starry, astral.

In the test phrase: 'SIDEREAL spaces', which appears in one of the English vocabulary tests, the word is thought by 23 per cent of adult readers to mean VAST. Both VAST and SIDEREAL may apply to the limitless space surrounding the world. VAST means boundless, great, immense; SIDEREAL means specifically pertaining to the constellations.

To the question: 'Measured by the apparent motion of any of the fixed stars', which appears in one of the physics vocabulary tests, 28 per cent answer SIDEREAL, nearly 29 per cent answer STELLAR, and 21 per cent ASTRAL. In the previous study of form C, based on 400 persons, where STELLAR was not one of the misleads, 127 persons or 32 per cent answered SIDEREAL, and 156 or 39 per cent ASTRAL. ASTRAL, STELLAR, and SIDEREAL, all come from words meaning star. ASTRAL goes back through the Latin *astrum*, a star, to the Greek ἀστήρ (aster), a star; STELLAR, to the Latin *stella*, a star; and SIDEREAL, to the Latin *sidus, sideris*, a star, constellation; but the three differ in modern usage. ASTRAL is poetical, almost synonymous with unknown, remote, mysterious. STELLAR means specifically pertaining to the stars. SIDEREAL is a scientific term, pertaining to the fixed stars which form the constellations. SIDEREAL time is determined by the motion of the earth in relation to the fixed stars.

From Ephraim Chambers' Cyclopaedia, the five-volume edition published in 1783, comes: 'SIDEREAL day is the time in which any star revolves from the meridian to the meridian again; viz. 23 hours, 56 minutes, 4 seconds, 6 thirds, of mean solar time'. The word THIRD, as used in this way by Chambers, is the 60th part of a second of time. From William Holder, 1616 to 1698, in his Discourse concerning Time: 'Divide the natural day into twenty-four equal parts, an hour into sixty minutes, a minute into sixty seconds, a second into sixty thirds'.

Returning to Chambers: 'There are 366 SIDEREAL days in a year, or in the time of 365 diurnal revolutions of the sun'. Still from Chambers: 'Year, SIDEREAL or astral, is the space of time

Measured by the apparent motion of any of the fixed stars.

FORM C. 43. NY		FORM CA. 33.	BO	NY	NY	SUM
SIDEREAL	127	SIDEREAL	32	513	71	616
standard	9	stellar	36	540	60	636
astral	156	astral	23	382	72	477
cosmic	23	cosmic	2	205	3	210
solar	60	solar	7	260	27	294
unmarked	25	unmarked	0	0	1	1
total	400	total	100	1900	234	2234

wherein the sun, going from any fixed star returns to the same. This consists of 365 days, 6 hours, 9 minutes, 14½ seconds; and is 20 minutes, 17½ seconds, longer than the true solar year'.

291. *SECANT* (*sē'-kănt*) *n.* A straight line which cuts a circle in two places, or a curve in several places, an unusual meaning of the word SECANT but still used by careful writers. Reread SECANT, the trigonometric function (281).

SECANT comes from the Latin *secare*, to cut, already met early in this book in BISECT (5), to cut in two. SECANT always refers in some way to a line which cuts another. Even when used for a trigonometric function, the SECANT was a line which cut the circumference, and extended beyond the circle to a tangent drawn at the end of the radius which formed the other side of the angle. This verb *secare*, to cut, with the past participle *sectus*, is the source of the familiar noun INTERSECTION, a cutting across; DISSECTION, a cutting apart; and SECTION, the act of cutting or a part cut from the rest.

Item 27 of form C reads: 'A straight line which, within its extremities, cuts a circle in two points'; and 41 persons out of 68, or 60 per cent, mark CHORD, instead of the correct answer SECANT. In the revised form CA, the wording is changed to: 'An unlimited straight line which cuts a circle at two points'. To this 94 persons out of 151, or 62 per cent, still mark CHORD. The CHORD is only a part of the SECANT. It is the line within the circle between the two intersections, the part of the SECANT intercepted by the circle. CHORD comes from the Latin *chorda*,

FORM C. A straight line which, within its extremities, cuts a circle in two points.

FORM CA. An unlimited straight line which cuts a circle at two points.

FORM C. 27.	CH	FORM CA.	CH	LA	PH	SUM
chord	41	chord	24	26	44	94
radius	1	radius	0	0	1	1
diameter	5	diameter	3	0	5	8
SECANT	18	SECANT	11	8	18	37
radian	3	radian	1	2	3	6
unmarked	0	unmarked	1	1	3	5
total	68	total	40	37	74	151

from the Greek χορδή (chorde), originally something made of gut, a string of gut, and so the string of a lyre or harp. A CHORD stretches from one end of an arc to the other much as a string stretches from one end of a bent bow to the other. A CHORD is that part of a straight line comprised between two of its intersections with a curve, specifically the straight line joining the extremities of an arc of a circle. A SECANT is the same straight line extending beyond the circle in both directions.

292. *CAPACITANCE* (kă-pă'-sĭ-tăns) *n.* The characteristic of an alternating current circuit which causes each phase of the current to lead the voltage by a quarter of a cycle.
Frederick Saunders, who gives in A Survey of Physics the clearest picture of this difference in phase between current and

voltage, asks the reader to imagine a small frictionless car on wheels, held in place by a coiled spring. Now move the car back and forth by hand with a regular periodic motion. At the extreme left the car is stationary, with no velocity, having finished its motion to the left and not yet started back to the right; but the force to the left against the spring is the greatest at this point. The greatest velocity toward the right is attained at the mid point; and the greatest force to the right is a quarter of a cycle later at the extreme right, for at the mid point the force is zero. From the mid point to the right the force increases as the velocity to the right decreases. The velocity to the right reaches its maximum 90 degrees ahead of the maximum force to the right. Replacing velocity by current, and force by voltage, the current leads the voltage by 90 degrees. This happens with CAPACITANCE in the circuit.

To the question: 'Property of an alternating current circuit which causes the current to lead the voltage by 90 degrees', 20 per cent of students answer correctly CAPACITANCE, and the remaining 80 per cent divide almost equally among the four other choices. With approximately 20 per cent of students guessing each of four choices, 20 per cent should also, it would seem, guess CAPACITANCE, the correct answer. Distributing the 5 per cent who do not mark this item at all among the five choices, 1 per cent to each, gives 21 per cent marking CAPACITANCE. Assuming that 20 per cent guess leaves 1 per cent as knowing this meaning of CAPACITANCE.

Students do not even divide as one might expect between INDUCTANCE and CAPACITANCE, one of which makes the current lag 90 degrees and the other lead; for returning to Professor Saunders' analogy imagine the car not held by a spring but running free. At the extreme left the greatest force to the right is needed to bring the car to a stop and start it back toward the right. At mid point the car has its greatest velocity, but at this point no force is needed, for the force which has been accelerating the car toward the right must start slowing it down. As the force to the left increases from this point to the extreme right the velocity decreases. The greatest velocity toward the right is attained 90 degrees after the greatest force to the right. The velocity in going through its cycle lags 90 degrees behind the force which causes it. Instead of FORCE use once more the word VOLTAGE, instead of VELOCITY use CURRENT, and the analogy with an alternating current circuit containing INDUCTANCE is nearly perfect.

INDUCTANCE, discussed under MUTUAL INDUCTANCE, is the same as SELF INDUCTION. It is electrical inertia and tends to retard changes in current. Why MUTUAL INDUCTANCE, word 86 in order of difficulty, should be marked correctly by 70 per cent of those who take the physics vocabulary test, while the present aspect of CAPACITANCE is almost unknown, is still a mystery. One would expect MUTUAL INDUCTANCE to be much more diffi-

Property of an alternating current circuit which causes the current to lead the voltage by 90 degrees.

FORM AB. 45.	%	FORM D. 42.	NY	%
impedance	23	impedance	82	23.4
resistance	6	resistance	41	11.7
CAPACITANCE	20	CAPACITANCE	64	18.3
reactance	15	reactance	52	14.9
inductance	35	inductance	91	26.0
unmarked	1	unmarked	20	5.7
total	100	total	350	100.0

FORM DA. 46.	%	FORM DB. 42.	NY
impedance	22	impedance	21
resistance	13	resistance	16
CAPACITANCE	20	CAPACITANCE	22
reactance	19	reactance	8
inductance	21	inductance	33
unmarked	5	unmarked	6
total	100	total	106

cult in comparison with other items than the figures indicate. The FARAD, a unit of CAPACITANCE, is marked correctly by 72 per cent; but this quality of CAPACITANCE, its characteristic of making the current lead the voltage, is marked correctly by only one fifth of those who have taken the test, the number one would expect by pure chance. Much is still to be discovered about the acquisition of technical concepts.

293. *EMPIRICAL LAW* (*ĕm-pĭr′-ĭ-kăl*). A general conclusion from observed data, based on experiments, derived from experience, depending upon observation of phenomena; according to Sir William Hamilton: 'The term EMPIRICAL means simply what belongs to or is the product of experience or observation', while Sir John Herschel adds, 1830: 'If the knowledge be merely accumulated experience, the fact is EMPIRICAL'.

EMPIRICAL is often used in an opprobrious sense, guided by mere experience without scientific knowledge, almost charla-

A conclusion from observed or experimental data only.

FORM C. 29.	NY	FORM CA. 46.	BO	NY HIGH	NY NEXT	NY REST	NY MISC.	SUM
postulate	23	postulate	8	23	53	200	22	306
EMPIRICAL		EMPIRICAL						
LAW	82	LAW	22	143	60	214	58	497
assumption	57	assumption	15	37	54	200	25	331
theory	134	theory	17	92	129	243	52	533
hypothesis	92	hypothesis	36	105	104	243	72	560
unmarked	12	unmarked	2	0	0	0	5	7
total	400	total	100	400	400	1100	234	2234

tanic. From Sir James Mackintosh, 1830, Progress of Ethical Philosophy, comes: 'Sextus, a physician of the EMPIRICAL, i.e. anti-theoretical school'.

The word EMPIRICAL comes from the Latin *empiricus*, from the Greek ἐμπειρικός (empeirikos), ἐμπειρία (empeiria), experience, from ἔμπειρος (empeiros), skilled, from ἐν (en), in, plus πεῖρα (peira), trial, experiment.

The nicest statement is that of John Stuart Mill in his Logic, 1846: 'An EMPIRICAL LAW is an observed uniformity, presumed to be resolvable into simpler laws but not yet resolved into them'. The relation between pressure and volume stated by Robert Boyle in 1662 was EMPIRICAL. The fourth-power relationship between the radiation from a black body and its temperature found by Stefan is always called EMPIRICAL. All modern science is EMPIRICAL, based on observation. But it does not stop there. It tries to connect and relate observed uniformities. It is called EMPIRICAL only so long as it remains a disconnected observed uniformity. The resolution of this into simpler uniformities, or into previously known uniformities, or even connecting it with other observed uniformities, entitles it to be called THEORETICAL. Thus Boltzmann is said to have derived the Stefan fourth-power relationship THEORETICALLY by starting with the Carnot cycle. Boltzmann really connected one EMPIRICAL relationship with another, for the Carnot cycle depends on Boyle's and Charles' EMPIRICAL laws.

To the question: 'A conclusion from observed or experimental data only', 22 per cent out of 2234 persons answer EMPIRICAL LAW; while 25 per cent answer HYPOTHESIS (hĭ-pŏth'-ĕ-sĭs), and another 24 per cent THEORY. Among the 400 New York persons, who score highest in the physics vocabulary test as a whole in a total group of 1900, 23 per cent mark THEORY; but in the 400 next highest, who know something of these words but are not quite certain, 32 per cent mark THEORY, an opposite of the correct answer; while in the low 1100 in this group of 1900, those who are more nearly guessing, only 22 per cent mark THEORY. One definition of an HYPOTHESIS is a proposition put forth without reference to its correspondence with facts. An HYPOTHESIS comes before observations, often serves as a guide in planning experiments for the collection of new facts. Inference and reasoning, which sets out from facts or observations, without relying on propositions accepted either on authority, or even provisionally for the sake of argument, may be called INDUCTIVE, MATERIAL, or EMPIRICAL. Reread THEOREM (130).

294. *HYPOCYCLOID* (hĭ-pō-sĭ'-kloid) *n.* The curve traced by a point on the edge of a circle which rolls around inside another circle. Reread CYCLOID (133).
The term HYPOCYCLOID commences with the Greek ὑπό (hypo), under, already met early in this book in HYPOTENUSE (29).

To the question: 'The curve made by a point on the circumference of a small circle rolling within a large circle', 22 persons out of 132 answer correctly HYPOCYCLOID; while 42 answer SPIRAL, and 34 EPICYCLOID. A SPIRAL is traced by a point which moves away from its starting point and at the same time moves about its starting point. It is made by a point which moves out along the spoke of a wheel as the wheel turns. The SPIRAL OF ARCHIMEDES is laid out by drawing a number of lines all radiating out like spokes from a center and all separated by equal angles. On one of these lines lay off a small distance from the center; on the next line double the distance from the center; and on the third line lay off three times the same distance from the center; and so on. The curve starting at the center and joining these points is the SPIRAL OF ARCHIMEDES.

The CYCLOID (133) is a curve traced by a point on the edge of a wheel which rolls on a straight line. It is a series of arches

The curve made by a point on the circumference of a small circle rolling within a large circle.

FORM A. 27.	BO	NY	SUM	FORM AA. 48.	NY
volute	2	4	6	volute	12
spiral	1	13	14	spiral	42
HYPOCYCLOID	5	7	12	HYPOCYCLOID	22
epicycloid	8	6	14	epicycloid	34
cycloid	3	10	13	cycloid	19
unmarked	1	1	2	unmarked	3
total	20	41	61	total	132

resting on the straight line. The EPICYCLOID is a similar series of arches resting on the outside of a larger circle; the HYPOCYCLOID, a similar series of arches inside a large circle.

295. *EXPONENTIAL METHOD* (*ĕks-pō-nĕn'-shăl mĕth'-ŏd*). Writing a large number as a power of ten, printing 100 as 10^2, 1000 as 10^3, and one million, 1,000,000, as 10^6. Figures less than one are written with negative exponents. Thus 0.10, or one tenth, is written 10^{-1}; 0.01, as 10^{-2}; and 0.001, as 10^{-3}.

A LIGHT-YEAR, the distance which light travels in a vacuum in a year, is 5.87837×10^{12} miles, or 587837×10^7 miles; or in the metric system 9.45988×10^{17} centimeters. Writing out seventeen zeros is laborious, time-consuming, and awkward to handle in computations.

To the question: 'Method of expressing a large number, as: 2.1984×10^{10}', 134 persons out of 357 answer EXPONENTIAL; while 141 answer LOGARITHMIC. In the expression 10^6, standing for one million, 6 is the logarithm of 1,000,000, for a LOGARITHM, by definition, is the EXPONENT of a base number, and in common logarithms the base is 10. The rule for determining the EXPONENT is the same as for determining the CHARACTERISTIC (208) of a logarithm. Both are one less than the number of digits to the left of the decimal, and one more than the number of zeros

Method of expressing a large number as 2.1984×10^{10}.

FORM B. 29.	NY	MISC.	SUM
factorial method	2	12	14
decimal method	2	33	35
logarithmic method	17	124	141
EXPONENTIAL METHOD	26	108	134
basic method	1	5	6
unmarked	0	27	27
total	48	309	357

to the right of the decimal. This method of expressing a large number might legitimately be called LOGARITHMIC, but is usually called EXPONENTIAL.

296. *ANTILOGARITHM* (*ăn-tĭ-lŏg'-ă-rĭthm*) *n*. The number which corresponds to a logarithm.

From the Penny Cyclopaedia of 1834 comes: 'ANTILOGARITHM, as used in this country, means the number to the logarithm. Thus in Briggs' system, 100 is the ANTILOGARITHM of 2, because 2 is the logarithm of 100'.

The prefix ANTI- comes from the Latin *anti-*, and this from the Greek ἀντί (anti-), opposite, over against. ANTI- occasionally suggests a process of the contrary kind, as in ANTICLIMAX; and in this sense ANTI- is used in ANTILOGARITHM.

To the question: 'The expression x in log x', 134 persons out of 525 answer ANTILOGARITHM, but 115 persons in the same group answer LOGARITHM, and 113 BASE. Among the 74 persons of this group who were tested in Philadelphia, 28 answer LOGARITHM, the most frequently marked of the five choices. Among the 40 tested in Chicago, 13 mark LOGARITHM, again the most frequently marked of the five choices. But among the 37 tested in Los Angeles only 3 mark LOGARITHM, the least frequently marked of the five choices. This disagreement is unusual for even with these small populations the tabulations from different laboratories agree surprisingly closely. The expression log x means the logarithm of x. To multiply the number x times the number y, find log x and log y and add these two logarithms. Then find the ANTILOGARITHM of this logarithm, the

The expression x in log x.

FORM CA. 45.	CH	LA	NY	NY	PH	SUM	FORM CB. 42. NY	
base	8	10	22	64	9	113	base	26
							ANTI-	
ANTILOGARITHM	9	10	23	72	20	134	LOGARITHM	11
logarithm	13	3	18	53	28	115	logarithm	18
							char-	
characteristic	6	7	14	33	7	67	acteristic	12
mantissa	3	7	17	46	6	79	mantissa	18
unmarked	1	0	3	9	4	17	unmarked	1
total	40	37	97	277	74	525	total	86

number to which this logarithm corresponds. Every natural number has a logarithm, sometimes called an ARTIFICIAL number. Every logarithm belongs to a natural number called its ANTILOGARITHM.

297. *Y INTERCEPT* (y ĭn'-ter-sĕpt) *n*. The distance on the y
    axis from the origin to the point at which a line or curve
cuts the y axis.
The word INTERCEPT comes from the Latin *interceptus*, to take between, a combination of *inter*, between, and *capere*, to take. The Y INTERCEPT is not the point on the y axis at which a line or curve crosses the axis but instead a distance, the distance along the y axis from the origin to the point of crossing.
    To the question: 'x = o, y = n', 113 persons out of 357 answer correctly Y INTERCEPT; but 123 answer LINEAR EQUATION. A LINEAR EQUATION is any equation of the first degree in its unknown quantities. The equation:
$$ax + by = c$$
is the usual form of a linear equation. The equation x = o represents a line, the y axis; y = n is another line, horizontal,

parallel to the x axis, and cutting the y axis at n. The combination of the two together is a point at n on the y axis.

The INTERCEPT FORM of a linear equation is:

$$\frac{x}{a} + \frac{y}{b} = 1.$$

When y = 0, x = a. This is the point at which the line crosses

B. 18. x = 0, y = n.

FORM B. 18.	NY	MISC.	SUM
quadratic root	0	52	52
Y INTERCEPT	23	90	113
x intercept	7	16	23
linear equation	17	106	123
conic-equation	1	21	22
unmarked	0	24	24
total	48	309	357

the x axis; and the distance a is the X INTERCEPT. When x = 0, y = b. This is the point at which the same line crosses the y axis and the distance y is the Y INTERCEPT.

298. *WESTON CELL* (*wĕs'-tŏn sĕl*). The accepted standard cell, a two-fluid cadmium cell which gives a remarkably constant voltage.

The WESTON CELL uses pure mercury (Hg) as the positive electrode, and a cadmium amalgam as the negative electrode. Mercurous sulphate (Hg_2SO_4) covers the mercury and a solution of cadmium sulphate ($CdSO_4$) covers the cadmium. The WESTON CELL is surprisingly independent of local conditions. It should be used at 20 degrees centigrade, for as the temperature rises the voltage drops; but it varies only 0.0000406 volts for each degree change. Furthermore the WESTON CELL does not polarize as do ordinary VOLTAIC cells, where hydrogen collects on the copper and reduces the voltage.

To the question: 'Cell which furnishes the legal definition of a volt', 22 persons in the group of 40 who score high in English vocabulary answer WESTON, and only 12 VOLTAIC. But of the group low in English vocabulary 13 out of 40 mark VOLTAIC and only 11 WESTON. In this instance the group who score low in English vocabulary and choose VOLTAIC is large enough to affect the total population studied, for of 537 persons tabulated 210 mark VOLTAIC and only 175 WESTON.

VOLTAIC (*vŏl-tā'-ĭk*) is the general term for any cell which produces electricity at the expense of one of two metals im-

Cell which furnishes the legal definition of a volt in the United States.

FORM E. 16.	BO	FW	LA	NY	NY	NY	NY	PH	TU	SUM
voltaic	9	22	15	8	6	14	86	38	12	210
WESTON	10	13	11	7	9	15	62	39	9	175
lead-storage	4	2	2	1	1	5	27	1	3	46
Leyden	2	6	5	3	3	5	28	20	3	75
photoelectric	1	5	0	1	1	1	13	2	1	25
unmarked	2	2	0	0	0	0	2	0	0	6
total	28	50	33	20	20	40	218	100	28	537

FORM E. 16. ENGLISH VOCABULARY

	HIGH	LOW
voltaic	12	13
WESTON	22	11
lead-storage	0	6
Leyden	6	8
photoelectric	0	2
unmarked	0	0
total	40	40

mersed in a fluid. A strip of copper, the positive, and zinc, the negative, in any dilute acid, usually sulphuric (H_2SO_4) or hydrochloric (HCl), is a VOLTAIC cell.

The WESTON CELL gives a current of only 0.0001 amperes, and is not used to produce a current. It plays something of the same part as the standard French meter, the measuring stick, a starting point for precise measurements. It is used with a potentiometer, an extremely accurate instrument for measuring electromotive forces, which balances an unknown voltage against the known voltage of the standard cell in such a way that no current flows.

The Bureau of Standards of the United States calibrates a WESTON standard cell to six significant figures; and the voltage should remain constant for a year or more to within one hundredth of one per cent. It has been said that each improvement in the WESTON CELL, each significant figure added to its accuracy, has initiated a wave of general technical advances throughout the entire electrical world.

299. *BODY CENTRODE* (*bŏd'-ē sĕn'-trōd*). The path of the instantaneous center of a plane figure moving so that all points in the figure move in parallel fixed planes.

The mathematical term CENTRODE is a combination of CENTER

Locus of the instantaneous center in a body.

FORM E. 48.	BO	FW	LA	NY	NY	NY	NY	PH	TU	SUM
space centrode	0	7	2	1	1	1	16	10	3	41
axis of rotation	5	16	8	11	5	14	88	28	5	180
axis of inertia	9	15	11	4	3	14	52	29	10	147
BODY CENTRODE	7	9	10	4	11	4	52	27	9	133
cyclic coordinate	3	1	1	0	0	4	7	4	0	20
unmarked	4	2	1	0	0	3	3	2	1	16
total	28	50	33	20	20	40	218	100	28	537

FORM E. 48.	ENGLISH VOCABULARY	
	HIGH	LOW
space centrode	3	1
axis of rotation	8	16
axis of inertia	5	15
BODY CENTRODE	20	6
cyclic coordinate	4	1
unmarked	0	1
total	40	40

and the Greek ὁδός (hodos), road, path, way. A CENTRODE is the path traced by the instantaneous center of a rotating or moving body.

To the question: 'Locus of the instantaneous center in a body', 133 persons out of 537 answer correctly BODY CENTRODE; while 180 answer AXIS OF ROTATION. In his first edition,

1828, Noah Webster says: 'Axis, the straight line, real or imaginary, passing through a body, on which it revolves, or may revolve. 2. In geometry, a straight line in a plane figure, about which it revolves to produce a solid'.

A plane figure which moves with a combination rectilinear motion and rotative may be considered as rotating about a moving point, even outside the figure itself, called the INSTANTANEOUS CENTER OF ROTATION. The CENTRODE is the path traced by this instantaneous center of rotation.

In Elements of Dynamics, 1878, the word CENTRODE was used perhaps for the first time by William Kingdon Clifford, an English mathematician and philosopher, part author with Karl Pearson of Common Sense of the Exact Sciences, published in 1885 after Clifford's death in 1879. From George M. Minchin, Uniplanar Kinematics of Solids and Fluids, published in 1882, comes: 'A locus traced out by the successive positions of an instantaneous centre of pure rotation has received the special name of a CENTRODE'.

300. *CATENARY* (kăt'-ē-nā-rē) *n.* The curve assumed by a flexible chain hanging in equilibrium between two points of support, the curve of a perfectly flexible, inextensible, infinitely fine cord when at rest under the action of forces, which in the common CATENARY are parallel, as a cord under the influence of gravity.

The word CATENARY comes from the Latin *catenarius,* from the noun *catena,* a chain.

Of the CATENARY John Harris, 1704, says: 'CATENAR, CATENARIA, is the Curve Line which a Rope hanging freely between two Points of Suſpenſion forms it ſelf into. What the nature of this Curve is, was enquired amongſt the Geometers in Galileus's time; but I don't find any thing was done towards a Diſcovery till in the Year 1690, James Bernoulli publiſhed it as a Problem; which about two Months after, Leibnitz declared he had found out, and would communicate within the Year: In December 1690, John the Brother of James Bernoulli communicated an Inveſtigation of it to the Editors of the Acta Eruditorum, which was publiſhed afterwards June 1691. This CATENARY or

FUNICULAR he faith he found not to be truly Geometrical, but of the Mechanical kind, becaufe its nature cannot be expreffed by a determinate Algebraick Equation; but Leibnitz gives its Conftruction Geometrically'.

Ephraim Chambers, writing in 1728, twenty-five years after John Harris, says of CATENARY: 'The nature of this curve was inveftigated by Galilaeo, who suppofed it to be the fame with the PARABOLA'. Even today to the question: 'The curve made

The curve made by a chain or cable hung by its ends.

FORM C. 43.	CH	FORM CA. 38.	CH	LA	NY	NY	PH	SUM
curtate	2	curtate	2	1	1	6	3	13
prolate	2	trochoid	3	1	2	4	1	11
parabola	29	parabola	15	15	40	106	29	205
concurve	16	concurve	11	5	26	77	11	130
CATENARY	19	CATENARY	9	15	26	82	27	159
unmarked	0	unmarked	0	0	2	2	3	7
total	68	total	40	37	97	277	74	525

FORM CB. 37.	NY
curtate	3
trochoid	5
parabola	37
concurve	21
CATENARY	19
unmarked	1
total	86

by a chain or cable hung by its ends', 159 persons out of 525 answer CATENARY; while 205 answer PARABOLA. To the eye the two curves are nearly identical. But the formula of the PARABOLA, or at least one way of writing it, is: $x^{1/2} - y^{1/2} = a^{1/2}$; while the formula of the CATENARY is:

$$y = \frac{a}{2} (e^{\frac{x}{a}} - e^{-\frac{x}{a}}).$$

The CATENARY is used obviously in the study of suspension bridges; and Chambers quotes Dr. D. Gregory as showing: 'That the inverted CATENARIA is the best figure for an arch'.

301. *REGELATION* (rē-jē-lā'-shŏn) *n.* The melting of ice under pressure and refreezing with the release of pressure. The word REGELATION comes from the Latin *regelare*, to thaw, warm. This in turn is a combination of *re-*, again, back, and the verb *gelare*, to freeze, congeal. From *gelare*, to freeze, come the unusual adjective GELID (*jĕl'-ĭd*), cold, icy, the verb to CONGEAL (*kŏn-jēl'*), to freeze, and the noun GELATIN (*jĕl'-ā-tĭn*), the animal substance. Although the Latin *regelare* meant to thaw, the English REGELATION means to freeze again, refreeze.

The word REGELATION for the phenomenon observed by Faraday, the freezing together of separate pieces of thawing

Phenomenon of melting below and freezing above a weighted wire resting on a block of ice.

FORM BA. 33.	NY	FORM D. 37.	NY	%
sublimation	14	sublimation	45	12.9
glaciation	24	glaciation	88	25.2
recalescence	24	recalescence	66	18.9
osmotic transfer	6	osmotic transfer	35	10.0
REGELATION	31	REGELATION	104	29.6
unmarked	1	unmarked	12	3.4
total	100	total	350	100.0

FORM DA. 35.	NY	FORM DB. 38.	NY
sublimation	13	sublimation	20
glaciation	30	glaciation	24
recalescence	16	recalescence	18
osmotic transfer	13	osmotic transfer	14
REGELATION	25	REGELATION	27
unmarked	3	unmarked	3
total	100	total	106

ice, was proposed by Dr. Joseph Dalton Hooker and was first used in 1857 in a memoir published by Mr. Huxley and Mr. Tyndall in the Philosophical Transactions.

As ice expands on freezing, so it contracts on melting. Pressure promotes this contraction, aids melting, lowering the melting point. Under a pressure of one atmosphere ice melts 0.0072 degrees centigrade below zero, the ordinary melting point.

Even this very slight lowering of the melting point plays its part in numerous phenomena.

A loop of thin wire hung over a block of ice, and weighted down by two or three kilograms, sinks gradually. The pressure of the wire lowers the melting point just enough for the ice to melt. Relieved of the pressure, the water above the wire refreezes. This refreezing under relieved pressure is REGELATION.

With a temperature just below freezing, snow stepped on melts under the weight of the body, and refreezes as ice when the pressure is released.

In 1850 Mr. Faraday observed that: 'Two pieces of ice at 32° Fahr., with moist surfaces, when placed in contact, freeze together to a rigid mass. This is called REGELATION'. Even in 1891 The Century Dictionary adds: 'The phenomenon, first observed by Faraday, is obscure'. Increased pressure at the various points of contact causes the ice there to melt. This melting cools the region. The water formed tends to escape. Relieved of pressure for an instant it refreezes and returns to the original temperature. This succession of melting and freezing, with the accompanying thermal effects, goes on until the two blocks are cemented into one.

To the question: 'The phenomenon of melting below and freezing above a weighted wire resting upon a block of ice', 25 per cent answer REGELATION, but 30 per cent answer GLACIATION, to form DA administered about 1934. In the earlier form BA, first administered about 1929, 31 per cent answered correctly, and 24 per cent GLACIATION. In 1953, 27 per cent answer correctly, and 24 per cent GLACIATION, closer than figures usually agree with these populations. There is a close historical association between GLACIATION and REGELATION. In 1854, on a visit to the Penrhyn slate quarries, John Tyndall became interested in slate cleavage. This led him to Switzerland to study glaciers. In opposition to James D. Forbes, who did so much for Clerk Maxwell as a boy, and who asserted that ice was viscous, Tyndall insisted that the flow of glaciers was due to fracture and REGELATION. In a lecture on Ice and Glaciers, Helmholtz opposed Tyndall's theory; but later in an appendix of 1865 he added that Tyndall had 'assigned the essential and principal cause of glacier motion in referring it to fracture and REGELATION'.

302. *JOULE-THOMSON EFFECT* (*jool-tŏm'-sŏn*). Cooling
caused by the gradual expansion of a gas due to work
done, and so to heat absorbed, in separating the molecules
against their slight attraction for one another.

James Prescott Joule, who lived from 1818 to 1889, took up
physics as a boy, perhaps because he could use the equipment
of his father's large brewery in his experiments, perhaps because
John Dalton, the chemist, was one of his tutors, though Dalton
died when Joule was sixteen. Joule was almost an invalid, with
spinal trouble, and so was educated at home. At the age of nine-

Cooling effect when a gas expands through a small hole.

FORM BA. 39.	NY	FORM D. 43.	NY	%
condensation	36	condensation	116	33.1
Hertzian effect	5	Hertzian effect	32	9.1
Compton effect	6	Compton effect	74	21.2
JOULE-THOMSON EFFECT	20	JOULE-THOMSON EFFECT	38	10.8
ebullition	30	ebullition	66	18.9
unmarked	3	unmarked	24	6.9
total	100	total	350	100.0

FORM DA. 41.	NY	FORM DB. 37.	NY
condensation	31	condensation	39
Hertzian effect	15	Hertzian	17
Compton effect	11	Compton	13
JOULE-THOMSON EFFECT	26	JOULE-THOMSON	19
ebullition	12	ebullition	14
unmarked	5	unmarked	4
total	100	total	106

teen he invented an electromagnetic engine. While still young
he tried and failed to measure the change in temperature of a
gas when it leaked through a small hole from one container
into an empty one and so expanded. On his honeymoon in
Switzerland he met William Thomson, who became Lord
Kelvin; and in 1884, repeating the experiment together with a

porous plug of cotton wool through which the gas escaped, they found a lower temperature in the second container.

After Joule's death Lord Kelvin said: 'Joule's discovery of a thermodynamic law, through the regions of electrochemistry, electromagnetism, and elasticity of gases, was based on a delicacy of thermometry which seemed impossible to some of the most distinguished chemists of the day'.

In the refrigeration process CONDENSATION is an important step and this may lead to the frequent marking of this word in answer to: 'The cooling of a gas or liquid on expanding through a small hole'. CONDENSATION, marked by 31 per cent, more often than the correct answer, and the corresponding verb, to CONDENSE, come from the Latin *com-*, together, and *densare,* to make thick, from *densus,* dense, thick, close. To CONDENSE may mean to make more dense, more compact, to reduce in volume, compress; or, as the word is more frequently used in physics, to change from a gas to a liquid. In refrigeration, gas is changed to a liquid, CONDENSED, by pressure. Then in a subsequent chamber this liquid is relieved of its pressure and so changes back to a gas. In so doing it absorbs heat from its surroundings which are thereby cooled.

The JOULE-THOMSON EFFECT cools the gas, not however through condensation and subsequent evaporation, not through changing from a gas to a liquid and back to a gas, but through the escape of rapidly moving molecules through a tiny hole into an empty chamber.

303. *COERCIVE FORCE* (*kō-er'-sĭv fors*). A measure of the characteristic which renders the impartation of magnetism slow and difficult and which retards the return of a bar usually of iron or steel once magnetized to the normal state when active magnetization ceases, the reversed magnetizing force that is just sufficient to reduce the residual magnetism in a material to zero.

The verb to COERCE (*kō-ers'*) is to restrain by authority, constrain to obedience by the force of law, compel to compliance. The word comes from the Latin *coercere,* to surround, encompass, control, curb. From this should come *coercitive,* which however is always shortened to COERCIVE. COERCIVE refers to the force or property within a substance which tends to hold the magnetism which has been produced, the power which causes HYSTERESIS ($h\breve{i}s$-$t\breve{e}$-$r\bar{e}'$-$s\breve{i}s$).

To the question: 'The value of the magnetizing field required to reduce the flux density to zero', 23 per cent answer COERCIVE FORCE, but 28 per cent answer MAGNETIC HYSTERESIS, almost an opposite of the question as worded. The popularity of HYS-TERESIS appears also in the previous study of form c, where 28 per cent marked COERCIVE FORCE and 33 per cent MAGNETIC

The value of the magnetizing field required to reduce the flux density to zero.

FORM C. 38. NY COERCIVE		FORM CA. 37. BO COERCIVE		NY HIGH	NY NEXT	NY REST	NY MISC.	SUM
FORCE	114	FORCE	26	111	99	221	52	509
permanence	28	permanence	5	21	37	199	22	284
permeability	50	permeability	16	80	77	216	39	428
magnetic		magnetic						
hysteresis	133	hysteresis	33	142	139	252	65	631
reluctance	50	reluctance	14	46	48	212	50	370
unmarked	25	unmarked	6	0	0	0	6	12
total	400	total	100	400	400	1100	234	2234

HYSTERESIS. HYSTERESIS is the phenomenon, the fact that a metal which has been magnetized keeps some of this magnetism even after the magnetizing force has been removed. The COERCIVE FORCE is an indication of the amount of magnetism which has been retained, it is the amount of reverse magnetization needed to remove the magnetism.

From Elementary Lessons in Electricity and Magnetism by Silvanus P. Thompson, 1896 (1894), comes: '(J. A.) Ewing has given the name HYSTERESIS (1881) to the subject of the lag of magnetic effects behind their causes'. Also from Thompson comes: 'If a new piece of iron or steel is subjected to an increasing magnetizing force, and then the magnetizing force is decreased to zero, some magnetism remains. The amount which remains is called the REMANENCE ($r\breve{e}m'$-$\breve{a}$-$n\breve{e}ns$). The amount of reverse magnetic force needed to demagnetize the iron is a measure of the retentivity of the material, and is known as the COERCIVE FORCE'.

304. *HYPERBOLA* (*hī-per'-bō-lah*) n. The locus (56) of
a point which moves in such a way that the difference of
its distances from two fixed points is always the same. Reread
CONIC (251).

The two fixed points are called FOCI; and the difference of the
distances to them is a positive constant less than the distance
between them.

The word HYPERBOLA comes from the Greek ὑπερβολή (hyperbola), a combination of ὑπέρ (hyper), over, and βάλλειν
(ballein), to throw. The term was used by Apollonius, who
was born about 262 B.C., the greatest of the Greek writers on

Curve whose equation is

$$\frac{x^2}{a^2} - \frac{y^2}{b^2} = 1.$$

FORM A. 19.	BO	NY	SUM	FORM AA. 46.	NY
parabola	3	6	9	parabola	32
ellipse	6	17	23	ellipse	27
HYPERBOLA	8	9	17	HYPERBOLA	46
circle	1	5	6	circle	12
helix	1	3	4	helix	13
unmarked	1	1	2	unmarked	2
total	20	41	61	total	132

the conic sections. He is said to have used the term because the
square of the rectangle on the abscissa equal to the square of the
ordinate overlaps the latus rectum.

To the question: 'Curve whose equation is:

$$\frac{x^2}{a^2} - \frac{y^2}{b^2} = 1',$$

46 persons out of 132 answer correctly HYPERBOLA; while 32
answer PARABOLA (111), and 27 ELLIPSE. The ELLIPSE (205) is
the locus of a point which moves in such a way that the sum
of its distances from two fixed points is always the same. The
equation of the ELLIPSE is:

$$\frac{x^2}{a^2} + \frac{y^2}{b^2} = 1,$$

the same as that of the HYPERBOLA except for the plus sign. In the ELLIPSE 2a is the sum of the distances from the two fixed points, the FOCI; while in the formula for the HYPERBOLA 2a is the difference of the distances to the FOCI.

305. *YAW* (*yaw*) *n.* The swing of an airplane to one side or the other about a vertical axis sometimes called the AXIS OF YAW.

The verb to YAW is primarily nautical and means to deviate from a straight course. The British navy captain, Frederick Marryat, writes: 'She steered wild, YAWED, and decreased in her rate of sailing'. From the verb comes the noun YAW, the temporary deviation of a ship from its direct course. Like so many nautical terms, YAW is related to both Norwegian and Icelandic words.

In an aircraft YAWING results in a difference between the direction of flight and the direction in which the plane is point-

An angular displacement about an axis parallel to the normal (i.e. vertical) axis of the aircraft.

FORM A. 18.	FW	LA	NY	NY	NY	PH	SUM	FORM AA. 39.	NY
pitch	4	9	4	18	23	31	89	pitch	10
bank	1	16	16	24	46	68	171	bank	9
sideslip	3	8	6	2	24	26	69	sideslip	13
skid	1	5	0	3	12	17	38	roll	8
YAW	9	16	10	15	34	51	135	YAW	22
unmarked	0	0	1	4	1	7	13	unmarked	1
total	18	54	37	66	140	200	515	total	63

ing. It is movement to right or left without banking so that one wing leads the other.

In answer to the question: 'An angular displacement about an axis parallel to the normal (i.e. vertical) axis of an aircraft', 135 persons out of 515 mark YAW; while a larger number, 171, mark BANK. One trouble may be the awkward wording of the definition. BANKING is rotation about the longitudinal axis extending front to back. It is controlled by the ailerons which lift one wing and lower the other. YAWING is rotation about the vertical axis extending up and down. It is controlled by the rudder.

In the revised form AA the definition has been simplified: 'A swing to one side or the other about the up-and-down axis'. Here 22 persons out of the 63 whose scores have been tabulated choose YAW, 35 per cent marking it correctly instead of 26 per cent as in the earlier form; but 13 persons now mark SIDESLIP. SIDESLIP occurs when one wing is below the other and the plane is moving forward, not turning; or when it is not turning fast enough to correspond with the tilt of the wings. The plane slides down sidewise. The purpose is to lose altitude without increasing the forward speed. In both a BANK and a SIDESLIP one wing is below the other. When a BANK is accompanied by a corresponding turn there is no SIDESLIP. In a YAW or in YAWING the wings are level. A YAW is a side-to-side motion with the wings horizontal.

306. *GEODETIC* (*jē-ō-dĕt′-ĭk*) *adj.* Lattice work, basket weave, a form of aircraft fusilage construction which distributes the stresses evenly over the entire structure by use of a large number of light members forming a network on the principle that on a curved surface the great circle is the shortest distance between two points.

GEODETIC is the adjective which corresponds to the noun GEODESY. Both come from the Greek γεωδαισία (geodaisia), the art of measuring, a combination of γῆ (ge), the earth, already met in the adjective GEOMETRIC (190), and δαίειν (daiein), to divide. GEODESY (*jē-ŏd′-ĕ-sē*) was originally land surveying in general; but the term is used today more specifically for measuring with exactness large areas of the earth's surface. In this sense the adjective occurs in the phrase: 'Coast and Geodetic Surveys'.

William Thomson, later Lord Kelvin, and P. G. Tait, in An Elementary Treatise on Natural Philosophy, on which they collaborated, wrote in 1879: 'If the shortest possible line be drawn from one point of a surface to another, its plane of curvature is everywhere perpendicular to the surface. Such a curve is called a GEODETIC line'. It is in this sense that the adjective GEODETIC is applied to fuselage construction; each strip follows the shortest line from one point to another on the curved surface. These lines crossing one another almost at right angles form a network or basket weave.

To the question: 'Type of fuselage in which the internal construction resembles a basket woven with fibers set at 45 degree angles', 120 persons out of 515 answer correctly GEODETIC; but 182 answer REINFORCED SHELL. The REINFORCED SHELL construction of the fuselage is one of the three classes into which the MONOCOQUE or shell-type fuselage is ordinarily divided. These are: FULL-MONOCOQUE, SEMI-MONOCOQUE, and REINFORCED

Form A. Type of fuselage in which internal construction resembles a basket woven with fibers set at 45° angles.

Form AA. Construction resembling a basket weave.

FORM A. 9.	FW	LA	NY	NY	NY	PH	SUM	FORM AA. 40.	NY
welded-steel-tube	0	8	3	3	10	17	41	welded-steel-tube	5
monocoque	5	6	6	11	29	42	99	monocoque	18
GEODETIC	8	20	11	16	24	41	120	GEODETIC	12
semi-monocoque	1	6	3	12	16	24	62	semi-monocoque	6
reinforced-shell	4	14	13	21	59	71	182	reinforced-shell	20
unmarked	0	0	1	3	2	5	11	unmarked	2
total	18	54	37	66	140	200	515	total	63

SHELL; and different parts of the same fuselage may be of any one of the three kinds. All three rely on the strength of the skin. The word MONOCOQUE comes from the French *coque*, egg-shell. It does not appear at all under M in the volume of the Oxford dictionary which came out in 1908; but is in the supplement of 1933. Here the first quotation gives MONOCOQUE as meaning egg-shaped, like an elongated egg, blunt at one end. It seems more likely that the derivation comes from the fact that the MONOCOQUE design depends for its strength upon the construction of the shell. The REINFORCED SHELL construction has the skin reinforced with a complete framework of structural members. The GEODETIC airplane construction resembles a basket weave in which the stresses are distributed substantially evenly over the entire structure.

307. *MATRIX* (*mă'-trĭks*) *n.* An ordered set of mn elements arranged in a rectangular array, with m rows and n columns. The plural is MATRICES (*mă'-trĭ-sēz*). The notation commonly used is:

$$A = \begin{matrix} a_{11} & a_{12} & a_{13} & \ldots & a_{1n} \\ a_{21} & a_{22} & a_{23} & \ldots & a_{2n} \\ a_{31} & a_{32} & a_{33} & \ldots & a_{3n} \\ \cdot & \cdot & \cdot & \ldots & \cdot \\ \cdot & \cdot & \cdot & \ldots & \cdot \\ a_{m1} & a_{m2} & a_{m3} & \ldots & a_{mn}. \end{matrix}$$

The word MATRIX comes directly from the Latin *matrix*, *matricis*, originally a breeding animal, from *mater*, mother, which occurs in the familiar phrase: ALMA MATER, literally nourishing mother, cherishing mother. MATRIX may be used in English today in a general sense for the mold or form in which anything is shaped, that which encloses something, like the womb. In mathematics, a MATRIX is a rectangular array of quantities, so called because it is thought of as a mold or set of compartments into which fit various quantities.

To the question: 'A square table of variables', 44 persons out of 132, whose scores have been tabulated, answer MATRIX as intended; but 33 answer QUADRANT; and 30 others DETERMINANT. QUADRANT seems clearly wrong. A QUADRANT is a quarter of a circle, an angle of 90 degrees, the area embraced by such an angle, or one of the quarters of a plane surface delineated by rectangular coordinates. Reread QUADRANT (188).

DETERMINANT is probably correct with the present wording of the question. A DETERMINANT can be formed from the elements of a square MATRIX. This is called the DETERMINANT of the MATRIX. Or a DETERMINANT can be formed by striking out rows or columns from a rectangular MATRIX. A DETERMINANT, when that word is used more or less incorrectly to mean merely the arrangement, and not the sum of the products, is always square. A MATRIX may be rectangular. The algebraic sum of all of the DETERMINANTAL PRODUCTS of a MATRIX is called the DETERMINANT of the MATRIX. By DETERMINANTAL PRODUCT from a square MATRIX, with n columns and n rows, is meant a product of n quantities, one from each column and one from each row.

A DETERMINANT is a homogeneous polynomial of the nth degree. A MATRIX is a system of n² elements arranged in the order in which they stand in the determinant, but not combined into

A square table of variables.

FORM A. 23.	BO	NY	SUM	FORM AA. 47.	NY
determinant	8	12	20	determinant	30
octant	2	3	5	octant	10
quadrant	4	12	16	quadrant	33
MATRIX	4	9	13	MATRIX	44
order	1	4	5	order	12
unmarked	1	1	2	unmarked	3
total	20	41	61	total	132

a polynomial. A single upright bar is drawn each side of a DETERMINANT; a double upright bar on each side of a MATRIX. A MATRIX is not a quantity, but a system of quantities. Interchanging rows and columns has no effect on a DETERMINANT, but gives a new MATRIX.

308. *POSTULATE* (*pŏs′-tū-lāt*) *n.* Something one is asked to take for granted, a geometrical premise put forward for acceptance without proof, a self-evident practical proposition. Reread THEOREM (130).

The word POSTULATE comes from the Latin *postulatus*, the past participle of *postulare*, to ask, demand, require. A POSTULATE is something one is asked to believe.

Euclid began with seven AXIOMS and six POSTULATES. His AXIOMS were of general application, partly definitions which he may have felt were already accepted. His POSTULATES were much the same but applied more specifically to geometry, as: A straight line may be drawn between any two points; a straight line may be produced indefinitely; about any point as a center a circle with any radius may be described; and all right angles are equal.

To the question: 'An assumption that a geometric operation may be performed', 15 persons out of 61 answer POSTULATE; while 23 answer PROPOSITION, and 14 THEOREM. All three probably fit this definition. In the revised form AA, the question has been changed to: 'A geometric assumption one is asked to accept without proof'. Here 62 persons out of 132 answer correctly POSTULATE, twice the percentage of the earlier study; while 30 answer THEOREM, and 25 PROPOSITION. A PROPOSITION,

Form A. An assumption that a geometric operation may be performed.
Form AA. A geometric assumption one is asked to accept without proof.

	FORM A. 29.	BO	NY	SUM	FORM AA. 44	NY
	theorem	4	10	14	theorem	30
	conclusion	1	2	3	conclusion	8
	induction	2	2	4	induction	6
	POSTULATE	5	10	15	POSTULATE	62
	proposition	7	16	23	proposition	25
	unmarked	1	1	2	unmarked	1
	total	20	41	61	total	132

from *pro*, forward, and *ponere*, to put, is anything put forward for acceptance, which cannot be proved because of its fundamental nature. Or a PROPOSITION may be a THEOREM which is provable, demonstrable. A PROPOSITION may be important or unimportant, general or specific, provable or axiomatic. PROPOSITION is the general term for anything put forward.

Both a THEOREM and a POSTULATE are PROPOSITIONS. Both are important. A THEOREM is more theoretical; a POSTULATE, more directly practical. A THEOREM must be provable, demonstrable; a POSTULATE is never proved, it is one of the assumptions with which one starts to prove a THEOREM.

309. *VISCOSITY* (*vĭs-kŏs'-ĭ-tē*) *n.* Resistance to steady flow, yielding to shearing stress, defined as imperfectly fluid, intermediate between solid and fluid.
Of VISCOSITY, Clerk Maxwell says in his Theory of Heat, published in 1871, the year he became professor of experimental physics at Cambridge, after retiring from King's College, London: 'When the very smallest stress, if continued long enough, will cause a constantly increasing change of form, the body must be regarded as a VISCOUS fluid, however hard it may be'.

The adjective VISCOUS comes from the Latin *viscosus*, sticky, and this in turn from *viscum*, a noun which means both mistletoe and bird-lime. The word VISCUM is used today for the genus of parasitic plants which includes the mistletoe. From the same source comes the adjective VISCID, sticky, glutinous, a word defined by Blount in his Glossographia in 1670. Although often defined in identical terms, VISCID should be used of a sticky surface; VISCOUS, for the internal structure.

To the question: 'The property of a substance by virtue of which it resists rapid distortion', 22 per cent of 2234 persons answer VISCOSITY; but 29 per cent answer TOUGHNESS. From Studies of Natural Philosophy, 1830, by Sir John Herschel comes: 'The TOUGHNESS of a solid, or that quality by which it will endure heavy blows without breaking'. TOUGHNESS goes back to 1580: 'TOUGHNESS, a clammie or gluish humous', and is really a literary rather than a technical term. But TOUGHNESS

The property of a substance by virtue of which it resists rapid distortion.

FORM C. 50. NY		FORM CA. 45. BO		NY HIGH	NY NEXT	NY REST	NY MISC.	SUM
VISCOSITY surface	80	VISCOSITY surface	23	101	84	209	65	482
tension	35	tension	9	26	61	216	30	342
elasticity	96	elasticity	15	84	86	216	37	438
plasticity	36	plasticity	9	34	44	205	20	312
toughness	130	toughness	41	155	125	254	77	652
unmarked	23	unmarked	3	0	0	0	5	8
total	400	total	100	400	400	1100	234	2234

and VISCOSITY are often used interchangeably, and frequently defined in nearly identical terms. From 1731, An Essay concerning the Nature of Aliments by John Arbuthnot, the Scottish physician, wit, and man of letters, physician extraordinary and later ordinary to Queen Anne, comes: 'The VISCOSITY or TOUGHNESS of the fluids'. Of the adjective TOUGH the Century Dictionary says: 'Of VISCOUS consistence or nature', also: 'Having the property of flexibility without brittleness, tenacious, stiff, ropey, viscous'. Still of TOUGH it says: 'Sticky, adhesive, tenacious, glutinous'. Of VISCOUS it says: 'Glutinous, tenacious, adhesive, sticky'. TOUGHNESS is just as satisfactory an answer to the present question as VISCOSITY, and must be removed as a mislead.

Although Maxwell speaks of the VISCOSITY of gases, the term should probably be limited to liquids; for the mechanism differs. The VISCOSITY of a liquid becomes less as the temperature goes up, that of a gas greater. The VISCOSITY of a liquid is due to the attraction of the molecules; the VISCOSITY of a gas to the interchange of molecules between one sliding layer and another.

The Century Dictionary opposes MOBILITY to VISCOSITY. Weld, in his Dictionary of Physics, opposes LIMPID to VISCOUS. But LIMPID comes from the Latin *limpidus*, shining; LIMPID means clear, bright, and is not the opposite of VISCOUS, except by implication. Pitch is VISCOUS and is not clear, not LIMPID. Tyndall gives treacle, honey, tar, and lava as VISCOUS substances. VISCOUS means resisting flow.

VISCOSITY is one of the important properties of a lubricating oil, which must have sufficient VISCOSITY to form a continuous layer between the moving parts, without causing waste of energy, for fluid friction varies directly as the VISCOSITY.

310. *DISPERSION* (*dĭs-per'-zhŏn*) *n.* The separation of different colored rays of light arising from their different wave lengths, ability of a prism to open up a spectrum, difference between the indices of refraction for extreme rays, dispersive power of an optical substance. Reread DIFFRACTION (256).

The word DISPERSION comes from the Latin *dispergere*, to scatter. This Latin verb, with the past participle *dispersus*, is a combination of *dis*, apart, and *spargere*, to strew, sprinkle, scatter, the source of the English word SPARSE, thinly scattered. To DISPERSE is to scatter, sprinkle around, strew. The more unusual word ASPERGE is also to sprinkle; while ASPERSE is to sprinkle with mud or dirt, bespatter with foul reports, a verb which corresponds to the more familiar noun ASPERSION.

Given the question: 'The separation of the components of white light on passing through a prism', 22 per cent answer correctly DISPERSION, but 32 per cent choose DIFFRACTION (256), and another 30 per cent REFRACTION. This mistake was actually made in the construction of the original form AB, where REFRACTION was scored as the correct answer.

The word REFRACTION comes from the Latin *refractus*, the past participle of *refringere*, literally to break back. This comes from the verb *frangere*, to break, with the past participle *fractus*, the source also of DIFFRACTION. REFRACTION is the bending of a ray on passing from one medium into another where its speed differs. REFRACTION is the bending of light when it strikes obliquely the dividing surface between one substance

Separation of the components of white light on passing through a prism.

FORM AB. 34.		FORM D. 32.		
REFRACTION	46	refraction	134	38.3
interference	1	interference	4	1.1
diffraction	52	diffraction	49	14.0
distortion	0	DISPERSION	149	42.6
deflection	1	deflection	11	3.1
unmarked	0	unmarked	3	0.9
total	100	total	350	100.0

FORM DA. 28.		FORM DB. 40.	
refraction	30	refraction	36
diffusion	13	diffusion	17
diffraction	32	diffraction	26
DISPERSION	22	DISPERSION	22
deflection	1	convergence	2
unmarked	2	unmarked	3
total	100	total	106

and another. Light which is REFRACTED the least is red; that which is REFRACTED the most is violet; so that a difference in REFRACTION causes DISPERSION. Violet light, or light of any color, entering a second prism is REFRACTED again, bent on entering, but is not DISPERSED. The success of an achromatic lens depends upon differentiating between these two phenomena; such a lens REFRACTS without a DISPERSION of the colors. There is REFRACTION without DISPERSION.

REFRACTION is the bending of a beam of light in passing from one medium to another due to a different velocity in the new medium. DIFFRACTION is the bending of a beam of light around the corner of an opaque object. DISPERSION is the separating of light into its component colors.

311. *CHARLES' LAW* (*charlz law*). The pressure of a gas when the volume is constant varies directly with the temperature, the pressure coefficients of all ordinary gases are the same, the volume coefficients of expansion of all gases are equal. The figure was later found accurately in about 1842 by Henri Victor Regnault (*rĕ-nō'*), who became director of the Sèvres porcelain works in 1854, to be 1/273.

Jacques Alexander César Charles, who lived from 1746 to 1823, began as a clerk in the Ministry of Finance, but soon turned to science, principally to an interest in the atmosphere, and gained note for his public experiments and demonstrations. In the same year in which Montgolfier sent up his hot-air

Law that the pressure of a given mass of a perfect gas at constant volume varies directly with its absolute temperature.

FORM C. 5.	NY	FORM CA. 8.	BO	NY HIGH	NY NEXT	NY REST	NY MISC.	SUM
CHARLES' LAW	324	CHARLES' LAW	32	219	151	279	69	750
Tycho Brahe's law	6	Boyle's law	55	167	214	424	126	986
Faraday's first law	27	Faraday's first law	4	3	12	150	19	188
Avogadro's law	38	Avogadro's law	5	6	21	142	13	187
Mariette's law	5	Mariette's law	1	5	2	105	6	119
unmarked	0	unmarked	3	0	0	0	1	4
total	400	total	100	400	400	1100	234	2234

balloon, Charles for the first time inflated one with hydrogen. A year later, 1783, a man ascended with it. In his work with gases Charles noticed that the coefficient of expansion was about the same for all. The law which now bears his name he announced in 1787. It states the relation of volume to temperature; as usually worded today it says that the volume is directly proportional to the absolute temperature.

Both Charles in England and Gay-Lussac a few years later in France, working independently, found that as a gas was heated its pressure increased directly with its temperature. To give both men credit, the relation of pressure and temperature is sometimes called CHARLES' LAW, and the relation of volume and temperature, GAY-LUSSAC'S LAW, for, when the pressure of a given mass of a gas is constant, the volume is directly proportional to the absolute temperature.

To the question: 'Law that the pressure of a given mass of a perfect gas at constant volume varies directly with its absolute temperature', 34 per cent of 2234 persons answer CHARLES' LAW; while 44 per cent answer BOYLE'S LAW. Of the 400 New York cases who score highest on the physics vocabulary test as a whole out of a total 1900, 55 per cent choose correctly CHARLES' LAW, and only 42 per cent BOYLE'S LAW. As this item appeared earlier in the original form C of the physics vocabulary test, the mislead BOYLE'S LAW was not included; and the item was marked correctly by 81 per cent. But in the revised form CA, with the mislead BOYLE'S LAW, the item becomes far more difficult. An early step in the learning process is knowing that CHARLES' LAW deals with the general relationship of pressure, volume, and temperature; and much later comes the distinction, the knowledge that CHARLES' LAW deals with pressure and temperature, BOYLE'S LAW (129) with pressure and volume.

Were each item of these vocabulary tests to be made as difficult as possible, the results would show only the final step in the learning process and not the series which must be taken toward the meaning of a word or phrase. CHARLES' LAW, without the mislead BOYLE'S LAW, will be included in an easy physics vocabulary test now under construction, and will also be retained in the difficult form, with the mislead BOYLE'S LAW.

The two laws were more than a hundred years apart in their discovery. During the interval the fahrenheit thermometer scale was devised. CHARLES' LAW, which comes after this discovery, deals with the change of volume with temperature; BOYLE'S LAW, which comes earlier, deals with the change of volume with pressure. Boyle seems to have been aware of the change of pressure with temperature; but Boyle, 1662, had no temperature scale, for, although it is said that Galileo invented the thermometer, his AIR-THERMOSCOPE was affected by variations of atmospheric pressure. The sealed thermometer of today was sponsored and made available by the Grand Duke Ferdinand the Second, of Tuscany, as early as 1654; but the fahrenheit scale was not proposed until about 1714, and some such scale was needed for the study of temperature and for CHARLES' LAW, 1787.

The modern explanation of CHARLES' LAW is that heating a gas, raising its temperature, increases the mean velocity of its molecules. The faster moving molecules hit the walls of the containing vessel more often and with greater momentum and as a result the pressure on the container increases.

The kinetic theory regards each gas as a collection of independently moving molecules, and by treating their collective motions statistically arrives at CHARLES' LAW. Substituting independently moving human beings in this statement gives the premises with which the Human Engineering Laboratory began its research. By measuring a sufficient number of independently moving individuals it is possible to build laws of human behavior, much as the kinetic theory derives CHARLES' LAW.

One practical difference is that physics started with the generalization, with the over-all law, and does not even today attempt to predict the future movements of individual molecules. The Human Engineering Laboratory starts with measuring numerous independently moving human beings with the hope of combining the accumulated results into laws; and laws are now actually emerging.

312. *BRAKE HORSEPOWER* (*brāk*). Horsepower measured by test at the propeller shaft, total computed horsepower minus friction, indicated horsepower less friction horsepower. Reread the easier word HORSEPOWER (77).

BRAKE HORSEPOWER is the result of laboratory tests. It is called BRAKE horsepower because it was formerly measured by tightening a brake, in the form of a U-shaped motionless belt, stretched around a pulley on the shaft. The pull or force on the

fixed belt caused by the friction of the revolving pulley, determined by attaching a spring balance to each end of the belt
and taking the difference between the two in pounds, multiplied by the distance through which the force acts per minute,
that is multiplied by the circumference of the wheel times its
number of revolutions per minute, gives the power. Foot-
pounds of power obtained in this way divided by 33,000 gives

Form A. Horsepower available at the propeller end of an airplane engine.
Form AA. Horsepower at the propeller shaft measured by test.

FORM A. 32.	FW	LA	NY	NY	NY	PH	SUM	FORM AA. 37.	NY
indicated horsepower	0	6	6	14	16	29	71	indicated	6
power peak	0	2	6	7	19	17	51	power peak	17
friction horsepower	0	3	3	3	11	6	26	available	6
rated horsepower	7	21	9	24	46	83	190	rated	13
BREAK HORSEPOWER	11	22	10	10	46	56	155	BREAK	21
unmarked	0	0	3	8	2	9	22	unmarked	0
total	18	54	37	66	140	200	515	total	63

the BRAKE HORSEPOWER of the engine driving the pulley. This
is horsepower produced by the engine under test conditions.
BRAKE HORSEPOWER is that part of the total horsepower of an
engine which can be used to perform work. In an aircraft
engine it may be as high as 85 to 90 per cent of the theoretically
computed horsepower.

To the question: 'Horsepower available at the propeller end
of an airplane engine', 155 persons in a population of 515, or
30 per cent, answer correctly BRAKE HORSEPOWER; but a larger
number, 190, answer RATED HORSEPOWER. The question: 'Horsepower available at the propeller' might easily suggest or even
mean available under cruising conditions, and so be answered
correctly as RATED HORSEPOWER, which is the maximum horsepower available for a prolonged operation. In the revised form
AA, the question reads: 'Horsepower at the propeller shaft

measured by test'. Here 21 persons out of the 63 whose scores have been tabulated answer BRAKE; 17, POWER-PEAK; with 13 still answering RATED. RATED HORSEPOWER is always less than the maximum BRAKE HORSEPOWER; it is the power which can be used safely for a long period. RATED HORSEPOWER is that given in the specifications by the manufacturer. It is based on many laboratory tests, each yielding a BRAKE HORSEPOWER. It is the manufacturer's judgment of the horsepower continuously available at the propeller shaft. Such manufacturer's specifications include the revolutions per minute of the crankshaft and the manifold pressure in inches of mercury at which the RATED HORSEPOWER can best be developed. BRAKE HORSEPOWERS are measured at different atmospheric pressures and for different revolutions per minute, and are one of the bases for stating RATED HORSEPOWER.

313. *WEIGHT* (*wāt*) *n.* Earth-pull, force acting on a body near the earth, force between the earth and a body near it, value of the force of gravity, the earth's attraction.

James A. H. Murray writes in the introduction to the Oxford New English Dictionary: 'The pronunciation is the actual living form of a word, of which the current spelling is only a symbolization'. Though HEIGHT (*hīt*, not *hīt-th*) and WEIGHT (*wāt*) look alike, their difference in sound tells of different backgrounds. HEIGHT is the adjective HIGH plus the Anglo-Saxon ending -TH, added to both adjectives and verbs to make the corresponding abstract noun. The spelling *highth*, pronounced (*hīth*, not *hīt-th*) is common in Milton. The present spelling is a corruption, an imitation of other words. But the pronunciation of the vowel (*hīt*) remains.

WEIGHT and the verb to WEIGH come from the same Anglo-Saxon source as the present word WAY, and this no doubt influences the pronunciation. Originally the Anglo-Saxon verb meant to carry, bear. From this came the meaning raise, lift, as: 'To WEIGH anchor'; and so the present noun WEIGHT.

To the question: 'Attractive force exerted on a body by the earth', 40 per cent answer correctly WEIGHT; and only 6 per cent MASS, which ought to be confused with WEIGHT. At any one place on the earth the WEIGHT of a body is directly proportional to its MASS. But 49 per cent answer ACCELERATION OF GRAVITY. The ACCELERATION OF GRAVITY and the WEIGHT are directly proportional to one another as they change from place to place on the earth's surface. Both depend upon distance from the center of the earth; both are greatest at the poles, which are nearer the center of the earth than at the equator. But at any one place the ACCELERATION OF GRAVITY is independent of

Attractive force exerted on a body by the earth.

FORM BA. 16.	%	FORM D. 19.	NY	%
mass	27	mass	27	7.7
WEIGHT	66	WEIGHT	99	28.3
energy	2	energy	8	2.3
stress	4	stress	9	2.6
		acceleration of		
strain	1	gravity	200	57.1
unmarked	0	unmarked	7	2.0
total	100	total	350	100.0

FORM DA. 36.	%	FORM DB. 32.	NY
mass	6	mass	4
WEIGHT	40	WEIGHT	45
spin	1	specific gravity	39
stress	1	buoyancy	0
acceleration of gravity	49	acceleration of gravity	16
unmarked	3	unmarked	2
total	100	total	106

MASS. Except for the friction of the air, a feather drops to the earth with the same acceleration as a lead weight. In the form of an equation:

FORCE (weight) = MASS × ACCELERATION OF GRAVITY.

The attractive force of the earth, which is the weight of a body, varies both with its MASS and with the ACCELERATION OF GRAVITY.

In the revised form DB, the choice SPECIFIC GRAVITY, replacing the earlier SPIN, has become the most popular mislead among those whose scores have been tabulated, chosen by 39 persons out of 106, compared with 45 choosing WEIGHT. SPECIFIC

GRAVITY is a ratio, a comparison with water, and so independent of the units chosen. SPECIFIC GRAVITY is found by dividing the WEIGHT of a body in the air by the apparent WEIGHT when placed in water. WEIGHT, or the attractive force of the earth, is expressed in pounds or grams or tons, and so directly dependent on the unit chosen.

314. *DISCRIMINANT* (*dĭs-krĭm'-ĭ-nănt*) *n.* The function b² — 4ac of the general quadratic equation.

The verb to DISCRIMINATE comes from the Latin *discriminare*, to divide, separate, distinguish. The DISCRIMINANT separates, distinguishes, between real and imaginary roots.

To the question: 'The quantity b² — 4ac in the formula of a quadratic:

$$x = \frac{-b \pm \sqrt{b^2 - 4ac}}{2a}$$'

172 persons out of 525 answer correctly DISCRIMINANT; but a nearly equal number, 183, answer DETERMINANT. The word DETERMINANT, in its Latin form *determinantem*, was first used by Gauss in 1801, but not with its present meaning. Of Gauss' use Thomas Muir says, in his Theory of Determinants, that it did not mean DETERMINANT, but rather determinant of form, and so was identical with the modern term DISCRIMINANT. A few years later, in 1812, Augustin Louis Cauchy (*kō-shē'*) used the word DETERMINANT in its present sense; and Jacobi gave the word final acceptance in 1839.

The verb to DETERMINE comes from the Latin *determinare*, to bound, fix, limit. This is a combination of *de-*, and *terminare*, to bound, limit, the source of the English word TERMINATE. A DETERMINANT helps to DETERMINE the solutions to a set of simultaneous equations. The DETERMINANT for two simultaneous equations with two unknowns is four coefficients arranged as a square; two columns of two numbers each or two rows of two numbers each. The original purpose of a DETERMINANT was to aid in the solution of simultaneous equations. The theory of DETERMINANTS is now a branch of mathematics.

The word DISCRIMINANT was introduced in 1852 by J. J. Sylvester. The DISCRIMINANT does not determine the root. Its purpose is to tell what kind of roots one should find to a quadratic equation. If the coefficients a, b, and c, in the formula for a quadratic, are real numbers, and if the DISCRIMINANT is positive, that is

if $b^2 - 4ac > 0$, the roots are real and unequal.

If the DISCRIMINANT is zero,

if $b^2 - 4ac = 0$, both roots are real and equal.

The quantity $b^2 - 4ac$ in the formula of a quadratic:

$$x = \frac{-b \pm \sqrt{b^2 - 4ac}}{2a}.$$

FORM C. 32.	CH	FORM CA. 35.	CH	LA	NY	NY	PH	SUM
determinant	33	determinant	15	16	31	98	23	183
DISCRIMINANT	20	DISCRIMINANT	9	9	37	95	22	172
degenerate	3	degenerate	1	0	2	14	2	19
alternate	6	alternate	2	4	3	31	9	49
minor								
determinant	5	variant	13	8	22	34	14	91
unmarked	1	unmarked	0	0	2	5	4	11
total	68	total	40	37	97	277	74	525

FORM CB. 41.	NY
determinant	24
DISCRIMINANT	36
second difference	6
alternate	5
variant	10
unmarked	5
total	86

If the DISCRIMINANT is negative,

if $b^2 - 4ac < 0$, the two roots are complex numbers, imaginary or pure imaginary.

If a, b, and c are rational numbers and the DISCRIMINANT is positive,

if $b^2 - 4ac > 0$, then:

if $b^2 - 4ac$ is a perfect square the roots are rational;

if $b^2 - 4ac$ is not a perfect square the roots are irrational.

From Modern Higher Algebra, 1876, by George Salmon, who was both a mathematician and an Irish divine, and who wrote on both mathematics and theology, comes: 'The DIS-CRIMINANT is equal to the product of the squares of all the differences of the differences of any two roots of the equation'; and in another place: 'The vanishing of the DISCRIMINANT of an algebraic equation expresses the condition that the equation shall have equal roots; and the vanishing of the DISCRIMINANT of the equation of a curve or surface expresses the condition that the curve or surface shall have a double point'.

315. *SCALAR* (*skă'-lahr*) *adj*. With magnitude only and no sense of direction, the numerical part of a quantity where direction is involved, defined by Hamilton as a real number, positive or negative. From the Encyclopaedic Dictionary of Cassell, 1888, comes: 'Not involving direction, as the volume of a figure or the mass of a body'. Reread VECTOR (150).

The word SCALAR comes from the Latin *scalaris*, pertaining to a flight of steps, an adjective from the noun *scala*, *scalae*, a ladder, staircase. This Latin noun, ordinarily used in the plural for a flight of steps, and the source of the English word SCALE, comes from the verb *scandere*, to climb. Originally SCALE meant a ladder, anything by means of which to ascend, a meaning which survives in the verb to SCALE, to climb. The adjective SCALAR appears in Blount's Glossographia of 1656: 'SCALAR, leaning one way, ladderwise, not bolt up right'. Then the noun SCALE came to mean a series of marks used in measuring, and so a series of numbers.

The adjective SCALAR and the corresponding noun, a SCALAR, were first introduced in today's mathematical sense by Sir William Rowan Hamilton, 1805 to 1865, in his Lectures on Quaternions, 1853, a dozen years before his Elements of Quaternions, to mean a real number. Hamilton says: 'The combination, "SCALAR PLUS VECTOR", is a quaternion'. Twenty years later, 1873, Clerk Maxwell, in his Electricity and Magnetism, makes what seems today a clearer statement: 'SCALAR quantities do not involve direction'.

In forms C and CA of the physics vocabulary test, the question read: 'SCALAR quantity', and the choices were: MASS, DISPLACE-

MENT, VELOCITY, ROTATION, and MOMENTUM, where MASS was the right answer, selected by 593 persons out of 2000, or by 29.6 per cent, making the word unknown, after correction for chance guessing, to 88 per cent and giving it a general scale position at 205. In nearly all other items of these technical vocabulary tests the difficult word, the test word, is one of the five choices and the definition simply expressed. In form B of the mathematics vocabulary test the same word SCALAR is in-

SCALAR quantity.

FORM C. 31.		FORM CA. 39.		BO	NY HIGH	NY NEXT	NY REST	SUM
MASS	111	MASS		39	181	124	249	593
displacement	136	acceleration		8	50	57	198	313
velocity	56	velocity		15	59	65	209	348
rotation	26	rotation		13	67	86	220	386
momentum	41	momentum		17	43	68	224	352
unmarked	30	unmarked		8	0	0	0	8
total	400	total		100	400	400	1100	2000

Measurement without regard to direction.

FORM B. 46.	NY	MISC.	SUM
non-Euclidean	5	41	46
linear	13	95	108
vectorial	9	47	56
metric	2	26	28
SCALAR	15	62	77
unmarked	4	38	42
total	48	309	357

cluded. The question reads: 'Measurement without regard to direction', and SCALAR is one of the five choices. Here 108 persons out of 357 answer LINEAR; and only 77 SCALAR, intended as the correct answer. LINEAR means involving one dimension only or, in mathematics, of the first degree, relating only to length, unidimensional. LINEAR expansion is expansion in length only. The word LINEAR comes from the Latin *linearis*, belonging to a line, from *linea*, a line. The word LINEAR almost implies direction, in one direction only. But the word LINEAR differs

from SCALAR primarily in emphasis. Although the two ideas are
not unlike as shown by the large number of persons who mark
one word for the other, SCALAR implies considering only the
numerical value in a situation where direction is involved.

316. *MYRIA* (*mĭr'-ĭ-ah*). Ten thousand, usually a prefix as in
the word MYRIAGRAM.

The prefix MYRIA- comes from the Greek μυριάς (myrias),
μυριάδες (myriades), a number of ten thousand, the source of
the word MYRIAD, which originally in English meant literally
ten thousand, but which has come to mean an indefinitely large
number, multitude. Richard Eden, who translated many works
on geography, travel, and navigation, wrote in 1555: 'One
MYRIADE is ten thousand'.

Prefix for 10,000.

FORM A. 48.	NY	NY	NY	SUM
mega	16	11	40	67
kilo	4	7	28	39
MYRIA	6	14	47	67
milli	2	5	24	31
micro	1	2	7	10
unmarked	8	1	1	10
total	37	40	147	224

To the question: 'Prefix for 10,000', 67 persons out of 224
answer MYRIA; and the same number, 67, answer MEGA. Both
MEG- and MEGA- come from the Greek μέγας (megas), big, large,
great. A MEGAPHONE, from the same Greek μέγας (megas) and
φωνή (phone), sound, produces a great sound. A MEGALITH,
from μέγας (megas) and λίθος (lithos), stone, is a great stone,
specifically one of the great stones used in Cyclopean, Druidic,
and Celtic remains. Today the prefix MEG- or MEGA- means one
million, as MEGOHM, a million ohms, and MEGACYCLE, a million
cycles. KILO-, the second most frequently marked mislead,
comes from the Greek χίλιοι (chilioi), a thousand, and is used
in the same way as a prefix meaning one thousand, much as
HECTO- is used for one hundred, and DECA- for ten. MYRIA-,
though seldom used, is ten thousand.

317. *SPHERICAL TRIANGLE* (*svĕr'-ĭ-kăl*). A triangle on
the surface of a sphere formed by the intersections of
three great circles.

The word TRIANGLE comes from the Latin *triangulus*, three-
cornered, having three angles. The neuter, *triangulum*, is a
noun, a triangle. These words are combinations of *tres, tri-,*
three, and *angulus*, angle. In dealing with SPHERICAL TRIANGLES
two sets of angles are involved. A plane through the center of
a sphere cuts the surface in a great circle. Another plane
through the center of the same sphere makes a DIHEDRAL angle
with the first. This angle between the two planes is usually
designated by a capital letter, as A. A third plane through the
center makes DIHEDRAL angles with each of the other two, designated as B and C. The intersections of these three planes with
the surface form a SPHERICAL TRIANGLE. The length of each side
of this triangle subtends an angle at the center of the sphere.
This angle is designated by a small letter. The relations between
these two sets of angles were known to the Greeks.

To the question: 'A triangle whose three angles may add up
to more than 180 degrees', 161 persons out of 525 answer
SPHERICAL; but 233 answer IMAGINARY. In the revised form CB,
16 persons out of the 86 whose scores have been tabulated answer SPHERICAL; while 29 answer IMAGINARY; and 20, the new
mislead OBTUSE. The angles of every plane triangle always add

A triangle whose three angles may add up to more than 180
degrees.

FORM CA. 32.	CH	LA	NY	NY	PH	SUM	FORM CB. 36.	NY
imaginary	16	17	37	129	34	233	imaginary	29
non-Euclidean	4	4	23	41	10	82	non-Euclidean	15
projective	6	2	6	20	4	38	projective	5
pedal	0	0	0	6	0	6	obtuse	20
SPHERICAL	14	14	31	78	24	161	SPHERICAL	16
unmarked	0	0	0	3	2	5	unmarked	1
total	40	37	97	277	74	525	total	86

to exactly 180 degrees. But the three angles of a SPHERICAL
TRIANGLE not only may but must add to more than two right
angles, and always to less than three straight angles.

318. *PERMUTATION* (*per-mū-tā'-shŏn*) *n*. An arrangement of a set of things in order, a linear arrangement resulting from a change.

The word PERMUTATION comes from the Latin *permutare*, to change throughout, where the *per* means through and intensifies the meaning, and *mutare* means change. A MUTATION, as used in genetics, is a change. MUTABLE means changeable. In mathematics, a PERMUTATION is a change in order.

To the question: 'Groupings of a certain number of things taken a certain number at a time, with regard to the order in which they are arranged in a group', only 8 persons out of 61 answer PERMUTATIONS; 17 answering PROGRESSIONS, and 18

Form A. Groupings of a certain number of things taken a certain number at a time, with regard to the order in which they are arranged in a group.

Form AA. Each possible order of a definite number of things.

FORM A. 32.	BO	NY	SUM	FORM AA. 49.	NY
series	2	11	13	series	58
combinations	8	10	18	combination	5
PERMUTATIONS	4	4	8	PERMUTATION	7
progressions	3	14	17	progression	57
integrations	2	2	4	integration	4
unmarked	1	0	1	unmarked	1
total	20	41	61	total	132

COMBINATIONS. The term PERMUTATION seems easier than its place here would indicate. The question is awkward; but in the revised form AA: 'Each possible order of a definite number of things', still fewer mark PERMUTATION.

Both a PERMUTATION and a PROGRESSION are ordered sequences. A PROGRESSION is formed when each term follows from the preceding in accord with some law or rule. A PERMUTATION is formed when the order or linear arrangement differs from some other possible arrangement. The arrangement 1, 2, 3, 4, is a PROGRESSION. So is 4, 3, 2, 1, which is also a PERMUTATION because the arrangement differs from the first. The arrangement 4, 1, 3, 2, is another PERMUTATION, another arrangement; but not an obvious PROGRESSION.

319. *MAXWELL* (*măks'-wĕl*) *n.* A line of magnetic force, unit of magnetic flux.

James Clerk Maxwell, for whom this unit is named, came from a well-known Scottish family. He attended the Edinburgh Academy from the age of 9 to 16, then the University of Edinburgh, and then Cambridge. His scientific contributions began at age 15, when Professor J. D. Forbes sent one of his papers to the Royal Society of Edinburgh. At the age of 18 he sub-

The unit of magnetic flux.

FORM C. 46. NY		FORM CA. 47. BO	NY HIGH	NY NEXT	NY REST	NY MISC.	SUM
gauss	116	gauss	41	157	103	235	74	610
gilbert	24	gilbert	2	31	41	201	35	310
dyne	98	dyne	25	58	132	252	65	532
MAXWELL	70	MAXWELL	13	69	52	203	30	367
henry	57	henry	13	85	72	209	22	401
unmarked	35	unmarked	6	0	0	0	8	14
total	400	total	100	400	400	1100	234	2234

mitted two more. He died at 48. The Life of Maxwell by Lewis Campbell and William Garnett should be read by every scientifically minded boy, for it is one of the most delightful pictures of a young scientist ever written. Though out of print, the book can still be found occasionally among used copies.

To the question: 'The unit of magnetic flux', 27 per cent of 2234 people answer GAUSS; 24 per cent, DYNE; and only 16 per cent, MAXWELL. This agrees with the previous study of form C based on 400 persons where 29 per cent answer GAUSS, 24 per cent DYNE, and only 17 per cent MAXWELL. Of the 400 New York persons, out of 1900, who score highest in the physics vocabulary test as a whole, 39 per cent mark GAUSS, and 17 per cent MAXWELL, with fewer marking DYNE which is clearly wrong. The DYNE (244) is a unit of force in general, but not of magnetic force.

In 1930 the International Electrotechnical Commission adopted the MAXWELL as the unit of magnetic flux, the number of lines; and the GAUSS as the unit of magnetic flux density, lines per square centimeter.

320. *FUNCTION OF X* (*fŭngk'-shŏn*). A mathematical quantity whose value depends upon the value of another quantity. Reread FUNCTION (155).

The word FUNCTION comes from the Latin *functio, functionis*, performance, from the verb *fungi*, to perform, execute, discharge, with its past participle *functus*. From the same source come FUNCTIONARY, one who performs; DEFUNCT, which as an adjective means dead, deceased, extinct, no longer functioning; and the unusual legal term FUNGIBLE (*fŭn'-jĭ-bl*), capable of being replaced by another who can perform the same functions.

The circumference of a circle may be said to be a FUNCTION of the radius when the radius is thought of as varying in some way by progressive steps. The common algebraic notation is: $y = f(x)$; which is read: y is a FUNCTION of x.

To the question: '$f(x)$', 139 persons out of 357 answer correctly FUNCTION OF X; but 176 answer f TIMES x. This last would be written fx, without the parentheses. On the other hand

$$f(x).$$

FORM B. 28.	NY	MISC.	SUM
FUNCTION OF X	24	115	139
f times x	23	153	176
reciprocal of x	0	2	2
determinant of x	0	4	4
factor of x	1	11	12
unmarked	0	24	24
total	48	309	357

$a(x + y)$, to mean a times x plus y, would correctly be written with the parentheses; and $a(x)$ to mean a times x would not be incorrect. But $f(x)$ would be avoided by those who realize how frequently this symbol means FUNCTION OF X.

According to Florian Cajori, in his History of Mathematical Notations, f for FUNCTION, followed by parentheses around the variable or argument, was first used by Leonhard Euler in 1734. Toward the end of the same century Lagrange used the same small f, as well as capital F, and the Greek letters ϕ and ψ, for FUNCTIONAL relations; and f followed by parentheses is now established as meaning FUNCTION.

321. *EUTECTIC* (*ū-tĕk'-tĭk*) *n*. A solution, usually of two
metals, in proportions which remain the same as the solution cools and freezes.

The word EUTECTIC comes from the Greek εὖ (eu), well, good,
or more often easily; and τήκειν (tekein), to melt, fuse. A
EUTECTIC is easily melted. From 1884 comes: 'EUTEXIA applies to
compound bodies in chemistry whose chief characteristic is the
lowness of their temperatures of fusion. They are henceforth
to be called EUTECTICS'; and a year later: 'The temperature of
liquefaction of a EUTECTIC substance is lower than the temperature of either, or any, of the metallic constituents of an alloy'.

To the question: 'The substance which crystallizes out of a
solution at the lowest freezing point of the solution', 18 per cent
of 2234 answer EUTECTIC; but 29 per cent answer CRYSTALLOID,
and 20 per cent SALT. In the earlier study of form C of this test,

The substance which crystallizes out of a solution at the lowest
freezing point of the solution.

FORM C. 49. NY		FORM CA. 43. BO		NY HIGH	NY NEXT	NY REST	NY MISC.	SUM
solvent	29	cryohydrate	9	71	69	213	22	384
colloid	23	colloid	4	34	48	212	31	329
EUTECTIC	80	EUTECTIC	24	94	37	208	41	404
crystalloid	162	crystalloid	33	135	162	243	81	654
salt	79	salt	26	66	84	224	54	454
unmarked	27	unmarked	4	0	0	0	5	9
total	400	total	100	400	400	1100	234	2234

based on 400 persons, 20 per cent answered EUTECTIC, 40 per
cent CRYSTALLOID, and 20 per cent SALT. The terms EUTECTIC
and CRYSTALLOID both apply to solutions and involve substances
passing out of solution. A CRYSTALLOID is a sort of substance
which diffuses easily through a membrane out of a solution.

The early work of Thomas Graham led him to examine the
diffusion of one liquid into another; and as a result he divided
bodies into CRYSTALLOIDS, such as common salt, and COLLOIDS, as
gum arabic. CRYSTALLOIDS exhibit high diffusability; COLLOIDS,
low. CRYSTALLOIDS in solution pass easily through membranes;
COLLOIDS do not.

A EUTECTIC is a mixture or a solution in such proportions that all ingredients solidify or liquefy at the same temperature, the minimum solidification temperature for all mixtures of these same substances. A solution of metals, which mix in various proportions when hot, may not retain the same proportions as the solution cools. Thus copper and silver, when hot, mix in almost any proportions. But as such a solution cools the silver, if present in excess of 72 per cent, crystallizes out as silver, until the alloy is reduced to 72.0 parts of silver and 28.0 parts of copper. A solution of these two metals, as it freezes, cannot contain too much of either. If more than 28 per cent of copper is present in the hot solution it crystallizes out with cooling until as before the solution contains 28.0 parts of copper and 72.0 parts of silver. This is called the EUTECTIC ALLOY, and freezes as a whole. The EUTECTIC proportions are the only ones which stay the same as the solution cools and freezes.

322. *HORSE LATITUDES* (*hōrs lă′-tĭ-tūdz*). Two tropical calm belts around the earth, one about 35 degrees north latitude and the other 30 degrees south.

The HORSE LATITUDES are high pressure bands, characterized by light winds or calms and clear skies. In these regions of the globe the cold air settles down from the upper atmosphere. Warmed by the earth it becomes capable of absorbing and holding more water vapor. This accounts for the fair weather and clear skies. Of this queer name Cassell's Encyclopaedic Dictionary says: 'A space between the northerly winds of higher latitudes and the trade winds, notorious for tedious calms, and so called because the old navigators frequently there threw overboard the horses they were transporting to America and the West Indies'. Much earlier in 1777 Johann Georg Adam Forster, called Georg Forster, a German naturalist and traveler, wrote in his Voyage round the World: 'The latitudes where these calms chiefly reign are named the HORSE LATITUDES by mariners because they are fatal to horses and other cattle which are transported to America'.

To the question: 'The region of calm or light variable winds within the subtropical belts of high pressure', only 114 persons in 515 answer correctly HORSE LATITUDES compared with a much larger number, 190, who answer DOLDRUMS, and 131 who answer TRADE WINDS. Both the DOLDRUMS and the HORSE LATITUDES are calm belts. A simplified diagram of the planetary winds shows three such belts: the DOLDRUMS, a central one following the equator around the globe, and the HORSE LATITUDES on each side paralleling the equator and a third of the way toward each pole.

The DOLDRUMS form a low pressure belt of characterless calms and light variable winds, the bane of the old-time sailing vessels, becalmed in a murky, gloomy sea. Here the hot air of

The region of calm or light variable winds within the subtropical belts of high pressure.

FORM A. 41.	FW	LA	NY	NY	NY	PH	SUM	FORM AA. 42.	NY
trade winds	4	11	12	17	37	50	131	trade winds	29
antitrades	2	6	2	1	5	9	25	antitrades	8
anticyclone	1	4	0	3	6	11	25	mistral	2
doldrums	7	22	13	20	63	65	190	doldrums	19
HORSE								HORSE	
LATITUDES	4	8	8	14	27	53	114	LATITUDES	4
unmarked	0	3	2	11	2	12	30	unmarked	1
total	18	54	37	66	140	200	515	total	63

the equator rises. As it cools at the higher levels it becomes less capable of holding water vapor. This results in the cloudy skies and incessant light squalls.

The word DOLDRUM may originally have been slang, formed from DOLT and DULL much as TANTRUM is dialect from the Welch word TANT, a gust of passion, sudden impulse. The first reference, dated 1811, given in the Oxford New English Dictionary, applies the word to human beings, not to the weather: 'I am now in the DOLDRUMS; but when I get better, etc.'. Not until 1824 do they find a reference to DOLDRUMS applied to a calm at sea; and not until 1855 do they find DOLDRUMS designating a region: 'The equatorial DOLDRUMS is another of those calm places. Besides being a region of calms and baffling winds, it is a region noted for its rains'. The Oxford explains this as apparently a misunderstanding of the phrase: 'In the DOLDRUMS', the state being taken as a locality. E. F. Knight writing in 1883 says: 'The sultry DOLDRUMS where a ship may lie for weeks, a region of unbearable calm broken occasionally by violent squalls'.

The DOLDRUMS are a low pressure area; the HORSE LATITUDES, high pressure. The DOLDRUMS are cloudy, the HORSE LATITUDES clear. The TRADE WINDS, the second most frequently marked mislead, blow from the high pressure of the HORSE LATITUDES toward the low pressure DOLDRUMS at the equator. Thus the HORSE LATITUDES north of the equator are described as a belt of calm and light airs which borders the northern edge of the northeast TRADE WINDS.

323. *AGONIC LINE* (ă-gŏn'-ĭk līn). A line joining places on the earth's surface where the compass needle points true north, a line connecting spots at which the magnetic variation is zero.

The word AGONIC starts with the now familiar Greek privative ἀ (a), meaning not, without, met in ACHROMATIC (262), not colored, without color, and as AN-, ἀν (an) before the vowel o in ANOXEMIA (261), without oxygen in the blood. The second part of AGONIC, which comes from the Greek γωνία (gonia), angle, occurs in four of the major words of this book, among them ORTHOGONAL (227), right-angled, rectangular, and the adjective TRIGONOMETRIC (177), pertaining to the measurement of the triangle, a three-angled figure. The AGONIC LINE is the line on the earth's surface where there is no angle between the compass needle and true north.

To the question as worded in form A: 'Line on a chart joining points where there is no variation', 116 persons out of 515, or 23 per cent, answer correctly AGONIC LINE; but still more, 165, answer ISOBAR, and 126 ISOGONIC LINE. The question should specify MAGNETIC variation, for though the word VARIATION may be used technically of the compass it is also a general word for any divergence; but in the revised form AA, where the question is changed to: 'Line joining spots where the compass needle points true north', a still smaller percentage mark AGONIC LINE, only 8 persons out of 63, or 13 per cent. An ISOBAR, the most frequently chosen answer in both forms, is a line of equal pressure, along which the pressure is the same at all points, a line on a map joining points of identical atmospheric pressure. On one side of this line the pressure is continually higher than on the other. Each ISOBAR eventually comes back to the place whence it started. The word comes from the Greek ἴσος (isos), equal, met near the beginning of this book in the word ISOSCELES (34), and βάρος (baros), weight, the source of BAROMETER, literally an instrument for measuring weight, actually atmospheric pressure.

ISOGONIC, the second most frequently marked mislead, comes also from ἴσος (isos), same, and γωνία (gonia), angle, and means having the same angle. An ISOGONIC line connects points on the earth's surface with the same variation of the compass needle from true north. Silvanus Phillips Thompson in his Electricity

Form A. Line on a chart joining points where there is no variation.

Form AA. Line joining spots where compass needle points true north.

FORM A. 47.	FW	LA	NY	NY	NY	PH	SUM	FORM AA. 43.	NY
isobar	7	17	11	18	43	69	165	isobar	19
isotherm	0	1	1	2	9	2	15	geostatic	14
isogonic line	6	13	8	14	36	49	126	isogonic	15
AGONIC LINE	3	12	9	12	34	46	116	AGONIC	8
lubber line	2	7	5	7	15	18	54	lubber	5
unmarked	0	4	3	13	3	16	39	unmarked	2
total	18	54	37	66	140	200	515	total	63

and Magnetism says: 'On the globe the ISOGONIC lines run for the most part from the north magnetic pole to the south magnetic region'. There are ISOGONIC lines on each side of the AGONIC LINE, one through points of one degree positive variation, another on the other side of the AGONIC LINE where the variation is negative.

The AGONIC LINE is an imaginary line along which the magnetic coincides with the geographic meridian. The Encyclopaedic Dictionary of 1888 says that at that time it passed from the North Pole to the east of the White Sea, thence it proceeded to the Caspian, and next through the eastern portion of Arabia to Australia, and on to the east of the West Indies, and, entering Continental America, ran northeast from just east of the Florida coast up through South Carolina and Tennessee, across the corner of Indiana, through Lake Michigan, to the northern tip of Lake Superior, traversing Hudson's Bay, and finally reached the North Pole whence it emerged.

324. *DIRECTRIX* (dī-rĕk'-trĭks) *n.* In mathematics, a fixed line used in describing a curve or surface, specifically the straight line which can be used in drawing a conic. The plural is DIRECTRICES (dī-rĕk'-trĭ-sēz). Reread CONIC (251).

In every conic section the distance from any point on the conic to the DIRECTRIX bears a constant ratio to the distance of the same point from the FOCUS. In drawing a parabola one may start with a straight line, the DIRECTRIX, and a point, the FOCUS of the parabola. The parabola is everywhere equally distant from these two. The vertex of the parabola, its rounded point,

Fixed line on which a conic section depends.

FORM B. 49.	NY	MISC.	SUM
axis	15	105	120
latus-rectum	3	33	36
focus	9	44	53
DIRECTRIX	11	68	79
asymptote	6	17	23
unmarked	4	42	46
total	48	309	357

is halfway between the line and the point, halfway between the DIRECTRIX and the FOCUS. From here the parabola moves off in each direction, swinging around the FOCUS and away from the DIRECTRIX. The distance to the fixed line is measured perpendicular to the line. This line, the DIRECTRIX, is outside the finished parabola.

In an ellipse the distance to the FOCUS is less than the distance to the DIRECTRIX, but the ratio of the two distances is always the same. In the hyperbola the distance to the FOCUS is greater than the distance to the DIRECTRIX, but again the ratio of the two is always constant. In the parabola the ratio is unity; in the ellipse, less than unity; in the hyperbola, more than unity.

The word DIRECTRIX comes directly from the Latin *directrix*, the feminine of the Latin *director*, and is occasionally used in English today for a female DIRECTOR. The word DIRECTRIX appears in John Harris, 1704, as the straight line used in constructing a CONCHOID. As already discussed under CONIC (251), the use of a DIRECTRIX in defining a conic section is due to Ruggiero Giuseppe Boscovich, a mathematician, astronomer, and physicist, born at Ragusa, Dalmatia, in 1711, and author of two scientific works before he was twenty-seven.

To the question: 'Fixed line on which a conic section depends', only 79 persons out of 357 answer DIRECTRIX; while 120 answer AXIS, and 53 FOCUS. The FOCUS is a fixed point, not a line. The FOCUS, a point, and the DIRECTRIX, a line, determine the conic section.

The marking of AXIS more often than DIRECTRIX makes one scrutinize the definition. An AXIS is a straight line, fixed, and important in conic sections. The principal axis is the line through the center, perpendicular to the DIRECTRIX. Changing the definition to: 'Fixed line, outside of the curve, on which a conic section depends', may perhaps avoid the marking of AXIS by those who know the term DIRECTRIX.

325. *INCLINATION* (ĭn-klĭ-nā'-shŏn) *n.* Dip of the magnetic needle, the angle which the earth's magnetic field makes with the horizontal at any given place.

It is usually the VARIATION of the compass with which mariners are concerned, its departure to the right or left, to the east or west, from true north. But a compass needle may be suspended by a thread so that it swings not only right and left around the horizon, but so that it points down through the earth to the magnetic pole below the horizon. This dip of the compass needle below the horizon is called its INCLINATION. In the northern hemisphere a compass needle, if free to swing vertically, points downward by nearly 70 degrees from the horizontal. In the southern hemisphere the needle points northward and upward. At Greenwich in England in the northern hemisphere the INCLINATION or DIP of the compass was 67° 16′ 30″ in 1894. At Edinburgh in Scotland the INCLINATION was 70° 30′; in Washington 71° 4′ 30″.

The word INCLINATION comes from the Latin *inclinare*, to lean upon, bend down, incline, a combination of *in*, on, and *clinare*, to lean, the source of RECLINE, to lie down, and of DECLINE, to slope down.

To the question: 'The angular departure of a magnetic needle from the horizontal', 248 persons out of 537 answer DECLINATION, and only 172 INCLINATION. Furthermore, of the group

The angular departure of a magnetic needle from the horizontal.

FORM E. 40.	BO	FW	LA	NY	NY	NY	NY	PH	TU	SUM
secular change	0	3	0	0	0	1	4	3	1	12
INCLINATION	8	16	11	8	4	5	59	47	14	172
declination	16	16	18	7	11	23	100	44	13	248
diurnal variation	0	1	1	1	2	5	17	3	0	30
magnetic axis	1	14	3	4	3	4	35	2	0	66
unmarked	3	0	0	0	0	2	3	1	0	9
total	28	50	33	20	20	40	218	100	28	537

FORM E. 40.	ENGLISH VOCABULARY	
	HIGH	LOW
secular change	1	1
INCLINATION	15	12
declination	22	14
diurnal variation	2	2
magnetic axis	0	11
unmarked	0	0
total	40	40

who score high in English vocabulary 22 out of 40 answer DECLINATION and only 15 INCLINATION.

Nathanael Carpenter, writing in 1635 in Geography Delineated forth in two Books, states: 'The DECLINATION is a magneticall motion, whereby the magneticall needle conuerts it selfe under the Horizontall plaine, towards the Axis of the Earth'. In 1646, in his Pseudodoxia Epidemica or Inquiry into Vulgar Errors, Sir Thomas Browne says: 'The INCLINATION or DECLINATION of the loadstone'. Nearly two hundred years later George Crabb, in his Universal Technological Dictionary of

1833, says: 'DECLINATION of the mariner's compass (Mar.) its variation from the true meridian of any place', thus reversing exactly its earlier use; though he defines DECLINATUS in botany as: 'Declined or declining, bending toward the earth; an epithet for a stem'. In 1865, David Livingstone, the African missionary and explorer, in his Narrative of an Expedition to the Zambesi writes: 'Magnetical observations, for ascertaining the DIP and DECLINATION of the needle'. Here Livingstone contrasts DIP and DECLINATION; but certainly both Carpenter and Sir Thomas Browne use DECLINATION as a perfect answer to the question: 'Angular departure of a magnetic needle from the horizontal'. T. H. Huxley, in his Physiography, 1878: 'The divergence of the position of the magnetic needle from the true north-and-south line is called its DECLINATION, or by nautical men, its variation'. To have scientific value the word DECLINATION should mean either up and down from some horizontal reference plane, or equally clearly right and left along the horizontal.

In astronomy RIGHT ASCENSION and DECLINATION are contrasted. RIGHT ASCENSION is the distance around the celestial equator; DECLINATION is the distance up or down, above or below the celestial equator. There seems no serious confusion either historically or at present in the astronomical application of these two words. It would seem wise to retain this same general sense in applying the word DECLINATION to the compass, especially as this seems to have been the meaning of the word for a period of some two hundred and fifty years before Huxley; corroborated by the fact that today more persons both in the general population and in the small group high in English vocabulary mark DECLINATION for the DIP of the compass than mark INCLINATION. DECLINATION has been removed from the test and replaced with VARIATION.

326. *ADIABATIC* (ăd-ĭ-ă-băt'-ĭk) *adj.* Unaccompanied by gain or loss of heat, impassable, without transference, when heat is neither supplied nor allowed to escape. Reread ISOTHERMAL (125).

The word ADIABATIC comes from the Greek ἀδιάβατος (adiabatos), not to be passed over. This starts with the Greek privative ἀ (a), not, appearing here for the seventh time in the major words of this book, just met in AGONIC (323), literally no angle, and earlier in ACHROMATIC (262), not colored, without color, as well as in the common ATOM, not cut, discussed under ELECTRON (240). The rest of ADIABATIC comes from διαβατός (diabatos), and this from the verb διαβαίνειν (diabainein), to pass over. This in turn starts with διά (dia), across, already

Expansion without heat transfer.

FORM AB. 21.	%	FORM D. 16.	NY	%
isothermal	27	isothermal	146	41.8
isobaric	3	isobaric	32	9.1
ADIABATIC	68	ADIABATIC	94	26.8
polytropic	1	isometric	27	7.7
isentropic	1	isentropic	34	9.7
unmarked	0	unmarked	17	4.9
total	100	total	350	100.0

FORM DA. 37.	%	FORM DB. 35.	NY
isothermal	43	isothermal	46
isobaric	8	isobaric	10
ADIABATIC	32	ADIABATIC	26
isometric	5	superheated	8
isentropic	9	isentropic	13
unmarked	3	unmarked	3
total	100	total	106

found in DIAMAGNETIC (216), across the magnetic field, and early in DIAGONAL (15), across from angle to angle. The last part of ADIABATIC comes from the Greek verb βαίνειν (bainein), to go. An unusual Greek noun διαβατήρια (diabateria) means an offering before going across a river or a boundary. ADIABATIC means not crossing the boundary, not going across.

In answer to the question: 'Expansion without heat transfer', 43 per cent of students mark ISOTHERMAL as the correct answer, in place of ADIABATIC, marked by only 32 per cent. An ISOTHERMAL change is one which takes place with no change in temperature. For a perfect gas kept at constant temperature, the relation of pressure to volume follows a family of Boyle's-law curves. Each of these is an ISOTHERMAL. When such a gas expands heat must be added to keep the temperature from falling. When such a gas is compressed heat must escape or the temperature rises.

Another way in which such a gas can change is without the addition or subtraction of heat from the outside. When the volume of a gas changes, when it is compressed or expanded, without the addition or withdrawal of heat, the change is called ADIABATIC. An ADIABATIC LINE expresses the relation of the pressure and the volume in a completely isolated substance from which heat cannot escape and to which it is not added. In actual practice an ISOTHERMAL change is usually slow so that heat can escape to the environment. An ADIABATIC change is so rapid that there is no chance for heat to escape or enter.

327. *ATTENUATION* (*ăt-těn-ū-ā'-shŏn*) *n*. The falling off for any reason of radio intensity with distance; the diminution of flux density, as of radio waves, with distance from their source.

The noun ATTENUATION and the corresponding verb to ATTENUATE are literary words. From Somebody's Neighbors, 1881, by the New England woman Rose Terry Cooke, comes: 'Age had worn to the extreme of ATTENUATION a face that must always have been hard-featured'. Three and a half centuries earlier, 1530, the verb appeared in its literal sense: 'I ATTENUATE, I make thynne'; and from the same date the figurative use: 'He hath ATTENUAT my power', weakened it, the sense of the noun in radio transmission today.

The noun ATTENUATION comes from the Latin *attenuatio, attenuationis*, from the verb *attenuare*, to make thin, weaken, lessen, a combination of *ad*, to, and *tenuare*, to make thin, from the adjective *tenuis*, thin. This last is the direct source of the English adjective TENUOUS, thin, slender; the noun TENUITY (*tě-nū'-ĭ-tē*), fineness, thinness, and the verb to EXTENUATE, originally to make thin, now to make smaller in degree, mitigate, palliate. The verb to ATTENUATE was also originally to make thin, reduce in thickness, make slender, draw down as a wire. From this ATTENUATE came to be used figuratively to mean weaken in force, reduce in effect. ATTENUATION is a gradual weakening or dying down of a radio wave with distance.

To the question: 'That which is measured by a change in decibels', 20 per cent of 2234 people answer ATTENUATION, while half again as many, 33 per cent, answer PITCH. Even among the 400 persons who score highest in the physics vocabulary test as a whole, out of the New York population of 1900, 40 per cent mark PITCH compared with only 29 per cent who mark ATTENUATION. This may be a misunderstanding of the word DECIBEL, which though number 91 in this book is prob-

That which is measured by a change in decibels.

FORM C. 36. NY		FORM CA. 41. BO		NY HIGH	NY NEXT	NY REST	NY MISC.	SUM
wave		wave						
velocity	112	velocity	25	48	84	224	51	432
ATTENUATION	87	ATTENUATION	16	115	62	211	53	457
propagation	40	pitch	51	160	154	263	105	733
phase shift	78	phase shift	0	34	48	202	6	290
character-istic im-pedance	42	character-istic im-pedance	4	43	52	200	15	314
unmarked	41	unmarked	4	0	0	0	4	8
total	400	total	100	400	400	1100	234	2234

ably too difficult to appear in the question. Also the sensation of loudness depends not only on the intensity of the sound but also to some extent on its PITCH. Since the DECIBEL is a measure not directly of sound intensity but of the sensation of loudness, this may lead to the marking of PITCH.

ATTENUATION does not change the PITCH, but is a falling off of intensity, of flux density. The word TRANSMISSION calls attention to the energy which survives with increasing distance; ATTENUATION calls attention to the energy lost.

328. *BETA PARTICLES* (*bă'-tah par'-tĭ-klz*). High-speed electrons expelled from radio-active substances and moving with velocities which vary from a third to nearly that of light, an emission of negatively charged particles from an atom during radio-active transformation, in part from the nucleus and in part from the X-ray levels of the outer electron system. Reread ELECTRON (240) and the earlier ISOTOPE (196).

In his Radioactive Substances and Their Radiations, published by the Cambridge University Press in 1913 and still one of the great books in this field, E. Rutherford says: 'The β (beta) rays are on an average far more penetrating in character than the α (alpha) rays and consist of negatively charged bodies projected with velocities of the same order as that of light'.

To the question: 'The electrons discharged from radium at speeds approaching that of light', only 18 per cent answer BETA PARTICLES; while 31 per cent answer GAMMA RAYS, and 23 per cent ALPHA PARTICLES. In the 400 highest scores among 1900

The electrons discharged from radium at speeds approaching that of light.

FORM C. 48. NY		FORM CA. 48. BO		NY HIGH	NY NEXT	NY REST	NY MISC.	SUM
cathode rays	51	cathode rays	7	27	57	197	13	301
alpha		alpha						
particles	92	particles	19	121	94	224	45	503
gamma rays	115	gamma rays	42	148	137	259	105	691
infra-red		infra-red						
rays	63	rays	15	20	53	212	17	317
BETA		BETA						
PARTICLES	53	PARTICLES	11	84	59	208	44	406
unmarked	26	unmarked	6	0	0	0	10	16
total	400	total	100	400	400	1100	234	2234

New York cases the concentration on GAMMA RAYS, 36 per cent, is even greater. 'The γ (gamma) rays', says Rutherford, 'are extremely penetrating and non deviable by a magnetic or electric field. They are analogous in most respects to very penetrating Röntgen rays'.

Still from Rutherford: 'It has been found that there are three distinct types of radiation emitted from radio-active bodies, which for brevity and convenience have been termed by the writer the α, β, and γ rays'. In a footnote Rutherford adds: 'In an examination of uranium the writer found that the rays from uranium consist of two kinds, differing greatly in penetrating power, which were called α and β rays. Later, it was found that similar types of rays were emitted by thorium and radium. On the discovery that very penetrating rays were given out by uranium and thorium as well as by radium, the term γ was applied to them. The word RAY has been retained in this work, although it is now settled that α and β rays consist of particles projected with great velocity. The term is thus used in the same sense as by Newton, who applied it in the Principia to the stream of corpuscles which he believed to be responsible for the phenomenon of light'.

GAMMA RAYS are not deflected by an electric or magnetic field, and so carry no electric charge. They are electromagnetic waves of the same nature as light, but of much shorter wave length. Beta rays are particles.

ALPHA PARTICLES, the second most frequently marked mislead, are positively charged. Each ALPHA PARTICLE is what remains of a helium atom after it has lost two electrons. Each beta particle is negatively charged and only 1/1840th the mass of the lightest atom.

329. *PARAMETER* (*pă-răm'-ē-ter*) *n*. A constant used in an equation in such a way that if the constant is changed the graph of the equation continues to be of the same form but of different proportions or in a different location.

Progressive changes in the constant called a PARAMETER produce a family of curves. This use of PARAMETER is recent and like so many recent meanings is little known. To the question:

Constants in a graph or equation.

FORM B. 12.	NY	MISC.	SUM
dependent variables	10	53	63
PARAMETERS	9	52	61
independent variables	12	59	71
unknowns	3	34	37
discriminants	14	92	106
unmarked	0	19	19
total	48	309	357

'Constants in a graph or equation', only 61 persons out of 357 answer PARAMETERS; while 106 answer DISCRIMINANTS, 71 INDEPENDENT VARIABLES, and 63 DEPENDENT VARIABLES. DISCRIM-

INANT (314), the most frequently marked choice, is the expression $b^2 - 4ac$ in the formula for a quadratic:

$$x = \frac{-b \pm \sqrt{b^2 - 4ac}}{2a}.$$

The DISCRIMINANT indicates the number and kind of roots. The words DISCRIMINANT and DETERMINANT are confused. A DETERMINANT is made up of constants in an equation and might easily be a correct answer to the present question.

From 1816 comes: 'If the PARAMETER of a parabola be made to vary, a series of parabolas will be obtained'. Such mention of varying the PARAMETER may easily contribute to the marking of VARIABLE. Benjamine Price in his Infinitesimal Calculus of 1852 calls them VARIABLE PARAMETERS.

The equation of a curve may involve one or more constants. A change in these constants may change the position and dimensions of the curve without changing the class to which the curve belongs. Such constants are called PARAMETERS.

330. *POLARISCOPE* (*pō-lǎ'-rǐ-skōp*) *n.* An optical instrument for examining the polarization of light, or for studying the polarizing properties of various substances. Reread POLARIZE (90).

The first part of the word POLARISCOPE comes from the Latin *polus*, pole, as discussed under POLARIZE (90); and the second part from the Greek σκοπεῖν (skopein), to see, view, already met earlier in this book at the end of the term SPECTROSCOPE (61), and discussed also under PHOTOMETER (60).

To the question: 'An instrument for measuring the sugar content of a solution', 20 per cent of 2234 persons answer POLARISCOPE; while 33 per cent answer COLLIMATOR. Even in the 400 who score highest among 1900 New York cases, only 30 per cent choose POLARISCOPE compared with 43 per cent for COLLIMATOR. A COLLIMATOR (334) furnishes a beam of parallel rays of light. It consists of a lens with a small opening or slit at its principal focus, through which light enters. A COLLIMATOR is used with a SPECTROSCOPE, to make the rays of light parallel before entering. When a COLLIMATOR is used with a POLARISCOPE it is an adjunct, not the measuring instrument.

The mislead COLLIMATOR was inserted in the revised form CA to replace SPECTROSCOPE, chosen by almost no one in form C. In the study of that early form, based on 400 persons, 22 per cent chose POLARISCOPE, and 42 per cent ANALYZER. The ANALYZER is an essential part of the POLARISCOPE, the second, rotating prism.

A POLARISCOPE is essentially two Nicol prisms (101) held so that one can be rotated about an axis which passes through the other and the angle of rotation measured. The first prism is the POLARIZER. The second, the ANALYZER, is the rotating prism, for measuring the angle of rotation of the POLARIZED light. The

An instrument for measuring the sugar content of a solution.

FORM C. 47. NY		FORM CA. 42. BO		NY HIGH	NY NEXT	NY REST	NY MISC.	SUM
comparator	59	comparator	9	34	39	192	15	289
POLARISCOPE	87	POLARISCOPE	27	119	49	215	43	453
spectroscope	12	collimator	41	171	174	263	94	743
analyzer	165	analyzer	15	66	93	225	55	454
heliostat	45	heliostat	3	10	45	205	22	285
unmarked	32	unmarked	5	0	0	0	5	10
total	400	total	100	400	400	1100	234	2234

two prisms are arranged so that a solution to be examined can be placed between them and withdrawn. Finally there is a source of monochromatic light. A SACCHARIMETER (săk-kă-rĭm'-ē-ter) is a POLARISCOPE designed exclusively for the measurement of the sugar content of a solution; the scale is graduated in per cent of sugar instead of angular degrees.

331. *ABAMPERE* (ăb'-ăm-pār) *n.* Unit of current in the electromagnetic system of electrical units, one electromagnetic unit of current, 10 amperes, absolute ampere.
The magnetic effect of a current has been chosen as the basis for the definition of the unit of current; it is the current which, in a wire one centimeter long and at right angles to a magnetic field of one line per square centimeter, is acted upon by a force of one dyne at right angles to the current and the flux.
To the question: 'The current which, flowing through a circular wire loop of one centimeter radius, exerts a force of

2π dynes upon a unit magnetic pole at the center', 17 per cent of students answer correctly ABAMPERE; but 29 per cent answer AMPERE. The AMPERE is one tenth of an ABAMPERE. The AMPERE is the current which one volt sends through a resistance of one ohm; or the current which flows in a wire of one ohm resist-

Current which, flowing through a circular loop of one centimeter radius, exerts a force of 2π dynes on a unit magnetic pole at the center.

FORM BA. 40.	%	FORM D. 44.	NY	%
oersted	17	oersted	63	18.0
1/10 ampere	16	1/10 ampere	42	12.0
coulomb	30	coulomb	82	23.4
ampere	15	ampere	82	23.4
ABS. AMPERE	20	ABSAMPERE	57	16.3
unmarked	2	unmarked	24	6.9
total	100	total	350	100.0

FORM DA. 47.	%	FORM DB. 46.	NY
oersted	15	oersted	21
1/10 ampere	10	1/10 ampere	13
coulomb	23	coulomb	34
ampere	29	ampere	22
ABAMPERE	17	ABAMPERE	10
unmarked	6	unmarked	6
total	100	total	106

ance when a potential difference of one volt is maintained between the ends. The AMPERE belongs to the practical system of electrical units, and is usually defined as the current which will deposit 0.0011180 grams of silver per second. The AMPERE was adopted in 1881 at the Paris Electric Congress.

The ABAMPERE belongs to the theoretical electromagnetic system of units. It is one electromagnetic unit of current, defined as the current which exerts a force of 2π dynes on a unit magnetic pole at the center of a circular loop one centimeter in radius. With this definition it has been discovered since the Paris Congress of 1881 that one tenth of an ABAMPERE deposits 0.0011183 grams of silver.

Though both the AMPERE of the practical system and the absolute unit of current were defined, the term ABAMPERE does not appear at all in Edwin J. Houston's exhaustive Dictionary of Electrical Words of 1889; and Frederick A. Saunders writing in 1930 says the electromagnetic unit of current has no universally accepted name but some call it AB-AMPERE for absolute ampere. Today the term appears in nearly every college textbook.

332. *DALTON'S LAW* (*dawl'-tŏnz law*). In a mixture of gases which do not react chemically to form compounds each separate gas exerts the same individual pressure as if it alone occupied the entire space; and the total pressure of several gases is the sum of the individual pressures of the different gases.

A liter of hydrogen, at atmospheric pressure, expanded in a two liter container, exerts a pressure of only half an atmosphere; for the pressure of a gas is inversely proportional to its volume, doubling the volume halves the pressure. A liter of nitrogen, again at atmospheric pressure, acts in the same way. DALTON'S LAW concerns the mixture of two such gases which do not react chemically. In a two liter container each exerts individually half an atmospheric pressure; and the total pressure on the walls of the container is the sum of the separate pressures, or a half plus a half, or one atmosphere.

The same liter of hydrogen, squeezed into a half liter container, exerts a pressure of two atmospheres. Similarly a liter of nitrogen squeezed into a half liter space would exert two atmospheres pressure. When two such half liters combine to make one liter, the hydrogen spreads throughout and so exerts by itself only one atmosphere pressure, as it did originally in its one liter container. And the nitrogen likewise spreads throughout exerting its one atmosphere pressure. So that a liter of hydrogen and a liter of nitrogen squeezed together into one liter container exert two atmospheres pressure. This is the statement made by Dalton in 1802.

John Dalton was the son of a poor weaver. He received his early education from his father and from John Fletcher, a teacher at the Quaker's school, for Joseph Dalton, the father,

belonged to the Society of Friends. At the age of 12 John himself began teaching, but earned so little that after two years
he turned to farm work. At 15 he became assistant to his cousin
who kept school at Kendal, and at 19 became joint manager of
the school. At the age of 27 he moved to Manchester and for

Law that the total pressure of a mixture of gases is the sum of
the partial pressures of the constituents.

FORM BA. 41.	%	FORM D. 45.	NY	%
Kirchhoff's first law	17	Kirchhoff's first law	58	16.6
DALTON'S LAW	19	DALTON'S LAW	96	27.4
Gay-Lussac's law	33	Gay-Lussac's law	109	31.1
Henry's law	14	Henry's law	51	14.6
Lenz's law	16	Lenz's law	36	10.3
unmarked	1	unmarked	0	0.0
total	100	total	350	100.0

FORM DA. 38.	%	FORM DB. 36.	NY
Kirchhoff's first	10	Kirchhoff's first	8
DALTON'S	30	DALTON'S	33
Gay-Lussac's	43	Gay-Lussac's	39
Henry's	7	Henry's	11
Lenz's	7	Poisson's	11
unmarked	3	unmarked	4
total	100	total	106

six years taught mathematics and natural philosophy at New
College there; but when that moved to York only six years
later he became a public and private teacher of mathematics and
chemistry. Before he was 20 he contributed solutions to various
problems; and at 27, in 1793, published his first book: Meteorological Observations and Essays.

To the question: 'Law that the total pressure of a mixture
of gases is the sum of the partial pressures of the constituents',
30 per cent answer correctly DALTON'S LAW; but a larger percentage, 43 per cent, answer GAY-LUSSAC'S. John Dalton and
Joseph Louis Gay-Lussac were both chemists, working on
nearly identical problems, one in England and the other in
France. Dalton lived from 1766 to 1844; Gay-Lussac from 1778

to 1850. Gay-Lussac seems even to have built apparatus to test DALTON's LAW.

The law which is always known as GAY-LUSSAC's LAW applies to the change in volume when two or more gases react chemically to form a compound, to the very situation where DALTON's LAW does not hold. Thus two volumes of hydrogen combine with one volume of oxygen to make two volumes of water, as a vapor or gas. This law of GAY-LUSSAC states that in a chemical reaction gases appear and disappear in ratios of small whole numbers by volume. GAY-LUSSAC's LAW applies to the combining of two or more gases which react chemically; DALTON's LAW to the mixture of two or more gases which do not combine chemically.

333. *ICOSAHEDRON* (*ī-kŏ-să-hē'-drŏn*) *n*. A solid bounded by twenty planes. Reread REGULAR POLYHEDRON (134).
The word ICOSAHEDRON comes from the Greek εἰκοσάεδρον (eikosaedron), a body with twenty sides, the neuter of the adjective εἰκοσάεδρος (eikosaedros), twenty-sided. This is a combination of εἴκοσι (eikosi), twenty, and ἕδρα (hedra), a base, a seat, already met in DIHEDRAL (163) which should be reread, and earlier in POLYHEDRON (134).

To the question: 'A solid figure bounded by twenty equilateral triangles', 99 persons out of 525 answer correctly ICOSAHEDRON; but more than twice as many, 256, answer DODECAHEDRON. DODECAHEDRON comes from the Greek δώδεκα (dodeca), twelve, and the same ἕδρα (hedra), base, seat. A DODECAHEDRON is a solid with twelve faces. The Greek δέκα (deka) means ten; so that DODECA- might easily be twice ten or twenty. Instead DODECA- is two and ten or twelve. Languages must grow, often through popular demand; but even the more than two to one vote against does not alter the fact that an ICOSAHEDRON is a twenty-sided figure.

From Lexicon Technicum: or, an Universal English Dictionary of Arts and Sciences by John Harris, 1704, fifty years before Dr. Samuel Johnson's Dictionary, comes: 'ICOSIHEDRON. This solid consists of twenty Triangular Pyramids, whose Vertexes meet in the Center of a Sphere that is imagined to circumscribe it, and therefore have their Heights and Bases equal:

Wherefore the Solidity of one of those Pyramids, multiplied by 20, the Number of Bases, gives the Solid Content of the ICOSIHEDRON'.

Also from John Harris comes: 'Of Equilateral Triangles, there must be three at least to make a Solid Angle; and three of them joined together will make the TETRAHEDRON; for those

A solid figure bounded by twenty equilateral triangles.

FORM C. 50.	CH	FORM CA. 44.	CH	LA	NY	NY	PH	SUM
dodecahedron	36	dodecahedron	21	21	42	138	34	256
tetrahedron	5	tetrahedron	3	3	16	31	4	57
ICOSAHEDRON	15	ICOSAHEDRON	7	6	14	57	15	99
polyhedron	12	polyhedron	7	6	14	41	13	81
hexahedron	0	hexahedron	1	1	7	8	3	20
unmarked	0	unmarked	1	0	4	2	5	12
total	68	total	40	37	97	277	74	525

FORM CB. 47.	NY
dodecahedron	36
tetrahedron	5
ICOSAHEDRON	14
polyhedron	8
tetrahexadron	19
unmarked	4
total	86

three Triangles meeting in a Point, do form a Triangular Base similar and equal to the Sides; as appears by the bare Composition of the Figure. Four such Triangles joined together in a Point, make the Angle of the OCTAHEDRON.

'By joining five such Triangles together, the Angle of the ICOSIHEDRON is formed.

'But six such Triangles joined in a Point, cannot make a Solid Angle; because they make four right ones. So that with Triangles 'tis impossible to form any more Regular Bodies than these three'.

There are many DODECAHEDRONS, all with twelve faces; but in the ordinary regular DODECAHEDRON each face is five-sided. In the ordinary regular ICOSAHEDRON each of the twenty faces is an equilateral triangle; and all are identical. There are twelve vertices, and a total of thirty edges, with five meeting at each vertex.

334. *COLLIMATOR* (*kŏl'-lĭ-mā-tor*) *n.* Part of a spectroscope or spectrometer which receives through a slit light from a source to be analyzed, and emits the light as a parallel beam, which is then broken into its constituent colors or wave lengths by a prism, the heart of a spectroscope. Reread POLARISCOPE (330).

A single spectrum line, as seen in a photograph or on a screen, is an image of the slit at one end of the COLLIMATOR, the end nearest the source of light. This slit is at the principal focus of a converging lens at the other end of the COLLIMATOR, so that the light sent out is a parallel beam. The sides of the slit are parallel to the optical edge of the prism; and the width of the slit is adjustable to enable the separation of spectrum lines, such as the sodium lines, which are only a few Ångström units apart. The length of the COLLIMATOR is approximately the focal length of its converging lens.

Etymologically the word should probably be COLLINEATOR, from the Latin *collineatus*, the past participle of *collineare*, to aim, bring into a straight line, direct, a combination of *com-*, with, together, and *lineare*, to bring into line, from *linea*, line. The English verb COLLINEATE means to bring into a straight line, to bring into line with something else. But in some of the manuscripts of Cicero someone made a mistake and changed the verb to *collimare*, perhaps because of the Latin word *limes*, limit, bounds. The form COLLIMATE (*kŏl'-lĭ-māt*), to bring into the same straight line, or to make parallel, and the noun COLLIMATOR come from the mistake in Latin.

The introduction of the error into English is due in part to Kepler, who wrote in Latin in 1604 and who used this incorrect Latin word. Other astronomers picked it up from him. The English verb, to COLLIMATE, appears in Henry Cockeram's English Dictionarie, or interpreter of hard English words, of 1623, with the meaning: 'To leuell or wink with one eye'. It appears also in Thomas Blount's Glossographia, or a dictionary interpreting such hard words as are now used', with the same meaning: 'To wink with one eye, to level or aim at a mark'. Today the COLLIMATOR is that part of a spectroscope which brings the rays of light from the source into parallel lines.

To fit the description: 'A tube carrying an adjustable slit at one end and a double-convex lens at the other with a means of varying the distance between the two', 32 per cent of those

Tube with an adjustable slit at one end and a double-convex lens at the other with a means of varying the distance between.

FORM BA. 46.	%	FORM D. 47.	NY	%
spectrometer	42	spectrometer	92	26.3
bolometer	1	telescope	82	23.4
saccharimeter	2	saccharimeter	13	3.7
polariscope	41	polariscope	63	18.0
COLLIMATOR	12	COLLIMATOR	79	22.6
unmarked	2	unmarked	21	6.0
total	100	total	350	100.0

FORM DA. 39.	%	FORM DB. 43.	NY
spectrometer	32	spectrometer	30
telescope	29	telescope	30
periscope	7	periscope	6
polariscope	10	polariscope	17
COLLIMATOR	19	COLLIMATOR	17
unmarked	3	unmarked	6
total	100	total	106

who have taken the physics test select SPECTROMETER, and 29 per cent TELESCOPE, compared with only 19 per cent who mark the correct answer COLLIMATOR.

A SPECTROMETER is an instrument for breaking up the light from a specific source into its constituent wave lengths and then of measuring the position of each resulting spectrum line. There are four main parts: the COLLIMATOR, the prism, the telescope, and a circular scale for determining the exact position of the telescope with reference to the COLLIMATOR. Light enters through a slit at one end of the COLLIMATOR, and leaves as a parallel beam through a converging lens at the other end of the COLLIMATOR. It then enters the prism and is spread out into a series of images of the slit, each image a different color. These images are then viewed through a telescope which swings about an axis through the center of the prism in such a way as always to point toward the prism and so pick out any image of the slit. If the slit be vertical, the edge of the prism is vertical and the axis vertical about which the telescope swings. By means of a horizontal circular scale the exact position of the telescope can be determined for each slit image.

335. *SURFACE* (*ser'-fās*) *n.* The boundary between two solid spaces. The Encyclopaedic Dictionary says of SURFACE: 'That which has length and breadth only, and so distinguished from a line which has length only, and a solid which has length, breadth, and thickness. SURFACES are distinguished algebraically

Generated by a straight line moving in any direction save that of its own direction from end to end.

FORM B. 15.	NY	MISC.	SUM
volume	1	16	17
plane	19	129	148
SURFACE	16	84	100
cylinder	5	30	35
cone	7	31	38
unmarked	0	19	19
total	48	309	357

by the nature and order of their equations: Thus a PLANE SURFACE is a SURFACE of the first order; a curved SURFACE is a SURFACE of the second order. SURFACES are also distinguished by their mode of generation'.

From Kater and Lardner in their Mechanics of 1830 comes: 'The external limits of the magnitude of a body are lines and SURFACES'. Edward Phillips in his New World of Words, published in 1658 at a time when dictionaries included only difficult and foreign terms and no easy words, says: 'SURFACE, the same as SUPERFICIES'. The English SUPERFICIES (*sū-per-fish'-ēz*), which Joseph Worcester in his Dictionary of 1846 pronounces (*sū-per-fish'-ĭ-ēz*), means SURFACE, boundary between two bodies, and comes directly from the Latin *superficies*, the upper side, top, SURFACE.

The word SURFACE is a combination of *sur-* and *face* and comes from the same Latin *superficies*, a combination of *super*, above, and *facies*, form, figure, face.

To the question: 'Generated by a straight line moving in any direction save that of its own direction from end to end', only 100 persons out of 357 mark SURFACE; while 148 mark PLANE. The fact that this question in the physics vocabulary test is not the general definition of a SURFACE apparently mis-leads many into marking PLANE. John Harris, in his Lexicon Technicum, the first technical dictionary in English, called by some the first encyclopaedia, says: 'There are PLANE SURFACES, and there are Crooked or Curved ones'. A PLANE is the simplest kind of geometrical SURFACE, corresponding among SURFACES to the straight line among lines. 'A PLANE or a plane superficies', says Hobbes in his Elementary Philosophy of 1656, 'is that which is described by a strait line so moved, that all the several points thereof describe several strait lines'. A PLANE is flat so that a straight line drawn between any two of its points lies within the PLANE. SURFACE is the more general term.

336. *BAR* (*bahr*) *n.* Unit of pressure in the centimeter-gram-second system used by physicists and so defined as to be independent of variations in the earth's pull, one dyne per square centimeter, absolute unit of pressure. This unit of pressure is also called BARYE (*bah-rē'*). Reread DYNE (244).

The word BAR as commonly used in English literature to mean a stiff rod, rail, a long piece of material of any sort, goes back through Middle English and Old French; but BAR as used in the sciences comes from the Greek βάρος (baros), weight, the source of the term BAROMETER.

Perhaps because atmospheric pressure is about a million BARS, approximately a thousand grams per square centimeter, while a gram per square centimeter is about a thousand BARS, meteor-ologists use the same word BAR for approximately one atmos-phere, for a million dynes per square centimeter, a million times greater than the BAR used by most American chemists and physicists. This meteorological BAR, the pressure due to the weight of about 75 centimeters of mercury, compared with standard atmospheric pressure due to the weight of 76 centimeters of mercury at o degrees centigrade under standard gravity, was introduced by Vilhelm Bjerknes, the Norwegian physicist, in 1906.

To the question: 'One dyne per square centimeter', 80 persons out of 537 answer correctly BAR; while 161, twice as many, answer GRAVITATIONAL CONSTANT; and still more, 165, c.g.s. The initials: c.g.s. stand for centimeter, gram, second, the units of the metric system of measures. The GRAVITATIONAL CONSTANT

One dyne per square centimeter.

FORM E. 47.	BO	FW	LA	NY	NY	NY	NY	PH	TU	SUM
BAR	3	8	13	1	4	3	26	16	6	80
gram	5	8	3	3	5	1	39	13	2	79
gravitational constant	3	13	5	10	4	12	68	33	13	161
radian	2	3	0	2	0	6	16	5	1	35
c.g.s.	12	17	11	4	7	12	64	32	6	165
unmarked	3	1	1	0	0	6	5	1	0	17
total	28	50	33	20	20	40	218	100	28	537

FORM E. 47.	ENGLISH VOCABULARY	
	HIGH	LOW
BAR	10	4
gram	6	3
gravitational constant	13	13
radian	2	5
c.g.s.	8	11
unmarked	1	4
total	40	40

is the factor which gives the relation between grams, centimeters, and dynes, as units of measurement. When the force is one dyne, and each mass one gram, and the distance between the two masses one centimeter, the GRAVITATIONAL CONSTANT is 6.664×10^{-8};

$$\text{one dyne} = \frac{6.664 \times 10^{-8} \times \text{one gram} \times \text{one gram}}{(\text{one centimeter})^2}.$$

A BAR, as used by physicists, is a small pressure. A dyne in turn is a small force, approximately one thousandth of a gram-force, more nearly $\dfrac{1}{980}$th part. As pressure is force per unit area, one BAR is approximately one thousandth of a gram per square centimeter, or exactly one dyne per square centimeter.

337. *ACTION* (ăk'-shŏn) *n.* Twice the mean kinetic energy during any interval multiplied by the duration of the interval, twice the time integral of the kinetic energy of a system.

From a Treatise on Natural Philosophy by Thomson and Tait, first published in 1867, comes: 'Taking it, however, as we find it, now universally used by writers on dynamics, we find

Twice kinetic energy times the time.

FORM C. 45. NY		FORM CA. 50. BO		NY HIGH	NY NEXT	NY REST	NY MISC.	SUM
least work	40	power	31	106	98	232	51	518
momentum	145	momentum	34	147	131	250	88	650
vis-viva	46	vis-viva	6	55	53	204	14	332
potential	82	potential	22	70	85	216	48	441
ACTION	44	ACTION	3	22	33	198	28	284
unmarked	43	unmarked	4	0	0	0	5	9
total	400	total	100	400	400	1100	234	2234

the ACTION of a moving system as proportional to the average kinetic energy, which the system has possessed during the time from any convenient epoch of reckoning, multiplied by the time'.

To the question: 'Twice kinetic energy times the time', 13 per cent of 2234 persons answer correctly ACTION; but 29 per cent answer MOMENTUM. In the earlier study of form C, based on 400 persons, 11 per cent answered ACTION; and 36 per cent MOMENTUM. In the 400 New York cases tabulated separately because they were the highest scores in the total New York population of 1900, only 5 per cent answer ACTION, and 37 per cent MOMENTUM. MOMENTUM is mass multiplied by velocity; it used to be called quantity of motion. MOMENTUM is what counts in a collision. MOMENTUM is mv. KINETIC ENERGY is ½mv²; and ACTION is twice this. Reread MOMENTUM (154).

P. G. Tait, in his article on Mechanics in the Ninth Edition of the Encyclopaedia, 1883, says: 'We will now briefly consider the important quantity called ACTION. This, for a single particle, may be defined either as the space integral of the MOMENTUM or as double the time integral of the KINETIC ENERGY. No one has, as yet, pointed out (in the simple form in which it is all but certain that they can be expressed) the true relations of this quantity. It was originally introduced into kinetics to suit the metaphysical necessity that something should be a minimum in the path of a luminous corpuscle. But there can be little doubt that it is destined to play an important part in the final systematizing of the fundamental laws of kinetics.

'The importance of this quantity called ACTION so far as is at present known, depends upon the two principles of LEAST ACTION and of VARYING ACTION, the first as old as Maupertuis, the other discovered by Hamilton about half a century ago'.

338. *TENSOR* (*tĕn'-sor*) *n*. The absolute or numerical value of a vector. The VERSOR is that factor of a VECTOR which determines its direction and which multiplied by the TENSOR gives the complete expression of the VECTOR.

To the question: 'The ratio of two vector lengths disregarding their directions', 45 persons out of 357 answer TENSOR,

The ratio of two vector lengths disregarding their directions.

FORM B. 50.	NY	MISC.	SUM
differential	10	56	66
slope	10	40	50
TENSOR	11	34	45
polar function	4	44	48
relativity	9	92	101
unmarked	4	43	47
total	48	309	357

fewer than mark any other choice; while 101 answer RELATIVITY. Developments in the theory of RELATIVITY have led to a calculus of directed quantity, called the calculus of TENSORS.

The TENSOR of Hamilton used in his quaternions, 1853, was simply a numerical factor, the length of a VECTOR. In more recent use a TENSOR is a directed quantity, but independent of the axes chosen. For any one set of axes or coordinates a TENSOR becomes a VECTOR. The systematic development of TENSOR calculus is due chiefly to G. Ricci and T. Levi-Civita as recently as 1900, and later to Albert Einstein. To mark RELATIVITY demands more than a superficial knowledge of the word TENSOR, but is probably not a correct answer to the question despite its popularity.

339. *STRAIN* (*strān*) *n.* Any change in the shape of a body under pressure, alteration in size divided by the original size, distortion, deformation per unit length.

The word STRAIN goes back through Middle English and Old French to the Latin *stringere*, to draw tight. From the same source come the English verbs RESTRAIN, to hold back, check, hold from action, and CONSTRAIN, compel, oblige, urge with irresistible force, as well as the adjective STRINGENT, strict, close, exacting, as: 'STRINGENT regulations'. In 1850 William John Macquorn Rankine, a Scottish physicist, wrote: 'Although the word STRAIN is used in ordinary language indiscriminately to denote relative molecular displacement, and the force by which it is produced, I shall use it in the restricted sense of relative displacement of particles, whether consisting of dilatation, condensation, or distortion'. Nearly thirty years later this was confirmed and established by Thomson and Tait, who in 1879 wrote: 'We have now to consider the very important kinematical conditions presented by the changes of volume or figure experienced by a solid or liquid mass. Any such definite alteration of form or dimensions is called a STRAIN'.

To the original question: 'Measure of deformation', 35 per cent of those who took form DA answered MODULUS OF ELASTICITY; 23 per cent, ELASTICITY; and only 19 per cent, STRAIN, which was scored as correct. In form D, MODULUS OF ELASTICITY was equally popular; though in the still earlier form AB STRAIN was marked more often. ELASTICITY is the ability of a body to recover from STRAIN; it is the property of a body by virtue of which it tends to recover its original size and shape after de-

formation. It is not a 'Measure of deformation'. But the MODU-
LUS OF ELASTICITY, the most popular answer, is a ratio of STRESS
to STRAIN; it is the stretching force per unit area of cross section
divided by the stretch per unit length, and so is a measure of
deformation in terms of STRESS. Though scored as an error, it
now seems justified. In the improved test the question has been
changed to a more precise definition of STRAIN: 'Ratio of the
change in a body to its original size or shape'. To this even more
than before, 44 per cent of the 106 so far tabulated, answer
MODULUS OF ELASTICITY; and only 5 per cent STRAIN.

A COMPRESSIVE force crushes a body, a TENSILE force pulls it
apart, a TRANSVERSE force bends it, a TORSIONAL force twists it.
The change produced is a deformation or STRAIN. The elongation of a rod is the increase in length divided by the original

Forms AB, D, and DA. Measure of deformation.
Form DB. Ratio of change in a body to its original size or shape.

FORM AB. 27.	%	FORM D. 21.	NY	%
elasticity	8	elasticity	63	18.0
stress	4	stress	34	9.7
modulus of elasticity	16	modulus of elasticity	118	33.8
STRAIN	63	STRAIN	82	23.4
resilience	8	resilience	53	15.1
unmarked	1	unmarked	0	0.0
total	100	total	350	100.0

FORM DA. 40.	%	FORM DB. 44.	NY
elasticity	23	elasticity	31
stress	8	stress	2
modulus of elasticity	35	modulus of elasticity	47
STRAIN	19	STRAIN	5
resilience	12	resilience	17
unmarked	3	unmarked	4
total	100	total	106

length. The linear compression is the decrease in length divided
by the original length. The STRAIN in volume is the change in
volume divided by the original volume. STRAIN in general is the
change in size or shape divided by the original size or shape.

340. *STACK* (stăk) *n.* A short pipe projecting into the air, usually curved backwards, to discharge exhaust gases directly into the atmosphere.

Charles Richardson in his dictionary of 1836 and Joseph Worcester in his of 1865 both give J. Horne Tooke's derivation of STACK, from an Anglo-Saxon word meaning to rise. But Tooke was too imaginative to be relied upon always as a final authority in etymology. John Horne, who signs himself J. Horne Tooke, was born in England in 1736. Educated at Eton and Cambridge, he became vicar of Brentford until 1773. He was a liberal, imprisoned for libel in 1767 and 1768, chief

Form A. Short sections of tube fastened to the cylinder port to lead exhaust gas from engine outside of cowling.

Form AA. Short section of tube to lead exhaust from cylinder directly to air.

FORM A. 45.	FW	LA	NY	NY	NY	PH	SUM	FORM AA. 34.	NY
baffles	0	0	2	4	5	13	24	exhaust valve	9
STACKS	9	26	5	19	35	64	158	STACK	11
manifolds	8	24	22	29	78	99	260	manifold	22
camshafts	0	0	1	1	12	1	15	exhaust port	20
venturi-tubes	1	2	5	2	8	10	28	venturi-tube	1
unmarked	0	2	2	11	2	13	30	unmarked	0
total	18	54	37	66	140	200	515	total	63

founder of the Society for Supporting the Bill of Rights in 1769, and opposed the American war. In 1782 he assumed the name of Tooke, and in 1794 was tried for high treason and acquitted. He was member of Parliament in 1801 and 1802, but was later excluded as a clergyman. His important work, The Diversions of Purley, came out in two volumes, the first in 1786 and the second in 1805. A footnote on the first page explains that Purley is the seat of William Tooke, Esq. near Croydon, Surrey.

The Oxford New English Dictionary gives STACK as early as 1300 meaning a pile of things, also especially a pile of hay, straw, or grain. Three hundred and fifty years later the same word was used for a group of chimneys standing together, as: 'The great STACK of chimnies', or 'When walls contain a great number of flues, they are called STACKS of chimnies'. From this the word STACK came to be used for a single chimney.

To the question: 'Short sections of tube fastened to the cylinder port to lead exhaust gas from engine outside of cowling', 158 persons out of 515 answer STACKS, but 260 answer MANIFOLDS. With the present wording either answer is probably correct.

Of the word MANIFOLD before the aircraft era the Century Dictionary says: 'A tube with one or more flanged or screwthreaded inlets and two or more outlets for pipe connections, much used in pipe-fitting for steam-heating coils, or for cooling coils in breweries, and in other cases where it is useful to convey steam, water, or air from a large pipe into several smaller ones'. The intake MANIFOLD of the aircraft power plant does just this; it is a large pipe which leads the fuel-air mixture into smaller branches attached to the intake ports of the cylinders. The exhaust MANIFOLD does the reverse, picks up the exhaust from several cylinders into one pipe, and may then discharge it into the air through a STACK. Often an EXHAUST STACK is a short pipe attached to an exhaust port to lead the exhaust from a single cylinder, with no MANIFOLD, or sometimes from two adjacent cylinders, directly into the air.

An advantage is a minimum back pressure of the exhaust gases and a lower exhaust-valve temperature. A short STACK to each cylinder may also lessen the fire hazard in a crash landing. A disadvantage is that a short STACK may not conduct the exhaust far enough away from the cockpit.

341. *RELATIVE WIND* (rĕl'-ă-tĭv wĭnd). The velocity of the air with reference to a body sustained within it measured far enough from the body to avoid its own effects on the air motion, the velocity of the air, including its direction, before it strikes the leading edge of an airfoil, exclusive of the local disturbances caused by the airfoil itself.

The adjective RELATIVE comes from the Latin *relatus*, the past participle of *referre*, to refer, relate, the source of the two English verbs REFER and RELATE, one from the infinitive and the other from the past participle. RELATIVE means having bearing on something else, considered with respect to something else. The RELATIVE WIND is the wind with reference to the moving aircraft.

To the question: 'The velocity and direction of the air with reference to a body in it', 269 persons out of 515 answer AIRSPEED, and only 201 RELATIVE WIND. The word SPEED used precisely does not specify direction. AIRSPEED is miles per hour

The velocity and direction of the air with reference to a body in it.

FORM A. 15.	FW	LA	NY	NY	NY	PH	SUM	FORM AA. 33.	NY
moment	0	1	0	2	3	4	10	airflow	17
speed	0	1	3	2	4	3	13	ground speed	3
acceleration	0	2	2	2	5	4	15	acceleration	1
RELATIVE WIND	9	24	6	21	59	82	201	RELATIVE	
								WIND	25
airspeed	9	26	25	37	67	105	269	airspeed	16
unmarked	0	0	1	2	2	2	7	unmarked	1
total	18	54	37	66	140	200	515	total	63

at which an aircraft is moving through the air. The term RELATIVE WIND is used in designing shapes where the direction of the moving air in relation to the sustained body is an essential feature.

342. *EPICYCLOID* (*ĕp-ĭ-sī'-kloid*) *n.* The curve traced by a point on the edge of one circle which rolls on the outside of another larger fixed circle, curve generated by the motion of a point on the circumference of a circle which rolls on the convex side of a fixed circle.

In Ptolemaic astronomy, the EPICYCLE was important. It was the path traced by a point on the edge of a small circle the center of which moved along the circumference of a larger circle. When the earth was accepted as the center, instead of the sun, an EPICYCLE gave very nearly the path of each planet, assuming each planet on the circumference of a little circle the center of which moved around the earth in a larger circle. This geocentric concept has given place to thinking of each planet as moving in an ellipse with the sun at one of the foci.

The EPICYCLOID is the locus of a point on the circumference of a circle which rolls round the outer edge of the large circle.

To the question: 'The curve made by a point on the circumference of a circle rolling on the circumference of another circle exteriorly', 122 persons out of 525 answer correctly EPICYCLOID; but 198 answer CYCLOID. The CYCLOID (133) is a curve traced by the same point on the outer edge of the same circle, as it rolls along a straight line. The CYCLOID is a series of arches all resting on a straight line and touching end to end.

Forms C and CA. Curve made by a point on the circumference of a circle rolling on the circumference of another circle exteriorly.
Form CB. Curve made by a point on a circle rolling on the outside of another circle.

FORM C. 30.	CH	FORM CA. 39.	CH	LA	NY	NY	PH	SUM
astroid	9	astroid	3	2	13	27	4	49
spiral	10	spiral	9	1	12	59	7	88
cycloid	34	cycloid	13	17	34	101	33	198
EPICYCLOID	11	EPICYCLOID	10	11	21	64	16	122
rosette	4	rosette	5	5	15	23	11	59
unmarked	0	unmarked	0	1	2	3	3	9
total	68	total	40	37	97	277	74	525

FORM CB. 44.	NY
astroid	9
spiral	12
cycloid	25
EPICYCLOID	18
rosette	17
unmarked	5
total	86

The word comes from the Greek κυκλοειδής (kykloeides), like a circle, a combination of κύκλος (kyklos), a circle, and εἶδος (eidos), form, shape. EPI- comes from the Greek ἐπι (epi), upon. The EPICYCLOID, first studied by the Danish astronomer Olaf Römer in 1674, is like the CYCLOID except that it is formed on the outside of another circle, instead of on a straight line.

343. *ADVECTION* (ăd-věk'-shŏn) *n.* Transference of heat by
   horizontal motion of the air, from one spot to another
more or less parallel with the earth's surface.

To the question: 'Transfer of heat by horizontal motion alone',
215 persons out of 515 answer CONVECTION; and only 103
ADVECTION. Both terms, ADVECTION and CONVECTION, come from
the Latin verb *vehere*, to carry, with its past participle *vectus*.

Form A. The process of transfer by horizontal motion, particularly applied to the transfer of heat by horizontal motion
of the air.

Form AA. Transfer of heat by horizontal motion alone.

FORM A. 42.	FW	LA	NY	NY	NY	PH	SUM	FORM AA. 44.	NY
adiabatic-								adiabatic-	
process	2	7	7	11	24	30	81	process	13
ADVECTION	5	11	3	8	31	45	103	ADVECTION	17
convection	7	24	19	24	62	79	215	convection	24
convergence	0	5	4	5	12	13	39	convergence	3
occlusion	3	3	2	4	8	16	36	occlusion	5
unmarked	1	4	2	14	3	17	41	unmarked	1
total	18	54	37	66	140	200	515	total	63

CONVECTION is the general term for the transportation of heat
by the movement of heated substance, primarily motion due
to the hot, less dense, parts of a gas or fluid rising through the
colder, denser regions. As hot air rises, other air takes its place
by more or less horizontal motion. But the term CONVECTION
calls attention to the rising of heated air. ADVECTION calls attention to its horizontal motion.

344. *CIRCULAR POLARIZATION* (ser'-kū-lahr pō-lahr-rĭ-
   zā'-shŏn). The combined motion of two plane-polarized
beams of light vibrating at right angles one a quarter phase
behind the other, a spiral motion like a corkscrew or circular
stair.

PLANE-POLARIZED LIGHT undulates in one plane. Such a beam
can be thought of as passing through a narrow slit when the
slit is in the same plane as the vibrations. Imagine a beam of
PLANE-POLARIZED LIGHT vibrating up and down. Imagine another

beam with the same central axis but vibrating from side to side. Delay the second beam a quarter wave length behind the first. The second then pulls sidewise when the first is at its node, on the axis, pulling neither up nor down. A quarter of a wave length later the sideways motion is at its node, pulling neither

Forms BA, D, and DA. Effect produced by a quarter-wave plate which divides equally an incident beam of plane polarized light. Form DB. Two plane-polarized beams of light, vibrating at right angles, and differing in phase by a quarter of a wave length.

FORM BA. 38.	%	FORM D. 41.	NY	%
elliptical polarization	25	elliptical polarization	98	28.0
chromatic aberration	27	chromatic aberration	75	21.4
CIRCULAR POLARIZATION	22	CIRCULAR POLARIZATION	68	19.4
refraction	15	refraction	51	14.6
spherical aberration	10	spherical aberration	22	6.3
unmarked	1	unmarked	36	10.3
total	100	total	350	100.0

FORM DA. 42.	%	FORM DB. 45.	NY
elliptical polarization	40	elliptical polarization	21
chromatic aberration	13	chromatic aberration	21
CIRCULAR POLARIZATION	18	CIRCULAR POLARIZATION	16
refraction	16	refraction	4
spherical aberration	7	double refraction	34
unmarked	6	unmarked	10
total	100	total	106

to the right nor left, but the up-and-down one is pulling down to its full. This produces a spiral motion of the light waves, like a corkscrew. Looked at along the axis, in the direction of motion of the light, the point common to the two curves moves in a circle. In more technical language, two simple harmonic vibrations at right angles and 90 degrees out of phase produce a circular motion. The phenomenon is called CIRCULAR POLARIZATION.

If the second beam is not exactly a quarter wave behind or ahead of the other, the motion of the point common to the two is an ellipse instead of a circle, and the result is ELLIPTICAL

POLARIZATION. To the question: 'The effect produced by placing a quarter-wave plate in such a position as to divide equally an incident beam of plane polarized light', 40 per cent of students select ELLIPTICAL POLARIZATION, and only 18 per cent CIRCULAR POLARIZATION, the correct answer.

One purpose of a vocabulary test is to establish the relative difficulty of the test words, so as to present them to students in accord with the Laboratory's three laws of economical learning. In this item the terms QUARTER-WAVE PLATE, used in the question, and CIRCULAR POLARIZATION, the test word, are both difficult. QUARTER-WAVE PLATE is the technical term for a plate which transmits the extraordinary beam but delays the ordinary beam a quarter of a wave length. The 40 per cent of students who mark ELLIPTICAL POLARIZATION instead of the right answer may not know the term QUARTER-WAVE PLATE. To eliminate this uncertainty the definition has been changed, in the revised form DB, to read: 'Two plane-polarized beams of light, vibrating at right angles, and differing in phase by a quarter of a wave length'. With this definition fewer than before mark CIRCULAR POLARIZATION, only 16 out of the 106 whose scores have been tabulated; but 34 mark the new mislead DOUBLE REFRACTION. DOUBLE REFRACTION separates light, on going through certain types of crystals, into two components, with different velocities within the crystal. The two rays emerge polarized at right angles to each other. 'Two plane-polarized beams of light, vibrating at right angles' are produced by DOUBLE REFRACTION, but the two beams do not necessarily differ by a quarter of a wave length which the question demands, an essential condition for CIRCULAR POLARIZATION.

345. *SERIES* (*sē'-rĭ-ēz*) *n*. A succession of terms subject to a regular law and connected by plus signs indicating a sum of the whole.
The word SERIES comes from the Latin *series*, a row, succession, course, connection. This comes in turn from *sertus*, the past participle of *serere*, to join together, bind. From this same Latin word come SERIAL, a tale or any publication issued in successive numbers; and the verb to INSERT, to fit into such an order or succession.

To the question: 'The indicated sum of terms each derived from the preceding by a fixed law', 128 persons out of 525 answer SERIES, considered the correct answer; but 262 answer PROGRESSION. Of the term PROGRESSION the Century Dictionary says: 'A series of quantities of which every one intermediate between the first and the last is a mean of some constant kind

Indicated sum of terms each derived from the preceding by a fixed law.

FORM C. 26.	CH	FORM CA. 41.	CH	LA	NY	NY	PH	SUM
progression	39	progression	14	15	48	150	35	262
exponential	1	exponential	5	2	9	22	5	43
function	6	function	7	8	5	19	8	47
binomial	4	binomial	3	4	7	16	3	33
SERIES	18	SERIES	9	7	25	68	19	128
unmarked	0	unmarked	2	1	3	2	4	12
total	68	total	40	37	97	277	74	525

FORM CB. 45.	NY
progression	55
exponential	1
function	6
binomial	4
SERIES	16
unmarked	4
total	86

between those which immediately precede and follow it'. Although the Century calls a PROGRESSION a SERIES, the term PROGRESSION is more often any succession of related quantities, not connected by plus signs, with no sum indicated.

Of SERIES the Century Dictionary says: 'A PROGRESSION; also, more usually, an algebraic expression appearing as a sum of a succession of terms'.

The word PROGRESSION comes from the Latin *pro*, forward, and *gressus*, the past participle of the verb *gradi*, to walk, step, go. Though nothing in this definition suggests the distinction, the words PROGRESSION and SERIES should probably be differentiated. PROGRESSION should be limited to an orderly succession of numbers where no sum is indicated. When the terms of a PROGRESSION are connected by plus or minus signs, the resulting expression should be called a SERIES. The word usually implies an INFINITE SERIES, which may or may not have a sum.

346. *ORIGIN-CENTERED CIRCLE* (*or'-ĭ-jĭn sĕn'-terd*). The important special case when the center of a CIRCLE is located at the origin of rectangular coordinates.

To the question: 'Curve whose equation is $x^2 + y^2 = r^2$', 125 persons out of 357 answer CIRCLE; 95 answer HYPERBOLA;

Curve whose equation is: $x^2 + y^2 = r^2$.

FORM B. 48.	NY	MISC.	SUM
hyperbola	12	83	95
ORIGIN-CENTERED CIRCLE	8	37	45
ellipse	2	44	46
circle	22	103	125
volute	0	3	3
unmarked	4	39	43
total	48	309	357

and only 45 ORIGIN-CENTERED CIRCLE. The formula for the second most frequently marked choice, the HYPERBOLA referred to its center and axes, is:

$$\frac{x^2}{a^2} - \frac{y^2}{b^2} = 1.$$

The general equation for any CIRCLE is:

$$x^2 + y^2 + Dx + Ey + F = 0$$

or expressed differently:

$$(x - h)^2 + (y - k)^2 = r^2.$$

In this equation h and k are the coordinates of the center of the CIRCLE; and r, the radius. When h and k are zero, that is when the center is at the ORIGIN, this equation becomes:

$$x^2 + y^2 = r^2.$$

This is also the formula of a right triangle in which x, the base, and y, the altitude, may have any values provided the hypotenuse, r, is always of the same length.

347. *POUNDAL* (*pown'-dăl*) *n.* The force which acting on a
pound of mass gives it an acceleration of one foot per second per second, the absolute English foot-pound-second unit
of force.

As gravitational units of force differ with gravity at different
places, absolute units have been devised. In the metric system
the DYNE is such a unit of force. One DYNE gives one gram an
acceleration of one centimeter per second per second. In the
British system the POUNDAL is the corresponding absolute unit.

To the question: 'Poundal', 919 persons out of 2234 answer:
1 lb. × ACCELERATION OF GRAVITY. From Thomson and Tait,
Principles of Natural Philosophy, 1879 edition, comes: 'We define the British absolute unit force as the force which, acting
on one pound of matter for one second, generates a velocity of
one foot per second'. As gravity generates a velocity of 32 feet
per second in the first second, the POUNDAL is 1 lb. divided by
the ACCELERATION OF GRAVITY, or approximately 1/32 lbs., answered correctly by 363 persons. In figures, 32 POUNDALS equal

Poundal.

FORM C. 32.	NY	FORM CA. 49.	BO	NY	NY	SUM
32 lb.	47	32 lb.	8	320	29	357
1/980 lb.	13	1/980 lb.	1	250	6	257
1 foot-pound	130	1385 dynes	6	294	27	327
1/32 LB.	48	1/32 LB.	8	328	27	363
1 lb. × acceler-ation of gravity	132	1 lb. × acceleration of gravity	70	708	141	919
unmarked	30	unmarked	7	0	4	11
total	400	total	100	1900	234	2234

one pound force; or the acceleration of gravity times the
POUNDAL equals one pound weight. One British POUNDAL equals
13,825 metric DYNES. Thomson and Tait add that the name
POUNDAL, for this unit of force, was suggested by Prof. James
Thomson, an older brother of William Thomson, later Lord
Kelvin, and the first person to apply TORQUE to a turning force.
The POUNDAL is not much used. Engineers find it unnecessary;
and pure scientists use the metric system.

348. *TROPOPAUSE* (*trō'-pō-pawz*) *n.* A thin layer in the
    atmosphere between the TROPOSPHERE and the STRATO-
SPHERE in which the temperature ceases to fall with height and
may even rise slightly.

The word TROPOPAUSE comes from the Greek verb τρέπειν
(trepein), to turn, through the noun τρόπος (tropos), a turn,
way, manner, style. From this comes the English TROPE (*trōp*),
a term in rhetoric which means a figure of speech, the turn of
a phrase. The second part is the English PAUSE, from the Latin
pausa, and the Greek παῦσις (pausis), a halt, stop, cessation.

To the question: 'The atmospheric boundary at which fall of
temperature with increasing height ceases abruptly', 210 persons out of 515 answer STRATOSPHERE; 85 answer the correct
TROPOPAUSE; and 82 TROPOSPHERE. The TROPOSPHERE extends
from the surface of the earth to a height of about seven miles,
or 10 to 12 kilometers, over the temperate zones, and more over

Form A. The point in the atmosphere at which the fall of temperature with increasing height abruptly ceases.
Form AA. The atmospheric boundary at which fall of temperature with increasing height ceases abruptly.

FORM A. 36.	FW	LA	NY	NY	NY	PH	SUM	FORM AA. 45.	NY
ionosphere	3	7	8	10	16	30	74	ionosphere	15
stratosphere	6	26	16	24	60	78	210	stratosphere	25
TROPOPAUSE	7	8	2	7	24	37	85	TROPOPAUSE	11
pressure									
altitude	0	3	3	7	11	9	33	photosphere	2
troposphere	2	9	6	7	25	33	82	troposphere	9
unmarked	0	1	2	11	4	13	31	unmarked	1
total	18	54	37	66	140	200	515	total	63

the equator. The observations of Teisserenc de Bort, published
between 1898 and 1907, show that in this lower region temperature drops with height at a rate of about 3 degrees fahrenheit
with every 1000 feet, or in the metric system 6 degrees centigrade for every kilometer. But a height is reached at about 12
miles or 18 kilometers over the equator and less over the polar
regions, 4 to 5 miles, 6 to 8 kilometers, where the temperature
no longer drops with height but remains stationary. This upper

region is the STRATOSPHERE, and with the present wording of the question seems justified enough to attract 210 persons. The first part of the word STRATOSPHERE comes from the same source as the English word STRATUM (*strā'-tŭm*), from the Latin *stratum*, the spread for a bed, coverlet, quilt, blanket, also pavement. The second part is the English word SPHERE, from the Latin *sphera*, and this in turn from the Greek σφαῖρα (sphaira), a ball, globe, sphere. Between the TROPOSPHERE and the STRATOSPHERE is a thin transition layer, the TROPOPAUSE. The TROPOSPHERE and the STRATOSPHERE were both named by De Bort in about 1899; and the TROPOPAUSE not until several years later.

349. *EXPONENTIAL SERIES* (*ĕks-pō-nĕn'-shăl*). An infinite series obtained by expanding the expression e^x in which the variable or unknown quantity enters as an exponent, and where e is the Napierian base.

The adjective EXPONENTIAL, from the noun EXPONENT, applies where the unknown or variable enters as the exponent or as part of the exponent. The EXPONENTIAL THEOREM is the theorem that

$$e = 1 + \frac{1}{1!} + \frac{1}{2!} + \frac{1}{3!} + \frac{1}{4!} + \cdots$$

FORM B. 16.	NY	MISC.	SUM
Taylor's series	9	51	60
EXPONENTIAL SERIES	8	41	49
arithmetic progression	14	122	136
Fourier's series	9	37	46
geometric progression	7	36	43
unmarked	1	22	23
total	48	309	357

every quantity is equal to the sum of all the positive integral powers of its logarithm, each divided by the factorial of its exponent. The noun EXPONENTIAL is the Napierian base raised to the power indicated by the variable.

To the question:

$$\text{'}e = 1 + \frac{1}{1!} + \frac{1}{2!} + \frac{1}{3!} + \frac{1}{4!} + \cdots\text{',}$$

136 persons out of 357 answer ARITHMETIC PROGRESSION, com-

pared with only 49 who answer EXPONENTIAL SERIES. Each term
of an ARITHMETIC PROGRESSION is obtained by adding the same
constant to the preceding term. Thus: a, a + d, a + 2d, a + 3d,
a + 4d, . . . , where a is the first term and d the common
difference, is the general expression for an ARITHMETIC PROGRES-
SION. The figures in the denominators of the EXPONENTIAL
SERIES: 1, 2, 3, 4, etc., probably lead to the popularity of ARITH-
METIC PROGRESSION. But 2! is FACTORIAL 2, 1 × 2; 3! is FAC-
TORIAL 3, 1 × 2 × 3. By means of the binomial theorem, the
expression e^x can be expanded into the series:

$$e^x = 1 + \frac{x}{1!} + \frac{x^2}{2!} + \frac{x^3}{3!} + \frac{x^4}{4!} + \cdots$$

This is known as the EXPONENTIAL SERIES, the variable x appearing as the exponent. The series as given in the present question
is really the numerical value of e, the base of the Napierian
logarithms, and not the EXPONENTIAL SERIES.

350. *ELECTRON-RAY TUBE* (*ē-lĕk′-trŏn rā*). A device to
       indicate when a radio receiver is properly tuned to the
carrier frequency of the desired station.
To the question: 'Unit which aids in tuning', 108 persons out
of 224 answer TRIMMER; and only 48 ELECTRON-RAY TUBE.

Unit which aids in tuning.

FORM A. 42.	NY	NY	NY	SUM
meter	3	5	14	22
ultraudion	3	2	7	12
trimmer	16	16	76	108
ELECTRON-RAY TUBE	6	7	35	48
autodyne	3	9	15	27
unmarked	6	1	0	7
total	37	40	147	224

TRIMMER is obviously a correct answer to the question as
worded, though this was not intended. A TRIMMER is an adjustable auxiliary condenser or capacitor used in tuning. A TRIMMER
connected in parallel with the tuning condenser increases its
range. The ELECTRON-RAY TUBE is an indicator of tuning.

In the ELECTRON-RAY TUBE electrons from the cathode strike a fluorescent target which glows with a faint green light when bombarded. Between the cathode and the target is a ray-control electrode. When the voltage of this and the target are the same the whole of the target is illuminated. When the voltage of the ray-control electrode is less than the target voltage, negative with respect to the target, fewer electrons reach the target and only a part is illuminated.

351. *FORCE* (*fors*) *n*. Work divided by distance, amount of work per unit distance.

Change in momentum is proportional to the force producing it; this is Newton's second law and is often accepted as a definition of FORCE. Le Roy D. Weld in his Glossary of Physics does

Space rate of doing work.

FORM AB. 43.	%	FORM D. 39.	NY	%
entropy	18	entropy	65	18.6
energy	37	energy	85	24.2
torque	4	torque	36	10.3
power	16	power	100	28.6
FORCE	25	FORCE	49	14.0
unmarked	0	unmarked	15	4.3
total	100	total	350	100.0

FORM DA. 49.	%	FORM DB. 48.	NY
entropy	14	entropy	10
energy	22	energy	33
torque	14	torque	20
power	36	power	14
FORCE	10	FORCE	22
unmarked	4	unmarked	7
total	100	total	106

not include the word FORCE at all among his definitions, perhaps because FORCE is so often the fundamental concept in terms of which other units are defined. Thus in most textbooks FORCE is discussed early and WORK when presented subsequently is defined in terms of FORCE. To the customary textbook definition:

'Product of force and distance', 456 students out of 537 answer WORK. But to a question expressing the same relation of work, force, and distance, but differently worded: 'Space rate of doing work', only 10 per cent of students answer FORCE, fewer than mark any other choice.

The phrase 'space rate' may be the trouble; but in answer to a letter asking if the question seemed unfair, Paul Wolff responded: 'Space rate of doing work is beautifully clear cut mathematically. It would become clear to most persons sooner if it were stated in the longer, old-fashioned classical way: The rate of change of work with respect to distance'.

For 'Space rate of doing work', the popular choice made by 36 per cent is POWER. POWER is time rate of doing work. It is WORK divided by time; while FORCE is WORK divided by distance. POWER is the amount of work done per unit time; FORCE is the amount of work done per unit distance.

352. *DIAMETER* (dī-ăm′-ē-ter) n. In a circle, any straight line across through the center from side to side; from Webster, first edition, 1828: 'A right line passing through the center of a circle or other curvilinear figure, terminated by the circumference, and dividing the figure into two equal parts'.

Isaac Newton extended this conception to other algebraic curves by the theorem: 'If on each of a system of parallel chords of a curve of the nth order there be taken the center of mean distances of the n points where the chord meets the curve, the locus of this center is a straight line, which may be called a DIAMETER of the curve'.

The word DIAMETER starts with the familiar Greek διά (dia), across, already met in ADIABATIC (326), not going across, and in DIAMAGNETIC (216), across a magnetic field. DIAMETER ends with METER from the Greek μέτρον (metron), meaning measurement. By derivation, a DIAMETER is a measurement across.

To the question: 'Line joining the mid points of a system of parallel chords of any conic', only 76 persons out of 525 answer correctly DIAMETER; while 197 answer PERPENDICULAR. In a circle, every DIAMETER is PERPENDICULAR to the family of chords which it bisects; but this is not true of other conic sections. In a conic the mid points of any family of parallel chords lie on a straight line; and this straight line is called a DIAMETER. In the ellipse, every such line goes through the center, as it does with the circle; and every straight line through the center is a DIAMETER. The same is true of the hyperbola, where the center is half way between the two foci; the mid points of any set of

Lines joining the mid points of a system of parallel chords of any conic.

FORM C. 41.	CH	FORM CA. 47.	CH	LA	NY	NY	PH	SUM
section	11	section	7	3	19	43	13	85
perpendicular	29	perpendicular	18	16	34	99	30	197
secant	14	secant	8	7	18	60	13	106
DIAMETER	6	DIAMETER	5	6	15	40	10	76
equator	6	equator	0	3	8	30	3	44
unmarked	2	unmarked	2	2	3	5	5	17
total	68	total	40	37	97	277	74	525

FORM CB. 48.	NY
section	9
perpendicular	40
secant	14
DIAMETER	11
equator	9
unmarked	3
total	86

parallel chords lie on a straight line, and this line goes through the center. In the parabola, the axis is a DIAMETER drawn through the mid points of all the chords when these are PERPENDICULAR to the axis. In a system of chords all parallel to one another, but not PERPENDICULAR to the axis, the mid points lie on a straight line parallel to the axis, and still called a DIAMETER.

353. *DYNAMIC FACTOR* (*dī-năm'-ĭk*). The load due to the acceleration of an aircraft divided by the basic load, the ratio of the load carried by any part of an aircraft when accelerating and the corresponding basic load.

The BASIC LOAD on any member is usually defined as the load when the aircraft is flying straight ahead at uniform speed. A change in speed changes this load; a sudden change may alter it materially. This new load, due to any acceleration, is called the DYNAMIC LOAD. The DYNAMIC FACTOR is then the ratio of this DYNAMIC LOAD to the BASIC LOAD.

The adjective DYNAMIC comes from the Greek δυναμικός (dynamikos), powerful, efficacious, from δύναμις (dynamis), power, might, strength. The first definition of DYNAMIC in the

Form A. Ratio between the load carried by any part of an air-craft when accelerating and the corresponding basic load.
Form AA. Specifically the ratio between the load when accelerating and the basic load.

FORM A. 7.	FW	LA	NY	NY	NY	PH	SUM	FORM AA. 48. NY	
lift-drag								lift-drag	
ratio	6	24	23	19	62	79	213	ratio	16
load factor	6	12	7	19	44	55	143	load factor	13
dynamic load	1	5	4	14	10	23	57	dynamic load	15
factor of								factor of	
safety	1	3	2	8	11	14	39	safety	5
DYNAMIC								DYNAMIC	
FACTOR	4	10	0	4	13	27	58	FACTOR	12
unmarked	0	0	1	2	0	2	5	unmarked	2
total	18	54	37	66	140	200	515	total	63

Century Dictionary is: 'Pertaining to mechanical forces not in equilibrium'. This is the sense in which the word is used in the phrase: DYNAMIC FACTOR.

To the question: 'Ratio between the load carried by any part of an aircraft when accelerating and the corresponding basic load', 58 persons out of 515 answer correctly DYNAMIC FACTOR; but 213 answer LIFT-DRAG RATIO. This is the ratio of the vertical lift up divided by the horizontal drag back. It is an indication of the aerodynamic effectiveness of a wing or airfoil.

The second most frequently marked mislead, chosen by 143, twice as many as DYNAMIC FACTOR, is LOAD FACTOR. This is the load put on a part by any sort of maneuver divided by the basic load. It is the ratio between two loads which have the same relative distribution. The numerator of the fraction may be the load applied in any way; the denominator is the BASIC

LOAD. LOAD FACTOR is a correct answer to the present question and a more usual term than DYNAMIC FACTOR. But LOAD FACTOR is a general term for the ratio of any load over the BASIC LOAD; DYNAMIC FACTOR is specifically the ratio of the load due to acceleration over the BASIC LOAD.

354. *LIMIT OF RESOLUTION* (*rĕ-sō-lū'-shŏn*). The angle
    subtended by two points which are just distinguishable
with a telescope or microscope.
The RESOLVING POWER of a lens is directly proportional to the

Characteristic of an optical instrument defined as the angle between two points just distinguishable.

FORM BA. 37.	%	FORM D. 40.	NY	%
		LIMIT OF		
LIMIT OF RESOLUTION	23	RESOLUTION	66	18.9
aperture	10	aperture	46	13.1
magnifying power	7	magnifying power	36	10.3
index of refraction	44	index of refraction	116	33.1
achromatism	14	achromatism	66	18.9
unmarked	2	unmarked	20	5.7
total	100	total	350	100.0

FORM DA. 44.	%	FORM DB. 39.	NY
		LIMIT OF	
LIMIT OF RESOLUTION	24	RESOLUTION	30
aperture	5	aperture	8
magnifying power	4	critical angle	31
index of refraction	53	index of refraction	26
achromatism	11	achromatism	8
unmarked	3	unmarked	3
total	100	total	106

diameter of the objective aperture and inversely proportional to the wave length of light.
To the question: 'The characteristic of any optical instrument which is defined as the angle subtended by two points which just appear separate', only 4 per cent of students mark MAGNIFYING POWER, which one might expect to be popular;

24 per cent mark LIMIT OF RESOLUTION, the correct answer; but 53 per cent mark INDEX OF REFRACTION. The INDEX OF REFRACTION is the speed of light in one substance divided by the speed in another. REFRACTION is the bending of a ray of light on entering a new medium at an angle. The magnifying power of a lens depends on REFRACTION, on the light rays bending as they enter the lens and bending again as they leave. But this is not what is known as the LIMIT OF RESOLUTION of a lens.

The LIMIT OF RESOLUTION of a lens depends on DIFFRACTION and INTERFERENCE. DIFFRACTION is the spreading out of light when it goes through a tiny hole due to the hole becoming a new point source of light. DIFFRACTION is the bending of light around the edge of an object, bending back into the shadow. DIFFRACTION rings form around the image of an object. These no more than blur the edge of a large object; but with details close together these DIFFRACTION rings overlap and make two points impossible to distinguish. The larger the aperture of the lens, that is, the greater its diameter, the smaller the rings and so the greater the RESOLVING POWER. Also the shorter the wave length of the light the smaller the rings, and so the greater the RESOLVING POWER.

355. *SURD* (*serd*) *n.* A quantity which cannot be expressed as a ratio of two whole numbers. The adjective applies to a quantity not expressible in rational numbers: 'A SURD expression', 'A SURD quantity'. Reread IRRATIONAL (287).

Ephraim Chambers, 1728, says: 'SURD, in arithmetic, denotes a number or quantity that is incommensurate to unity; or that is inexpressible by any known way of notation, otherwise than by its radical sign or index. This is otherwise called an IRRATIONAL or INCOMMENSURABLE number and an IMPERFECT POWER.

'When any number or quantity hath its root proposed to be extracted, and yet is not a true figurate number of that kind; that is, if its square root be demanded, and it is not a true square, if its cube root be required and itself be not a true cube, etc., then it is impossible to assign, either in whole numbers, or in fractions, any exact root of such number proposed'. Part of this is quoted, word for word, a century later by George Crabb in his Technological Dictionary of 1833.

The word SURD comes from the Latin *surdus*, deaf. The English ABSURD may be a combination of the Latin *ab*, which intensifies the meaning, and the same Latin *surdus*, deaf, dull, indistinct. The Encyclopaedic Dictionary of 1881 and the Etymological Dictionary of the Rev. Walter W. Skeat both say: 'Latin *surdus*, deaf; hence, deaf to reason, irrational'; for the word

Any number which is neither a whole number nor a fraction.

FORM B. 8.	LA	MISC.	SUM
imaginary number	23	132	155
SURD	6	45	51
radical	12	104	116
prime	3	17	20
proper fraction	3	6	9
unmarked	1	5	6
total	48	309	357

RATIONAL is used of human beings to mean sane, capable of reasoning. But the Century Dictionary says the word SURD arose from a mistranslation into Latin of the Greek ἄλογος (alogos), a combination of the privative ἀ (a), meaning not, and λόγος (logos), words, which does not mean stupid or unreasonable, but inexpressible.

To the question: 'Any number which is neither a whole number nor a fraction', only 51 persons out of 357 choose SURD, the correct answer; while 155 choose IMAGINARY NUMBER and 116 RADICAL. An IMAGINARY NUMBER is one which cannot actually be obtained, one which is of only theoretical value. The IMAGINARY NUMBERS are the even roots of negative numbers, roots which cannot be extracted; for any positive number multiplied by itself gives a positive answer, and any negative number multiplied by itself also gives a positive answer. There is no number which multiplied by itself gives a negative answer. So that it is impossible to get the square root of a negative number, or any even root of a negative number. Such a root is called IMAGINARY and is handled in mathematical manipulations much as if it were a real number but without the root actually being taken. An IMAGINARY NUMBER cannot be approximated; it just cannot be obtained at all.

Both a SURD and an IRRATIONAL number can be obtained to any number of decimal places but never quite accurately. There is some effort to differentiate the two words, using IRRATIONAL in a more general sense to include such constants as π, the ratio of the diameter to the circumference of a circle, which can be carried to any number of decimal places but never to the final one; and to limit the word SURD to a root which can never be obtained absolutely accurately. It is perhaps this which leads to the confusion of SURD with RADICAL. A RADICAL is a root sign: $\sqrt{}$. A SURD is the square root of two: $\sqrt{2}$; or the cube root of four: $\sqrt[3]{4}$; or the cube root of ten: $\sqrt[3]{10}$. These roots can be carried to any number of decimal places, but never determined exactly. SURDS are real numbers which can be used for practical purposes, which can be obtained as accurately as an engineer or mathematician desires, but never precisely.

356. *CREST FACTOR* (*krĕst făk'-tor*). The maximum value of an alternating current divided by its effective value, the ratio of the maximum value to the square root of the mean of the squares of the instantaneous values of an alternating current over a complete cycle. Called also PEAK FACTOR and AMPLITUDE FACTOR.

The effective value of an alternating current, its root-mean-square value, is in many ways the same as the corresponding value of a direct current. Most electrical instruments show the effective or root-mean-square value of an alternating current. The CREST VALUE is the peak it reaches during each half cycle. This is above the corresponding figure for a direct current of the same indicated amperes, volts, or watts. The CREST FACTOR is the mean value of an alternating current or more exactly its root-mean-square value divided into its CREST VALUE.

To the question: 'The ratio of root-mean-square current to maximum current', only 15 per cent of those persons whose scores have been tabulated for form DA answer correctly CREST FACTOR, 20 per cent in the earlier form D, and 30 per cent for the still earlier form AB given to a more selected group; while with every form more and with form DA nearly three times as many, 44 per cent, answer POWER FACTOR. Both POWER FACTOR and CREST FACTOR apply to alternating currents. Both involve in their computation the effective value of the alternating current, the square root of the mean of the squares of the instantaneous values of the alternating current over a cycle. The POWER FACTOR gives the true power determined from the apparent power. The latter is the product of volts and amperes. As in a direct current circuit power equals volts times amperes, so in a non-inductive alternating current circuit the same holds true.

Forms AB, D, and DA. Factor obtained by dividing root-mean-square current into maximum current.

Form DB. Factor which equals maximum current divided by root-mean-square current.

FORM AB. 39.	%	FORM D. 38.	NY	%
reactive factor	10	reactive factor	51	14.6
leakage factor	11	leakage factor	45	12.9
form factor	5	form factor	38	10.8
power factor	42	power factor	119	34.0
CREST FACTOR	30	CREST FACTOR	69	19.7
unmarked	2	unmarked	28	8.0
total	100	total	350	100.0

FORM DA. 43.	%	FORM DB. 47.	NY
reactive factor	10	safety	10
leakage factor	10	leakage	24
form factor	16	form	9
power factor	44	power	34
CREST FACTOR	15	CREST	19
unmarked	5	unmarked	10
total	100	total	106

In a circuit of this sort which contains resistance only the POWER FACTOR is 1.00 or 100 per cent. But in an inductive circuit the lag between the current and voltage causes the true power to be less than the product of the current and voltage. In this case:

VOLTS × AMPERES × POWER FACTOR = TRUE POWER.

The CREST FACTOR is the ratio of maximum current in a half cycle to its effective value. Reread POWER FACTOR (228).

357. *OCTANT* (ŏk'-tănt) *n.* One of the eight parts into which
     space is divided by three coordinate planes. Reread the
adjective CARTESIAN (276).

The word OCTANT comes from the Latin *octans, octantis*, a
half quadrant, from *octo*, eight, a word which occurs also in
OCTAGONAL, eight cornered. OCTANT in English is ordinarily
used with the Latin meaning of a half quadrant, an eighth of a
flat circle, as when two heavenly bodies, especially the sun and
a planet, are distant from one another by an eighth of a circle,
45 degrees. From Edward Phillips, in his World of Words of
1658, comes: 'OCTANT or OCTILE (in Astrol.), where a Planet is
in such an Aspect or Position with respect to another, that their
Places are only distant an eighth part of a Circle, or 45 Degrees'.

On the other hand OCTANT is occasionally used for one of the
eight parts into which a solid, or the space around a central
point, is divided by three planes, usually at right angles. From
1790 comes: 'The eight OCTANTS of a regular parallelopipedon';
from 1875: 'Four lower and four upper OCTANTS of a sphere';
and from 1895: 'These planes divide the space round the origin
into eight hollow quoins or OCTANTS'. But this use of OCTANT is
rare as shown by the fact that to the question: 'Division of space
determining whether x, y, and z measurements are plus or
minus in sign', only 95 persons out of 525 answer OCTANT; while
252 answer QUADRANT.

In the rectangular or Cartesian coordinate system two lines at
right angles called axes divide the plane in which they lie into
four parts. Each of these quarters is called a QUADRANT (188).
Noah Webster, in his first edition, 1828, says: 'QUADRANT, in
geometry, the quarter of a circle; the arc of a circle containing
ninety degrees; also, the space or area included between this
arc and two radii drawn from the center to each extremity'.
Today, in analytical geometry, the word QUADRANT is used for
any of the four parts into which a plane is divided by rectangular coordinate axes.

In much the same manner OCTANTS divide solid space and
determine the signs of three coordinates. The x axis is horizontal, with positive values to the right and negative to the left,
as in plane coordinates. In locating a point in three-dimensional
space the z axis runs up and down, vertically, with positive

values up and negative down; while the y axis runs out toward
the observer, horizontally and at right angles to the other two,
with positive values toward the observer, and negative away.
In drawing such a three-dimensional system on a flat piece of
paper, the x and z axes are drawn at right angles to each other;
and distances in this plane, parallel to these two axes, the plane

Division of space determining whether x, y, and z measurements
are plus or minus in sign.

FORM C. 9.	CH	FORM CA. 48.	CH	LA	NY	NY	PH	SUM
absolute	5	absolute	4	2	13	31	9	59
quadrant	38	quadrant	23	21	48	130	30	252
OCTANT	11	OCTANT	6	6	16	50	17	95
pole	5	pole	3	4	13	13	2	35
meridian	9	meridian	2	2	4	50	12	70
unmarked	0	unmarked	2	2	3	3	4	14
total	68	total	40	37	97	277	74	525

FORM CB. 46.	NY
absolute	16
quadrant	39
OCTANT	16
pole	7
meridian	3
unmarked	5
total	86

of the paper, are measured directly to scale. The y axis, coming
toward the observer, is represented by a line which makes an
angle of 135 degrees with each of the other two. Distances
parallel to the y axis are foreshortened in the ratio of $\sqrt{2}$ to 2.
Equal lengths along the three axes are represented by the sides
of a square and half its diameter.

358. *COL* (kŏl) *n.* A low-pressure valley or defile between two
    barometric highs.
The word COL belongs to the dialects of the Alps, it goes
back through the French *col*, neck, pass, defile, to the Latin
collum, neck. A COL is a marked depression in the summit line

of a mountain chain, a narrow pass between two mountain peaks, a defile leading from one side of a mountain range to the other. The word is used in this way by Tyndall in his Hours of Exercise in the Alps. The same word meaning a depression in barometric pressure between two barometric highs is so recent that this meaning appears in neither the Century Dictionary of 1891 nor the Oxford New English Dictionary started at almost the same time but not finished until 1913.

To the question: 'A neck of relatively low pressure between two anticyclones', 97 persons out of 515 answer correctly COL; but two and a half times as many, 248, answer LINE SQUALL. One trouble may be the term ANTICYCLONE in the definition, an area of high pressure. The word SQUALL comes from the Swedish *squal*, a rush of water. A SQUALL is a violent gust of

A neck of relatively low pressure between two anticyclones.

FORM A. 12.	FW	LA	NY	NY	NY	PH	SUM	FORM AA. 46.	NY
COL	4	9	5	13	29	37	97	COL	10
line squall	8	28	17	31	66	98	248	line squall	35
chinook	3	5	5	6	17	26	62	chinook	8
foehn	2	6	6	6	17	13	50	white squall	2
monsoon	1	4	3	4	10	24	46	monsoon	6
unmarked	0	2	1	6	1	2	12	unmarked	2
total	18	54	37	66	140	200	515	total	63

wind, succession of sudden gusts, usually accompanied by rain, snow, or sleet. A LINE SQUALL is the kind of SQUALL which is caused by the passage of a V-shaped barometric trough. It is named LINE SQUALL because the SQUALLS form a line coincident with the axis of the trough which sweeps across the country broadside on. A LINE SQUALL is wind and rain; a COL is the low pressure valley which may cause the LINE SQUALL.

359. PHUGOID OSCILLATION (fū'-goid ŏs-sĭl-lā'-shŏn).

A fore-and-aft oscillation of long period about a horizontal straight line, caused by a sudden disturbance.

The word PHUGOID, first used about 1908, comes from the Greek φύγη (phuge), flight. The English FUGITIVE, one in flight, and the musical term FUGUE, although both from Latin, come from the same original source as the Greek word. The ending -OID, from the Greek εἶδος (eidos), form, shape, resemblance, likeness, already met in CYCLOID (133), and earlier in ANEROID (93), is the termination of many scientific adjectives and means in the form of, like, resembling, but often suggests not exactly like, as: ANTHROPOID, like man.

The noun OSCILLATION and the corresponding verb to OSCIL-LATE go back to the Latin *oscillatus*, the past participle of *oscil-*

A long-period oscillation characteristic of the disturbed longitudinal motion of an aircraft.

FORM A. 31.	FW	LA	NY	NY	NY	PH	SUM	FORM AA. 49. NY	
spiral instability	0	2	4	15	26	11	58	spiral	19
stable oscillation	0	5	7	12	45	32	101	stable	5
unstable oscillation	15	24	13	16	39	98	205	unstable	24
PHUGOID OSCILLATION	2	11	4	7	19	22	65	PHUGOID	12
catastrophic instability	1	7	6	4	9	20	47	catastrophic	1
unmarked	0	5	3	12	2	17	39	unmarked	2
total	18	54	37	66	140	200	515	total	63

lare, to swing, from *oscillum*, a swing. This Latin word is identical in spelling with *oscillum*, a little mask hung on a tree and swaying in the wind, the diminutive of *os*, mouth, face.

To the question: 'A long-period oscillation characteristic of the disturbed longitudinal motion of an aircraft', 205 persons in a population of 515 mark UNSTABLE. There are three types of oscillation in aviation terminology: UNSTABLE, STABLE, and PHUGOID. All of these oscillations are up-and-down motions of the aircraft in flight, first above and then below the horizontal course. In UNSTABLE OSCILLATION each motion up and down is greater than the preceding, the amplitude of each increasing continuously until an attitude of the craft is reached from which there is no tendency to return to the original. A STABLE OSCILLATION, marked by 101 persons, also more frequently than the correct answer, is an oscillation like the preceding but whose amplitude does not increase. A PHUGOID OSCILLATION, marked by only 65 persons, is one of long period. The PHUGOID theory deals with longitudinal stability.

360. *GNOMONIC PROJECTION* (*nō-mŏn′-ĭk*). Type of projection where a great circle on the globe appears as a straight line on a flat surface, map on which a straight line is the shortest distance between two points on the earth.

A GNOMONIC PROJECTION represents lines on the surface of the earth projected out from the center of the earth onto a flat plane. As seen from the center of the earth every great circle on the surface appears as a straight line; for each great circle is the intersection with the surface of a plane through the center of the earth, which cuts the earth in half. Picture the earth as a hollow ball with a light at the center casting a shadow of each surface line on a screen. With the screen held above the north pole the meridians radiate out in all directions as straight lines equally spaced, while the lines of latitude are circles around the pole.

GNOMONIC is an adjective from the noun GNOMON (*nō′-mŏn*), the rod or triangle on a sun-dial which casts a shadow and so indicates the time. GNOMONIC originally meant pertaining to the GNOMON or sun-dial, pertaining to measuring time with the sun-dial. The adjective GNOMONIC comes through the Latin *gnomonicus*, from the Greek γνωμονικός (gnomonikos), an adjective from γνώμων (gnomon), the triangular upright on a sundial which by its shadow shows the time of day. The name applies to this type of projection because each line on a GNOMONIC chart might be the shadow of a line on the surface of a glass globe cast on a flat screen by a light at the center of the globe.

To the question: 'A chart projection on which all great circles are exactly represented by straight lines', GNOMONIC is chosen by only 76 persons out of 515, MERCATOR CHART attracting far more, 257, more than three times as many. MERCATOR's projection is named for a Flemish geographer who lived from 1512 to 1594. His real name was Gerhard Kremer. But in Low German Kremer, spelt Kramer in Dutch, means merchant, beggar. MERCATOR (*mer-kā'-tor*) is the Latin translation of merchant, beggar. In both MERCATOR'S projection and a GNOMONIC PROJECTION the meridians are straight lines. In MERCATOR'S projection they run up and down parallel to one another and never meet; in a GNOMONIC PROJECTION they radiate out from the pole as they do on the globe. In MERCATOR'S projection the

Form A. A chart projection on which all great circles are exactly represented by straight lines.
Form AA. Type of projection where all great circles are straight lines.

FORM A. 48.	FW	LA	NY	NY	NY	PH	SUM	FORM AA. 47.	NY
log	1	1	1	0	5	3	11	Admiralty	2
Lambert chart	4	12	9	12	25	36	98	Lambert	10
Mercator chart	8	27	21	25	71	105	257	Mercator	32
GNOMONIC CHART	5	7	1	13	26	24	76	GNOMONIC	13
synoptic chart	0	3	2	3	10	15	33	synoptic	4
unmarked	0	4	3	13	3	17	40	unmarked	2
total	18	54	37	66	140	200	515	total	63

latitude lines are straight and horizontal; in a GNOMONIC PROJECTION they are circles around the pole. On MERCATOR'S projection a compass course is a straight line, and a great circle is a curve which in the northern hemisphere bends above a straight line. The first American edition of the Encyclopaedia Britannica, 1798, says: 'It is of consequence to navigators in a long voyage to take the nearest way to their port; but this can seldom be done without considerable difficulty. The shortest distance is measured by an arch of a great circle intercepted between two points; and therefore it is advisable to direct the ship along a great circle.' On a GNOMONIC PROJECTION a great circle is a straight line.

Aeronautical charts on the GNOMONIC principle are used for laying out long great-circle courses. The course is then transferred, section by section, to another type of chart.

361. *DRAG STRUT* (drăg strŭt). A fore-and-aft compression member of the internal bracing system of an aircraft
wing.

A STRUT is the compression member in any truss frame. A
DRAG STRUT is a fore-and-aft STRUT, lying in a horizontal position, compressed by drag, a horizontal force parallel to the
direction of motion of the plane.

To the question: 'A fore-and-aft compression member of the
internal bracing system of an airplane wing', only 48 persons
out of 515 answer DRAG STRUT, while 243 answer COMPRESSION
RIB. This is a correct answer to the present question. A COM-
PRESSION WING RIB performs the two functions of a rib, it gives

Form A. A fore-and-aft compression member of the internal
bracing system of an aircraft.

Form AA. A fore-and-aft piece primarily to resist compression
in the internal bracing of a wing.

FORM A. 30.	FW	LA	NY	NY	NY	PH	SUM	FORM AA. 50.	NY
stringer	8	20	9	24	38	70	169	stringer	3
spats	0	1	3	0	5	4	13	truss	6
tab	0	1	1	3	11	7	23	lift strut	13
compression rib	7	29	15	30	70	92	243	compression rib	35
DRAG STRUT	3	3	7	3	13	19	48	DRAG STRUT	4
unmarked	0	0	2	6	3	8	19	unmarked	2
total	18	54	37	66	140	200	515	total	63

the wing section its form and shape and also transmits air loads
from the covering to the spars, but a COMPRESSION RIB also
takes the compression load between the front and rear spars,
replacing a COMPRESSION STRUT which would otherwise be a
separate member. The choice COMPRESSION RIB might be omitted
from this item leaving DRAG STRUT as the only correct answer;
or the question might be made more precise so that DRAG STRUT
would fit and COMPRESSION RIB would not. This last has been
attempted: 'A fore-and-aft piece used primarily to resist compression in the internal bracing of a wing; but 35 out of 63 still
mark COMPRESSION RIB, and only 4 DRAG STRUT.

362. *TRAPEZOID* (*trăp'-ĕ-zō-ĭd*) *n.* Correctly, an enclosed four-sided plane figure with no sides parallel; but commonly used in English, originally by mistake, for an enclosed four-sided figure with two opposite sides parallel and the other two not so.

Both TRAPEZOID and TRAPEZIUM (*tră-pē'-zĭ-ŭm*) come from the Greek τραπεζοειδής (trapezoeides), a combination of τράπεζα (trapeza), table, and εἶδος (eidos), form. In his Philosophy of the Inductive Sciences, 1840, William Whewell says: 'TRAPE-ZIUM (τραπέζιον) originally signifies a table, and thus might denote any form; but as the tables of the Greeks had one side shorter than the opposite one, such a figure was at first called a TRAPEZIUM. Afterwards the term was made to signify any figure with four unequal sides, a name being more needful in geometry for this kind of figure, than the ordinary form'.

Euclid, who wrote about 300 B.C., did not differentiate among the TRAPEZIA. Seven hundred and fifty years later Proclus, surnamed Diadocus, A.D. 450, in his Commentaries on the First Book of Euclid's Elements, used TRAPEZOID, τραπεζοιδές (trapezoides), for a figure with no sides parallel; and TRAPEZIUM, τραπέζιον (trapezion), for the same figure with two sides parallel. These meanings survive today in all European languages, and held in English until the last of the seventeen hundreds. John Harris, 1704, says: 'TRAPEZOID, a solid irregular Figure, having four Sides not parallel to one another'. The Chambers of 1753 says of TRAPEZOID: 'A plane irregular figure, having four sides, no two of which are parallel to each other'.

The Oxford New English Dictionary blames Charles Hutton, not for the mistake but for not correcting it. Hutton, professor of mathematics at the Royal Academy, Woolwich, published a Mathematical and Philosophical Dictionary in 1795 in which he gives both meanings but takes no definite stand at a time when the mistake was just being made and might have been corrected more easily than today. Today of TRAPEZOID the Oxford New English Dictionary says: 'With some: A quadrilateral figure having only two sides parallel', and then adds: 'A misapplication of the term peculiar to English; now generally given up'.

Despite this statement, when given a choice between TRAPE-
ZIUM and TRAPEZOID, 366 persons out of 525 answer TRAPEZOID
to the question: 'A four-sided figure with only two sides
parallel', while only 22 answer TRAPEZIUM, which the Oxford
Dictionary and all writers from A.D. 450 to 1750 would consider
correct. In nearly every population studied, Chicago, Los Angeles, and New York, roughly ten times as many mark TRAPE-
ZOID as TRAPEZIUM. To the same question in form CB, where as
an experiment the incorrect choice TRAPEZOID is omitted, 46
persons out of 86 answer TRAPEZIUM.

When the question is asked in reverse, in form B, item 9, of
this same worksample 280: 'A plane figure with four sides, no
one of which is parallel to another', 54 persons answer TRAPE-
ZOID and 46 TRAPEZIUM. For no sides parallel, more persons

A four-sided figure with only two sides parallel.

FORM C. 13.	CH	FORM CA. 7.	CH	LA	NY	NY	PH	SUM
quadrilateral	8	quadrilateral	4	1	9	31	8	53
TRAPEZIUM	1	TRAPEZIUM	2	3	5	10	2	22
trapezoid	49	trapezoid	20	21	69	190	56	366
rhombus	9	rhombus	2	11	10	36	6	65
rhomboid	1	rhomboid	2	1	4	10	2	19
unmarked	0	unmarked	0	0	0	0	0	0
total	68	total	40	37	97	277	74	525

FORM CB. 50.	NY
quadrilateral	5
TRAPEZIUM	46
rectangle	1
rhombus	22
rhomboid	10
unmarked	2
total	86

mark TRAPEZOID than TRAPEZIUM; but the vote is not so clear
and overwhelming as the present item. Nevertheless English
should return to the original meanings of the two words, both
to agree with present European languages and to be consistent
with itself prior to 1750. A TRAPEZOID should be a four-sided

figure with no sides parallel; and a TRAPEZIUM, a four-sided figure with two sides parallel. From now on TRAPEZIUM will be scored as the correct answer to the present item. This moves the item from among the easy words to the present position among the most difficult words of this book, where it will be of interest to persons with scientific background, who score generally high.

363. *QUADRIC* (*kwŏd'-rĭk*) *n.* An equation of the second degree involving more than two variables. As an adjective QUADRIC means of the second degree and is used specifically where the variables are more than two.

To the question: 'Any equation of the second degree involving three variables', 253 persons out of 525 answer QUADRATIC; and only 46 QUADRIC, the correct answer. Both QUADRIC and

Any equation of the second degree involving three variables.

FORM C. 45.	CH	FORM CA. 23.	CH	LA	NY	NY	PH	SUM
cubic	20	cubic	12	11	23	60	19	125
quadratic	33	quadratic	22	14	51	131	35	253
polyhedral	3	polyhedral	1	2	7	34	8	52
QUADRIC	5	QUADRIC	3	4	5	29	5	46
conic	6	conic	2	5	9	19	4	39
unmarked	1	unmarked	0	1	2	4	3	10
total	68	total	40	37	97	277	74	525

FORM CB. 49.	NY
cubic	26
quadratic	41
polyhedral	2
QUADRIC	11
conic	4
unmarked	2
total	86

QUADRATIC come from the Latin *quattuor*, equivalent to the English four. The Latin adjective *quadratus* means square. The neuter *quadratum* is a noun and means a square. The verb *quadrare* is to make four cornered, to square, and is the source of the English QUARRY, both the verb to QUARRY, to dig and cut stone from the ground, and QUARRY, the pit or cavern left after removing the stone, usually for building. QUADRIC goes back no earlier than 1850, whereas QUADRATIC goes back to 1650.

John Harris, who gave the seventh series of Boyle lectures in 1698: Atheistical Observations against the Being of God and His Attributes fairly considered and fully refuted, says in his Lexicon Technicum, 1704: 'QUADRATICK equations, are ſuch as retain on the unknown Side, the Square of the Root or Number ſought'. The Encyclopaedia printed in Philadelphia in 1798 by Thomas Dobson, a year after the completion of the third edition of the Encyclopaedia Britannica in 1797, says: 'QUADRATIC EQUATIONS, in algebra, thoſe wherein the unknown quantity is of two dimenſions or raiſed to the ſecond power'. Where there is only one variable, the word QUADRATIC is usually employed; where the number of nonhomogeneous variables exceeds two, QUADRIC.

364. *ÅNGSTRÖM UNIT* (ĕng′-strŏm ū′-nĭt). Unit of length for the measurement of wave lengths of light, one tenthousandth of a micron, 10^{-10} meter, called also tenth-meter. Anders Jonas Ångström, 1814 to 1874, was a Swedish physicist who in 1868 published his great map of the solar spectrum. Although his measurements were inexact to the extent of one part in seven or eight thousand, because his standard meter was just too short, his work long remained authoritative in questions of wave length.

A ten-millionth of a millimeter is thought by only 20 per cent of students to be an ÅNGSTRÖM UNIT, and by 63 per cent to be a MILLIMICRON. A MICRON is one millionth of a meter, 10^{-6} meter, 1/1,000,000th meter. A MILLIMICRON is one thousandth of a MICRON, 10^{-9} meter, 1/1,000,000,000 meter. A MICRON is 10,000 ÅNGSTRÖM UNITS; so that a MILLIMICRON is ten ÅNGSTRÖM UNITS. Those who take the physics vocabulary test have a close idea of an ÅNGSTRÖM UNIT. No one marks KILOMETER, used in form BA as an opposite in suggestion; and only one in a hundred marks CENTIMETER. MILLIMICRON, substituted for KILOMETER, is by far the most popular answer in form D, and remains the popular answer in forms DA and DB.

Visible light rays extend from about 3900 ÅNGSTRÖM UNITS to about 7800. The two well-known sodium lines are 5896 and

Ten-millionth of a millimeter.

FORM BA. 42.		FORM D. 46.		
ÅNGSTRÖM UNIT	18	ÅNGSTRÖM UNIT	66	18.9
micrometer	20	micrometer	19	5.4
centimeter	1	centimeter	2	0.6
micron	58	micron	21	6.0
kilometer	0	millimicron	223	63.7
unmarked	3	unmarked	19	5.4
total	100	total	350	100.0

FORM DA. 45.		FORM DB. 41.	
ÅNGSTRÖM UNIT	20	ÅNGSTRÖM UNIT	17
micrometer	5	micrometer	5
megohm	2	X-unit	4
micron	7	micron	10
millimicron	63	millimicron	65
unmarked	3	unmarked	5
total	100	total	106

5890 ÅNGSTRÖM UNITS. X rays are much shorter, from ten to as short as one tenth ÅNGSTRÖM UNITS. Radio waves are much longer, measured in meters, not ÅNGSTRÖM UNITS.

365. PENCIL (pĕn'-sĭl) n. In geometry, a number of lines which meet in one point.

The word PENCIL comes from the Latin penicillum, a painter's brush, the diminutive of peniculus, brush. This in turn is the diminutive of penis, tail.

To the question: 'A group of lines in 3-dimensional space meeting at a single point', 5 persons out of 132 answer PENCIL, the correct answer, while 101 answer VORTEX. In the earlier study, 2 out of 61 answer PENCIL, and 49 VORTEX. A VORTEX, from the Latin vortex, a variant of vertex, a whirl, eddy, whirlpool, is a rapid movement of particles round an axis, a whirl of vapor or of fluid. A VORTEX-LINE, according to W. K. Clifford, is: 'A curve such that its tangent at every point is in the direction of the spin at that point'. A VERTEX, in geometry, is a point at which two lines meet to form an angle; and this no doubt leads to the overwhelming popularity of VORTEX.

In optics, a PENCIL of rays is all the rays of light which diverge from or converge to a given point. From George Crabb's Technological Dictionary, 1833, comes: 'PENCIL of rays (Opt.) a double cone of rays joined together at the base; the one cone having its VERTEX in some point of the object, and the crystalline humour or glass for its base, and the other having its base on the same glass, but its VERTEX on the point of convergence'. VERTEX, as thus used, is the point; PENCIL, the group of lines.

From the Penny Cyclopaedia of the Society for the Diffusion of Useful Knowledge, published in sections between 1833 and 1843, comes: 'A PENCIL of lines is a number of lines which meet

A group of lines in 3-dimensional space meeting at a single point.

FORM A. 50.	BO	NY	SUM	FORM AA. 50.	NY
PENCIL	1	1	2	PENCIL	5
sheaf	3	3	6	sheaf	14
vortex	14	35	49	vortex	101
class	0	0	0	class	6
tensor	0	2	2	tensor	5
unmarked	2	0	2	unmarked	1
total	20	41	61	total	132

in one point'. From 1859, collected works of Arthur Cayley, not published until 1895, comes: 'A system of lines through a point is said to be a PENCIL'.

366. *ARGUMENT* (ahr'-gū-mĕnt) *n.* Independent variable, a quantity on which the value of another quantity depends, usually a quantity which is varied in regular steps in computing the corresponding values of another quantity.

The term ARGUMENT is used by the Century Dictionary for the quantity on which a series of numbers depend in a numerical table. It gives as an illustration a table of the sun's declination for each degree of longitude, so that the longitude being

known, the declination might be found. The longitude is the
ARGUMENT of the table. Much earlier, 1704, John Harris gives:
'ARGUMENT, in astronomy, is an Ark by which we seek another Ark unknown, and proportional to the first'. More than
a hundred years later, 1828, Noah Webster, in the first edition
of his dictionary, quotes this but gives credit to Chambers.

The word ARGUMENT comes from the Latin *argumentum*,
proof, evidence, token, subject, contents. This comes in turn
from the verb *arguere*, to prove, argue, show, make clear.

To the question: 'A variable upon whose assigned values the
value of another variable depends', only 17 persons out of 357
answer ARGUMENT; while 183 answer DEPENDENT VARIABLE; and
85 FUNCTION. A FUNCTION is a mathematical expression whose

A variable upon whose assigned values the value of another
variable depends.

FORM B. 35.	NY	MISC.	SUM
ARGUMENT	4	13	17
function	11	74	85
tensor	0	25	25
dependent variable	25	158	183
parameter	4	1	5
unmarked	4	38	42
total	48	309	357

value depends upon another quantity, or upon other quantities,
called ARGUMENTS or INDEPENDENT VARIABLES, the value of the
FUNCTION or DEPENDENT VARIABLE changing in accord with a
fixed relationship.

367. ∵ In mathematical logic this symbol means since, because,
inasmuch as, considering, for, as, seeing that.

To the question "∵", only 5 persons out of a total of 68, whose
scores have been tabulated for the original form c, answer
SINCE; while 49 answer THEREFORE. In printing the five choices
across the page in the vocabulary test, THEREFORE came first,
followed by SINCE. Because of the similarity of the two signs:
∵ and ∴, it seemed as if those who saw THEREFORE might mark
it instantly without reading through the line. To test this possi-

bility, the choice UNEQUAL, the fourth choice in form C, was put first in the revised form CA, and THEREFORE put fourth, with SINCE still in second position. This means that a person reading across the row of choices from left to right must reject SINCE, the correct answer, in order to mark THEREFORE; and yet 373 persons out of 535 mark THEREFORE under these conditions, compared with only 57 marking SINCE.

Under the heading Symbols in Mathematical Logic, Florian Cajori traces the history of these two notations. J. H. Rahn, as early as 1659, used both ∴ and ∵ for THEREFORE, the first, ∴, predominating. Both forms are found in many early writings. The sign ∵, meaning BECAUSE, SINCE, Cajori finds first

FORM C. 35.	CH	FORM CA. 49.	CH	LA	NY	NY	PH	SUM
therefore	49	unequal	0	1	4	5	1	11
SINCE	5	SINCE	2	3	11	34	7	57
proof	5	proof	3	2	8	15	3	31
unequal	1	therefore	28	28	62	199	56	373
not propor-tionate	8	not propor-tionate	4	1	10	29	2	46
unmarked	0	unmarked	3	2	2	5	5	17
total	68	total	40	37	97	287	74	535

in 1805. The sign ∴ meaning THEREFORE and ∵ meaning SINCE or BECAUSE, are clearly differentiated in the Elements of Euclid edited at the University of Cambridge in 1827. But among those who have taken the vocabulary of mathematics there is certainly no universal recognition of ∵ as meaning SINCE or BECAUSE, the opposite of THEREFORE, WHEREFORE, CONSEQUENTLY.

368. CENTER OF PERCUSSION (per-kŭsh'-shŏn). Point at

which if a physical pendulum is struck there is no reaction of the axis, one of two conjugate points of a free body acted upon by an impulse the other of which lies on the axis of instantaneous rotation.

The word PERCUSSION comes from the Latin percussio, percussionis, a striking, beating, from the verb percutere, to strike, beat. This in turn is a combination of per, through, and quatere, to shake, strike. A DISCUSSION, a combination of *dis*, apart, and the same *quatere*, is by derivation a shaking apart of a subject. A CONCUSSION is a striking together. Though by derivation a PERCUSSION is a striking through, the word appears most frequently in a technical context as: CENTER OF PERCUSSION.

To the question: 'The point at which the mass of a physical pendulum may be considered as concentrated', 65 per cent answer CENTER OF GRAVITY and 12 per cent CENTER OF PERCUSSION. To this question either answer is probably correct. The CENTER OF GRAVITY of a body is the point at which, if its mass were concentrated, the gravitational force would be the same as on the body as a whole. It is the point at which the weight of a

Forms AB, D, and DA. The point at which the mass of a physical pendulum may be considered as concentrated.
Form DB. Center of physical pendulum used in determining period with ideal pendulum equation.

FORM AB. 49.		FORM D. 50.		
NO POINT	2	NO POINT	41	11.7
center of gravity	93	center of gravity	189	54.0
geometric center	0	geometric center	23	6.6
		instantaneous		
instantaneous center	2	center	21	6.0
		center of		
center of percussion	2	percussion	58	16.6
unmarked	1	unmarked	18	5.1
total	100	total	350	100.0

FORM DA. 50.		FORM DB. 50.	
NO POINT	1	suspension	30
center of gravity	65	gravitational	43
geometric center	7	geometric	13
instantaneous center	11	instantaneous	7
center of percussion	12	PERCUSSION	7
unmarked	4	unmarked	6
total	100	total	106

body may be considered as concentrated. In problems which deal with the attraction of the earth for a relatively small body the CENTER OF GRAVITY is for practical purposes a definite point. But actually a solid sphere or a hollow sphere is the only body whose center of gravity is always the same for different relative positions and orientations. For every other body or system the CENTER OF GRAVITY differs with changes in orientation.

For a pendulum the CENTER OF SUSPENSION, the CENTER OF GRAVITY, and the CENTER OF PERCUSSION, lie on the same straight line. The CENTER OF SUSPENSION is one of two conjugate points of a gravity pendulum of which the other is the CENTER OF PERCUSSION. CONJUGATE in this sense means that if the CENTER OF PERCUSSION be used as the CENTER OF SUSPENSION, the CENTER OF SUSPENSION becomes the CENTER OF PERCUSSION.

369. *LAMBERT* (*lăm'-bert*) *n.* Metric unit of brightness of an extended surface, unit of intensity per unit area whether self luminous or lighted by an outside source.

Unit of intensity of light per unit area of an extended surface.

FORM E. 45.	BO	FW	LA	NY	NY	NY	NY	PH	TU	SUM
candle power	17	37	15	13	7	27	126	67	18	327
lux	1	1	5	0	4	2	17	4	3	37
LAMBERT	2	7	7	4	4	1	23	12	1	61
standard candle	4	2	3	3	1	4	20	10	2	49
meter candle	1	3	3	0	4	4	28	6	4	53
unmarked	3	0	0	0	0	2	4	1	0	10
total	28	50	33	20	20	40	218	100	28	537

FORM E. 45.	ENGLISH VOCABULARY	
	HIGH	LOW
candle power	20	31
lux	4	2
LAMBERT	6	1
standard candle	2	2
meter candle	8	4
unmarked	0	0
total	40	40

To the question: 'Unit of intensity of light per unit area of an extended surface', 327 persons out of 537 answer CANDLE

POWER; while only 61 answer LAMBERT. CANDLE POWER, which is sometimes hyphenated, sometimes a single word, and sometimes printed as two words, a practice which has been followed here, is the intensity of the light source. Originally one CANDLE POWER was the intensity of an actual candle made to rigid specifications, a sperm candle burning at the rate of 120 grains of spermaceti per hour. A newer definition is one sixtieth of the intensity in one direction of one square centimeter of a blackbody radiator at the temperature of freezing platinum (1755 degrees). The term CANDLE POWER applies specifically to the source of light.

Strictly the term CANDLE POWER applies to a point source of light, not to a surface emitting light or reflecting it. One occasionally sees the phrase: CANDLE POWER per square centimeter; but for this purpose the word LAMBERT should be used. To reduce CANDLES per square centimeter to LAMBERTS multiply by π; one CANDLE per square centimeter equals π LAMBERTS.

370. *TRAPEZIUM* (*tră-pē'-zē-ŭm*) *n.* Correctly a four-sided figure with two sides parallel; but defined by most dictionaries as a four-sided figure with no sides parallel.

To the question: 'A plane figure with four sides, no one of

A plane figure with four sides, no one of which is parallel to another.

FORM B. 9.	NY	MISC.	SUM
rhombus	7	56	63
trapezoid	10	44	54
quadrilateral	24	156	180
TRAPEZIUM	5	41	46
parallelopiped	1	8	9
unmarked	1	4	5
total	48	309	357

which is parallel to another', 54 persons mark TRAPEZOID, which is correct, as compared with only 46 who mark TRAPEZIUM. These statistics probably mean little, for 180 persons mark QUADRILATERAL, the general term for any four-sided figure, whether the sides are parallel or not. For a four-sided figure with no sides parallel, the French use *trapezoide*, similar to the English TRAPEZOID; and the Germans also *trapezoid*. To be consistent with these languages, where the meaning is clear, English should go back to the earlier use of TRAPEZOID to mean a four-sided figure with no sides parallel; and TRAPEZIUM for the four-sided figure with two sides parallel. For additional discussion reread TRAPEZOID (362).

371. *CORIOLIS* (*kor-ĭ-ō'-lĭs*). The combined effect of an acceleration and a velocity, the acceleration of a particle toward the center of a curved path when the center of the path is also moving, the acceleration of a particle toward an axis about which the path on which it is moving is itself revolving.

A projectile shot from a gun moves on a curved path; and at the same time, because of the revolution of the earth, the

Force produced by the rotation of the relative velocity of a particle on a rotating curve.

FORM AB. 48.		FORM D. 49.		
tangential force	17	tangential force	37	10.6
radial force	7	radial force	29	8.3
centrifugal force	42	centrifugal force	167	47.7
centripetal force	27	centripetal force	37	10.6
CORIOLIS FORCE	7	CORIOLIS FORCE	48	13.7
unmarked	0	unmarked	32	9.1
total	100	total	350	100.0

FORM DA. 48.		FORM DB. 49.	
tangential	8	tangential	7
radial	0	gyroscopic	10
centrifugal	71	centrifugal	56
centripetal	12	centripetal	14
CORIOLIS	5	CORIOLIS	12
unmarked	4	unmarked	7
total	100	total	106

path itself revolves about the earth's axis. The CORIOLIS effect is a third term which appears in the formula when two such motions are combined.

To the question: 'The force produced by the rotation of the relative velocity of a particle on a rotating curve', only 5 per cent of students answer correctly CORIOLIS; while 71 per cent answer CENTRIFUGAL. The word CENTRIFUGAL is a combination of the Latin *centrum*, the center, and *fugere*, to flee, and by derivation means fleeing from the center. CENTRIFUGAL FORCE is due to inertia; it is the reaction exerted on a body constrained to move in a curved path. CENTRIFUGAL FORCE is not an actual force, but is often a convenient term for the inertia reaction equal and opposite to CENTRIPETAL FORCE. A body moving about another toward which it is drawn by CENTRIPETAL FORCE follows a curved path. Without CENTRIPETAL FORCE such a rotating body would move straight ahead on the tangent to its curved path. CENTRIPETAL FORCE causes it to fall back constantly from its tangent toward the center of the curve on which it is moving. Mathematically CENTRIPETAL FORCE results in a constant acceleration toward the center. Ordinarily ACCELERATION causes a body to move with an increasing or decreasing speed. Uniform motion about a center is the one instance where the word ACCELERATION is used with reference to a body moving at constant speed. This is because the direction of motion is constantly changing and therefore the velocity, though the speed is constant.

Paul Wolff writes: 'CORIOLIS is that particular part of the total acceleration (or total inertia force) due inherently only to the combined effects of rotational angular velocity and radial linear velocity. The magnitude of the CORIOLIS acceleration is twice the product of these two velocities; the direction is tangential to the path of absolute motion.

'CORIOLIS acceleration is the sum of two equal parts:

1. Due simply to the fact that, if a point moves along a radius which rotates at constant angular velocity, the tangential velocity will be different from one instant to the next; hence there is tangential acceleration without change in either rotational angular velocity or radial linear velocity. The magnitude of this part is the product of these two velocities.

2. Due (like centripetal acceleration) to the fact that an acceleration is produced by the change in direction of the radial velocity from one instant to the next even though its magnitude

does not change. As in 1, the direction of this acceleration is tangential in the same direction, and the magnitude is also equal to the product of angular and radial velocities.

'It is thus apparent that part 1 above is a simple linear acceleration and part 2 is neither more complex, mysterious, nor new than is centripetal velocity. In part 1, the change is merely one in magnitude of tangential velocity, hence the acceleration is tangential. In part 2 the change is one in direction of radial velocity; in this case, the velocity being radial, the acceleration is tangential.'

INDEX

abacus, *n.* 272
ABAMPERE, *n.* 331
abate, *v.* 83
Abbot, C. G., 193
a. b. c., 191
a. b. d. c., 191
Abelard, Peter, 121
aberration, *n.* 215, 262, 284, 19
able, *adj.* 131, 27, 218
about, *adv.* 23, 31
abscind, *v.* 260
ABSCISSA, *n.* 260, 187, 247, 259, 155, 274
abscissa difference, 259
abscissae, *pl. n.* 260
absolute, *adj.* 39, 131, 357, 225
absolute ceiling, 73
absolute constant, 104, 203
absolute scale, 268
absolute temperature, 268, 110, 311, 255
ABSOLUTE ZERO, 39, 178
absolve, *v.* 39
absorb, *v.* 110
absorber, *n.* 110
absorption, *n.* 124
absorption coefficient, 41
absorption lines, 148
absorption spectrum, 237
absorptivity, *n.* 110
abstract, *n.* 313
abstract noun, 28
absurd, *adj.* 355
abundant, *adj.* 21
accelerate, *v.* 117
acceleration, *n.* 85, 116, 117, 371, 150, 353, 341, 315, 347

acceleration of gravity, 64, 313, 75, 347
access, *n.* 52
accident, *n.* 207, 49
accommodate, *v.* 145, 230
ACCOMMODATION, *n.* 145, 230
accompanying, *adj.* 70
accomplish, *v.* 52, 180
accord, *v.* 160
account, *n.* 266
accumulating, *adj.* 285
accurate, *adj.* 287
acentric, *adj.* 31
ACHROMATIC, *adj.* 262, 93, 310, 143, 284
achromatism, *n.* 354
acid, *n.* 184, 13
acoustic, *adj.* 91
across, *adv.* 15, 125, 216, 227, 352
act, *n.* 49
ACTION, *n.* 337, 85
actual, *adj.* 225
acumen, *n.* 22
ACUTE, *adj.* 22, 4, 16, 227, 189
addition, *n.* 105, 259, 128, 212
adhesion, *n.* 142, 258
adhesive, *adj.* 309
ADIABATIC, *adj.* 326, 125, 264, 352
adiabatic process, 343
ADJACENT, *adj.* 82, 207
adjoining, *adj.* 82, 207
adjustment, *n.* 145
Admiralty, *n.* 360
adorn, *v.* 154
adornment, *n.* 154
advantage, *n.* 180
ADVECTION, *n.* 343

B

collineate, *v.* 334
collineation, *n.* 231
collision course, 252
colloid, *n.* 321
color, *n.* 262, 61, 284, 310, 93
coloration, *n.* 262
colored, *adj.* 93
colored print, 284
colorless, *adj.* 262
colure, *n.* 204
comb, *n.* 58
comb, *v.* 58
COMBINATION (math.), *n.* 189, 318
combine, *v.* 189
COMMENSURABLE, *adj.* 221, 3, 168
commensurate, *adj.* 160
commodious, *adj.* 145
common cycloid, 133
common difference, 190
common logarithm, 113, 128, 208
common ratio, 190
Common Sense of the Exact Sciences, 299
commutant, *n.* 3
commutator, *n.* 118
COMMUTATOR RIPPLE, 118
compact, *adj.* 153, 302
compactness, *n.* 153
comparator, *n.* 330
compass, *n.* 138, 164, 323, 325, 151
compass course, 360, 164
compass point, 252
compel, *v.* 339
complement, *n.* 250, 273, 120, 288

complementary, *adj.* 82, 224, 120, 160, 183
complementary angles, 224
complete, *adj.* 39
complete, *v.* 52, 180
completing, *adj.* 224
complexion, *n.* 262
compliance, *n.* 303
complicated, *adj.* 14
complication, *n.* 194
component, *n.* 42
compose, *v.* 42
composite, *adj.* 10
compound motor, 289
compound pendulum, 197
compress, *v.* 74, 326, 302
compressibility, *n.* 118, 242
compression, *n.* 339, 18, 165, 210, 242
compression ratio, 170
compression rib, 361
compression strut, 361
compressive, *adj.* 339
Compton, 264
Compton effect, 302
computer, *n.* 213
Comus, 218
con-, 31, 3
concave, *adj.* 31, 186, 182
concave-convex, *adj.* 262
concavity, *n.* 186
concavo-convex, *adj.* 186
concealed, *adj.* 199
CONCENTRIC, *adj.* 31, 229, 67
conchoid, *n.* 324
conclave, *n.* 31
conclusion, *n.* 293, 207, 308
concurrent, *adj.* 257
concurve, *n.* 300

copy, *n.* 67, 140
copy, *v.* 62, 140
cord, *n.* 139, 171, 300
Corinthian, *adj.* 271
CORIOLIS, *n.* 371
corkscrew, *n.* 59
corn, *n.* 146
cornea, *n.* 184
corner, *n.* 134
corollary, *n.* 200
corpuscle, *n.* 109, 240, 328, 275
corpuscular theory, 151
correct, *adj.* 287
correlation, *n.* 46, 189
correspond, *v.* 174
correspondence, *n.* 174
corresponding, *adj.* 160, 82
COSECANT, *n.* 273, 177, 250, 120, 281, 288
COSINE, *n.* 120, 103, 177, 250, 273, 281, 288, 228
cosmic, *adj.* 290, 193
cosmic radiation, 193
cosmos, *n.* 193
COTANGENT, *n.* 250, 177, 120, 103, 281, 288
coulmeter, *n.* 279
COULOMB, *n.* 236, 126, 102, 240, 331
Coulomb, Charles Augustin, 236, 286
coulometer, *n.* 279
count, *v.* 33
countenance, *n.* 170
counter-, 175
counterbalance, *v.* 175
COUNTERCLOCKWISE, *adv.* 175, 188

COUPLE, *n.* 257, 241
coupled, *adj.* 246
coupling, *n.* 115
courage, *n.* 201, 213, 267
courageous, *adj.* 201
course, *n.* 164, 9, 89, 96, 345
course (airplane), *n.* 89
coverlet, *n.* 348
coversine, *n.* 288, 120, 273
cowling, *n.* 122
Cowper, 218
Crabb, George, 15, 267, 131, 187, 325, 355
crammed, *adj.* 51
crankshaft, *n.* 191, 18
Crayfish, 8
create, *v.* 2
credibility, *n.* 219
credible, *adj.* 219
Cremona, 160
crescent, *n.* 182, 280
crest, *n.* 254
CREST FACTOR, 356
crest value, 356
critical angle, 354
critical pressure, 54, 38
CRITICAL TEMPERATURE, 132, 199
crocodile, *n.* 10
crooked, *adj.* 80, 241
Crookes, 109
Crookes tube, 24
crossing, *n.* 32
crotchets, *pl. n.* 11
crowd, *n.* 51
crowd, *v.* 74
crowded, *adj.* 51
crown, *n.* 200

Dewar, Sir James, 132
DEW POINT, 41
dia-, 125
Diadocus, 362
diagonal, *adj.* 15, 125, 227, 216,
    134
DIAGONAL, *n.* 15, 87
DIAMAGNETIC, *adj.* 216, 352,
    326
DIAMETER, *n.* 352, 15, 17, 26,
    87, 139, 84, 23, 291
diaphragm, *n.* 24, 97
diatom, *n.* 196, 88
diction, *n.* 135
dictionaries
    Arts, Sciences, and Manu-
        factures, 124
    Aviation, 1, 147
    Bailey, 17, 29, 32, 84, 130,
        217, 260
    Blancard, 230
    Blount, 334
    Brande, 242
    Builder's, 87
    Cassell, 53, 113, 101, 210,
        315, 322, 270
    Century, 1, 66, 98, 121, 231,
        242, 51, 53, 58, 76, 82,
        130, 140, 210, 263, 301,
        309, 345, 353, 355, 358,
        366, 223
    Chambers, 56, 6, 29, 42, 82,
        43, 75, 104, 111, 120, 225,
        230, 267, 278, 366, 370,
        151, 154, 155
    Chemistry, 26, 13, 124
    Chemistry and Mineralogy,
        26
    Cockeram, 334

dictionaries—(*Cont'd*)
    Coles, 4
    Crabb, 15, 187, 267, 325, 355
    Electrical, 331
    Encyclopaedic, 53, 76, 113,
        13, 101, 210, 315, 322, 323,
        335, 355, 223, 270
    English Synonyms, 187
    Etymological, 38, 355
    Glossographia, 334
    Harris, 204, 29, 66, 111, 127,
        231, 253, 363, 81, 124, 267,
        278, 333, 335, 366, 370,
        212
    Hawkins' Mechanical, 241
    Hutton, 87, 197, 370, 208
    Illustrated Aviation, 1
    Imperial, 121, 231, 55, 242
    Johnson, 29, 111, 130, 333,
        17
    Jordanoff, 1
    Kersey, 29, 47
    Larousse, 1
    Mathematical and Philo-
        sophical, 87, 197, 370, 208
    Mechanical, 241
    Modern English Usage, 11
    Oxford, 1, 66, 121, 310, 322,
        49, 53, 77, 82, 90, 120, 7,
        8, 122, 196, 288, 340, 358,
        370, 223, 125
    Oxford Supplement, 243
    Phillips, 66, 116, 29, 130,
        209, 335
    Physical, 230
    Richardson, 340
    Skeat, 38, 355
    Smith, 124
    Stormonth, 20

electro-, 50
electro-chemical equivalent, 50, 88
electro-chemistry, *n.* 50
electrode, *n.* 50, 211, 13, 350, 88, 123, 98
electrode tube, 123
electrodynamics, *n.* 27
electrology, *n.* 26
ELECTROLYSIS, *n.* 50, 88, 98, 236, 196, 109
electrolyte, *n.* 9, 50, 13, 88, 211
electromagnet, *n.* 2, 53
electromagnetic, *adj.* 331
electromagnetic inertia, 86
electromagnetics, *n.* 27
electromagnetic unit, 240
electromagnetic waves, 328
electrometer, *n.* 107, 166
electromotive force, 30, 285, 228, 234
ELECTRON, *n.* 98, 240, 109, 196, 328, 50, 78, 88, 123, 211, 275, 350, 236
electronic, *adj.* 123
ELECTRON-RAY TUBE, 350, 123
Electrons, Protons, etc., 98
electron tube, 78
electrophoresis, *n.* 50
electrophorus, *n.* 60
electroplating, *n.* 50, 211
electroscope, *n.* 93
electrostatics, *n.* 50
electrostatic unit, 102, 240
electrostriction, *n.* 26
electrotyping, *n.* 50
electrum, *n.* 98
element, *n.* 47, 5, 275, 240

element (chemical), *n.* 196, 255
Elements of Geometrie, Euclid, 22, 4, 276, 160, 239, 362, 84
element (tube), *n.* 123
elevation, *n.* 144, 233
elevator, *n.* 48, 36
eliminator, *n.* 2
Eliot, George, 59
ELLIPSE, *n.* 205, 111, 239, 251, 280, 304, 84, 156, 324, 342, 87, 346, 352
ellipsis, *n.* 205
elliptical polarization, 344
ELLIPTIC FOCI, 239
Ellis, Alexander J., 136, 168, 51
elongation, *n.* 339, 165, 210
embellishment, *n.* 154
e. m. f., 234
emission spectrum, 237
emissive power, 255
emmetropic, *adj.* 230
EMPENNAGE, *n.* 48, 1
empirical, *adj.* 293
EMPIRICAL LAW, 293
-ence, 215
encompass, *v.* 303
encyclopaedia, *n.* 55
Encyclopaedia Britannica, 8, 77, 107, 131, 165, 215, 258, 363, 196
Encyclopaedia (Philadelphia), 84, 92, 214, 129, 108, 205
encyclopaedias
   Chambers (see dictionaires)
   Diderot, 56
   Harmsworth, 90

Galvani, Luigi, 166

GALVANOMETER, *n.* 166, 107, 285

gamma, *n.* 222

gamma rays, 328, 109

Ganot, Adolphe, 136, 143, 257, 270

gap, *n.* 37

garland, *n.* 200

Garnett, William, 244

gas, *n.* 132, 20, 149, 157, 129

gassing factor, 94

gauss, *n.* 319, 102, 275

Gauss, 271

Gay-Lussac, Joseph, 311, 332

Gay-Lussac's law, 129, 332

Geissler, Heinrich, 148

Geissler tube, 148

gelatin, *n.* 301

gelid, *adj.* 301

generate, *v.* 2

generation, *n.* 2

GENERATOR, *n.* 2, 118, 172, 6

genus, *n.* 2

geodesy, *n.* 306

GEODETIC, *adj.* 306

geographic meridian, 323

Geography, Carpenter, 325

Geology and Geography of Great Britain, 121

Geometria, 276

geometric, *adj.* 33, 190

Geometrical Practice, 29, 34

geometric center, 368

GEOMETRIC PROGRESSION, 190, 33, 278, 46, 206, 349

geometry, *n.* 26, 276

Geometry, Elements, 84

Geometry, Lardner, 160

germ cell, 262

gift, *n.* 200

gilbert, *n.* 102, 319

giro, *n.* 59

glaciation, *n.* 301

glass, *n.* 184, 217

globe, *n.* 84, 348, 360

gloomy, *adj.* 146

Glossary of Physics, 351

Glossographia, 315, 334

glutinous, *adj.* 309

gnomon, *n.* 360

gnomonic, *adj.* 360

GNOMONIC PROJECTION, 360

go, *v.* 88, 9, 62, 125, 326, 98

goad, *n.* 31

goad, *v.* 31

gold, *n.* 98, 216

Golden Legend, 122

gold foil, 36

gold-leaf, *n.* 36

good, *adj.* 146, 321, 219

Good, John Mason, 8

gradient, *n.* 269

Graham, Thomas, 158, 321

gram, *n.* 64, 74, 91, 244, 336

gram-calorie, *n.* 179, 193

gram-centimeter, *n.* 244

graphic, *adj.* 150

Graphic Arts, 185

grapnel, *n.* 137

grating, *n.* 151, 61

GRATING, DIFFRACTION, 148

grave, *adj.* 258

gravitate, *v.* 258

GRAVITATION, *n.* 258, 214

gravitational constant, 336

gravity, *n.* 313, 49, 64, 258, 347

great, *adj.* 69, 316, 78, 290

inscribed, *adj.* 31

insecure, *adj.* 152

insert, *v.* 345

inspect, *v.* 170

instability, *n.* 359

instantaneous center, 368, 299

INSTRUMENT FLYING, 147

instrument landing, 147

insulation, *n.* 270

intact, *adj.* 206

intake, *n.* 18

intake closes, 191

intake opens, 191

integer, *n.* 127, 206, 221, 83, 113

integral, *adj.* 208

INTEGRAL, *n.* 206, 14, 259

integral combination, 278

integral invariant, 119

integral permutation, 278

integrate, *v.* 206

integrating, *adj.* 285

integration, *n.* 206, 189, 220, 318

intensity, *n.* 60, 49, 153

intensity (heat), *n.* 282

intensity (light), *n.* 369

intensity (radio), *n.* 327

intensity (sound), *n.* 91

interaction, *n.* 215

intercept, *n.* 32, 159, 297, 176, 260

intercept, *v.* 260

intercepted, *adj.* 260, 161

interception, *n.* 231

interchangeable, *adj.* 183

interfere, *v.* 215

INTERFERENCE, *n.* 215, 40, 148, 151, 310, 354

INTERFEROMETER, *n.* 151, 60, 215

interior, *adj.* 224

interior angle, 22

intermeddle, *v.* 215

intermediate, *n.* 37

interrupt, *v.* 260

intersect, *v.* 5

INTERSECTION, *n.* 32, 5, 249, 194, 291

invalidation, *n.* 200

invariant, *n.* 119

inverse, *adj.* 46, 200, 108, 175

inversely, *adv.* 46

INVERSE PROPORTION, 46, 108, 233

INVERSION, *n.* 233

invert, *v.* 200, 46

inverted, *adj.* 233, 46, 288

invisible, *adj.* 110

involute, *n.* 253

involved, *adj.* 14

i. o., 191

ION, *n.* 88, 50, 98, 13, 109, 211, 240

-ion, 121

ion effect, 232

Ionic, *adj.* 271

ionization, *n.* 144

ionosphere, *n.* 144, 348

iron, *n.* 258, 216

irradicate, *v.* 223

IRRATIONAL, *adj.* 287, 225, 173, 355, 105, 108

irrational root, 140

isentropic, *adj.* 326

iso-, 125

isobar, *n.* 34, 125, 323, 279

isobaric, *adj.* 125, 326

O

object, *n.* 246
objective, *n.* 354, 246
oblige, *v.* 339
oblique, *adj.* 16, 80, 231
oblique coordinates, 227
observation, *n.* 293
obtund, *v.* 4
OBTUSE, *adj.* 4, 22, 317, 16, 227, 28, 34
obtuseness, *n.* 28
obverse, *adj.* 46
obverse, *n.* 46
occident, *n.* 207
occlusion, *n.* 343
occur, *v.* 207
octagon, *n.* 29
octagonal, *adj.* 15, 357, 227
octahedron, *n.* 134, 163, 333
OCTANT, *n.* 357, 188, 307
odd, *adj.* 80, 173, 44
odds, *n.* 219
oersted, *n.* 126, 275, 331
offer, *v.* 42
Ogilvie, John, 121, 231, 242
ohm, *n.* 30, 126, 100
Ohm, Georg Simon, 30
ohmmeter, *n.* 107
OHM'S LAW, 30, 286
-oid, 53, 359
oil, *n.* 309
Old Testament, 74
one, *n.* 127
Onnes, H. Kammerlingh, 132
opacity, *n.* 309
opal, *n.* 217
opalescence, *n.* 65
open, *v.* 74

open circuit, 9
opening, *n.* 74
operating, *adj.* 72
operating load, 99
operation, *n.* 99, 72
operational function, 46
operator, *n.* 176
opine, *v.* 121
opinion, *n.* 121
opposed, *adj.* 194
opposed-type engine, 18
opposite, *adj.* 43, 296, 224
opposite, *n.* 200
opposite angles, 224
oppress, *v.* 74
optical center, 7
optician, *n.* 143
optics, *n.* 143, 230, 245
Optics, Brewster, 90, 143, 215, 256, 262, 267
Optics, Parkinson, 262, 267
Opus Palatinum de Triangulis, 120
oral, *adj.* 18
orb, *n.* 51, 133
orbit, *n.* 9, 119, 51
ordain, *v.* 247
ordained, *adj.* 247
ORDER, *n.* 271, 189, 307
order, *v.* 187, 247
ordered, *adj.* 187, 247
ordinal, *adj.* 287, 248
ordinal, *n.* 248
Ordinance Survey, 121
ordinary, *adj.* 72
ORDINATE, *n.* 247, 187, 188, 155, 260, 249
ordinate, normal curve, 274
orientation, *n.* 121, 277

BIBLIOGRAPHY

Dictionaries and Books on Words
in the Author's Collection

1599 MINSHEU, JOHN, Dictionarie in Spanish and English. Bound together with the next with Minsheu's signature on the title page.

1617 MINSHEU, JOHN, Guide into Tongues. One volume, folio. A dictionary in thirteen languages.

1673 COTGRAVE, RANDLE, A French and English Dictionary. (First Edition 1611)

1678 PHILLIPS, EDWARD, New World of Words. A dictionary by a nephew of John Milton.

1704 HARRIS, JOHN, Lexicon Technicum.

1721 BAILEY, NATHAN, Universal Etymological English Dictionary.

1724 COLES, E., English Dictionary, a small dictionary: 'explaining the difficult terms that are used in Divinity, Husbandry, Physick, Philosophy, Law, Navigation, Mathematicks and other Arts and Sciences'.

1755 JOHNSON, SAMUEL, Dictionary of the English Language. Two volumes, folio.

1771 DYCHE, REV. THOMAS, English Dictionary.

1775 ASH, JOHN, Dictionary of the English Language. Two volumes.

1778 DIDEROT, M., Encyclopédie, ou Dictionnaire Raisonné des Sciences, des Arts, et des Métiers.

1786 CHAMBERS, EPHRAIM, Cyclopaedia or An Universal Dictionary of Arts and Sciences. Five volumes. (First Edition 1728 two volumes).

1790 SHERIDAN, THOMAS, Dictionary of the English Language. By the father of the playwright. (First Edition 1789)

1798– TOOKE, JOHN HORNE, Diversions of Purley. Printed for
1805 the author.

1807 AIKEN, A. & C. R., Dictionary of Chemistry and Mineralogy. Two volumes.

1813 GOOD, JOHN MASON; GREGORY, OLINTHUS; BOSWORTH, NEWTON; Pantologia, a New Cyclopedia.

1818 JOHNSON, SAMUEL, A Dictionary of the English Language. First American Edition from the Eleventh London Edition.

1828 WEBSTER, NOAH A., An American Dictionary of the English Language.

1850 OGILVIE, JOHN, Imperial Dictionary, English, Technological, and Scientific. Three volumes. Based on Webster, 1828.

1863 WATTS, HENRY, Dictionary of Chemistry. Longmans, Green. Five volumes.

1873 LITTRÉ, E., Dictionnaire de la Langue Française.

1875 RICHARDSON, CHARLES, Dictionary of the English Language. Two volumes.

1878 ENCYCLOPAEDIA BRITANNICA, Scribner's. Ninth Edition. Twenty-five volumes.

1879 JAMIESON, JOHN, Etymological Dictionary of the Scottish Language. (First Edition 1808).

1881 OGILVIE, JOHN, Imperial Dictionary, New Edition. Four volumes.

1882 SKEAT, REV. WALTER W., Etymological Dictionary of the English Language.

1885 STORMONTH, REVEREND JAMES, Dictionary of the English Language. (First Edition 1871).

1888 ENCYCLOPAEDIC DICTIONARY, Robert Hunter, and Cassell. Seven volumes bound as fourteen.

1888 NEW ENGLISH DICTIONARY ON HISTORICAL PRINCIPLES, Murray, James A. H. Oxford. Ten volumes bound as twelve.

1889 CENTURY DICTIONARY. Ten volumes. Based on the Imperial, 1850. Own these ten volumes and use them.

1937 WELD, LE ROY D., Glossary of Physics. McGraw-Hill.

1937 ENCYCLOPAEDIA BRITANNICA.
Fourteenth Edition. Twenty-four volumes.

Original Research before 1900:

1833 BREWSTER, SIR DAVID, Treatise on Optics.
(First American Edition)

1839 FARADAY, MICHAEL, Electricity. Philosophical Transactions.

1845 YOUNG, THOMAS, Natural Philosophy. Taylor and Walter. Two volumes.

1875 HELMHOLTZ, HERMANN L. F., Sensations of Tone, Longmans, Green. Translated by Alexander J. Ellis.
One of the great translations of a scientific work.

1884 JOULE, JAMES PRESCOTT, Scientific Papers. Physical Society of London. Two volumes.

1897 HUMBOLDT, ALEXANDER VON, Cosmos.
A translation from the German 1845–1858.

Text Books:

1880 ARNOTT, NEIL, Elements of Physics. Appleton.
(First Edition 1827)

1881 GANOT's Eléments de Physique, Translated by E. Atkinson. William Wood. (First Edition 1863)

1892 BARKER, GEORGE F., Physics. Henry Holt.

1896 STEWART, BALFOUR & GEE, W. W. HALDANE, Elementary Practical Physics. Macmillan.

1896 THOMPSON, SILVANUS P., Electricity and Magnetism. Macmillan.

1897 THOMPSON, SILVANUS P., Light, Visible and Invisible. Macmillan.

1904 DANIELL, ALFRED, Principles of Physics. Macmillan.

1905 WATSON, W., Physics. Longmans, Green.

1906 MILLIKAN, ROBERT ANDREWS & GALE, HENRY GORDON, First Course in Physics. Ginn.

1907 LODGE, SIR OLIVER, Electricity. Macmillan. (First Edition 1889)

1910 UNDERHILL, CHARLES R., Solenoids, Electromagnets, and Electromagnetic Windings. Van Nostrand.

1911 GRANVILLE, WILLIAM ANTHONY, Differential and Integral Calculus, Ginn. Every scientific boy should own this book long before he needs it.

1912 SODDY, FREDERICK, Matter and Energy. Henry Holt.

1913 RUTHERFORD, E., Radio Active Substances. Cambridge. A classic.

1916 MILLER, D. C., Science of Musical Sounds. Macmillan. For the musician as well as the scientist.

1925 LODGE, SIR OLIVER, Ether and Reality. Doran.

1930 SAUNDERS, FREDERICK A. (Harvard), Survey of Physics. Henry Holt.

1933 RICHTMYER, F. K., Modern Physics. McGraw-Hill. Read aloud to your son the first three historical chapters. Black says: 'Wonderfully interesting introduction to modern physics'.

1935 MILLIKAN, ROBERT A., Electrons (+ and −), Protons, Photons, Neutrons, Mesotrons, and Cosmic Rays. University of Chicago Press. Black calls this a classic.

1941 BLACK, NEWTON HENRY (Harvard), College Physics. Macmillan.

1946 CLIFFORD, WILLIAM KINGDON, Commonsense of the Exact Sciences. Knopf. This book first appeared in 1885, carefully edited by Karl Pearson, six years after Clifford's death.

History of Science:

1855 BREWSTER, SIR DAVID, Sir Isaac Newton. Thomas Constable.

1870 BREWSTER, SIR DAVID, Martyrs of Science: Galileo, Tycho Brahe, Keppler. By a great scientist. Out of print, but find it and read it aloud.

1884 CAMPBELL, LEWIS and GARNETT, WILLIAM, Life of James Clerk Maxwell. Macmillan.

1895 CAJORI, FLORIAN, History of Mathematics. Macmillan.

1899 CAJORI, FLORIAN, History of Physics. Macmillan.

1918 SEDGWICK, W. T. and TYLER, H. W., History of Science. Macmillan.

1924 PEARSON, KARL, Life, Letters, & Labours of Francis Galton. Cambridge University Press.